S0-AIH-200

ORGANOMETALLIC REACTIONS

Volume 3

ADVISORY BOARD

G. E. COATES, Professor of Chemistry

Chairman, Department of Chemistry
University of Wyoming
Laramie, Wyoming 82070

H. GILMAN, Professor

Department of Chemistry
Iowa State University
Ames, Iowa 50010

F. HEIN, Professor

Director, Institute of Coordination Compounds
Academy of Sciences of DDR
Jena, East Germany

A. N. NESMEYANOV

Institute for Elementoorganic Compounds
Moscow, U.S.S.R.

G. WITTIG, Professor

Department of Chemistry
University of Heidelberg
Heidelberg, W. Germany

ORGANOMETALLIC REACTIONS

Volume 3

EDITED BY

Ernest I. Becker

Department of Chemistry
University of Massachusetts
Boston, Massachusetts

Minoru Tsutsui

Department of Chemistry
Texas A & M University
College Station, Texas

Wiley-Interscience

A Division of John Wiley & Sons, Inc.

NEW YORK . LONDON . SYDNEY . TORONTO

Copyright © 1972, by John Wiley & Sons, Inc.

All rights reserved. Published simultaneously in Canada.

No part of this book may be reproduced by any means, nor transmitted, nor translated into a machine language without the written permission of the publisher.

Library of Congress Catalogue Card Number: 74-92108

ISBN 0-471-06136-0

Printed in the United States of America.

10 9 8 7 6 5 4 3 2 1

Preface

The primary literature on organometallic chemistry has undergone phenomenal growth. The number of papers published from 1955 to 1970 is about equal to all prior literature. Together with this intense activity there has developed a complexity in the literature. Thus specialized texts and teaching texts, a review journal, an advances series, and a research journal have all appeared during this period. The present series also reflects this growth and recognizes that many categories of organometallic compounds now have numerous representatives in the literature.

The purpose of *Organometallic Reactions* is to provide complete chapters on selected categories of organometallic compounds, describing the methods by which they have been synthesized and the reactions they undergo. The emphasis is on the preparative aspects, although structures of compounds and mechanisms of reactions are briefly discussed and referenced. Tables of all of the compounds prepared in the category under consideration and detailed directions for specific types make these chapters particularly helpful to the preparative chemist. While the specific directions have not been refereed in the same way as are those in *Organic Syntheses* and *Inorganic Syntheses*, the personal experiences of the authors often lend special merit to the procedures and enable the reader to avoid many of the pitfalls frequently encountered in selecting an experimental procedure from the literature.

We acknowledge a debt of gratitude to the contributing authors whose dedication and skill in preparing the manuscripts cannot adequately be rewarded. It has been gratifying to note that virtually all invitations to contribute have been accepted at once. We also owe thanks to the publisher for encouragement and even the "gentle prod" when necessary to see these volumes to their completion.

Ernest I. Becker
Minoru Tsutsui

September 1970

Editors

Contents

Contents for Volume 1

Contents for Volume 2

ORGANOMETALLIC REACTIONS

Volume 3

Olefin Oxidation and Related Reactions with Group VIII Noble Metal Compounds

REINHARD JIRA AND WERNER FREIESLEBEN

Consortium für elektrochemische Industrie GmbH, Munich, Germany

I. INTRODUCTION

In 1959 the Consortium für elektrochemische Industrie GmbH*[342] presented a new process for the commercial production of acetaldehyde from ethylene by direct oxidation. This new process not only filled a gap in the availability of basic organic intermediates from petrochemical resources but also, by its intricate catalysis, stimulated elementary investigations in organometallic chemistry.

The reaction between ethylene and oxygen to yield acetaldehyde is effected by an aqueous solution of palladium chloride and cupric chloride, which brought to memory a reaction described by Phillips in 1894:[295]

$$C_2H_4 + PdCl_2 + H_2O \longrightarrow CH_3CHO + Pd + 2HCl \qquad (1)$$

At this time Phillips studied the behavior of various hydrocarbons toward oxidizing agents. He observed a black precipitate of palladium metal when he passed ethylene into an aqueous solution of palladium chloride. The olefin was oxidized to acetaldehyde. Evidently, the stoichiometric reaction of a noble metal salt with a scarce olefin found little commercial interest. Phillips' reaction was suggested for analytical application or for the separation of palladium from other noble metals.[276]

Only the discovery that catalytic quantities of palladium salt could be successfully employed for oxidation reactions in the presence of a suitable oxidant (which prevents the precipitation of the palladium metal) turned broad attention to palladium chemistry and reactions of other noble metals. A variety of new specific reactions performed with $PdCl_2$ was elaborated: the oxidation of olefinic to carbonyl compounds in aqueous or nonaqueous solutions; the allylic oxidation of olefins; oxidative coupling; as well as a great many specific catalytic reactions without the accompanying oxidation, e.g., hydrolysis of substituted olefins, transvinylation, carbonylations, oligomerization, isomerization, etc.

All of these reactions proceed through organometallic intermediates. In most cases the initial step is formation of a π-complex of an olefin with a noble metal atom. Such complexes have been known since 1831 when Zeise[421] described a compound $KCl \cdot PtCl_2 \cdot C_2H_4$, the "sal Kalico Platinicus inflammabilis," which he had obtained by treating a boiling alcoholic solution of hexachloroplatinic acid with potassium chloride. Zeise's salt remained a dubious academic curiosity rather than an inspiring event. It took nearly a century to turn the attention of researchers to such compounds. The first palladium-olefin complex was described in 1938 by Kharasch et al.[190] With the impulse of commercial success, extensive research flared up in this field. The engagement grew worldwide after Moiseev and co-workers[250] had reported a synthesis of vinyl acetate from ethylene in acetic acid solution with $PdCl_2$.

---

* Research organization of Wacker-Chemie GmbH, Munich, Germany.

Within a few years a multitude of publications appeared on new reactions with palladium or other noble metal salts; on new complexes, e.g., π-allyl-palladium compounds;[340] or on kinetics and mechanisms. These compounds will be critically reviewed in the following chapters.*

II. BONDS AND STRUCTURES OF π-COMPLEXES

Bonds and structures of π-complexes have been extensively described in summarizing publications, e.g.,[21,22,99,100,116,124,130] We confine ourselves in this paper to a presentation of the model generally accepted for metal-olefin complexes. It has been shaped by Dewar[85] for silver-olefin compounds and was applied by Chatt and Duncanson[47] for the interpretation of platinum-olefin complexes. We use the same model for describing palladium-olefin complexes and their behavior, as well as olefin complexes of other metals of the platinum group. According to this model the olefin should be bonded to the metal by the concerted action of two types of bonds: a σ-type which is brought about by the overlapping of the π-orbital of the olefin with a $5d\,6s$ $6p^2$ hybrid orbital of the platinum and a π-type by the overlapping of a filled $5d$ orbital of the metal with the antibonding orbitals of the olefin. Since the electron donor property of the olefin prevails, its carbon atoms carry a partial positive charge. See Fig. 1.

In Zeise's salt the ethylene is symmetrically bonded to the platinum atom, its C—C axis being oriented perpendicular to the plane of the four-coordinated planar complex. The plane of the hydrogen atoms lies parallel to the cis-Cl-Z-plane, but the hydrogen atoms are repelled away from the metal behind the olefinic carbon atoms which, therefore, adopt a partial sp^3 character. Nevertheless, the C—C double bond remains almost unchanged.

Coordination of the olefin only causes a lengthening of the C—C distance. This could be demonstrated by the lowering of the C—C stretching frequency for about 100 wave numbers.[47] Infrared spectroscopic reinvestigation of Zeise's salt—including far infrared, to determine the metal-olefin bond strength—has been published recently.[127,302] For spectroscopic data on $[Pt(C_2H_4)Cl_2]_2$ and its deuterio- and palladium-analogues, see Ref. 128. The structure outlined above was essentially confirmed by a crystal structure determination of $K(PtCl_3C_2H_4)\cdot H_2O$.[414] The distances between the platinum atom and the cis-chloro atoms are both the same (2.32 Å); only the distance between the platinum atom and the chlorine atom in trans position to the olefin was found to be slightly longer (2.42 Å). This lengthening is attributed to the "trans effect" of the olefin.[15,116]

---

* Patent literature is cited only where examples that have not been published elsewhere are given. But no warranty shall be deduced or construed from the literature cited for priorities.

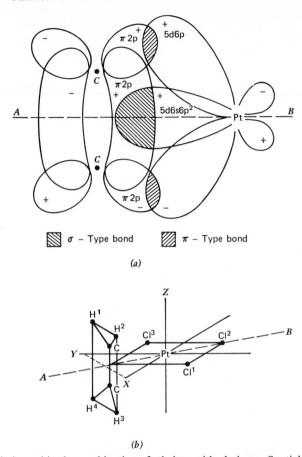

(a)

(b)

Fig. 1. Orbitals used in the combination of ethylene with platinum. Spatial arrangement of atoms in $C_2H_4PtCl_3^-$. σ-Type bond; π-type bond.

The olefin need not be rigidly fixed to the metal atom, since for rhodium[62,67a] and platinum[30] olefin complexes there is evidence of a rotation of the olefin about its coordination axis with an activation energy of 15 kcal for $[(C_2H_4)_2Rh(C_5H_5)]$.[67a] An analogous structure was determined by Dempsey and Baenziger[83] by X-ray analysis of the binuclear chloro-bridged ethylene palladium chloride complex prepared by Kharasch et al.[190] In this complex the axes of the ethylene molecules are also perpendicular to the plane of the Pd_2Cl_2 system with the planes intersecting in the centers of the ethylenic double bonds.

Substituted ethylenes are asymmetrically bonded to the central metal in analogous complexes. This was found for the corresponding binuclear styrene palladium chloride complex by Holden and Baenziger.[157] The carbon atoms of the aromatic ring of the complexed styrene are out of plane, whereas free styrene has a planar structure. The C—C axis of the ethylenic group is tipped away from the plane of the chloro-bridges, its bond being off-center and shifted to the terminal carbon atom. Angles and distances can be seen in Fig. 2.

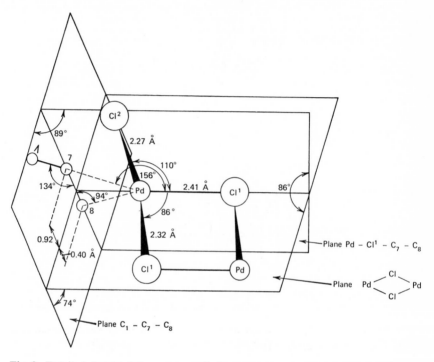

Fig. 2. Detailed sketch of the styrene-palladium chloride complex. The large atoms are chlorine; the medium-size atoms are palladium; and the smallest are the carbon atoms C_1, C_7, and C_8 of styrene.

The prototype of π-allyl complexes of palladium $[C_3H_5PdCl]_2$ was first described by Smidt and Hafner.[340] The allylic anion is bonded to the palladium atom as a bidentate ligand by two delocalized electron pairs and symmetrically oriented to the $(PdCl)_2$ bridge. Therefore, they occupy two square planar coordination sites. This proposal for a "sandwich-type" bond and structure was confirmed by nuclear magnetic resonance (NMR) studies[82] and by X-ray analysis.[272,321,351] According to Oberhansli and Dahl,[272] the plane of the three allylic carbon atoms is declined by an angle of 108° to

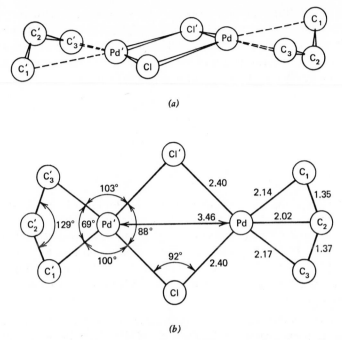

(a)

(b)

Fig. 3. The molecular configuration of $(C_3H_5)PdCl_2$, intramolecular distances and angles by Smith.

the Pd_2Cl_2-bridge system with the central carbon atom tipped away from the palladium. The five hydrogen atoms are coplanar with the allylic plane.[351] Bond angles and distances are shown in Fig. 3.

The allylic carbon atoms are equidistant to the palladium atom;[351] the Pd—Cl distances agree fairly with the *trans*-Pd—Cl bonds in olefin palladium complexes. This lengthening of the Pd—Cl bonds in [π-allyl $PdCl$]$_2$ leads to the assumption that beyond a σ-type bond formed by the overlap of the two π-hybrid orbitals of the allylic ligand with unoccupied square planar dsp^2 orbitals of the metal atom, other π-type back bondings—similar to the ones proposed for olefin complexes—are present. The nature of the bonding in π-allyl complexes of transition metal ions was discussed using bonding energy data.[189]

Allylic groups in mononuclear complexes of platinum group metals with different ligands that can be obtained, e.g., from bis(π-allyl $PdCl$) complexes by reactions with *tert*-phosphines or arsines are bound unsymmetrically. From NMR spectra three different conformational rearrangements have been discussed:[402,405]

1. Collapse of the signals of protons 3 and 4 in phosphine systems suggests an equilibrium between π- and σ-bonded allyl groups. This has first been interpreted by the formation of a structure with simultaneous π- and σ-olefin bondings between the allyl group and the metal.[299,300] The equilibrium lies almost completely on the side of the π-allylic structure.[223]

2. Collapse of the signals of protons 1 and 4, and of 2 and 3, respectively, indicates rotation of the π-allyl group in its own plane. This occurs at higher temperatures and with an excess of ligand through a pentacoordinate species.

3. Collapse of the signals of all four protons in arsine[403] and phosphine[404,406] systems (L = AsR_3; PR_3) indicates a π-σ interchange of the allyl group at even higher temperatures and with excess of ligand (dynamic allyl group).

With allyl complexes of rhodium and platinum, similar observations have been made.[400,407] Further NMR investigations of asymmetric bonding in π-allyl complexes of platinum metals were published by other authors.[60,306,307,358] The formation of σ-allyl bondings may be the first step in the reaction of π-allyl complexes with nucleophiles (see Section III-D).

III. OXIDATION OF OLEFINS WITH PdCl$_2$

A. Aqueous Medium

1. Kinetics and Mechanism

First experimental evidence for an intermediate olefin-palladium π-complex in the oxidation of ethylene to acetaldehyde by palladium chloride was presented by Anderson.[7] He obtained acetaldehyde by heating the aqueous solution of Zeise's salt:

$$K[PtCl_3C_2H_4] + H_2O \longrightarrow CH_3CHO + Pt + KCl + 2HCl \qquad (2)$$

A similar behavior is to be expected for Kharasch's ethylene palladium complex, which probably dissociates into mononuclear ionic species in aqueous medium, if an analogous complex is the intermediate in Phillips' reaction. In fact, on treatment with water, Kharasch's compound yielded acetaldehyde actually at room temperature.[342]

$$[PdC_2H_4Cl_2]_2 + 2H_2O \longrightarrow 2CH_3CHO + 2Pd + 4HCl \qquad (3)$$

Similarly, from the corresponding propylene complex acetone[261] is obtained, and from complexes with higher olefins[263] the corresponding ketones.

One of the feasible reaction routes—hydration of the olefin and subsequent dehydrogenation of the alcohol by the noble metal salt—had been envisaged by Chatt and Duncanson[47] for the hydrolysis of Zeise's salt. The postulated alcohol, however, could not be found.[178] Ethanol, furthermore, is dehydrogenated by PdCl₂ only at elevated temperatures,[213,268] while Kharasch's complex decomposes immediately at room temperature. Finally, there are only negligible quantities of by-product alcohol in the oxidation of ethylene to acetaldehyde with a PdCl₂-containing catalyst on a technical scale. An intermediate alcohol must, therefore, be excluded.

Apparently, the reaction takes place within the complex sphere of the metal atom.

Buttressing this conclusion were experimental results by Smidt et al.[339,342,343] They observed an impeding effect on the reaction between ethylene and an aqueous solution of $PdCl_2$ by chloride and hydrogen ions. The rate of absorption of ethylene by a standard solution of $PdCl_2$ (100 mM/liter) decreased with increasing Cl^- ion concentrations (Fig. 4).

This effect was attributed to a shift of the equilibrium of complex formation:

$$[PdCl_4]^{2-} + C_2H_4 \rightleftharpoons [C_2H_4PdCl_3]^- + Cl^- \tag{4}$$

Complex formation as such was deduced from the fact that, in kinetic experiments, ethylene was absorbed by aqueous $PdCl_2$ solution at the beginning much more rapidly than would have been expected from its solubility in water,[150,174] while later on the rate of absorption corresponded to the rate of the overall reaction. For the rate of absorption of ethylene by aqueous solutions of various platinum metal salts, see Ref. 282.

Equilibrium constants for complex formation of $PdCl_2$ with various olefins have been determined by Moiseev et al.[251,292,294] and Henry[150,152] (see Table I). Attempts to isolate complexes of $PdCl_2$ with ethylene and propylene in polar solvents were not successful.[260,261,343] However, in nonpolar solvents (benzene, p-xylene, n-paraffins, CCl₄), a variety of olefins such as ethylene,[260] propylene,[261] 1-butene, 1-pentene, cis-2-pentene, cyclohexene, and styrene[262,263,303,304] could be reacted with suspended PdCl₂ to give the appropriate complexes of the Kharasch type [olefin-PdCl₂]₂.*

* No complex could be obtained from isobutene. It is noticeable that, from a mixture of cis- and trans-2-pentene, the complex obtained consisted of a mixture of the complexes of 1-pentene and cis-2-pentene. No complex containing trans-2-pentene could be isolated. From 1-hexene and 1-heptene no complexes could be obtained. From styrene two sterically different complexes with PdCl₂ seem to have been formed in a similar reaction,[263] but no assignment of the structure has been presented.

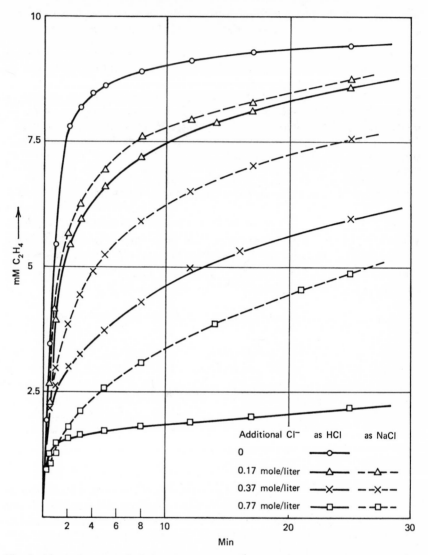

Fig. 4. Absorption rate of ethylene in aqueous $PdCl_2$-solution (100 mM/liter) at various Cl^- and H^+ ion concentrations.

When hydrochloric acid was added to the reaction mixture instead of equimolar NaCl, the rate of ethylene absorption decreased even further. However, since complex formation is independent of the pH-value (Moiseev[251] conducted appropriate experiments in strong acid solutions), the

TABLE I
Equilibrium Constants for π-Complex Formation in Aqueous Solution

1. $[PdCl_4]^{2-} + \text{olefin} \underset{}{\overset{K_1}{\rightleftharpoons}} [\text{olefin} \cdot PdCl_3]^- + Cl^-$

2. $[PdCl_4]^{2-} + \text{olefin} + H_2O \underset{}{\overset{K_2}{\rightleftharpoons}} [\text{olefin} \cdot PdCl_2OH_2] + 2Cl^-$

$$K_1 = \frac{[\text{olefin} \cdot PdCl_3^-][Cl^-]}{[PdCl_4^{2-}][\text{olefin}]} \qquad K_2 = \frac{[\text{olefin} \cdot PdCl_2OH_2][Cl^-]^2}{[PdCl_4^{2-}][\text{olefin}]}$$

Olefin	Temperature	K_1	K_2	Ref.
Ethylene	8.0	15.6	9.0	292
	13.4	16.3	6.5	251
	15.0	18.7	—	150
	20.0	15.2	4.3	292
		16.9	3.8	294
	25.0	13.1	2.7	292
		17.4	—	150
	35.0	9.7	—	150
Propylene	10.3	8.4	4.0	292
	14.9	8.6	4.8	292
	20.1	7.9	4.6	292
		7.6	4.0	294
	25.0	14.5	—	152
1-Butene	5.0	13.9	3.1	292
	10.0	12.6	3.5	292
	14.8	13.6	4.5	292
	20.0	12.4	3.4	292
		14.3	3.4	294
	25.0	11.2	—	152
cis-2-Butene	25.0	8.7	—	152
trans-2-Butene	25.0	4.5	—	152

Note: While K_1 is independent of the ionic strength, for K_2 an influence has been observed.[293] Thus, for ethylene (for 1-butene in parentheses) K_2 changes from 0.5 to 6.5 (0.3 to 8.9), when the ionic strength is increased from 2.1 to 4.5 (2.1 to 5.1).

H^+ ion must somehow exert an influence on complex hydrolysis according to the overall equation:

$$[C_2H_4PdCl_3]^- + H_2O \longrightarrow CH_3CHO + Pd + 3Cl^- + 2H^+ \qquad (5)$$

This effect is consistent with the stabilization of Zeise's salt against hydrolysis by hydrochloric acid.[51,178]

The impeding of the reaction by H^+ ions and the partial positive charge on the complexed olefin led to assuming the attack of an OH^- ion on the olefin.[131,339,342,343] It was inferred that the nucleophilic agent could be a hydroxo ligand at the Pd ion.[131,339,342]

Solvent molecules also appeared feasible as the attacking species. This premise brought about various propositions for the mechanism,[249,250] among others a route via vinyl alcohol. Tracer studies with D_2O [131,339,342] disproved this assumption, since all four hydrogen atoms of the aldehyde originate from the ethylene used. Kharasch's complex on hydrolysis in D_2O yields an acetaldehyde free of deuterium if secondary isotope exchange is avoided. Nevertheless, the hypothesis of an intermediate vinyl alcohol is remarkable because it led to a new synthesis for vinyl acetate, vinyl ethers, and acetals from ethylene when the reaction was carried out in acetic acid containing acetate ions or in alcohols, respectively.

The inference of a free OH^- ion as nucleophilic agent* was disproved by Moiseev and Vargaftik.[253,393] At the low pH-value of the reaction mixture it was, moreover, improbable a priori. Vargaftik additionally studied the salt effect on the reaction rate. It should be positive if a free OH^- ion reacted with the negatively charged Zeise-type olefin-palladium complex. However, a negative salt effect was observed which indicates that either oppositely charged ions react or that a dipole is formed in the transition state.

Moiseev determined the ratio of the rate constants of the ethylene oxidation by $PdCl_2$ in water and D_2O. If a free OH^- ion were the nucleophilic agent, this ratio should be consistent with the ratio of the dissociation constants of H_2O and D_2O:[415]

$$\frac{k_{H_2O}}{k_{D_2O}} = 5.08$$

The measured value turned out to be 4.05.[253] This value corresponds with the ratio found for the dissociation constants of weak acids in H_2O and D_2O.[322] Therefore, it led to assuming the dissociation of an olefin-Pd-aquo complex to yield an olefin-Pd-hydroxo complex.

Such an olefin-Pd-hydroxo complex was derived by Moiseev et al. and by Henry from kinetic investigations.[150,252,379,393,395] For the reaction rate the authors found the expression:

$$\text{reaction rate} = k \frac{[C_2H_4][Pd^{2+}]}{[Cl^-]^2[H^+]} \tag{6}$$

i.e., a first-order reaction with respect to ethylene and $PdCl_2$ concentrations and a dependence of the inverse H^+ ion concentration and the inverse square of the Cl^- ion concentration.†

Expression (6) can be interpreted by the following sequence of equilibria:

1. Complex formation (see Eq. (4))

* Henry[150] estimated the rate constant for the hydrolysis of the ethylene-$PdCl_2$ complex and concluded that it should be higher by several powers of 10 if a free OH^- ion were the attacking agent.

† As a first consequence, a mononuclear complex can be derived as reacting species. This is confirmed by results from spectroscopic investigations of aqueous $PdCl_2$ solutions which show that chloro-bridged binuclear palladium complexes do not exist in aqueous solutions.[210b,224,409]

2. Substitution of a further chloro ligand by a water molecule:

$$\left[\begin{array}{c} Cl \\ | \\ \pi\text{-}C_2H_4\text{—Pd—Cl} \\ | \\ Cl \end{array} \right]^- + H_2O \rightleftharpoons \left[\begin{array}{c} Cl \\ | \\ \pi\text{-}C_2H_4\text{—Pd—H}_2O \\ | \\ Cl \end{array} \right] + Cl^- \qquad (7)$$

$$(1) \qquad\qquad\qquad\qquad (2)$$

3. Dissociation of the aquo complex:

$$\left[\begin{array}{c} Cl \\ | \\ \pi\text{-}C_2H_4\text{—Pd—H}_2O \\ | \\ Cl \end{array} \right] + H_2O \rightleftharpoons \left[\begin{array}{c} Cl \\ | \\ \pi\text{-}C_2H_4\text{—Pd—OH} \\ | \\ Cl \end{array} \right]^- + OH_3^+ \qquad (8)$$

$$(3)$$

In this sequence one inhibiting H^+ ion and two impeding chloride ions are involved.*

The interpretation is in accordance with experimental results published by Leden and Chatt,[210] who found in acidic solution the *trans*-chloro ligand of Zeise's salt to be easily substituted by a water molecule from which a H^+ ion dissociates. Based on these results Joy and Orchin[178] had postulated a complex type analogous to (3) as the first intermediate in the hydrolysis of Zeise's salt.

Analogous to the platinum complex,[210] the monohydroxo-bis-chloro-ethylene palladium complex (3) should have *trans* configuration. To enable an interaction between the olefin and the hydroxo ligand to occur, the latter should be in a *cis* position.

Evidence for a *trans-cis* isomerization of complex (3) was revealed by a more detailed kinetic study of the interaction between lower olefins and aqueous palladium chloride solutions.[174] It could be demonstrated that H^+ and Cl^- ions not only impede the reaction but also accelerate it (Figs. 5, 6).

The curves found by plotting the experimental results satisfy the simplified expression:†

$$\text{reaction rate} = \frac{a \cdot [H^+][Cl^-]}{b + [H^+]^2[Cl^-]^3} \qquad (9)$$

Equation (9) transmutes into the rate equation (6) previously given at higher H^+ and Cl^- ion concentrations if Pd^{2+} and olefin concentrations remain constant. This transmutation is readily perceived from the plots in Figs. 5 and 6; the accelerating effect of H^+ and Cl^- ions predominates with their lower concentrations, whereas the inhibition prevails at higher concentrations of H^+ and Cl^- ions.

---

* Equilibrium constants of the sum of the equilibria (4) and (7) with various olefins have been determined by Moiseev et al.[251,291,292] see Table I.

† A similar dependence of the reaction rate on H^+ and Cl^- ion concentrations has been found for styrene oxidation.[279]

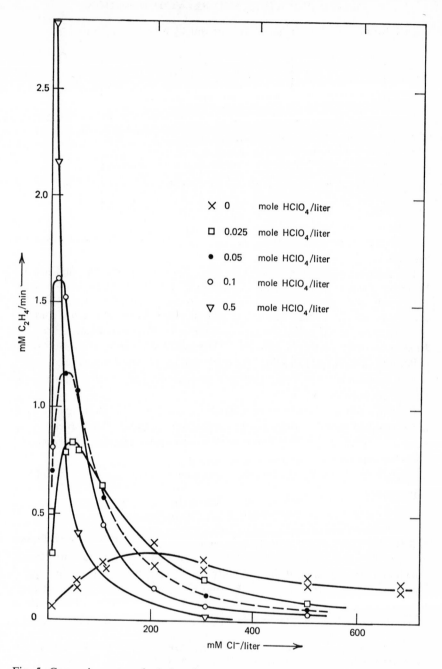

Fig. 5. Conversion rates of ethylene in aqueous $PdCl_2$ (0.002 molar) versus Cl^- ion concentrations.

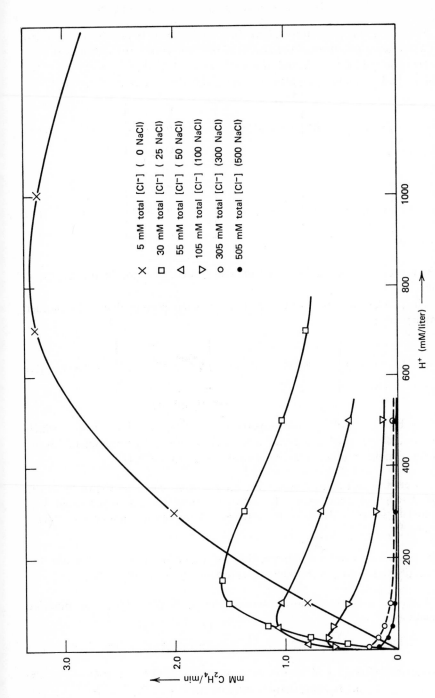

Fig. 6. Conversion rates of ethylene in aqueous $PdCl_2$ (0.002 molar) versus H^+ ion concentrations.

X 5 mM total [Cl⁻] (0 NaCl)
□ 30 mM total [Cl⁻] (25 NaCl)
△ 55 mM total [Cl⁻] (50 NaCl)
▽ 105 mM total [Cl⁻] (100 NaCl)
○ 305 mM total [Cl⁻] (300 NaCl)
● 505 mM total [Cl⁻] (500 NaCl)

Following the suggestions of Moiseev and Henry, it has been concluded that the augmentation of the order of the concentrations means a further substitution of a chloro ligand by a water molecule and the dissociation of the chloro-hydroxo-aquo complex to yield a dihydroxo complex according to:

$$\left[\begin{array}{c} Cl \\ | \\ C_2H_4—Pd—OH \\ | \\ Cl \end{array}\right]^- + H_2O \rightleftharpoons \left[\begin{array}{c} Cl \\ | \\ C_2H_4—Pd—OH \\ | \\ OH_2 \end{array}\right] + Cl^- \qquad (10)$$
$$\qquad\qquad (3) \qquad\qquad\qquad\qquad (4)$$

$$\left[\begin{array}{c} Cl \\ | \\ C_2H_4—Pd—OH \\ | \\ OH_2 \end{array}\right] + H_2O \rightleftharpoons \left[\begin{array}{c} Cl \\ | \\ C_2H_4—Pd—OH \\ | \\ OH \end{array}\right]^- + H_3O^+ \qquad (11)$$
$$\qquad\qquad\qquad\qquad\qquad\qquad (5)$$

which accounts for the increased impeding effect of chloride and hydrogen ions.

The accelerating effect of Cl^- and H^+ ions has been explained by another equilibrium:

$$\left[\begin{array}{c} Cl \\ | \\ \pi\text{-}C_2H_4—Pd—OH \\ | \\ OH \end{array}\right]^- + H_3O^+ + Cl^- \rightleftharpoons \left[\begin{array}{c} Cl \\ | \\ \pi\text{-}C_2H_4—Pd—Cl \\ | \\ OH \end{array}\right]^- + 2H_2O \qquad (12)$$
$$\qquad (5) \qquad\qquad\qquad\qquad\qquad (6)$$

i.e., substitution of the *trans*-hydroxo ligand by a chloro ligand, which lowers the activation energy for the attack of the *cis*-hydroxo ligand on the olefin by polarization across the central metal (*trans* effect).

An electron withdrawal across the central metal could be shown by NMR spectroscopy of Zeise's salt. The proton peaks of the complexed olefin were shifted to lower fields under the influence of increasing chloride ion concentration.[174]

The postulated *trans-cis* isomerization for a fruitful interaction between the *cis*-hydroxo ligand and the olefin is represented by Eqs. (10)–(12).

According to these premises a rate equation can be derived from the following equations:

$$[PdCl_4]^{2-} + C_2H_4 + 2H_2O \xrightarrow{K_1} [C_2H_4PdCl(OH)_2]^- + 3Cl^- + 2H^+ \qquad (13)$$

$$[C_2H_4PdCl(OH)_2]^- + H^+ + Cl^- \xrightarrow{K_2} cis[C_2H_4PdCl_2(OH)]^- + H_2O \qquad (12a)$$

$$cis[C_2H_4PdCl_2(OH)]^- \longrightarrow H_3CCHO + Pd + 2Cl^- + H^+ \qquad (14)$$

If, in a simplified manner, equilibria (4), (7), (8), (10), and (11) are summarized (13), and if it is assumed that there are no other preequilibria accounting for palladium complexes other than $[PdCl_4]^{2-}$ in (13)* (this was also assumed by Moiseev and Henry), Eq. (14) in a summarized form includes the rate-determining step. There is no influence on intermediate equilibria by any agent in solution.

The rate equation derived from (13), (12a), and (14) adopts the form:

$$\text{reaction rate} = \frac{k \cdot K_1 \cdot K_2 [Pd][C_2H_4][H^+][Cl^-]}{K_1[C_2H_4] + K_1K_2[C_2H_4][H^+][Cl^-] + [H^+]^2[Cl^-]^3} \qquad (15)$$

If we assume K_2 to be very small, the middle term in the denominator can be neglected and Eq. (15) agrees with Eq. (9) at constant palladium and C_2H_4 concentrations, supporting the mechanism proposed.†

Moiseev et al.[248] published a further kinetic study on the oxidation of ethylene, propene, and 1-butene. With the results the rate law (Eq. (6)) was extended by another term:

$$\text{reaction rate} = k_2^{\text{I}} \cdot \frac{[PdCl_4^{2-}][\text{olefin}]}{[Cl^-]^2[H_3O^+]} + k_2^{\text{II}} \frac{[PdCl_4^{2-}]^2[\text{olefin}]}{[Cl^-]^3[H_3O^+]} \qquad (16)$$

Apart from Eq. (19) a binuclear palladium complex with a penta-coordinated palladium atom should also be involved:‡

$$[PdCl_4]^{2-} + [\pi\text{-}C_nH_{2n}PdCl_2OH]^- \underset{-Cl^-}{\overset{}{\rightleftharpoons}} \left[\begin{array}{c} Cl \quad Cl \\ Cl_2Pd \overset{\diagup}{\underset{\diagdown}{}} \overset{|}{Pd}{-}C_nH_{2n} \\ Cl \quad OH \end{array} \right]^{2-} \longrightarrow$$

$$\textbf{(6a)}$$

$$\left[\begin{array}{c} Cl \quad\quad Cl \quad\quad Cl \\ Pd Pd \\ Cl Cl C_nH_{2n}OH \end{array} \right]^{2-} \qquad (17)$$

$$\textbf{(7a)}$$

For corresponding rate constants, see Table II.

Complexes (6) exhibit all prerequisites for a *cis*-ligand insertion reaction. This term is generally applied for reactions of the type[139, 271]

$$\begin{array}{c} R \\ | \\ {-}M{-}L \end{array} \longrightarrow {-}M{-}L{-}R \qquad (18)$$

which represents formally the insertion of a ligand L between a central metal of a complex and a σ-bonded ligand R in *cis*-position. The term does not describe

---

* System Pd^{2+}—Cl^-—H_2O has been investigated by spectroscopic and electrometric methods, equilibrium constants have been reported by various authors.[90, 409]

† Henry[155] questioned the kinetic feasibility of the equilibria mentioned but did not contradict the necessity of the *cis*-hydroxo-ethylene-$PdCl_2$ complex.

‡ The same authors mention in a more recent paper[210b] that no binuclear complexes of palladium exist in aqueous solution.

TABLE II
Second-Order Rate Constants

$$-\frac{d[\text{olefin}]}{dt} = k_2^{\text{I}} \cdot \frac{[\text{PdCl}_4^{2-}][\text{olefin}]}{[\text{Cl}^-]^2[\text{H}^+]} + k_2^{\text{II}} \cdot \frac{[\text{PdCl}_4^{2-}]^2[\text{olefin}]}{[\text{Cl}^-]^3[\text{H}_3\text{O}^+]} \qquad (16)$$

Olefin	Temperature °C	k_2^{I}	k_2^{II}	Refs.
		Mole$^2 \cdot 1^{-1} \cdot \sec^{-1} \cdot 10^4$		
Ethylene	15	9.9		150
	25	34.8		150
	35	56.3		150
		11.3	35.0	248
Propylene	25	9.4		152
		3.5	25.0	248
1-Butene	25	3.9		152
		5.4	32.8	248
cis-2-Butene	25	3.0		152
trans-2-Butene	25	3.4		152

Note: The values of k_2 are valid for a Cl$^-$ ion concentration of higher than 0.1 moles/liter at a constant ion strength of 2 moles/liter checked with NaClO$_4$. The second term in the rate equation with k_2^{II} as rate constant appears if Pd^{II} concentration of $1 \cdot 10^{-2}$ to $2 \cdot 10^{-1}$ moles/liter are used. At lower Pd^{II} concentrations the reaction rate follows an expression involving only the first term (Eq. (6)).

the mechanism of the reaction which might rather be an attack or a migration of ligand R on ligand L. A proposal has been made by P. Cossee for a quantum-chemical treatment of this type of reaction.[59] Olefin rotation around its coordination axis[30,62] (cf. Section II) facilitates cis-ligand insertion.

The intramolecular reaction between a positive (olefin) and a negative (OH) ligand, which also explains the negative salt effect found by Vargaftik et al.,[393] results in a σ-compound according to:*

$$cis[\text{C}_2\text{H}_4\text{PdCl}_2(\text{OH})]^- \rightleftharpoons \left[\text{HOCH}_2 \cdot \text{CH}_2 \cdot \text{Pd} \begin{matrix} \diagup \text{Cl} \\ \diagdown \text{Cl} \end{matrix} \right]^- \qquad (19)$$

(6)   (7)

Species like (7) have been postulated as intermediates in olefin oxidations by Hüttel et al.,[164] Moiseev et al.,[252] and Henry.[150] Stable compounds of this type, e.g., $\text{Cl} \cdot \text{Hg} \cdot \text{CH}_2 \cdot \text{CH}_2\text{OH}$, are obtained in similar reactions with mercuric compounds. If this compound is reacted with PdCl$_2$, acetaldehyde is obtained. From the corresponding ClHgCH$_2$CH$_2$OEt and ClHgCH$_2$CH$_2$OAc, vinyl ether and vinyl acetate, respectively, were formed in analogous reactions.[247]

* Empty coordination sites of complexes in this or one of the following formulas might be occupied by a solvent molecule or any other ligand.

Stable palladium and platinum complexes with a metal–carbon σ-bond from an original π-bond are described in Section III-B (see also Table IV). Reactions leading to metal compounds of the type (7) are generally termed oxymetallations. *Cis*-ligand insertion as described or the addition of a metal hydroxide to an olefinic double bond, e.g.,

$$\text{M—OH} + \overset{|}{\underset{|}{C}}=\overset{|}{\underset{|}{C} } \longrightarrow \text{M}-\overset{|}{\underset{|}{C}}-\overset{|}{\underset{|}{C}}-\text{OH} \qquad (20)$$

are feasible mechanisms. The stereochemical aspects to be deduced from these concepts are discussed in detail in Section III-B-5.

The experimental fact that all four hydrogen atoms of the aldehyde originate from the ethylene forces a hydride transfer from the β-carbon atom across the original double bond.* For the hydride transfer in question, E. W. Stern[359] believed that an intermediate hydrido-palladium complex could not be excluded. Jira et al.[174] formulated the transfer in two consecutive reactions, the formation of the hydrido-vinyl alcohol complex (8) by β-hydrogen abstraction:†

$$\left[\text{HO—CH}_2\text{—CH}_2\text{—Pd} \begin{smallmatrix} \text{Cl} \\ \diagup \\ \diagdown \\ \text{Cl} \end{smallmatrix} \right]^- \rightleftharpoons \left[\begin{smallmatrix} \text{H} \quad\; \text{OH} \\ \diagdown \diagup \\ \text{C} \\ \| \quad\quad\longrightarrow \text{Pd—Cl} \\ \text{CH}_2 \quad\quad | \\ \quad\quad\quad \text{H} \end{smallmatrix} \begin{smallmatrix} \text{Cl} \\ \\ \end{smallmatrix} \right]^- \qquad (21)$$

$$(7) \qquad\qquad\qquad (8)$$

and another *cis*-ligand insertion reaction to yield σ-complex (9):‡§

$$(8) \rightleftharpoons \left[\begin{smallmatrix} \text{OH} \\ | \\ \text{CH}_3\text{—C—Pd—Cl} \\ | \quad\; | \\ \text{H} \;\; \text{Cl} \end{smallmatrix} \right]^- \qquad (22)$$

$$(9)$$

It is known that β—C—H bonds are weakened in metal alkyl compounds. Reversible β-hydrogen abstraction takes place from the alkyl group of a metal

---

* This result contradicts the postulation by Matveev et al.[224] that a proton could be abstracted from the olefin ligand of a binuclear complex to form, e.g., [(C$_2$H$_4$)ClPdCl$_2$-PdCl(C$_2$H$_3$)]. Furthermore, as already mentioned, the existence of such binuclear complexes in diluted aqueous solutions is rather doubted.[409]

† This equilibrium represents the inverse *cis*-ligand insertion equilibrium.

‡ Complex (9) has already been formulated by Pestrikov.[287]

§ Intramolecular hydride transfer via analogous reactions including π- and σ-intermediates is also assumed in olefin isomerization catalyzed by transition metal compounds, including noble metals. (See Section IV-C.)

alkyl to form hydrides or hydrido complexes and olefins, e.g., the reversible formation of magnesium and aluminum alkyls by interaction of the metal hydrides with olefins. With transition metals, similar reactions are described:[48]

$$trans[PtHCl(PEt_3)_2] + C_2H_4 \longrightarrow trans[PtCl(C_2H_5)(PEt_3)_2] \qquad (23)$$

with an intermediate hydrido-olefin-Pt-complex[46] and the formation of an olefin complex of cyclopentadienyl iron dicarbonyl from the corresponding alkyl compound.[123]

The particular ability of platinum metals to form hydrido complexes enables the hydride transfer in the manner shown (Eqs. (21) and (22)). This ability has been demonstrated by the deuteration of 1-butene[64] (see also Section IV-C-1) through exchange of H against D, according to

$$CH_2{=}CH{-}CH_2{-}CH_3 + rhD \longrightarrow \underset{\substack{| \quad | \\ rh \quad D}}{CH_2{-}CH{-}CH_2{-}CH_3} \longrightarrow$$

$$CH_2{=}CD{-}CH_2{-}CH_3 + rhH \quad (24)$$

Another example for an iridium-catalyzed hydride exchange has recently been reported with the following sequence:[333]

$$+ HCl \quad (25)$$

Compounds of thallium, lead, and mercury (which essentially lack the ability to form hydrido complexes analogous to complex (7) are preferably already cleaved heterolytically at this stage of the reaction chain to form glycol derivatives.[151]

In the technical manufacture of acetaldehyde, some ethylene chlorohydrin as a by-product in quantities below 1% is formed. As a feasible route for its formation the heterolytic cleavage of the oxypalladation adduct (7) may be assumed, followed by the addition of a chloride ion to the carbonium ion formed. However, the cupric ions present in the technical catalyst play an essential role in this reaction. With high $CuCl_2$ concentrations (up to 3 moles/liter) the formation of ethylenechlorohydrin becomes the main reaction. It has been suggested that $CuCl_2$ assists the heterolytic cleavage by coordination with the palladium; or the organic ligand is transferred to the $CuCl_2$ followed by an analogous cleavage of the ϱ-compound.[357]

$$(7) \quad \xrightarrow{2CuCl_2 \ Cl^-} \quad \left[HOCH_2CH_2-Pd \overset{\displaystyle Cl-CuCl_2}{\underset{\displaystyle Cl}{\overbrace{}Cl-CuCl_2}} \right]^{2-} \quad \longrightarrow \quad HOCH_2CH_2Cl \ + $$

$$[PdCl_4]^{2-} \ + \ 2CuCl \quad (26)$$

or

$$(7) \quad \xrightarrow{2CuCl_2, \ 2Cl^-} \quad [PdCl_4]^{2-} \ + \ \left[HOCH_2CH_2 \overset{\displaystyle -Cu-Cl-CuCl_2}{\underset{\displaystyle Cl}{}} \right]^- \quad \longrightarrow$$

$$HOCH_2CH_2Cl \ + \ 2CuCl \ + \ Cl^- \quad (27)$$

Another mechanism for the formation of ethylene chlorohydrin comprises "ligand transfer oxidation" reactions *via* radical intermediates which have been presented by *Kochi*.[197]

$$\left[HOCH_2-CH_2 \overset{\displaystyle |}{\underset{\displaystyle Cl \ \ \ \ Cl}{Pd\cdots Cl\cdots CuCl}} \right]^- \quad \longrightarrow \quad \begin{array}{l} HOCH_2-CH_2\cdot \\ + \ [PdCl_3]^- \ + \ CuCl \end{array} \quad (28)$$

$$HOCH_2-CH_2\cdot \ + \ ClCuCl \quad \longrightarrow \quad HOCH_2-CH_2Cl \ + \ CuCl \quad (29)$$

For analogous reactions in acetic acid medium, cf. Section III-B-2.

Only complex (9) is cleaved into a carbonium ion (10) or its solvation product, the oxonium species (11), and the palladium metal which leaves with the electron pair of the σ-bond.

$$\left[\overset{\displaystyle OH}{\underset{\displaystyle H}{CH_3-C-PdCl_2}} \right]^- \quad \longrightarrow \quad \overset{\displaystyle OH}{\underset{\displaystyle H}{CH_3-C^\oplus}} \ + \ Pd \ + \ 2Cl^- \quad (30)$$

$$(9) \qquad\qquad\qquad\qquad (10)$$

$$\overset{\displaystyle OH}{\underset{\displaystyle H}{CH_3-C^\oplus}} \ + \ H_2O \quad \longrightarrow \quad \overset{\displaystyle OH \ \ H}{\underset{\displaystyle H \ \ \ H}{CH_3-C\overset{}{}O^\oplus}} \quad (31)$$

$$(11)$$

$$\overset{\displaystyle OH \ \ H}{\underset{\displaystyle H \ \ \ H}{CH_3-C\overset{}{}O^\oplus}} \quad \longrightarrow \quad CH_3-C\overset{\displaystyle O}{\underset{\displaystyle H}{\diagup}} \ + \ H_3O^+ \quad (32)$$

Evidence for the carbonium or oxonium ion corresponding to (10) and (11) was given by Moiseev,[245] who carried out the reaction in nonaqueous deuterio-methanol. The acetal formed did not contain any deuterium. This, however, should have been found if the acetal was formed by the addition of the deuterio-alcohol to the vinyl ether primarily present (see Section III-B-1). The heterolysis of complex (9) can also be understood as an attack of a solvent (water) molecule or of an OH^- ion, both either free or complexed, to the central metal atom. Then Eq. (30) changes into

$$\left[\begin{array}{c} OH \\ | \\ CH_3-C-PdCl_2 \\ | \quad | \\ H \quad OH_2 \end{array}\right]^- \longrightarrow (11) + Pd + 2Cl^- \qquad (32a)$$

$$(9')$$

or $\qquad \qquad \qquad \qquad \Big\downarrow \begin{array}{l} -H^+ \\ -H^+ \end{array}$

$$\left[\begin{array}{c} OH \\ | \\ CH_3-C-PdCl_2 \\ | \quad | \\ H \quad OH \end{array}\right]^{2-} \longrightarrow CH_3-CH\Big\langle \begin{array}{c} OH \\ \\ OH \end{array} + Pd + 2Cl^- \qquad (32b)$$

$$(9'')$$

Some authors [224,252,287] claim that, after the electron pair is withdrawn, the palladium exists in a complex with zero valent state. Matveev et al. [224] drew this conclusion from the observation that no metallic palladium precipitated when the reaction was carried out in the presence of cupric chloride. Though metallic palladium, depending on its particle size, is quickly dissolved by cupric chloride solution, there is still indication of the existence of a palladium complex with zero valent state of the central metal. If the reaction is carried out in the presence of sodium nitrite,[346] a complex PdNOCl precipitates, according to

$$C_2H_4 + PdCl_2 + NaNO_2 \longrightarrow CH_3CHO + PdNOCl + NaCl \qquad (33)$$

Since its nitrosyl group is considered as positive NO^+ ion by the N—O infrared valence frequency,[125,211] the palladium is left with zero valence.

Other evidence for a zero valent palladium complex was derived by Moiseev and Pestrikov,[242] who explained in this way their observation of an isomerization of butenes, during oxidation. If the existence of such complexes is accepted, Eq. (30) can be substituted by

$$(9) \longrightarrow (10) + [PdCl_2]^{2-} \qquad (34)$$

$$[PdCl_2]^{2-} \longrightarrow Pd + 2Cl^- \qquad (35)$$

Similar considerations hold for Eq. (32a) and (32b).

The question remains: which one of all these reactions is the rate-determining step? Since the overall reaction is not diffusion-controlled, the rate-determining step must be any of the reactions after the formation of the olefin-palladium complex.

Henry[150] suggested the formation of σ-compound **(7)** to be rate-determining. The small isotope effect he had found studying the rates with C_2H_4 and C_2D_4:

$$\frac{k_{C_2H_4}}{k_{C_2D_4}} = 1.07$$

led him to assume as the rate-determining step a reaction prior to the cleavage of a C—H bond in the hydride transfer. His result, however, can be interpreted differently: no or only a small isotope effect should be observed if the hydride transfer takes place before the rate-controlling step in equilibrium reactions.

If the hydride ligand in complex **(8)** has bonding relations to both carbon atoms (in consequence of equilibria (21) and (22), complex **(8)** can be approximately considered as a transition state.* In such a symmetrical arrangement oscillation of the carbon atoms with respect to hydride does not require different energies if H^- is replaced by D^-.[410] Only small differences in energy are to be expected if the carbon atoms are not quite equal.

It appears logical that only the irreversible heterolysis (30), (32a), (32b) or (34) requires the highest activation energy. It is therefore suggested to be the rate-determining step. The order of values for $\Delta H^\ddagger$ and $\Delta S^\ddagger$, calculated by Henry[150] (19.8 kcal and -8.7 e.u., respectively), account for the separation of charges in Eq. (30).[118]

With these results the oxidation of ethylene with $PdCl_2$ in aqueous medium can be described as a reaction proceeding through the following steps.

1. Absorption of the olefin by the $PdCl_2$ solution, yielding an olefin palladium complex:

$$C_2H_4 + [PdCl_4]^{2-} \rightleftharpoons \left[\begin{array}{c} CH_2 \\ \| \longrightarrow Pd-Cl \\ CH_2 \end{array} \begin{array}{c} Cl \\ | \\ | \\ Cl \end{array}\right]^- + Cl^- \qquad (4)$$

2. Hydrolysis of this complex and subsequent dissociation of the *trans*-aquo complex, yielding a *trans*-hydroxo complex:

$$\left[\begin{array}{c} CH_2 \\ \| \longrightarrow Pd-Cl \\ CH_2 \end{array} \begin{array}{c} Cl \\ | \\ | \\ Cl \end{array}\right]^- + 2H_2O \rightleftharpoons \left[\begin{array}{c} CH_2 \\ \| \longrightarrow Pd-OH \\ CH_2 \end{array} \begin{array}{c} Cl \\ | \\ | \\ Cl \end{array}\right]^- + OH_3^+ + Cl^- \qquad (7)+(8)$$

---

* Actually it is an intermediate step but of higher energy than both σ-complexes **(7)** and **(9)**.

*3. trans-cis–*Isomerization via a dihydroxo complex:

$$
\begin{bmatrix} \begin{array}{c} CH_2 \\ \| \\ CH_2 \end{array} \!\!\longrightarrow \begin{array}{c} Cl \\ | \\ Pd\!-\!OH \\ | \\ Cl \end{array} \end{bmatrix}^{-} + 2H_2O \; \rightleftharpoons \; \begin{bmatrix} \begin{array}{c} CH_2 \\ \| \\ CH_2 \end{array} \!\!\longrightarrow \begin{array}{c} Cl \\ | \\ Pd\!-\!OH \\ | \\ OH \end{array} \end{bmatrix}^{-} + OH_3^+ + Cl^- \qquad (10)+(11)
$$

$$
\begin{bmatrix} \begin{array}{c} CH_2 \\ \| \\ CH_2 \end{array} \!\!\longrightarrow \begin{array}{c} Cl \\ | \\ Pd\!-\!OH \\ | \\ OH \end{array} \end{bmatrix}^{-} + H_3O^+ + Cl^- \; \rightleftharpoons \; \begin{bmatrix} \begin{array}{c} CH_2 \\ \| \\ CH_2 \end{array} \!\!\longrightarrow \begin{array}{c} Cl \\ | \\ Pd\!-\!Cl \\ | \\ OH \end{array} \end{bmatrix}^{-} + 2H_2O \qquad (12)
$$

*4. cis–*Insertion of the olefin:

$$
\begin{bmatrix} \begin{array}{c} CH_2 \\ \| \\ CH_2 \end{array} \!\!\longrightarrow \begin{array}{c} Cl \\ | \\ Pd\!-\!Cl \\ | \\ OH \end{array} \end{bmatrix}^{-} \; \rightleftharpoons \; \begin{bmatrix} HO\!-\!CH_2\!-\!CH_2\!-\!Pd\begin{array}{c} {}^{\nearrow Cl} \\ {}_{\searrow Cl} \end{array} \end{bmatrix}^{-} \qquad (19)
$$

5. Hydride transfer via a hydrido olefin complex:

$$
\begin{bmatrix} HO\!-\!CH_2\!-\!CH_2\!-\!Pd\begin{array}{c} {}^{\nearrow Cl} \\ {}_{\searrow Cl} \end{array} \end{bmatrix}^{-} \; \rightleftharpoons \; \begin{bmatrix} \begin{array}{c} OH \\ | \\ H_3C\!-\!C\!-\!Pd \\ | \\ H \end{array}\begin{array}{c} {}^{\nearrow Cl} \\ {}_{\searrow Cl} \end{array} \end{bmatrix}^{-} \qquad (21)+(22)
$$

6. The rate-determining cleavage of this σ-complex, forming a carbonium or oxonium ion and a Pd(O) complex from which acetaldehyde and palladium metal, respectively, are obtained:

$$
\begin{bmatrix} \begin{array}{c} OH \\ | \\ H_3C\!-\!C\!-\!Pd \\ | \\ H \end{array}\begin{array}{c} {}^{\nearrow Cl} \\ {}_{\searrow Cl} \end{array} \end{bmatrix}^{-} + H_2O \longrightarrow \begin{bmatrix} \begin{array}{c} OH \\ | \\ H_3C\!-\!C\!-\!O^{\oplus}{\begin{array}{c} {}^{\nearrow H} \\ {}_{\searrow H} \end{array}} \\ | \\ H \end{array} \end{bmatrix} + [PdCl_2]^{2-} \qquad (30)+(34)
$$

$$
H_3C\!-\!\underset{\underset{H}{|}}{\overset{\overset{O}{\|}}{C}} + H_3O^+ \qquad\qquad Pd + 2Cl^-
$$

$$
(32) \qquad\qquad\qquad (35)
$$

This mechanism for the ethylene oxidation should also apply for other olefinic compounds.* For the propylene oxidation a rate equation was derived, analogous to Eq. (6).[89,152] Apparently, the kinetic measurements have not been carried out at chloride concentrations low enough to notice the activating effect of Cl^- and H^+ ions, which has been observed for propylene, as well as for 1-butene.[174]

2. Influences on Reaction Rate

Complexing agents block or impede the ability of the Pd^{2+} ion to coordinate olefins and, therefore, affect the overall rate of reaction. Figure 7 gives rates of absorption of ethylene by Pd^{2+} ion solutions with different complexing agents added.[339,340]

Halide ions lower the absorption rate in the order of increasing atomic numbers. Because they form insoluble palladium compounds, iodide and sulfide ions block the absorption completely. Other complexing agents such as CN^-, NH_3, amines, and the like also block the reaction, since they prevent the formation of an olefin complex. Compared with the less complexing perchlorate ion, even sulfate ions exhibit a retarding effect.[174]

Poor complexing anions of weak acids such as acetate or other carboxylates increase the reaction rate by buffering the acid solution. Since the H^+ ion concentration affects the reaction, independent of the acid used, the addition of acetate ions also buffers the acid solution in the presence of $CuCl_2$, a component of the technical catalyst that will be outlined below (see Section III-A-3).

3. Addition of Oxidants

During the stoichiometric reaction between an olefin and palladium chloride, according to

$$C_2H_4 + PdCl_2 + H_2O \longrightarrow CH_3CHO + Pd + 2HCl \qquad (1)$$

Pd^{2+} ions are reduced to zero valence state. Whether zero-valent palladium is complexed or is in the metallic form, it can be reoxidized by all oxidants having a higher potential than the couple Pd^0/Pd^{II}. Among such oxidants the following have been reported:[207,219,249,341,342] oxygen; ozone; peroxides; persulfate; oxometallates, e.g., potassium permanganate and potassium chromate; ferric salts; cupric salts; chlorates, bromates, and iodates; $(IO_6H_4)^-$; Hg^{2+}; PbO_2, MnO_2, V_2O_5, $VOSO_4$, Ce^{4+}; quinones; and HNO_3. Some of these compounds, e.g., $VOSO_4$[207] and HNO_3[219] have been claimed in the patent literature to avoid the use of chloride ions that give rise to

---

* An exception, so far, was found to be cyclohexene. Its oxidation rate is obstructed by Cl^- ions; however, H^+ ions do not show any influence on the reaction.[392] Probably, the reaction is controlled by a different limiting step that is not yet known.

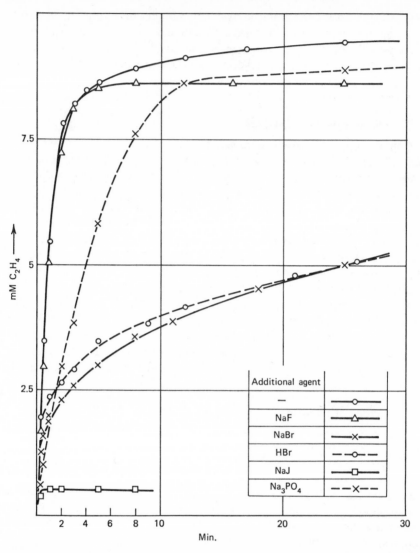

Fig. 7. Absorption rate of ethylene in aqueous PdCl₂ solutions containing various complexing agents.

chlorinated by-products. In the presence of such oxidants, the precipitation of metallic palladium can be avoided.

In the technical processes for the manufacture of acetaldehyde, acetone, and methylethylketone (also of vinyl acetate) from the corresponding olefins in homogeneous phase, cupric chloride is used as the oxidant, since the cuprous chloride formed, according to

$$2CuCl_2 + Pd(O) \rightleftharpoons PdCl_2 + 2CuCl \qquad (36)$$

is easily reoxidized by oxygen or air:

$$2CuCl + 2HCl + \frac{1}{2}O_2 \longrightarrow 2CuCl_2 + H_2O \qquad (37)$$

The ability of cupric chloride to oxidize metallic palladium is brought about by the presence of Cl^- ions. They decrease the normal potential of the couple Pd^0/Pd^{2+} and increase simultaneously the potential of the couple Cu^+/Cu^{2+} because they stabilize the Pd^{2+} and the Cu^+ by complexing.[209]

Actually, the oxidation of metallic palladium with free or hydrated cupric ions is not possible, since the equilibrium constant for Eq. (38)

$$Pd_{met} \rightleftharpoons Pd^{2+} + 2e^- \qquad E_0 = 0.987$$
$$2Cu^{2+} + 2e^- \rightleftharpoons 2Cu^+ \qquad E_0 = 0.153$$
$$2Cu^{2+} + Pd_{met} \overset{K}{\rightleftharpoons} 2Cu^+ + Pd^{2+} \qquad (38)$$

which was calculated[171] from the normal potentials of the half-reactions[209] is very low; $K = 10^{-28.2}$.

In the presence of Cl^- ions, these potentials are changed:

$$Pd_{met} + 4Cl^- \rightleftharpoons [PdCl_4]^{2-} + 2e^- \qquad E_0 = 0.62$$
$$2Cu^{2+} + 4Cl^- + 2e^- \rightleftharpoons 2[CuCl_2]^- \qquad E_0 = 0.47*$$
$$2Cu^{2+} + Pd_{met} + 8Cl^- \overset{K'}{\rightleftharpoons} 2[CuCl_2]^- + [PdCl_4]^{2-} \qquad (39)$$

and the equilibrium constants adopt the values

$$K'_{25°} = 7.9 \times 10^{-6}$$
$$K'_{100°} = 7.9 \times 10^{-5}$$

which simultaneously reveal that a rise of temperature favors the oxidation of metallic palladium by cupric chloride. Similar consideration of the thermodynamics of this process has been given by Matveev et al.[224]

Equilibrium (36), which is identical with Eq. (39), determines the $PdCl_2$ concentration that can be kept in solution.

Apart from these thermodynamic considerations the mechanism of the reoxidation of Pd(O) by CuCl has to be discussed. Finely divided metallic palladium is easily oxidized by $CuCl_2$ solutions. A ligand-transfer oxidation mechanism[376] is assumed, probably according to[171] (cf. [2]):

$$CuCl^+ + Pd^0 \longrightarrow [Cu\cdots Cl\cdots Pd]^+ \longrightarrow Cu^+ + PdCl \qquad (40)$$
$$CuCl^+ + PdCl \longrightarrow [Cu\cdots Cl\cdots PdCl]^+ \longrightarrow Cu^+ + PdCl_2 \qquad (41)$$

* E_0 for this half-reaction is calculated from the value $E_0 = 0.538$ for $Cu^{2+} + Cl^- + e \rightleftharpoons CuCl$ and from the equilibrium constant $K = 6.5 \times 10^{-2}$ for $CuCl + Cl^- \rightleftharpoons CuCl_2^-$, both listed in Ref. 209.

The Pd(O) may be present as a zero valent complex or in metallic form.

Another proposal that should be relevant to the nonprecipitation of metallic palladium during olefin oxidation involves as the active species a binuclear chloro-bridged complex of palladium and copper of the type

$$
\left[
\begin{array}{c}
\;\;\overset{\displaystyle CH_2}{\underset{\displaystyle Pd}{\overset{\parallel}{\underset{}{C}}}} \\
\end{array}
\right]^{-}
$$

which accounts for the electron acceptance of the Cu^{II} by ligand transfer simultaneously with the cleavage of the Pd-σ-complex formed.[327] Since two electrons must be accepted, either metallic copper is intermediately formed or the electron transfer must occur in two steps or the two electrons are divided over two copper atoms in a trinuclear complex.

Oxidizing agents do not generally exert an influence on the formation of carbonyl compounds if they do not contain inhibiting substances or produce these when reduced. Benzoquinone, for instance, has been used as the oxidant in kinetic investigations,[174,252,393] since in its presence there is no change of H^+, Cl^-, and Pd^{2+}-concentrations.*

Cupric chloride exerts an inhibiting influence because of its chloride ions and the acid produced when reduced during the reaction (cf. Eq. (42)). But if the total H^+ and Cl^- concentrations present in the solution are taken into account, the reaction rate follows the same rate law (e.g., Eq. (6)) in the presence of $CuCl_2$[101b] as well as in its absence, similarly as for benzoquinone.

$$C_2H_4 + 2CuCl_2 + H_2O \xrightarrow{PdCl_2} H_3CCHO + 2CuCl_2^- + 2H^+ \tag{42}$$

The same result has been deduced from kinetic investigations, carried out with olefin–oxygen mixtures.[89,236]

In the presence of $CuCl_2$ the olefin reaction (oxidation to carbonyl compounds) and the oxidation of cuprous chloride formed can proceed simultaneously if an olefin-oxygen mixture is used. The olefin oxidation then becomes catalytic (43).

$$C_2H_4 + \tfrac{1}{2}O_2 \xrightarrow{PdCl_2,\ CuCl_2} H_3CCHO \tag{43}$$

In this case a stationary state characterized by constant oxidation degree ($[Cu^{2+}]/[Cu^+] + [Cu^{2+}]$) is reached when the rates of reduction of $CuCl_2$ (Eq. (42)) and the rate of oxidation of CuCl (Eq. (37)) are equal.[339,342,343] The oxidation degree of the stationary state depends on the presence of agents affecting the reduction and oxidation rates, and on the ethylene and

* Benzoquinone has no effect on the rate of oxidizing ethylene,[169] as it has been reported for CO.[98]

oxygen partial pressures. Thus it can be shifted to higher degrees of oxidation by agents inhibiting the olefin reaction (reduction of $CuCl_2$) and by increasing the oxygen concentration. On the other hand, the oxidation degree of the stationary state can be reduced e.g., when chloride and hydrogen ion concentrations are decreased or the ethylene concentration is increased. The latter measure can reduce the oxidation degree, even until CuCl precipitates.

The oxidation of ethylene in the presence of oxygen is linearly dependent on the palladium chloride concentration and the partial pressure of ethylene up to an ethylene/oxygen ratio that does not yet cause CuCl precipitation (in the corresponding stationary state). When CuCl precipitates, the rate will be controlled by oxygen concentration.[237]

For the first condition (no precipitation of CuCl), the rate equations for the oxidation of ethylene and propylene are fully in accordance with those in the absence of $CuCl_2$ established by Moiseev and Henry (see Eq. (6)). Thus Kiryu and Shiba[192] found the rate equation for the ethylene oxidation in the presence of $CuCl_2$ (Eq. (44))

$$\text{reaction rate} = k \cdot [PdCl_2]^{0.81} \cdot [CuCl_2]^{-1.06} \cdot [H^+]^{-0.91} \cdot p_{C_2H_4} \qquad (44)$$

and Dozono and Shiba[89] found for the propylene oxidation (Eq. (45)):

$$\text{reaction rate} = \frac{k[PdCl_2]p_{C_3H_6}}{[Cl^-]^{2.21}[H^+]} \qquad (45)$$

Both equations can be compared with the simplified expression (6), since the experiments leading to them have been carried out with high Cl^- ion concentrations.

Since the oxygen concentration does not influence the reaction rate, the rate equations derived might also be valid for the reaction in the absence of oxygen, i.e., the reaction rate in the presence of oxidants is determined by the same rate-controlling step as in the absence of oxidants.

It must be noted that all of these studies were carried out with Cl^- ion concentrations high enough to correspond with the concentration of the copper ions in the bivalent state. Lower chloride ion concentrations are important for the technical processes.

For the manufacture of acetaldehyde two technical versions have been elaborated. The *one-stage process* uses a mixture of ethylene and oxygen; the reaction is governed by the above-mentioned conditions, which bring about a stationary state with a given oxidation degree. In the *two-stage process* ethylene and oxygen are reacted separately with the catalyst solution, which is first reduced by the olefin and subsequently reoxidized by air.

Both processes use Cl^- ion concentrations in the catalyst solution lower than those corresponding to the $CuCl_2$ concentration. This leads to an increased rate of reaction because of the formation of cupric oxychloride and the increase of the pH value. During the reduction, according to Eq. (42), the

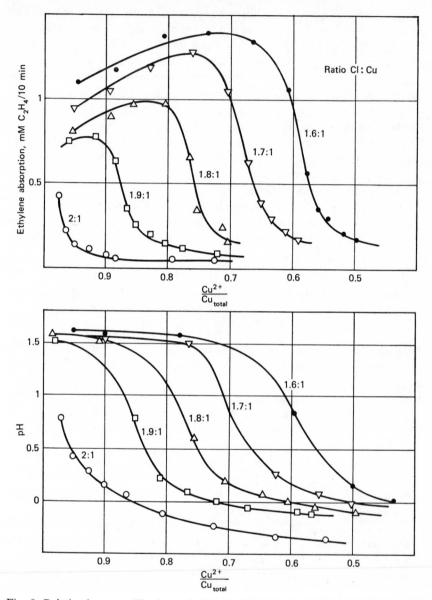

Fig. 8. Relation between pH value and the rate of the reaction of ethylene with aqueous PdCl₂ solutions containing CuCl₂.

high pH value is maintained until all cupric oxychloride present has been neutralized by the H^+ ions formed. Then the pH value drops suddenly. The lower the Cl^-/Cu ratio, the broader the range of fast reaction (see Fig. 8). The technical processes are carried out in this range. The initial increase of the reaction rates with decreasing oxidation degree, as shown in Fig. 8 can be attributed to a lowering of the Cl^- ion concentration due to complexing as $[CuCl_2]^-$.

Technical processes have also been developed for the oxidation of propylene and butene.[347] The oxidation of butenes in the presence of $PdCl_2$ and cupric salts was particularly studied.[202,203,288,290] For descriptions of the technical processes, see Refs. 23, 170, 171, 347.

The presence of $CuCl_2$ in the technical catalyst causes a number of secondary reactions, predominantly chlorinations of the carbonyl compounds. From acetaldehyde, mono-, di-, and trichloro-aldehydes are formed, as well as ethylene chlorohydrin. Among other side products acetic acid, oxalic acid, and condensation products, e.g., chloro-crotonaldehyde can be named. From acetone the main by-product (about 1–2%) is chloroacetone; from methylethylketone 3-chloro-2-butanone. In the latter case the reaction can be conducted in such a way that the 3-chloro-2-butanone is obtained as the main product.[201,289] Other by-products in the butene oxidation are butyraldehyde and the products of oxidative degradation: propionaldehyde or acetaldehyde, respectively (see Section III-F). If nitric acid is used as the additional oxidant, glyoxal[119,297] or glyoxylic acid[32] can be obtained.

The oxidation of ethylene to acetaldehyde is accompanied by liberation of a heat of reaction of 58.2 kcal/mole. Attempts have been made to make use of this heat of reaction in fuel cells to produce electric energy.[194,371]

Papers with prevailing technical aspects on the oxidation of olefins in the presence of $PdCl_2$ and $CuCl_2$ have appeared in various countries.[42–44,366,422]

4. Noble Metal Compounds Other Than PdCl₂

Palladium salts seem to be the most suitable agents for the oxidation of olefins to carbonyl compounds, although other noble metal salts show similar reactions.

As mentioned, Zeise's salt, an ethylene platinum(II) complex $K(C_2H_4PtCl_3)$, yields acetaldehyde with water. Platinum complexes are more stable than comparable palladium compounds. Therefore, the decomposition with water requires elevated temperatures but is also impeded by Cl^- and H^+ ions.[174] Analogous mechanisms are assumed.

The outlined mechanism must also be inferred for the reaction between hexafluoroplatinate(IV) and olefins,[183] according to

$$R \cdot CH = CHR' + [PtF_6]^{2-} + H_2O \longrightarrow R \cdot CO \cdot CH_2 \cdot R' + Pt^{2+} + 4F^- + 2HF$$

(46)

Bi- and tetravalent platinum compounds such as $PtCl_2$, $[PtCl_4]^{2-}$, $[PtCl_6]^{2-}$, $[PtCl_4(OH)_2]^{2-}$, and $[Pt(OH)_6]^{2-}$ have been reported as catalysts for the oxidation of olefins in the presence of oxygen.[342] Among compounds of other platinum metals, $RhCl_3$, $IrCl_4$, and $IrCl_3$ exhibited catalyzing activity. Carbonyl compounds are also formed in reactions between olefins and chloroauric acid[81] or mercuric chloride.[151] The use of Ru^{III} complexes in the presence of cupric salts has also been reported. It could be shown that citric acid increased the activity of Ru^{III} complexes in the oxidation of ethylene to acetaldehyde but only with Cu^{2+} salts present.[283]

When $RhCl_3$ was reacted in aqueous solution with a mixture of ethylene and oxygen, no metal was precipitated. This suggested a Rh^{I} intermediate as parallel to Pd^{0}.[342] In fact, from $RhCl_3$ and ethylene in aqueous methanol, a chloro-bridged binuclear ethylene Rh^{I} complex[61] was isolated:

$$2RhCl_3 + 2H_2O + 6C_2H_4 \longrightarrow [(C_2H_4)_2RhCl_2Rh(C_2H_4)_2]$$
$$+ 2H_3CCHO + 4HCl \quad (47)$$

This reaction was also kinetically studied in dimethylacetamide.[167]

5. Reactions of Various Olefinic Compounds

Olefinic compounds reacted with aqueous $PdCl_2$ solution are listed in Table III. Polarizing effects govern the nature of the reaction products, which generally form according to the following equation:*

$$CH_2 = CH-R \xrightarrow{PdCl_2, H_2O} CH_3-\underset{\underset{O}{\|}}{C}-R \quad (48)$$

if R represents an electron-releasing group such as alkyl, etc.

$$-CH=CH-X \xrightarrow{PdCl_2, H_2O} -\underset{\underset{O}{\|}}{C}-CH_2-X \quad (49)$$

if X represents an electron-attracting group such as

$$-COOH$$
$$-COOR$$
$$-NO_2$$
$$-CN$$
$$-OH, etc.$$
$$-CO$$

the directing effect of these groups depends on the stability of the transition state in the rate-determining step which is influenced by such groups. If the rate-controlling reaction is the heterolysis of a σ-compound corresponding

---

* Products formed are essentially the same as expected by the electrophilic addition of water, according to Markovnikov's rule.

TABLE III

Oxidation of Olefinic Compounds in Aqueous Medium

Substrate	Oxidant	Reaction temperature °C	time, min	Products	Yield % (conversion)	Description in section	Mechanism	Example in section	Refs.
a. Aliphatic mono-olefins:									
Ethylene	PdCl$_2$	20	5	Acetaldehyde	99 (90)	III-A	ol	VI-A-1, VI-A-3	342
	RhCl$_3$·3H$_2$O—MeOH	20	7 hr	Acetaldehyde [(C$_2$H$_4$)$_2$RhCl]$_2$	(77)	III-A-4	ol		61
	PdCl$_2$/CuCl$_2$/O$_2$			Acetaldehyde	95	III-A-3	ol	VI-B-1	23,170, 171,339, 343
	PdCl$_2$/CuCl$_2$/O$_2$			Ethylene chlorohydrin, acetaldehyde				VI-B-2	357
Propene	PdCl$_2$	20	5	Acetone Propionaldehyde	ca. 96 (85) 2-3	III-A-5 III-A-6	ol	VI-A-1, VI-A-4	342 131
1-Butene	PdCl$_2$/CuCl$_2$/O$_2$	100		Acetone, propionaldehyde	ca. 90		ol	Cf. VI-A-1	347
	PdCl$_2$	20	10	Methylethylketone	ca. 95 (80)	III-A-5	ol	VI-A-1	342
2-Butene	PdCl$_2$			Butyraldehyde	2-3	III-A-6	ol	VI-A-4	131
				Methylethylketone	ca. 95	III-A-5	ol	Cf. VI-A-1	342
1-Butene, 2-butene	PdCl$_2$/CuCl$_2$/O$_2$			Methylethylketone	ca. 88		ol	VI-A-1	347
	PdCl$_2$/CuCl$_2$/O$_2$			3-Chlorobutan-2-one, methylethylketone		III-D-2			201
Isobutene	PdCl$_2$	Reflux	1 hr	α-Methacrolein	30-40	III-D-2	all. ol	VI-B-3	342,164
				Isobutyraldehyde	ca. 10	III-F	degr		
				Traces methylethylketone, acetone					

(continued)

35

TABLE III (continued)

Substrate	Oxidant	Reaction temperature °C	time, min	Products	Yield % (conversion)	Description in Section	Mechanism	Example in Section	Refs.
1-Pentene	PdCl$_2$	20	20	n-Propylmethylketone, pentanal	(81)	III-A	ol		342,131
2-Methyl-1-, -2-butene	PdCl$_2$/50% HOAc	90	4 hr	α-Methylcrotonaldehyde	18	III-D-2	all.		160
				2-Methylbutanal	2				
1-Hexene	(pH3)	90	30	β-Methylcrotonaldehyde	8.5–9.5	III-A	ol		160
	PdCl$_2$	30	30	n-Butylmethylketone, hexanal	(75)		all.		342,131
	PdCl$_2$/CuCl$_2$/O$_2$ (in EtOH—H$_2$O)	40		Hexan-2-one	95	III-A-5	ol	Cf. VI-A-2, VI-A-4	126
				Hexanal	5 (100)		ol		
2-Methyl-1-pentene	PdCl$_2$/50% HOAc	90	75	Mesityl oxide	20	III-D-2	(all.?)		160
2-Methyl-2-pentene	PdCl$_2$/50% HOAc	90	75	Mesityl oxide	20	III-D-2	(all.?)		160
				2-Methylpentan-3-one	1		ol		
3-Methyl-2-pentene	PdCl$_2$/50% HOAc	90	6 hr	trans-cis-3-Methylpent-2-en-4-one	62	III-D-2	all.		160
4-Methyl-1-pentene	PdCl$_2$/CuCl$_2$/Cu(OAc)$_2$	85		Methyl isobutylketone	58		ol		134
2,2-Dimethyl-1-butene	PdCl$_2$			t-Butylmethylketone (pinacolone)	Good		ol		164
1-Heptene	PdCl$_2$	50	30	Heptan-2-one, n-heptanal	(65)	III-A	ol	VI-A-2, VI-A-4	342,131
3-Ethylpent-2-ene	PdCl$_2$/H$_2$O—HOAc	90		3-Ethylpent-2-en-4-one	(42)	III-A	all.		160
1-Octene	PdCl$_2$	50	30	Octan-2-one, n-octanal		III-A	ol	VI-A-2, VI-A-4	342
	PdCl$_2$/CuCl$_2$/O$_2$ (in EtOH—H$_2$O)	40		Octan-2-one, octanal	96		ol		126
1-Nonene	PdCl$_2$	70	45	Nonan-2-one	(35)	III-A	ol		342
	PdCl$_2$/CuCl$_2$/O$_2$ (in EtOH—H$_2$O)	40		Nonan-2-one, nonanal	94		ol		126
1-Decene	PdCl$_2$	70	60	Decan-2-one	(34)	III-A	ol		342
	PdCl$_2$/CuCl$_2$/O$_2$	40		Decan-2-one	92		ol		126

1-Dodecene	0.02 mole $PdCl_2$ 0.02 mole $CuCl_2$ (in 50 ml DMF + 7 ml H_2O)	60	150	Dodecan-2-one	85	III-A	ol	VI-B-4	56
1-Tetradecene	$PdCl_2$/$CuCl_2$/O_2 (in EtOH—H_2O)	40		Tetradecan-2-one	92	III-A	ol		126
1-Hexadecene	$PdCl_2$/$CuCl_2$/O_2 (in EtOH—H_2O)	40		Hexadecan-2-one	88	III-A	ol		126
1-Octadecene	$PdCl_2$/$CuCl_2$/O_2 (in EtOH—H_2O)	40		Octadecan-2-one	90	III-A	ol		126
b. Cycloolefins									
Cyclopentene	$PdCl_2$	30	30	Cyclopentanone	61	III-A-5	ol		342
Cyclohexene	$PdCl_2$	30	30	Cyclohexanone	65	III-A-5	ol		342
Cyclohexene	$PdCl_2$(H_2O/AcOH)	20	120	Cyclohexanone, benzene (75%), cyclohexane (25%)	60		ol	VI-A-7	161,164
1-Methylcyclohexene	$PdCl_2$(H_2O/AcOH)	20	30 hr	Toluene, methylcyclohexane	Low; 13.5, 8		disprop; disprop	VI-A-7	161,164
Cycloheptene	$PdCl_2$(H_2O/AcOH)	20	14 hr	Cycloheptanone	10.5	III-A-5	ol		161
Indene	$PdCl_2$	50	60	β-Indanone	66	III-A-5	ol		342
c. Aromatic olefins									
Styrene	$PdCl_2$	50	180	Acetophenone, phenylacetaldehyde, benzaldehyde	57	III-A-5, III-A-6	ol, degr	VI-A-4	131,342 277,279
	$PdCl_2$(H_2O/THF)	50		Acetophenone, phenylacetaldehyde	35	III-A-5	ol		349
m-Nitrostyrene	$PdCl_2$	50	120	m-Nitroacetophenone	35	III-A-5	ol		349
p-Methoxystyrene	$PdCl_2$	20	10	p-Methoxyacetophenone	45	III-A-5	ol		342
p-Chlorostyrene	$PdCl_2$	30	30	p-Chloroacetophenone	36	III-A-5	ol		342
α-Methylstyrene	$PdCl_2$/H_2O, HOAc, NaOAc	105	180	Acetophenone	See Table XII	III-F	degr		164
				2,4-Diphenyl-4-methylpent-2-one		IV-B	olig		
				2,5-Diphenylhexa-2,4-diene	See Table IX	III-E	coupl		
β-Methylstyrene (propenylbenzene)	$PdCl_2$/H_2O, HOAc	Reflux	60	Benzyl methyl ketone	65	III-A-5	ol		164
Allylbenzene	$PdCl_2$	40	30	Benzyl methyl ketone	76	III-A-5	ol		342

(continued)

TABLE III (continued)

Substrate	Oxidant	Reaction temperature °C	time, min	Products	Yield % (conversion)	Description in section	Mechanism	Example in Section	Refs.
Anethol H$_3$C—O—C$_6$H$_4$—CH=CH—CH$_3$	PdCl$_2$	70	270	p-Methoxybenzyl methyl ketone 1-p-Methoxyphenyl-2-methylglyoxal Anisaldehyde	55	III-A-5 III-F	ol ol, ox degr		342,169 169
Estragol H$_3$C—O—C$_6$H$_4$—CH$_2$—CH=CH$_2$	PdCl$_2$	Reflux	180	p-Methoxybenzyl methyl ketone 1-p-Methoxyphenyl-2-methylglyoxal Anisaldehyde		III-A-5 III-F	ol ol, ox degr		169
Isosafrol (methylenedioxyphenyl)CH=CH—CH$_3$	PdCl$_2$	70	150	3,4-Methylenedioxybenzyl methyl ketone (methylenedioxyphenyl)CH$_2$—C(=O)—CH$_3$	69	III-A-5	ol		342
α,β-Dimethylstyrene (2-Phenylbut-2-ene)	PdCl$_2$/H$_2$O—HOAc	100	60	2-Phenylbutan-3-one 2,4-Diphenyl-3,4-dimethylhex-2-ene	4, 5 —	III-A-5 IV-B	ol olig		164
1,1-Diphenylethylene	PdCl$_2$/H$_2$O—HOAc	Reflux	120	Benzophenone, acetophenone 1,1,4,4-Tetraphenylbutadiene	Poor See Table VIII	III-F III-E	degr coupl		164 164
Stilbene	PdCl$_2$ PdCl$_2$/H$_2$O—HOAc	Reflux	12 hr	Acetophenone Desoxybenzoin (benzyl phenyl ketone)	Poor 92.5 (low conversion)	III-F III-A-5	degr ol		342 164
Phenylcyclopropane	PdCl$_2$ (substr.: Pd = 1:1)	75	2 hr	Propiophenone Phenylacetone	60 35	III-A-5	ol iso		285a
	PdCl$_2$ (subtr.: Pd = 1:4)	75	2 hr	(*trans*-Propenylbenzene) Propiophenone	95	III-A-5	ol		285a

d. α,β-Unsaturated acids and their derivatives

								Cf.	
Acrylic acid	PdCl₂	50	180	Acetaldehyde	(50)	III-A-5	ol, dec	VI-A-2	342
n-Butyl acrylate	PdCl₂	20	180	Acetaldehyde	(ca. 80)		ol, hy, dec		169
Methylacrylic acid	PdCl₂	40	60	Propionaldehyde	(61)	III-A-5	ol, dec		342
n-Butyl methacrylate	PdCl₂	20	180	Propionaldehyde,	(low)	III-A-5	ol, hy, dec		169
Methacrylic amide	PdCl₂	5	30	Acetaldehyde Propionaldehyde	82	III-F III-A-5, IV-A-1	degr hy, ol		169 349
β,β-Dimethylacrylic acid	PdCl₂	50	300	Acetone	(15)	III-F	degr		342
Crotonic acid	PdCl₂	50	60	Acetone	(75)	III-A-5	ol, dec		342
Crotonic amide	PdCl₂	50	30	Acetone	(80)	III-A-5, IV-A-1	hy, ol		349
α,β-Pentenoic acid	PdCl₂	35	45	Methyl ethyl ketone	(88)	III-A-5	ol, dec		342
α,β-Pentenoic amide	PdCl₂	50	30	Methyl ethyl ketone	70	III-A-5, IV-A-1	hy, ol		349
trans-α-Methylcrotonic acid (tiglic acid)	PdCl₂	50	120	Methyl ethyl ketone	(40)	III-A-5	ol, dec		342
α-Ethylacrylic acid	PdCl₂/H₂O—HOAc	90	60	Crotonaldehyde	9.4		(all. ?)		160
α,β-Hexenoic acid	PdCl₂	35	70	Pentan-2-one	(94)	III-A-5	ol, dec		342
α,β-Hexenoic amide	PdCl₂	50	30	Pentan-2-one	68	III-A-5, IV-A-1	hy, ol, dec		349
Sorbic acid	PdCl₂	65	15	Pent-2-en-4-one	(35)	III-A-5	ol, dec		342
α,β-Heptenoic acid	PdCl₂	50	50	Hexan-2-one	(86)	III-A-5	ol, dec		342
α,β-Heptenoic amide	PdCl₂	50	30	Hexan-2-one	53	III-A-5, IV-A-1	hy, ol, dec		349
α,β-Octenoic acid	PdCl₂	50	60	Heptan-2-one	(95)	III-A-5	ol, dec		342
Cinnamic acid	PdCl₂	50	10 hr	Acetophenone	(35)	III-A-5	ol, dec		342
Cinnamic amide	PdCl₂	50	80	Acetophenone	48	III-A-5, IV-A-1	hy, ol, dec		349
p-Chlorocinnamic-acid	PdCl₂	70	9 hr	p-Chloroacetophenone	(25)	III-A-5	ol, dec		342
m-Nitrocinnamic amide	PdCl₂	50	6 hr	m-Nitroacetophenone	38	III-A-5, IV-A-1	hy, ol, dec		349
Maleic acid	PdCl₂	50	180	Pyruvic acid	(25)	III-A-5	ol, dec		342
Itaconic acid	PdCl₂	50	60	Succinic aldehyde acid	(30)	III-A-5	ol, dec		342

(continued)

39

TABLE III (continued)

Substrate	Oxidant	Reaction temperature °C	time, min	Products	Yield % (conversion)	Description in section	Mechanism	Example in section	Refs.
e. Diolefins									
1,3-Butadiene	PdCl$_2$	90	30	Crotonaldehyde	34	III-A-5	ol		342,176
1,3-Pentadiene	PdCl$_2$	Reflux	8 hr	Methyl propenyl ketone Methyl propyl ketone Acetone	Traces	III-A-5			176
1,4-Pentadiene	PdCl$_2$	Reflux	6 hr	Methyl propenyl ketone Methyl propyl ketone Acetone	15 10	III-A-5	iso, ol		176
1,5-Hexadiene	PdCl$_2$	Reflux	5 hr	3-Methylcyclopentanone	13	III-F III-A-5	degr ol, condens		176
1,5-Heptadiene	PdCl$_2$	Reflux	6 hr	Acetonylacetone 3-Ethylcyclopentanone 3-Methylcyclo-2-hexen-1-one 2,5-Heptanedione	5 Small	VI-A-6 III-A-5	ol		176
3-Methyl-1,5-heptadiene	PdCl$_2$	Reflux	7 hr	2-Hexanone 2-Methyl-4-ethylcyclopentanone 3-Methyl-3-hepten-1-one 3,6-Dimethyl-2-cyclohexen-1-one 2-Chloro-p-xylene p-Xylene 3-Methyl-2,5-heptandione	6	III-A-5	ol, condens		176
Cyclopentadiene	PdCl$_2$	20–100		[C$_5$H$_5$PdCl]$_x$	Quantitative				345a
1,5-Cyclooctadiene	Pd(OAc)$_2$			Cyclooct-4-enone					4, 5
f. Substituted aliphatic olefins (olefins with hydrolyzable substituents, see Table IV)									

40

Substrate	Temp	Time	Catalyst	Products	Yield (%)	Section	Mechanism	Ref
Nitroethylene	70	60	PdCl$_2$	Nitroacetaldehyde	5.5	III-A-5	ol	349
1-Nitroprop-1-ene	70	60	PdCl$_2$	Nitroacetone	37	III-A-5	ol	349
Acrylonitrile	30	30	PdCl$_2$	Cyanoacetaldehyde	88	III-A-5	ol	131
Allyl alcohol	25	5	PdCl$_2$	Acrolein	75	III-A-5	ol	172,342
Acrolein	20		PdCl$_2$	Acetaldehyde	Traces	III-A-5, III-D	ol, dec	173
Crotyl alcohol	20		PdCl$_2$	Butan-3-on-1-ol		III-A-5	ol	388
				Acetaldol, methyl vinyl ketone		III-A-5	ol	172
				Crotonaldehyde				
Methyl vinyl carbinol	20		PdCl$_2$	Acetaldol, butan-3-on-1-ol		III-A-5	ol	172
				Crotonaldehyde, methyl vinyl ketone				
Crotonaldehyde	25	180	PdCl$_2$	1,3,5-Triacetylbenzene	35	III-A-5	ol, condens	342
Methyl(but-1-en-4-yl)sulfone	50	120	PdCl$_2$	Methyl(butan-2-on-4-yl)sulfone	92(54)	III-A-5	ol	350
5-Bromo-1-pentene	25	30	PdCl$_2$	5-Bromopentan-2-one	(53)	III-A-5	ol	342
1-Hexen-5-one (allylacetone)	67	5 hr	PdCl$_2$/CuCl$_2$/O$_2$ (in DMF—H$_2$O)	Hexan-2,5-dione(acetonylacetone)	70–80	III-A-5	ol	416
10-Undecenoic acid	60	120	0.02 mole PdCl$_2$ 0.02 mole CuCl$_2$ (in 50 ml DMF + 7 ml H$_2$O)	10-Keto-undecanoic acid	85	III-A	ol	56

Note: The following abbreviations for mechanisms are used in the tables in this chapter.

all.	Allylic oxidation (as described in Section III-D).
condens	Any condensation reaction (as secondary reaction).
coupl	Oxidative coupling (as described in Section III-E).
dec	Decarboxylation (as secondary reaction).
degr	Oxidative degradation (as described in Section III-F).
disprop	Disproportionation.
hy	Hydrolytic reactions (as described in Section IV-A-1).
iso	Isomerization (as described in Section IV-C).
ol	Olefin oxidation (as described in Sections III-A, III-B, III-C).
olig	Oligomerization (as described in Section III-B).
ox	Any oxidation reaction (not described here).

to (9) in the case of propylene oxidation, acetone is the main product because of the two possible structures

$$
\begin{array}{cc}
\overset{\displaystyle OH}{\underset{\displaystyle CH_3}{CH_3-\overset{|}{\underset{|}{C}}-PdCl_2}} & \overset{\displaystyle OH}{\underset{\displaystyle H}{CH_3-CH_2-\overset{|}{\underset{|}{C}}-PdCl_2}} \\
\textbf{(9a)} & \textbf{(9b)}
\end{array}
$$

heterolysis of (9a) is favored by the two electron-releasing CH_3 groups.

With electron-withdrawing groups, e.g., in the oxidation of acrylonitrile

$$
\begin{array}{cc}
\overset{\displaystyle OH}{\underset{\displaystyle CN}{H_3C-\overset{|}{\underset{|}{C}}-PdCl_2}} & \overset{\displaystyle OH}{\underset{\displaystyle H}{NC-CH_2-\overset{|}{\underset{|}{C}}-PdCl_2}} \\
\textbf{(9c)} & \textbf{(9d)}
\end{array}
$$

heterolysis of structure (9d) is favored and cyanoacetaldehyde is formed.[131]

Another or additional way to explain the directing effect of substituents is to consider the metal–carbon distances in the olefin complexes. NMR studies have shown[102] that, in Zeise-type complexes of 1-olefins, the terminal CH_2 group is situated nearer to the platinum, thus preforming the carbon–metal σ-bond and, therefore, directing the attack of the OH-ligand to the adjacent carbon atom. For styrene it could be demonstrated by X-ray analysis[157] that in (styrene·$PdCl_2)_2$ the distance between the palladium atom and the terminal carbon atom of the ethylenic group is likewise shorter. In the case of acrylonitrile also, a structurally preferred entering of the OH-group can be assumed, since in the corresponding olefin complex, the palladium might be bonded nearer to the carbon atom adjacent to the CN-group because there are additional bonding relations between palladium and nitrogen. In the only stable complex of $PdCl_2$ with acrylonitrile, the palladium is solely bonded to the nitrogen.[324] Consequently, methylketones are primarily obtained when 1-olefins are reacted, such as acetone from propylene. The corresponding aldehydes are formed only to a minor extent (see Section III-A-6).

While lower olefins give good yields of the ketones desired, higher 1-olefins yield by-products and also isomeric ketones. One can assume that the olefins are already isomerized to some extent in the presence of $PdCl_2$ (see Section IV-C). A laboratory method to improve the yield of methylketones from 1-olefins was described by Clement and Selwitz for the manufacture of dodecanone, using aqueous dimethylformamide as the solvent.[56] Cyclic olefins give cyclic ketones. From cyclooctene no ketone could be obtained.[161]

From α,β-unsaturated carbonyl compounds or α,β-unsaturated carboxylic acids β-dicarbonyl compounds or β-oxo-carboxylic acids, respectively, are primarily formed. But these compounds are unstable and subject to secondary reactions, such as condensation or decarboxylation.

The main products from α,β-unsaturated carboxylic acids are carbonyl compounds with one carbon atom less than the acid fed. In agreement with this, acrylic and crotonic acid give rise to acetaldehyde and acetone, whereas methacrylic acid forms propionaldehyde. Other α,β-unsaturated carboxylic acids react analogously. Esters[169] and amides of such acids react with aqueous $PdCl_2$ to give the same carbonyl compounds as the free acids. Since such derivatives of β-oxocarboxylic acids are stable, the $PdCl_2$ must somehow exert an additional influence on their hydrolysis and decarboxylation.

According to the general scheme, acetylacetaldehyde should be expected as the oxidation product of crotonaldehyde. However, it can be isolated only as its condensation product: 1,3,5-triacetylbenzene.

From acrolein, only a small amount of acetaldehyde beside side products could be obtained.[169] The reaction might proceed via malondialdehyde, the usual oxidation product, which would be oxidized to β-oxo-butyric acid followed by decarboxylation, or via acrylic acid and then by the normal route just described.

Allyl alcohol is easily oxidized to acrolein by aqueous $PdCl_2$, even at room temperature.[172,342] Since butan-3-on-1-ol has been obtained from crotyl alcohol,[388] the oxidation of allylic alcohols occurs apparently with the hydroxy group directing the carbonyl group into the β-position to form β-hydroxy carbonyl compounds. These are normally dehydrated in acidic medium to form α,β-unsaturated carbonyl compounds.

Starting from either crotyl alcohol or α-methylallyl alcohol (which are known to isomerize into each other[305,418] crotonaldehyde and methylvinylketone are obtained. In the reaction medium both alcohols, butan-3-on-1-ol and acetaldol have been determined. Since β-oxypropionaldehyde could be determined in the reaction of allyl alcohol for its oxidation, an analogous route is therefore assumed:[172]

$$H_3C\!-\!CH\!=\!CH\!-\!CH_2OH \xrightarrow{\text{PdCl}_2,\ \text{H}_2\text{O}} H_3C\!-\!CO\!-\!CH_2\!-\!CH_2OH \longrightarrow$$
$$H_3C\!-\!CO\!-\!CH\!=\!CH_2$$

$$H_3C\!-\!CH(OH)\!-\!CH\!=\!CH_2 \xrightarrow[-\text{Pd},\,-2\text{HCl}]{\text{PdCl}_2,\ \text{H}_2\text{O}} H_3C\!-\!CH(OH)\!-\!CH_2\!-\!CHO \longrightarrow$$
$$H_3C\!-\!CH\!=\!CH\!-\!CHO$$

Butadiene reacts with aqueous palladium chloride to yield crotonaldehyde. The reaction proceeds via vinylacetaldehyde, which is easily isomerized under the reaction conditions.[176] (For isomerization reactions, see Section IV-C.) Also, 1,4- and 1,3-pentadiene give n-propenylmethylketone in the reaction with aqueous palladium chloride.

1,5-Hexadiene yields the appropriate diketone, 2,5-hexanedione. The main product, however, is 3-methylcyclopentanone. Cyclic products are obtained also from other 1,5-dienes.[176]

Acetophenone is the main product in the reaction of aqueous palladium chloride solution with styrene. Evidently, the phenyl group acts like an electron-releasing group. Under certain conditions, however (see Section III-A-6), the corresponding aldehyde, phenylacetaldehyde, can be obtained as the main product.

Phenylcyclopropane reacts with aqueous $PdCl_2$ to give propiophenone and phenylacetone.[285a] Propiophenone is the exclusive product if phenylcyclopropane and palladium chloride are used with a mole ratio of 1:4, while with the inverse mole ratio in the first two hours only isomerization to *trans*-propenylbenzene takes place. It is, therefore, assumed that propiophenone is the product of oxidative ring cleavage, whereas phenylacetone is derived from *trans*-propenylbenzene.

6. Aldehyde–Ketone Ratio

Ketones are the main products in the oxidation of 1-olefins. The corresponding aldehydes are obtained under the usual conditions to only a minor extent (about 1–3% of the carbonyl compounds formed). Efforts have been made to increase the ratio of aldehyde to ketone; successful measures found were: increasing the temperature or the H^+ and Cl^- or Pd^{2+} ion concentration.[131,277,279,311] Under these conditions the unfavored carbon atom becomes more ready for the nucleophilic attack of the OH^- ligand. The effect of temperature can well be explained, for at elevated temperatures more OH^- ions have an energy high enough to attack the unfavored carbon atom also. The effect of increasing the H^+ and Cl^- or Pd^{2+} concentration is still obscure. A decrease of the activation energy caused by a "*trans* effect" of the chloro ligands in *trans* position cannot be solely responsible, since a *trans*-chloro ligand is necessary in any case for the interaction between the complexed olefin and the OH^- ligand. Different aldehyde-ketone ratios are observed when different α-olefins are reacted under same conditions.[131] (See also Section VI-A-4.) For industrial purposes these conditions are not advantageous, since increasing the Cl^- and H^+ ion concentration decreases the overall reaction rate considerably.

B. Nonaqueous Media

1. Mechanism and Kinetics

If an olefin is allowed to pass into the solution of a palladium salt in a nonaqueous proton-active solvent, an interaction takes place between the anions of the solvent and the olefin, while the palladium salts are reduced to the metallic form. As oxidation products vinyl compounds such as vinyl esters or vinyl ethers or their formal solvent adducts are obtained. If the solution contains water, the corresponding carbonyl compounds are also formed.

In nonaqueous solvents the olefin oxidation seems to be a reaction that is quite analogous to the oxidation in aqueous solution. It is assumed that the essential step is also an insertion reaction between the olefin and the solvent anion, both complexed to the metal. Because of the lower nucleophilicity of the solvents compared to water, the concentration of the solvent anions must be increased by the addition of the alkaline or alkaline earth salts.

Thus vinyl acetate and ethylidene diacetate are obtained if ethylene is reacted with an acetic acid solution of $PdCl_2$ or $Pd(OAc)_2$ and additional alkaline acetates. In an alcoholic solution of $PdCl_2$, vinyl ethers and the corresponding acetals are formed.[250,362] The same products are obtained if olefin palladium chloride complexes of the type $[olefin \cdot PdCl_2]_2$ are reacted with the nucleophile, instead of the olefin and palladium salt separately.[250,261]

The mechanism of this reaction can easily be derived from the oxidation mechanism in aqueous solution if an OR^- ligand (in which R represents an alkyl or acyl group) instead of an OH^- ligand is assumed to react with the complexed olefin. Moiseev and Vargaftik[245] carried out the reaction in H_3COD and CH_3COOD. They found that the acetal or ethylidene diacetate formed did not contain any deuterium atoms. Therefore, a mechanism must be excluded that involves the formation of a vinyl compound followed by the addition of a solvent molecule. The formation of a deuterium-free acetal or diacetate, respectively, requires an oxonium ion (11′) as intermediate which can either result from complex (9′) via a carbonium ion (10′) or directly in a bimolecular reaction of complex (11′) with a solvent molecule without the carbonium ion intermediate. From the oxonium ion (11′) a D^+ ion dissociates.

For the formation of the vinyl compounds, three different ways can be discussed:

1. Dissociation of vinyl complex (8′), after the metal has taken up the β-hydrogen (Eqs. (50), (51))*

2. Stabilization of carbonium ion (10′) by H^+ ion release (Eq. 52); cf. Moiseev et al.[246]

3. Cleavage of the diacetate or acetal (Eqs. (50), (52), (54), (55))

---

* Cf. hydride transfer in aqueous medium. (Hydride transfer is completed in the route forming the diacetate and the acetal.)

In the following equations R is alkyl or acyl. Inert diluents can be used in these reactions.

$$[ROCH_2CH_2-PdX_2]^- \rightleftharpoons \left[\begin{array}{c} H \quad OR \\ \diagdown \diagup \\ C \\ \| \longrightarrow Pd(H)X_2 \\ C \\ \diagup \diagdown \\ H \quad H \end{array} \right]^- \qquad (50)$$

$$(7') \qquad\qquad\qquad\qquad (8')$$

$$(8') \nearrow \quad \begin{array}{c} H \quad OR \\ \diagdown \diagup \\ C \\ \| \\ CH_2 \end{array} \quad + [Pd(H)X_2]^- \qquad (51)$$
$$\downarrow$$
$$Pd + H^+ + 2X^-$$

$$(8') \searrow \left[\begin{array}{c} OR \\ | \\ H_3C-C-PdX_2 \\ | \\ H \end{array} \right]^- \longrightarrow \left[\begin{array}{c} OR \\ | \\ H_3C-C^\oplus \\ | \\ H \end{array} \right] + PdX_2^{2-} \qquad (52)$$

$$(9') \qquad\qquad\qquad (10')$$
$$\downarrow$$
$$Pd + 2X^-$$

$$(10') \nearrow \quad H_2C=CH-OR + H^+ \qquad (53)$$

$$\searrow +ROD \quad \begin{array}{c} O^\oplus \diagup D \\ H_3C-CH \diagdown R \\ \diagdown OR \end{array} \longrightarrow H_3C-CH \begin{array}{c} \diagup OR \\ \diagdown OR \end{array} + D^+ \qquad (54)$$

$$(11')$$

$$H_3C-CH \begin{array}{c} \diagup OR \\ \diagdown OR \end{array} \longrightarrow H_2C=CH-OR + ROH \qquad (55)$$

If 2-deuteriopropene is reacted with acetic acid in iso-octane in the presence of $PdCl_2$ and Na_2HPO_4, the deuterium atom is found in the isopropenyl acetate formed.[359] This rather curious behavior is not consistent with the hydrogen abstraction and transfer mechanism discussed. It was explained by a proton loss followed by or concurrent with a Pd-assisted 2,1-hydrogen shift.

Kinetic investigations on the reaction of ethylene with $PdCl_2$ and NaOAc in acetic acid led to the rate equation:[269]

$$\text{reaction rate} = \frac{k \cdot [PdCl_2][HOAc]^2[NaOAc][C_2H_4]}{1 + K \cdot [NaOAc]^2} \tag{56}$$

It reveals a first-order dependence with regard to Pd^{2+} and ethylene concentrations (see also [54a, 148]) and a maximum rate dependency on the NaOAc concentration. This has been confirmed by Belov et al.[17,18] For constant concentrations of $PdCl_2$, ethylene, acetic acid, and chloride ions, Eq. (56) resembles Eq. (9) if

$$[NaOAc] = \frac{1}{[H^+]}$$

Since Eq. (9) has been used to conclude the *cis*-ligand insertion mechanism, it is safe to assume parallel mechanisms for the reactions in water and in acetic acid.

The rate maximum dependency on the sodium acetate concentration has also been differently interpreted.[238] Cleavage of oligonuclear palladium complexes by acetate ions should be responsible for the activating influence, while the inhibiting effect should be caused by the competition between acetate ions and the olefin complexing with the palladium salt. Of course, the result of this interpretation is also an acetato-palladium complex with the prerequisite for a *cis*-ligand insertion reaction (oxypalladation). This is in accordance with results of kinetic studies.[54a,148]

cis-Ligand insertion reactions result in the formation of intermediate σ-complexes, which cannot generally be isolated. From nonconjugated cyclic diolefins, however, metal σ-compounds have been obtained in which the metal–carbon, σ-bond is stabilized by a π-bond between the metals palladium, platinum, and the residual double bond, e.g., from cyclooctadiene

(12)   (13)   (14)

Similarly stabilized σ-compounds are formed with amine derivatives.[286] Such complexes are listed in Table IV. Platinum σ-complexes are summarized in Cross.[70]

In these oxymetallation products the nucleophile and the metal are in *trans* position to each other, the metal being endo with respect to the coordinating double bond, the nucleophile being exo.[5,363,364,411]

TABLE IV

Stable σ-Complexes of Palladium(II) and Platinum(II) Derived from Cyclic Diolefins or Allylamines (for example see Section VI-H-1)

Types:

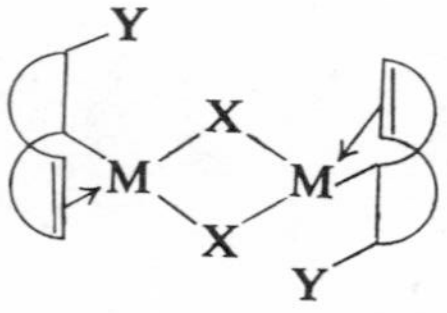

(17)

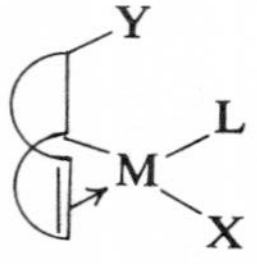

(18)

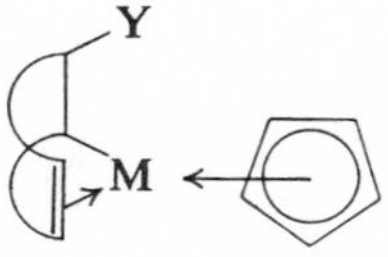

(19)

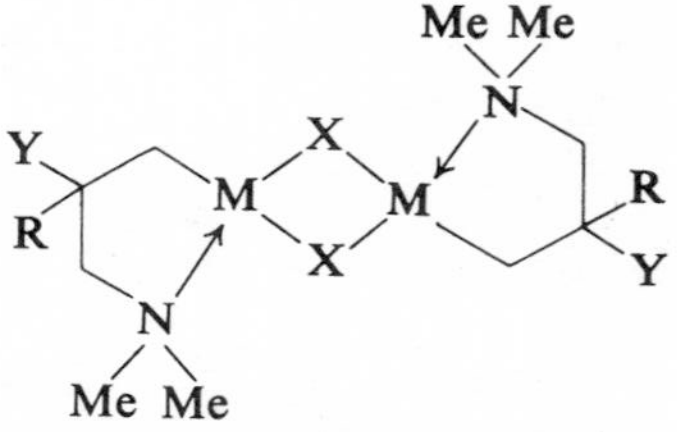

(20)

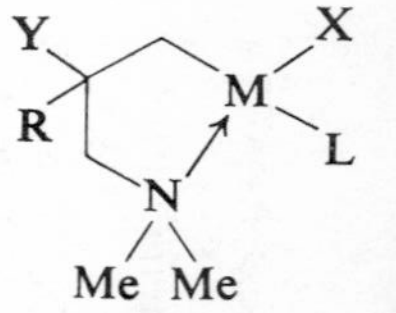

(21)

Examples:

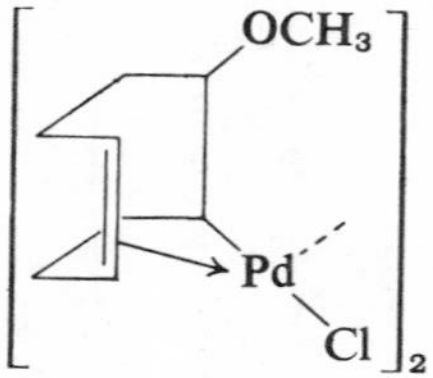

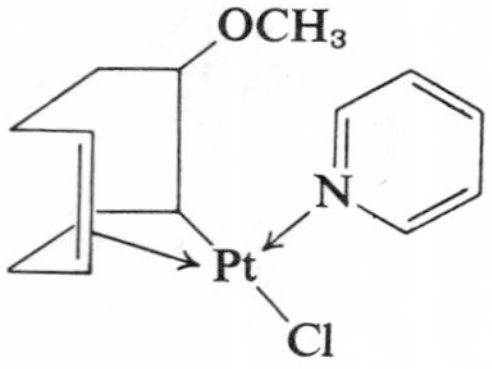

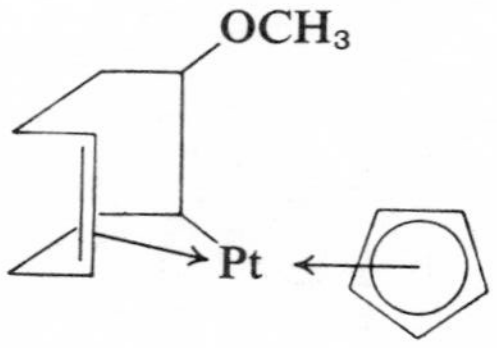

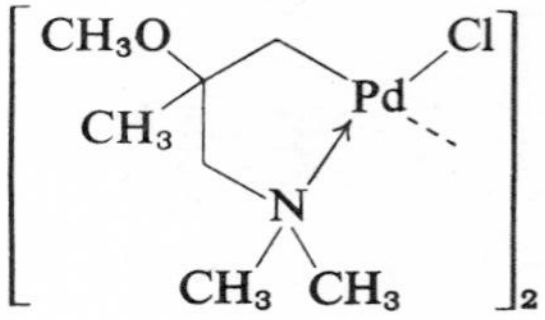

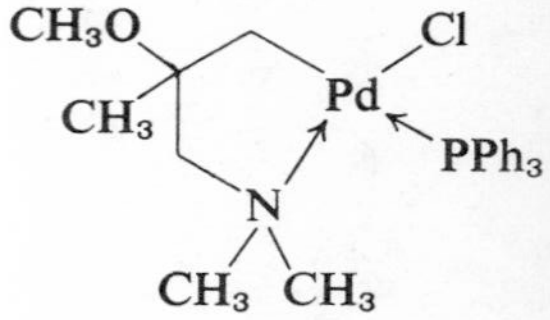

For Dicyclopentadiene:

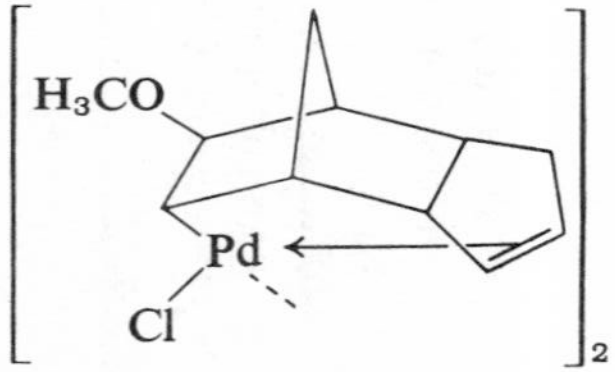

Metal	Original diolefin or allylamine	X	Y	L	Complex type	Refs.
Pd	Cycloocta-1,5-diene	Cl, Br	CH_3O	—	(17)	50
		Cl	CH_3COO	—	(17)	4
		CH_3COO	CH_3COO	—	(17)	4
		CH_3COO	CH_3O	—	(17)	4
		Cl	$CH(COOC_2H_5)_2$ $COCH_3$	—	(17)	386
		Cl	$CH{\big<}{}^{COOC_2H_5}$	—	(17)	386
	Dicyclopentadiene	Cl	RO (R=CH_3, C_2H_5, $n-$, $i-C_3H_7$)	—	(17)	50
		Cl	CH_3O	p-Toluidine	(18)	50
		Cl	CH_3O	Pyridine	(18)	363
		—	CH_3O	—	(19)	363
		Cl	CH_3O	—	(17)	363
Pd	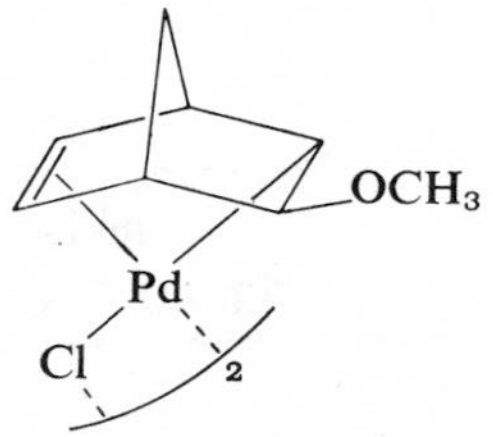 Norbornadiene	—	Internal Insertion	—	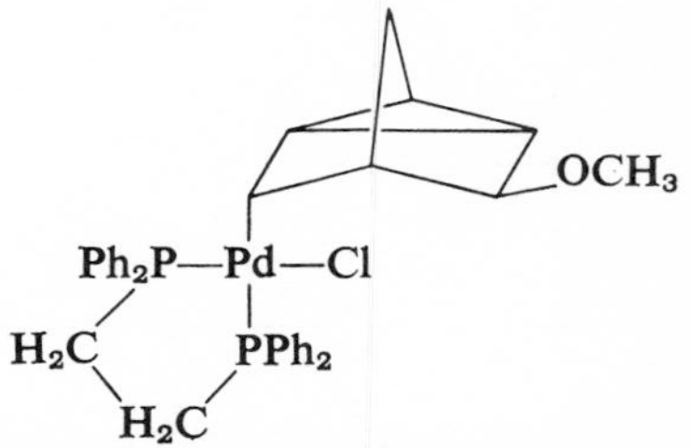 (17)	60a

(continued)

49

TABLE IV (continued)

Metal	Original diolefin or allylamine	X	Y	L	Complex type	Refs.
	+ 1,2-Bis(diphenylphosphino)-ethane					
	4-Vinylcyclohexene	Cl	CH_3COO	—	$\left[\text{OCOCH}_3\text{-cyclohexenyl–Pd}\rightarrow\text{Cl}\right]_2$	286
	N,N-Dimethylallylamine	Cl	CH_3O	—	(20) (R = H)	58
		Cl	CH_3O	Aniline, PPh_3	(21) (R = H)	58
	N,N-Dimethyl-2-methylallyl-amine	Cl	CH_3O	—	(20) (R = CH$_3$)	58
		Cl	CH_3O	Aniline, PPh_3	(21) (R = CH$_3$)	58
		Cl	C_2H_5O	—	(20) (R = CH$_3$)	58
		Cl	C_2H_5O	Aniline, PPh_3	(21) (R = CH$_3$)	58
		Cl	$HOCH_2CH_2O$	—	(20) (R = CH$_3$)	58
		Cl	$HOCH_2CH_2O$	Aniline, PPh_3	(21) (R = CH$_3$)	58
		Cl	(phenyl)CH_2NH—			
Pd, Pt	1,5-Cyclooctadiene, norbornadiene, 4-vinylcyclohexene,	Cl	(phenyl)CH—NH—CH_3	—	(17)	286

	1,5-hexadiene		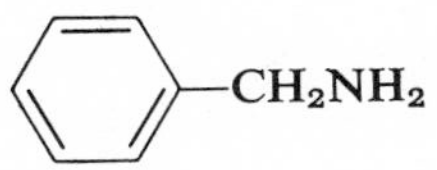			
			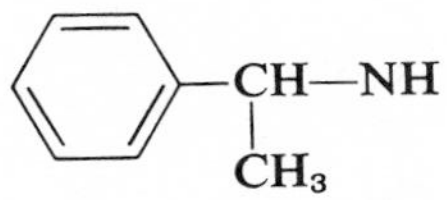			
Pd, Pt	1,5-Cyclooctadiene, norbornadiene, 4-vinylcyclohexene, 1,5-hexadiene	Cl		PPh_3	**(18)**	286
Pt	1,5-Cyclooctadiene	Cl, I	CH_3O	—	**(17)**	49
		Cl	CH_3O	*p*-Toluidine	**(18)**	49
		Cl	CH_3O	Pyridine	**(18)**	363
		—	CH_3O	—	**(19)**	363
	Dicyclopentadiene	Cl, I, SCN, SEt	CH_3O	—	**(17)**	49
		Cl	n-C_3H_7O	—	**(17)**	49
		Cl	CH_3O	*p*-Toluidine	**(18)**	49
		Cl	CH_3O	Pyridine	**(18)**	363
		—	CH_3O	—	**(19)**	363
	Dipentene	Cl	CH_3O	—	**(17)**	49
	Norbornadiene	Cl	CH_3O	—	**(17)**	363

It cannot yet be decided whether these complexes are always intermediates (cf. Section III-B-5), although oxidation products have been obtained therefrom, e.g., 1- and 2-methoxy-1,3-cyclooctadiene from complex (12a)[325] and the isomeric diethyl bicyclo-[6.1.0]-non-4-ene-9,9-dicarboxylate and diethyl cycloocta-3,5-dienylmalonate from complex (12e)[386] (see Table IV).

Ultraviolet irradiation of the insertion product of Pd—OAc and cyclooctadiene (12) gave exo-2-acetoxy-bicyclo[3.3.0]oct-6-ene;[5]

On heating in HOAc at 75° without irradiation, no bicyclic ester but mainly hydrocarbons and some cyclooctenone, cyclooct-2-enyl acetate, and cycloocta-3,5-dienyl acetate are formed.

Oxypalladation products are similarly obtained when N,N-dimethylallyl amine is reacted with $PdCl_2$ or Li_2PdCl_4 in alcohols (e.g., methanol, ethanol, and glycol). The Pd—C σ-bond is stabilized by a Pd—N bond in chloro-bridged binuclear complexes (15) or mononuclear complexes (16). (See Table IV.)

(15)   (16)

2. Reactions with Carboxylic Acids and Carboxylates

Olefins reacted with palladium salts in anhydrous acetic acid in the presence of alkali acetates and their reaction products are listed in Table V. In the patent literature also, other carboxylic acids are claimed as reaction media. As alkali acetate lithium salts (chloride or acetate) are often claimed in patents because they increase the solubility of palladium and cupric chloride to form very soluble chloro complexes.[375a]

With increasing molecular weight of the olefins, the uniformity of the reaction products decreases. While ethylene yields predominantly vinyl acetate, propylene forms i-propenyl acetate along with some n-propenyl acetate and allyl acetate.[19,241] Higher olefins react to form allylic esters.[16,193,394] 1-Olefins give mainly primary allylic esters beside secondary esters and, to some extent also, enol esters. With 2-olefins the formation of enol esters is very low. The results published differ from each other, probably because of different reaction conditions and composition of reaction mixtures that strongly influence the ratio of the products formed. With higher olefins an increasing preisomerization of the olefins gives rise to an even broader spectrum of products.

Surveys of the conversion of higher olefins have been given by Schultz and Gross,[327] for ethylene by van Helden.[148] No enol acetate could be obtained from cyclohexene and cyclopentene.[6,122,275] (See Sections III-B-5, III-D). Butadiene reacts with sodium acetate and $PdCl_2$ in anhydrous acetic acid to give butadien-1-yl acetate.[362] Styrene reacts to form α-acetoxystyrene,[353] β-acetoxystyrene, and other acetoxylated and chlorinated products.[389] Also, diacetates, e.g., those corresponding to n- and i-propenyl acetate have been obtained.[19] Phenyl acetate was obtained from benzene.[76,97] Since a benzene complex of palladium, $[C_6H_6Pd(H_2O)ClO_4]_n$ could be isolated during these investigations,[75] it is safe to assume that benzene can also be activated by complex formation with Pd^{II}. Toluene and other methylbenzenes are acetoxylated preferably in the side chain (see allylic oxidation, Section III-D). These acetoxylations of aromatic compounds occur beside coupling reactions (see Section III-E), which lead to biphenyls or phenyl-substituted ethanes.

Acetaldehyde and acetic anhydride are formed from vinyl acetate and acetic acid under the catalytic influence of $PdCl_2$, according to[55]

$$H_2C{=}CH{-}O{-}COCH_3 + HOOCCH_3 \xrightarrow{\text{PdCl}_2} O(OCCH_3)_2 + H_3CCHO \qquad (57)$$

Ethylidene diacetate was excluded as intermediate but was determined in the reaction mixture.[169] Mechanisms for this reaction, e.g.,[328] which assume the attack of a palladium-complexed acetate ion on an adjacent π-complexed vinyl acetate, do not account for the presence of diacetate.

This reaction, together with the preceding formation of vinyl acetate from ethylene has been claimed as a new process for the manufacture of acetic anhydride from ethylene in the presence of palladium chloride.[31]

As in the aqueous medium the noble metal compound is also reduced to the metallic form in nonaqueous media, and oxidants can be added to prevent metal precipitation. Suitable oxidants are the same as those mentioned in Section III-A-3. For technical purposes also, cupric chloride and acetate are used. Similarly, as described for the reaction in aqueous medium (see Section III-A-3) the palladium(0) may be reoxidized via a binuclear chloro-bridged Pd—Cu complex by ligand (chloride) transfer oxidation.[375b] In the presence of nitric acid glycol mono- and diacetates have been reported as products.[208,335,373]

In the technical process to manufacture vinyl acetate from ethylene, acetaldehyde is found as a by-product. Its formation can be attributed to the three following reactions:

1. From Pd-catalyzed oxidation of ethylene in the presence of water, which is formed in the reoxidation of CuCl according to Eq. (37):

$$2CuCl + 2HCl + \tfrac{1}{2}O_2 \longrightarrow 2CuCl_2 + H_2O \qquad (37)$$

(The amount of acetaldehyde is controlled by the water content of the reaction liquid.)

2. Pd-catalyzed hydrolysis of vinyl acetate (see Section IV-A).

3. Pd-catalyzed decomposition of vinyl acetate according to Eq. (57). Other by-products are ethylidene diacetate, acetic acid and butenes.[148,342,344]

The amount of these by-products formed during vinyl acetate manufacture can be reduced by the addition of acid amides, such as N,N-dimethylformamide, acetamide, N-methylacetamide, and N,N-dimethylacetamide.[52]*

A description of the technical process for vinyl acetate manufacture was given by Krekeler et al.[204,205] and by S. A. Miller,[231] who also summarized. the patent literature. (See also Ref. 327.)

With lower straight-chain olefins, saturated chloroalkyl and glycol-di- and glycol monoacetates are formed as by-products in the presence of cupric salts.[153] This reaction is analogous to the formation of ethylene chlorohydrin in aqueous medium[357] (see Section III-A-1). In acetic acid solution or suspension of $CuCl_2$ and $PdCl_2$, ethylene yields β-chloroethyl acetate, glycol diacetate, and in the presence of water glycol monoacetate. 1-Butene, and cis- and trans-2-butene give different isomers from the various oxypalladation and isomerization products possible (see Table V).

Similarly, cyclohexene reacts in the presence of $CuCl_2$ to yield saturated diesters, such as cis- and trans-1,2-chloro acetates and cis-1,2- and 1,3-diacetates. In the absence of $CuCl_2$ only 2- and 3-cyclohexen-1-yl acetates were found. It is assumed that first the unsaturated ester is formed by the reaction of the olefin with $PdCl_2$, which is then converted to the saturated diester by $CuCl_2$ in the presence of alkali acetate.[154]

Since these reactions have only been observed in the presence of cupric salts, $CuCl_2$ should assist in the formation of glycol derivatives, e.g. β-chloroethyl acetate from the acetoxypalladation intermediate[153] analogously to ethylene chlorohydrin formation in the aqueous medium[357] (see Section III-A-1) via a heterolytic cleavage or ligand transfer oxidation with radical intermediates:

$$[AcOCH_2CH_2-PdCl_2]^- \xrightarrow{2CuCl_2,\ Cl^-} \left[AcOCH_2CH_2-Pd \begin{array}{c} Cl-CuCl_2 \\ \\ Cl\quad Cl-CuCl_2 \end{array} \right]^{2-} \longrightarrow$$

$$AcOCH_2CH_2Cl + [PdCl_4]^{2-} + 2CuCl \quad (58)$$

or

$$[AcOCH_2CH_2-PdCl_2]^- \xrightarrow[-[PdCl_3]^-,\ -CuCl]{CuCl_2} AcOCH_2-CH_2 \cdot \xrightarrow{CuCl_2}$$

$$AcOCH_2CH_2Cl + CuCl \quad (59)$$

* Increasing proportions of dimethylacetamide in the catalyst solution increase the mount of allyl acetatate found in propene oxidation.[54a]

TABLE V

Olefin Oxidation in Carboxylic Acids (see Sections III-B, III-D)

Substrate olefin	Solvent, nucleophile	Oxidant	Reaction temperature °C	time, hr	Products	Yield, %	Mechanism	Example	Refs.
a. Aliphatic olefins and diolefins									
[$C_2H_4PdCl_2$]$_2$	HOAc/NaOAc	[$C_2H_4PdCl_2$]$_2$	20	3	Vinyl acetate	60	ol		250
	HOAc/Na$_2$HPO$_4$/i-C$_8$H$_{18}$	[$C_2H_4PdCl_2$]$_2$			Vinyl acetate		ol		362
Ethylene	HOAc/NaOAc	PdCl$_2$	20	16	Vinyl acetate	20	ol	VI-C-1	250
Ethylene	HOAc/Na$_2$HPO$_4$/i-C$_8$H$_{18}$	PdCl$_2$	20	120	Vinyl acetate	22.2	ol		362
Ethylene	HOAc/NaOAc	PdCl$_2$/benzoquinone	18	63	Vinyl acetate		ol	VI-C-2	250
Ethylene	HOAc/KOAc	PdCl$_2$/CuCl$_2$/O$_2$			Vinyl acetate, acetaldehyde		ol	VI-C-3	356a
Ethylene	HOAc/Li(Na,K)OAc (4 moles)	{PdCl$_2$(0.01 mole)/CuCl$_2$ (2 moles)	100 33 atm	1	(Vinyl acetate) Glycol diacetate, 2-Chloroethyl acetate	See Section VI-C-5	(ol)	VI-C-5	153
Ethylene	HOAc/LiOAc/Licl	Pd(OAc)$_2$/Cu(OAc)$_2$/O$_2$	105		Vinyl acetate, acetaldehyde, ethylidenediacetate, glycoldiacetate 2-Chloroethyl acetate		ol		54a
Ethylene	HOAc/LiCl/Fe(OAc)$_3$	Pd(OAc)$_2$	50		Vinyl acetate, acetaldehyde	66 11	ol		148 148
Ethylene	HOAc	PdCl$_2$/LiNO$_3$, Pd(OAc)$_2$/NaNO$_3$		2	{Glycol monoacetate Glycol diacetate		ol	VI-C-6	373 208
Ethylene	HOAc(gas phase)	Rh, Ru, Ir/C/O$_2$			Vinyl acetate				408
Ethylene	HOAc/NaOAc	Pd/C	100		Vinyl acetate	90	ol	VI-C-4	158
Vinyl chloride (7.5 atm)	HOAc/NaOAc	PdCl$_2$/Cu(OAc)$_2$	75	3	1,2,2-Triacetoxyethane		ol	VI-C-9	199
Propene	HOAc/NaOAc	PdCl$_2$			*n*-Propenyl acetate Isopropenyl acetate Allyl acetate		ol ol all.		241 327 359 394

(*continued*)

TABLE V (*continued*)

Substrate olefin	Solvent, nucleophile	Oxidant	Reaction temperature °C	time, hr	Products	Yield, %	Mechanism	Example	Refs.
Propene	HOAc/Na$_2$HPO$_4$/i-C$_8$H$_{18}$	PdCl$_2$	20	118	Isopropenyl acetate		ol		362
Propene	HOAc	Pd(OAc)$_2$			Allyl acetate (90%)		all.		35
					Isopropenyl acetate (9%)		ol		35
Propene	HOAc	Pd(OAc)$_2$	25		Isopropenyl acetate (98.6%)		ol		193
					n-Propenyl acetate (0.5%)		ol		193
					Allyl acetate (0.9%)		all.		193
Propene	HOAc/NaOAc	PdCl$_2$			n-Propylidene diacetate		ol		19
					Isopropylidene diacetate				19
Propene	HOAc	PdCl$_2$/LiNO$_3$	50	2	CH$_3$CH(OAc)—CH$_2$OH, CH$_3$—CH(OH)—CH$_2$OAc				373
Allyl acetate	HOAc—MgCl$_2$	PdCl$_2$/Cu(OAc)$_2$			Glyceryl diacetate Glyceryl triacetate	75	ol		138a
1-Butene	HOAc	Pd(OAc)$_2$			*trans*-Crotyl acetate (40%)		ol (all.), iso		35
					H$_3$C—CH—CH—CH=CH$_2$ (17%) OAc		all.		35
					CH$_2$=CH—CH$_2$—CH$_2$OAc (34%)		all., iso		35
					Enol acetates (9%)		ol		35
1-Butene	HOAc	Pd(OAc)$_2$	25		Crotyl acetate (*trans : cis* = 80:20 (9%))		all., iso		193
					H$_3$C—CH$_2$—C=CH$_2$ (80%) OAc		ol		193
					H$_3$C—CH$_2$—CH—CH—CHOAc (9%)		ol		193
					H$_2$C=CH—CH$_2$—CH$_2$OAc (2%)		all., iso		193
1-Butene	HOAc/NaOAC	PdCl$_2$, benzoquinone			H$_2$C=CH—CH—CH$_3$ OAc		all.		16

Olefin	Solvent/base	Catalyst	Temp (°C)	Products	Type	Ref.
1-Butene	HOAc/NaOAc(4 M)	PdCl$_2$, CuCl$_2$(2M)		H$_2$C=C(OAc)—CH$_2$—CH$_3$	ol	16
				cis,trans-H$_3$C—C(OAc)=CH—CH$_3$	ol, iso	16
				cis,trans-H$_2$C(OAc)—CH=CH—CH$_3$	ol, iso	16
1-Butene	HOAc	PdCl$_2$/LiNO$_3$		1-Chloro-2-acetoxybutane (58.9%)	ol	153
				2-Chloro-1-acetoxybutane (11.6%)		153
				1,2-Diacetoxybutane (16.5%)		153
				Some 2,3-, 1,3-, and 1,4-isomers		153
				C$_2$H$_5$—CH(OAc)—CH$_2$OH, C$_2$H$_5$—CH(OH)—CH$_2$OAc		373
cis-2-Butene	HOAc/Na$_2$HPO$_4$/i-C$_8$H$_{18}$	PdCl$_2$	100	sec-Butyl acetate		359
cis-2-Butene	HOAc—NaOAc(4M)	PdCl$_2$/CuCl$_2$(2M)		1-Chloro-3-acetoxybutane (35%)		153
				3-Chloro-1-acetoxybutane (26%)		
				1,3-Diacetoxybutane (10%)		
				2-Chloro-3-acetoxybutane (15%)		
				2,3-Diacetoxybutane (14%)		
trans-2-Butene	HOAc—NaOAc(4M)	PdCl$_2$/CuCl$_2$(2M)	100	1-Chloro-3-acetoxybutane (18%)		153
				3-Chloro-1-acetoxybutane (15%)		
				1,3-Diacetoxybutane (7%)		
				2-Chloro-3-acetoxybutane (44%)		
				2,3-Diacetoxybutane (17%)		
cis,trans-2-Butene	HOAc	Pd(OAc)$_2$		trans-Crotyl acetate (58%)	all.	35
				H$_3$C—CH(OAc)—CH=CH$_2$ (40%)	all., iso	35
	HOAc/NaOAc	Pd(OAc)$_2$	25	H$_3$C—CH(OAc)—CH=CH$_2$ (97%)(+ enol acetates)	all.	193
Butadiene	HOAc/Na$_2$HPO$_4$/i-C$_8$H$_{18}$	PdCl$_2$	65	H$_2$C=CH—CH=CH—CH$_2$—OAc	ol	362
1-Pentene	HOAc/NaOAc	Pd(OAc)$_2$	25	H$_2$C=C(OAc)—CH$_2$—C$_2$H$_5$ (85%)	ol	193

(continued)

57

TABLE V (*continued*)

Substrate olefin	Solvent, nucleophile	Oxidant	Reaction temperature °C	time, hr	Products	Yield, %	Mechanism	Example	Refs.
cis-2-Pentene	HOAc/NaOAc	Pd(OAc)₂	25		H₂C—CH=CH—CH—C₂H₅ (10%), OAc		all.		193
					Other enol acetates (5%)		ol.		193
					CH₂=CH—CH—CH₂CH₃ (65%), OAc		all.		193
					CH₃—CH—CH=CH—CH₃ (28%), OAc		all.		193
1-Hexene	HOAc/NaOAc	PdCl₂	25–100	15 min	Enol acetates (7%)		ol.		394
	HOAc/NaOAc	PdCl₂			2-Hexen-1-yl acetate		all.		394
					Hexen-1-yl acetate				
		PdCl₂/CuCl₂	118	15 min	Hexen-2-yl acetate	70–80	ol, all.	VI-C-7	{327, 210a}
					Hexen-3-yl acetate				
1-Heptene	HOAc/NaOAc	PdCl₂			2-Hepten-1-yl acetate		all.		394
1-Decene	HOAc/NaOAc	PdCl₂			2-Decen-1-yl		all.		394
b. Aromatic and cyclic olefins and diolefins									
Styrene	HOAc/KOAc	PdCl₂	100		α-Acetoxystyrene		ol		353
	HOAc/NaOAc	PdCl₂/CuCl₂/O₂			β-Acetoxystyrene		ol		389
					α-Chloroethylbenzene				389
					α-Acetoxyethylbenzene				389
					α,β-Dichloroethylbenzene				389
					α-Chloro-β-acetoxyethylbenzene				389
					α,β-Diacetoxyethylbenzene				389
	HOAc	Pd(OAc)₂	95	4	α-Acetoxystyrene (5%)		ol		391
					cis-β-Acetoxystyrene (11%)		ol		391
					trans-β-Acetoxystyrene (22%)		ol		391
					trans,trans-1,4-Diphenylbutadiene (57%) (see Table VIIIb)		coupl		391

Olefin	Solvent	Oxidant			Products			Ref.
	HOAc—NaOAc	PdCl$_2$	95	4	β-Acetoxystyrene (1.9%)		ol	391
					cis-β-Acetoxystyrene (22.9%)		ol	391
					trans-β-Acetoxystyrene (49.2%)		ol	391
					Acetophenone (3.8%)		ol	391
					trans,trans-1,4-Diphenylbutadiene (12%) (see Table VIII)		coupl	391
α-Methylstyrene	HOAc	Pd(OAc)$_2$	95	4	$C_6H_5-C(=CH_2)-CH_2OAc$ (18.2%)		all.	391
		Pd(NO$_3$)$_2$	95	4	trans,trans-2,5-Diphenylhexa-2,4-diene (41.0%)		coupl	391
					Acetophenone (51.5%)		degr	391
					$C_6H_5-C(=CH_2)-CH_2OAc$ (33.8%)		all.	391
β-Methylstyrene	HOAc	Pd(OAc)$_2$	95	4	$trans\text{-}C_6H_5-CH=CH-CH_2OAc$		all.	391
Cyclopentene	HOAc—NaOAc	PdCl$_2$			2-Cyclopenten-1-yl acetate		all.	122
					1-Cyclopenten-3-yl acetate		all., iso	122
Cyclohexene	HOAc—NaOAc	Pd(OAc)$_2$, PdCl$_2$	75		Cyclohex-2-enyl acetate		all.	6,122
					Cyclohex-3-enyl acetate		all., iso	6,122
	HOAc	—	20		Cycloocta-3,5-dienyl acetate	Low	ol	5
					Cyclooct-2-enyl acetate	Low		5
					Cyclooct-4-enone	Low	ol	5

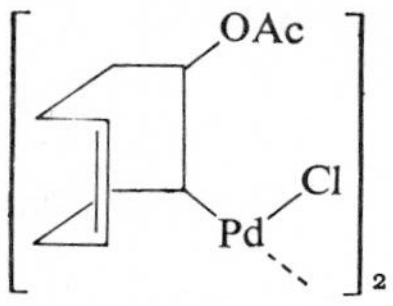

[Pd complex structure: bis(μ-chloro) dimer with OAc and bicyclic ligand, shown as $\left[\text{OAc}\cdots\text{Pd}\cdots\text{Cl}\right]_2$]

+ ultraviolet

[Product: bicyclopentane OAc structure] 20   5

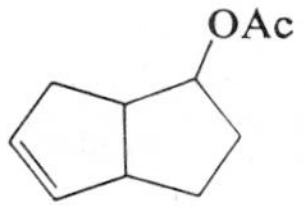

(continued)

59

TABLE V (*continued*)

Substrate olefin	Solvent, nucleophile	Oxidant	Reaction temperature °C	time, hr	Products	Yield, %	Mechanism	Example	Refs.
c. Aromatics									
Benzene	HOAc—NaOAc	Pd(OAc)₂	100	16	Phenyl acetate (Biphenyl, see Table VIII)		ol		76
	HOAc—LiOAc—NaNO₂(N₂O₄)	Pd(OAc)₂/carrier	160–180	18	Phenyl acetate	1–2	ol		97
Benzene		Pd(OAc)₂ or Pd + NaNO₂	100		Nitrobenzene	1–2			380a
Toluene	HOAc—NaOAc	Pd(OAc)₂	100	4	Benzyl acetate (3,3′-Dimethylbiphenyl, see Table VIII)		all.		76
	HOAc—KOAc	Pd(OAc)₂	100	5	Benzyl acetate	92.5	all.		33
					Benzylidene diacetate	6	all.		33
	HOAc—KOAc	PdCl₂			Benzyl acetate (Bitolyls, see Table VIII)	Traces	all.		149
	HOAc—KOAc	Pd/Al₂O₃/O₂	120	10 min	Benzyl acetate	93 (19)	all.	VI-C-8	206
	HOAc—KOAc—Sn(OAc)₂	Pd(OAc)₂—O₂/C	100	9	Benzyl acetate	41	all.	VI-C-8	34
					Benzylidene diacetate	0.5			34
					Benzaldehyde	4.2			34
					Methyl benzoate	0.2			34
[(PPh₃)₂ClPdCH₂-C₆H₅]	AgOAc/HOAc			10.5	C₆H₅CH₂OAc	24.0			101a
					C₆H₅CH(OAc)₂	7.0			101a
	KOAc/HOAc			22.0	C₆H₅CH₂OAc	6.0			101a
[PPh₃Pd(CH₂C₆H₅)-Cl]₂	AgOAc/HOAc			10.5	C₆H₅CH₂OAc	33.0			101a
					C₆H₅CH(OAc)₂	24.0			101a
	KOAc/HOAc			22.0	C₆H₅CH₂OAc	22.0			101a
Toluene	EtCOOH—EtCOOLi—Sn(OAc)₂	Pd—O₂/C	100	6	Benzyl propionate	20.8	all.		34
					Benzyl acetate	0.5	all.		34
					Benzaldehyde	0.2			34
					Benzylidene dipropionate	0.8			34

Substrate	Reagent	Solvent	Temp. (°C)	Time (h)	Product(s)	Yield (%)		Ref.
	Pd(OAc)$_2$ (1 equiv)	HOAc	90	13	Benzyl acetate	81	all.	36b
					Benzaldehyde	4		36b
					Benzylidene diacetate	6		36b
	Pd(OAc)$_2$ (2 equiv)	7% HOAc—H$_2$O			Benzyl acetate	32	all.	36b
					Benzaldehyde	28		36b
p-Methoxytoluene	Pd(OAc)$_2$	HOAc	90	13	p-Methoxybenzyl acetate	96	all.	36b
o-Methoxytoluene	Pd(OAc)$_2$	HOAc	90	13	o-Methoxybenzyl acetate	85	all.	36b
p-Chlorotoluene	Pd(OAc)$_2$	HOAc	90	13	p-Chlorobenzyl acetate	25	all.	36b
p-Nitrotoluene	Pd(OAc)$_2$	HOAc	90	13	p-Nitrobenzyl acetate	1	all.	36b
					p-Nitrobenzaldehyde	1		36b
Xylenes	Pd(OAc)$_2$	HOAc—NaOAc	110	1	Methylbenzyl acetates		all.	76
o-Xylene	Pd(OAc)$_2$—O$_2$/C	HOAc—KOAc—Sn(OAc)$_2$	100	24	o-Methylbenzyl acetate	24.7	all.	34
					o-Methylbenzylidene diacetate	1.4		34
					o-Xylene diacetate	12.1		34
	Pd(OAc)$_2$ (2 equiv)	HOAc	90	13	o-Methylbenzyl acetate	38	all.	36b
					o-Xylylene diacetate	16	all.	36b
					Benzyl acetate	4		36b
					Toluene	4		36b
m-Xylene	Pd(OAc)$_2$—O$_2$/C	HOAc—KOAc—Sn(OAc)$_2$	100	24	m-Methylbenzyl acetate	16.2	all.	34
					m-Methylbenzylidene diacetate	2.5		34
					m-Xylylene diacetate	18.0		34
					m-Tolualdehyde	6.8		34
p-Xylene	Pd(OAc)$_2$—O$_2$/C	HOAc—KOAc—Sn(OAc)$_2$	100	8	p-Methylbenzyl acetate	33	all.	34
					p-Methylbenzylidene diacetate	1.9		34
					p-Xylylene diacetate	15.7		34
p-Xylene	Pd(OAc)$_2$ (2 equiv)	HOAc	90	13	p-Methylbenzyl acetate	38	all.	36b
					p-Xylylene diacetate	16	all.	36b
					Benzyl acetate	6		36b
					Toluene	6		36b
Mesitylene	Pd(OAc)$_2$—O$_2$/C	HOAc—KOAc—Sn(OAc)$_2$	100	24	3,5-Dimethylbenzyl acetate	5	all.	34
					by-products			34
Durene	Pd(OAc)$_2$—O$_2$/C	HOAc—KOAc—Sn(OAc)$_2$	100	4 days	1,4,5-Trimethylbenzyl acetate	27.7	all.	34
Hexamethylbenzene	Pd(OAc)$_2$—O$_2$/C	HOAc—KOAc—Sn(OAc)$_2$	110	4 days	Pentamethylbenzyl acetate	21.9	all.	34
	Pd(OAc)$_2$	HOAc—NaOAc	100	1	Pentamethylbenzyl acetate		all.	76
	Pd(OAc)$_2$—O$_2$/C	EtCOOH—EtCOOLi—Sn(OAc)$_2$	145	4 days	Pentamethylbenzyl propionate	26.5	all.	34

Analogous is the reaction of norbornene with palladium halides in acetic acid containing sodium acetate and cupric halides. Because of steric reasons (see Section III-B-5), and also because of the stability of the carbonium ion formed, hydride abstraction or transfer does not take place. Already the first σ-compound (according to (7′)) is cleaved heterolytically and after rearrangement—typical for this ring system—*exo*-2-chloro-*syn*-7-acetoxynorbornane[13] is formed, according to

(60)

3. Reactions with Alcohols

Reactions of olefinic compounds with alcoholic solutions of palladium salts lead mainly to acetals or ketals. Corresponding vinyl ethers are obtained only to a minor extent.[247] Their formation can, however, be favored by diluting the reaction mixture with an inert solvent,[362] or by selecting other special reaction conditions, e.g., for the formation of vinyl ethyl ether.[353] The presence of water causes the formation of carbonyl compounds. With glycols cyclic acetals, e.g., dioxolanes from 1,2-glycols and 1,3-dioxanes from 1,3-glycols are obtained.[212] Examples are listed in Table VI.

The directing effect of the site of a nucleophilic attack is quite analogous to the reaction in aqueous solution. Thus electron-releasing alkyl groups cause the formation of a ketal group at the adjacent double-bonded carbon atom (i.e., from 1-olefins, ketals of methyl ketones are obtained), while electron-attracting groups direct the nucleophile into the β-position, e.g., from acrylonitrile the acetal of cyanoacetaldehyde is obtained.

1,5-Cyclooctadiene results in the formation of 1- and 2-methoxycycloocta-1,3-diene. It has already been mentioned that in this case an intermediate σ-complex can be isolated[325] (Table IV). From styrene the formation of β-ethoxystyrene beside traces of α-ethoxystyrene was observed.[353]

As in aqueous solution cupric salts or other oxidants can be used to regenerate the Pd^{II} salt, which is reduced to the metallic form during the reaction.

The use of glycols as solvents has been claimed as an improved method for the manufacture of carbonyl compounds via cyclic acetals or ketals because of the excellent solubility of the catalyst components and the high reaction rate.[212]

4. Reactions with Other Nucleophiles

The success of the olefin oxidation with palladium salts in aqueous and acetic acid media for the manufacture of acetaldehyde and vinyl acetate, respectively, stimulated the use of other nucleophiles. Since most of them are rather strong complexing agents, olefin complexing is obstructed. Nevertheless, oxidation products were obtained.

In polar solvents, such as esters, ethers, nitriles, etc., it has been claimed that ethylene reacts with HCl, O_2, and $PdCl_2$ in the presence of $CuCl_2$ to form vinyl chloride.[39] A mechanism similar to those mentioned, i.e., ligand-insertion reaction, may be involved.

It may hold also for the thermal decomposition of $K[C_2H_4PdCl_3]$[174] and $[C_2H_4PdCl_2]$[120] which form vinyl chloride on heating along with ethylene, according to

$$K[C_2H_4PtCl_3] \longrightarrow C_2H_3Cl + Pt + HCl + KCl \qquad (61)$$

From the propylene analog $K[C_3H_6PtCl_3]$, isopropenyl chloride and allyl chloride are obtained.[172]

The reaction of ethylene and propylene with $PdCl_2$ and alkali metal fluoride leads to the formation of vinyl fluoride and 2-fluoropropene, respectively.[67] With $Pd(CN)_2$ in solvents such as benzonitrile or acetonitrile from ethylene, the principal product is acrylonitrile, together with some propionitrile.[274] Dimethylformamide and dimethylsulfoxide decrease the amount of acrylonitrile formed.

From amines and acid amides no vinyl compounds could be isolated. However, hydrogenation of the intermediates formed results in the formation of the corresponding saturated compounds:[362] butyl isopropyl amine and N-isopropylacetamide were obtained from propylene and n-butylamine or acetamide, respectively. The interaction of acetamide with $[C_2H_4PdCl_2]_2$ gave N-ethylacetamide after hydrogenolysis.

Carbanions as nucleophiles are treated in Section III-E.

Sodium nitrite or dinitrogen tetroxide reacts with benzene in acetic acid-lithium acetate solution only in the presence of palladium chloride to form nitrobenzene and phenyl acetate.[380a] Since the formation of phenyl acetate has been described as an analogous reaction to olefin oxidation (see Section III-B), the palladium chloride-catalyzed nitration of benzene can be assumed as the nucleophilic attack of a nitrite ion on the aromatic substrate.

TABLE VI
Oxidation of Olefins and Nonhydrolyzable Olefinic Compounds in Alcohols

Substrate olefin	Nucleophile, solvent	Oxidant	Reaction temperature °C	press. atmg	time, hr	Products	Yield %	Mechanism	Example described	Refs.
a. Reaction of olefins with monohydric alcohols										
Ethylene	Methanol	PdCl$_2$				H$_3$CCH(OCH$_3$)$_2$		ol		246
	Ethanol/ether	PdCl$_2$/benzoquinone	18		6	H$_3$CCH(OC$_2$H$_5$)$_2$	72	ol	VI-D-1	250
	Ethanol	PdCl$_2$				Ethyl vinyl ether				353
						Diethylacetal	Traces			353
[C$_2$H$_4$PdCl$_2$]$_2$	Ethanol	Pd^{II}	20		2	H$_3$CCH(OC$_2$H$_5$)$_2$	63	ol		250,187b
	Isopropanol/*i*-C$_8$H$_{18}$	Pd^{II}	5		4	H$_2$C=CH—O—CH(CH$_3$)$_2$	1.6	ol		362
Ethylene	Isopropanol/*i*-C$_8$H$_{18}$	PdCl$_2$	20		16	H$_3$CCH(O—CH(CH$_3$)$_2$)$_2$	15.8	ol		362,187b
						Vinyl isopropyl ether	1.5	ol		362
						Acetaldehyde isopropyl acetal		ol		362
1-Octene	Methanol, ethanol	PdCl$_2$/CuCl$_2$	60		2	Octan-2-one and isomers	20.2	ol		212
Styrene	Ethanol, *sec*-butanol	PdCl$_2$/CuCl$_2$	50		3	Acetophenone, phenylacetaldehyde		ol		212
	Ethanol	PdCl$_2$				β-Ethoxystyrene				353
						α-Ethoxystyrene	Traces			353
Cyclohexene	Ethanol	PdCl$_2$/CuCl$_2$	50		3	Cyclohexanone		ol		212
Acrylonitrile	ROH	PdCl$_2$/CuCl$_2$	100			Cyanacetaldehyde acetals		ol		212
Cyclooctadiene	Methanol	PdCl$_2$				1- and 2-Methoxy-1,3-cyclooctadiene		ol		325
b. Reaction of olefins with di- and trihydric alcohols										
Ethylene	Glycol	PdCl$_2$/CuCl$_2$/O$_2$	100	20		2-Methyl-1,3-dioxolane	91	ol	VI-D-2	212
	1,3-Propandiol	PdCl$_2$/CuCl$_2$/O$_2$	50	4-12	0.7	2-Methyl-1,3-dioxane		ol		212

64

Olefin	Diol	Catalyst			Product		Ref.
Propylene	Glycol	$PdCl_2/CuCl_2/O_2$	50	6–10	0.7	2,2-Dimethyl-1,3-dioxolane	ol	212
	1,2-Propylene glycol	$PdCl_2/CuCl_2/O_2$				2,2,4-Trimethyl-1,3-dioxolane	ol	212
	2,4-Pentandiol	$PdCl_2/CuCl_2/O_2$				2,2,4,6-Tetramethyl-1,3-dioxane	ol	212
	Glycerol	$PdCl_2/CuCl_2/O_2$				2,2-Dimethyl-4-hydroxymethyl-dioxolane	ol	212
1-Butene	Glycol	$PdCl_2/CuCl_2/O_2$	50	6–10	0.7	2-Methyl-1-ethyl-1,3-dioxolane	ol	212
1-Octene	1,3-Propanediol	$PdCl_2/CuCl_2/O_2$	100	2	3	2-Methyl-2-n-hexyl-1,3-dioxane	ol	212
					Small	2-n-Heptyl-1,3-dioxane		
Cyclopentene	Glycol	$PdCl_2/CuCl_2/O_2$				1,4-Dioxaspiro[4,4]nonane	ol	212

Structure for 1,4-Dioxaspiro[4,4]nonane:

```
H2C—CH2       O—CH2
          \  /
           C
          /  \
H2C—CH2       O—CH2
```

| Cyclohexene | Glycol | $PdCl_2/CuCl_2/O_2$ | 20 | 5 days | | 1,4-Dioxaspiro[4,5]decane | ol | 212 |

Structure for 1,4-Dioxaspiro[4,5]decane:

```
       CH2—CH2     O—CH2
                CH
H2C
       CH2—CH2     O—CH2
```

| | 1,3-Propanediol | $PdCl_2/CuCl_2/O_2$ | 85 | 2 | 2 | 1,5-Dioxaspiro[5,5]undecane | ol | 212 |

Structure for 1,5-Dioxaspiro[5,5]undecane:

```
       CH2—CH2     O—CH2
                CH       CH2
H2C
       CH2—CH2     O—CH2
```

Styrene	Glycol	$PdCl_2/CuCl_2/O_2$	85	2	0.5	2-Benzyl-1,3-dioxolane	ol	212
Acrylonitrile	Glycol	$PdCl_2/CuCl_2/O_2$	85	2	0.5	2-Cyanomethyl-1,3-dioxolane	ol	212 (VI-D-3)
	Propylene glycol	$PdCl_2/CuCl_2/O_2$				2-Cyanomethyl-3-methyldioxolane	ol	212
	1,3-Propanediol	$PdCl_2/CuCl_2/O_2$	100	2	3	2-Cyanomethyl-1,3-dioxane	ol	212
	2,3-Butylene glycol	$PdCl_2/CuCl_2/O_2$				2-Cyanomethyl-4,5-dimethyl-dioxolane	ol	212

65

TABLE VII

Oxidative Reactions in Nonaqueous Medium with Nucleophiles Other Than Carboxylates and Alcohols (see Section III-B-4)

Substrate olefin	Nucleophile, solvent	Oxidant	Reaction temperature °C	time, hr	Products	Yield %	Mechanism	Example	Refs.
$[C_2H_4PdCl_2]_2$	Thermal decomposition	Pd^{II}	170		Vinyl chloride, ethylene		ol		120
$K[C_2H_4PtCl_3]$	Thermal decomposition	Pt^{II}	200		Vinyl chloride, ethylene		ol		174
Ethylene	HCl, polar solvents	$PdCl_2/O_2$	150		Vinyl chloride		ol		39
	{LiF, CsF / $C_6H_5NO_2$—H_2O	$PdCl_2$ or $[C_6H_5CNPdCl_2]_2$	190	20	Vinyl fluoride		ol		67
	HF, gas phase	$PdCl_2$—$FeCl_3$—$CuCl_2$/C			Vinyl fluoride	Low	ol		317
	CN^-, benzonitrile acetonitrile	$Pd(CN)_2$			Acrylonitrile (propionitrile)	51 7	ol	VI-E-1	274 274
	HCl, gas phase	$PdCl_2/CuCl$/carrier/O_2			Vinyl chloride				168,320
	HCl, gas phase	Pd/carrier/O_2			Vinyl chloride				93
	HCN, gas phase	Pd/carrier/O_2			Acrylonitrile				10,96
$[C_2H_4PdCl_2]_2$	Acetamide/Na_2HPO_4/THF	Pd^{II}			*After hydrogenation:* N-ethylacetamide				362
$K[C_3H_6PtCl_3]$	Thermal decomposition	Pt^{II}	200		2-Chloropropene, allyl chloride	High	ol, all.		169
Propylene	HCl	PdO/carrier/O_2			Allyl chloride		all.	VI-E-2	155a
	CsF, $C_6H_5NO_2$—H_2O	$PdCl_2$ or $[C_6H_5CNPdCl_2]_2$	190	20	2-Fluoropropene				67
	n-Butylamine/Na_2HPO_4/THF	$PdCl_2$			*After hydrogenation:* butyl-isopropylamine				362
	Acetamide/Na_2HPO_4/THF	$PdCl_2$			*After hydrogenation:* N-isopropylacetamide				362
Benzene	HOAc—LiOAc—$NaNO_2(N_2O_4)$	$Pd(OAc)_2$ or $Pd + NaNO_2$	100	18	Nitrobenzene	1–2			380a
					Phenyl acetate (see Table V)	1–2			
Cyclohexene	H_2NCOOR	$PdCl_2$			N-(Cyclohexen-1-yl)carbamidic esters		ol		236

5. Stereochemistry

Olefin oxidation with palladium salts to form carbonyl and vinyl compounds, acetals, diacetates, and the like has been interpreted from kinetic data as a *cis*-ligand insertion reaction. The reaction must be necessarily thought of as a stereospecific *cis* addition to C=C double bonds.

This assumption has found support by other evidence: the course of the isomerization of *cis*-2-butene in the presence of a deuterio-rhodium complex leads to *trans*-2-D-2-butene. The first step in this reaction is the *cis*-addition of a deuterio-rhodium complex to *cis*-2-butene,

$$
\begin{array}{ccc}
\underset{\text{H}_3\text{C}}{\overset{\text{H}}{>}}\text{C}=\text{C}\underset{\text{CH}_3}{\overset{\text{H}}{<}} & \xrightarrow{+\text{rhD}} & \underset{\text{H}_3\text{C}}{\overset{\text{rh}}{>}}\text{HC}-\text{CH}\underset{\text{CH}_3}{\overset{\text{D}}{<}} & \xrightarrow{\text{rotation}}
\end{array}
$$

$$
\underset{\text{H}_3\text{C}}{\overset{\text{rh}}{>}}\text{HC}-\underset{\text{D}}{\overset{\text{H}}{\text{C}}}-\text{CH}_3 \xrightarrow{-\text{rhH}} \underset{\text{H}_3\text{C}}{\overset{\text{H}}{>}}\text{C}=\text{C}\underset{\text{D}}{\overset{\text{CH}_3}{<}} \qquad (62)
$$

which releases a rh-H-complex, leaving a deuterated *trans*-butene apparently after rotation of the σ-compound.[64] (For a detailed description of olefin isomerization, see Section IV-C.) *Trans* addition and subsequent *trans* elimination must be excluded since no free hydride ion would be stable under the reaction conditions. The same considerations can be applied for the hydride transfer (β-hydride abstraction and subsequent *cis* insertion) postulated as an essential step in the olefin oxidation (see Eqs. (21), (22), (50), (52)). This hydride transfer should depend on the possibility of rotation of the original double bond in the σ-intermediate, complex (7) and (7'). If such stereochemical requirement is obstructed, the course of oxidation deviates at this stage, e.g., the reaction of norbornene with $PdCl_2$ in acetic acid/sodium acetate (see Section III-B-2) in which the σ-intermediate according to (7') is already heterolytically cleaved. The rigid norbornane skeleton blocks the normal course of oxidation with hydride transfer.

The absence of enol acetates in the reactions of cyclohexene and cyclopentene with Pd^{II} in HOAc/NaOAc has been explained by the impossibility for the palladium in position 2 (with respect to the acetoxy group) to abstract the *trans*-hydrogen from carbon 1. Hydrogen abstraction, however, is possible from carbon 3 and carbon 4, leading to 2- and 3-enyl acetates.[122] It may be noted that in aqueous solution cyclohexanone and cyclopentanone are obtained, which indicates a 1,2-hydrogen shift.

This concept of *cis* addition must not exclude a *trans* addition in cases that favor such addition by suitable reaction conditions. From the coupling constants of the adjacent hydrogen atoms, for instance, it could be shown with complexes of dicylopentadiene[256,363,364] and norbornadiene[121] that

the OR-groups are in *trans*-exo-position with regard to the palladium.

Also, for the acetoxylation products and the corresponding products from cyclooctadiene a *trans* configuration (exo with regard to the double bond) is assumed, which might be peculiar for these ring systems.[5] The reactions resemble oxymercuration[214] and oxythallation.[155] The configuration is maintained if 1-chloro-1-propene is converted to *n*-propenyl acetate[361] (see Section IV-A). This can only be explained by assuming the opposite stereo-chemical course of addition and elimination.

C. Heterogeneous Reactions

The oxidation of olefin to carbonyl compounds was carried out with a heterogeneous catalyst, when a mixture of ethylene, oxygen, and hydrogen was passed over a catalyst consisting of palladium metal supported on charcoal.[342] The reaction was assumed to proceed through a bivalent palladium that was formed by oxygen in the presence of residual traces of hydrogen chloride. Water as nucleophile was formed by the combustion of hydrogen.[345]

Therefore, the first experiments for the development of a continuous process for acetaldehyde manufacture were carried out by passing a mixture of ethylene, oxygen, and water vapor over $PdCl_2$ and additional ferric and cupric chlorides as cocatalysts supported on charcoal.[342,345] In this reaction the reduction of $PdCl_2$ by ethylene and its regeneration by oxygen in the presence of the cooxidants, as described for the aqueous medium, occur simultaneously, so that the overall reaction was catalytic. The space-time yield has been found to have a maximum with a stoichiometric ethylene–oxygen ratio (60–70% ethylene).[238] The reaction in the gaseous phase, however, is not carried out on a technical scale because of the insufficient lifetime of the catalyst. A rapid decrease of the catalytic activity was also observed by other authors,[238] who furthermore found acetaldehyde formation in the absence of water vapor. As water exerts only a catalytic function in the overall reaction and the catalytic activity is increased if steam is added to the reaction mixture, the same mechanism has to be assumed.

Similarly, vinyl acetate is obtained by passing ethylene, oxygen, and acetic acid vapor over $PdCl_2$ and $CuCl_2$ on a charcoal carrier.[417] Alkali acetate, which is an essential component of the liquid contact, is not needed at all in this reaction, since probably sufficient acetate ions are formed by solvolysis of $PdCl_2$. The yields are low because of an extensive combustion of ethylene to carbon dioxide.

The formation of vinyl chloride has resulted from passing ethylene, oxygen, and hydrogen chloride over $PdCl_2$ and $CuCl_2$ on an inert carrier.[168,320] Vinyl fluoride has been obtained by passing ethylene, oxygen, and HF over a catalyst prepared from $PdCl_2$, $FeCl_3$, $CuCl_2$, and coal at 175°.[317] Also, metallic palladium has been used as a catalyst for olefin oxidation. The metal can be supported on a carrier or be used as palladium black. If ethylene and oxygen are passed over such a catalyst, acetic anhydride and acetic acid are obtained.[182] Acetaldehyde was assumed as an intermediate, which could, however, not be isolated, probably because of rapid oxidation to acetic anhydride. Acetaldehyde was, in fact, a product of ethylene oxidation, together with acetic acid and acetic anhydride in the presence of palladium metal if the residence time of the gas mixture was drastically reduced (1% conversion).[114] The gas was circulated until about 30% ethylene oxidation was obtained. Partial oxidation represented 30–40% of the ethylene conversion beside total oxidation. The selectivity was strongly improved (70% partial oxidation) by using a palladium-gold alloy containing 20% gold as catalyst, which was prepared by reducing the metal chlorides with hydrazine.[331]

In the patent literature the use of metallic catalysts for olefin oxidation has been reported. Procedures were claimed for the manufacture of acetaldehyde[95] (cf. 345), vinyl acetate,[9,316] vinyl chloride,[93] acrylonitrile,[10,96] and allyl chloride (from propylene, HCl, and O_2).[94] Palladium metal supported on a carrier or as palladium black can also be used as a catalyst in a liquid phase reaction of acetic acid (containing sodium acetate) with ethylene.[158] For the manufacture of vinyl acetate a Pd/Au contact has also been claimed,[331] as well as Rh, Ru, and Ir catalysts on carbon in a liquid phase reaction.[408]

Metal catalysis for the manufacture of vinyl acetate from ethylene reached technical importance.[204,329] The process operates with a high conversion rate of ethylene (space-time yield = more than 150 g vinyl acetate per hr and per liter catalyst) and a high yield (91–94%) of vinyl acetate. Remarkable is the almost complete absence of by-product acetaldehyde. A detailed report on the patent literature is given by S. A. Miller.[231]

D. Allylic Oxidation

The type of reaction in which the olefin is oxidized at the α-carbon atom next to the double bond (allylic position) is termed allylic oxidation. It takes place in aqueous medium as well as in nonaqueous systems. In aqueous solutions allylic alcohols or their reaction products are obtained as main products from olefins branched at the double bond, e.g., from isobutene or similar compounds. From straight-chain olefins, allylic compounds are formed only in very minor proportions, while the main course of the reaction follows the "normal" olefin oxidation mechanism. In acetic acid, allylic esters result from propene and particularly from higher olefins (cf. Section III-B).

1. Proposals for a Mechanism

Two mechanisms have been proposed for the allylic oxidation:

1. The use of π-allyl complexes as intermediates.[160,241,394]

2. A route via the olefin palladium complex and the σ-type species formed by oxypalladation and followed by a β-hydrogen abstraction,[193] according to

$$Pd(OAc)_2 + RCH{=}CHCH_2R' \rightleftharpoons RCH{-}\underset{\substack{| \\ OAc}}{}CH{-}\underset{\substack{| \\ PdOAc}}{}CH_2R' \xrightarrow{-HPdOAc} \qquad (63)$$

$$\longrightarrow R{-}CH{-}CH{=}CH{-}R'$$
$$\qquad\quad \underset{OAc}{\overset{|}{}}$$

Contrary to the normal olefin oxidation, the hydride ion is not abstracted from the carbon atom which had been added to the nucleophile.

The first proposal can be deduced from the observation that the same products are formed in the allylic oxidation of olefins and in the reaction of bis-π-allyl complexes derived from these olefins with nucleophiles (see below). This reaction may proceed through a mononuclear species which originates from cleavage of the chloro-bridge. It could be shown by NMR spectroscopy[299,300] and X-ray analysis[223] that in mononuclear π-allyl palladium complexes, in which the two ligands except the allyl group are different (Cl and PR$_3$), the allyl group is unsymmetrically bonded, indicating a certain sp^3 character of one of the outer carbon atoms. Moreover, in investigating the NMR spectra of such π-allyl palladium and Rh complexes, it has been found that at elevated temperatures the protons of the allyl group become magnetically equivalent. This has been interpreted by a rapid interchange of the two σ-allyl forms and the π-allyl form (dynamic allyl form).[60,93,307,358,400,403] (See Section III-D-2.)

It can therefore be assumed that a preformed σ-bond may be cleaved, forming the allylic compound. Several mechanisms for this cleavage could be suggested: (*1*) as S_N1 reaction, forming a carbonium ion, which adds the nucleophile; (*2*) a S_N2 mechanism as an interaction of the nucleophile with the σ-compound; and (*3*) a pseudomonomolecular reaction between the σ-bonded allyl group and the complexed nucleophile. The olefinic group may be bonded to the metal or not (which is indicated by a dotted arrow in the equations).

$$
\begin{array}{c}
\underset{\text{CHR}^3}{\overset{\text{CHR}^1}{R^2C}} \overset{L}{\underset{X}{\xrightarrow{}}} Pd \longrightarrow \underset{\text{CHR}^3}{\overset{\text{CHR}^1}{R^2C}} \overset{L}{\underset{X}{\cdots\cdots\xrightarrow{}}} Pd
\end{array}
$$

$$\Big\downarrow +\,Y \tag{64}$$

$$
\underset{\substack{\oplus\text{CHR}^3 \\ +\,Pd+L+X^-}}{\overset{\text{CHR}^1}{\underset{R^2C}{\|}}}
\qquad
\underset{\substack{\text{CHR}^3Y \\ +\,Pd+X^-+L}}{\overset{\text{CHR}^1}{\underset{R^2C}{\|}}}
\qquad
\underset{\substack{\text{CHR}^3X \\ +\,Pd+L}}{\overset{\text{CHR}^1}{\underset{R^2C}{\|}}}
$$

Mechanism 2 has been derived from the experimental observation[193] that 2-olefins yield almost exclusively secondary allylic esters. However, the formation of crotyl acetate beside α-methylallyl acetate from 2-butene and palladium acetate in the presence of sodium acetate has also been observed.[35,169] Although this primary acetate can also be formed by isomerization of the secondary one, the preferred formation of secondary esters might also be a consequence of intermediate asymmetric mononuclear π-allyl complexes caused by different ligands or by the asymmetry of the π-allyl group. It would be an analogue to the formation of ketones in olefin oxidation.

It cannot yet be decided which one of both mechanisms applies for allylic oxidation, or, whether in one case the first, and in other cases the second, route governs the reaction.

2. Allylic Oxidation in Aqueous Medium

1-Olefins branched at the double bond cannot yield ketones with aqueous palladium chloride by the normal olefin oxidation route. The formation of the corresponding aldehyde is even more suppressed than in the case of unbranched olefins (cf. Section III-A) by the influence of two electron-releasing alkyl groups. Thus the amount of 2-methylalkanals formed from 2-methyl-1-alkenes (Eq. (65)) is very small[160,342]

$$
\underset{RH_2C}{\overset{H_3C}{\diagdown}} C{=}CH_2 + PdCl_2 + H_2O \longrightarrow \underset{RH_2C}{\overset{H_3C}{\diagdown}} CH{-}CHO + Pd + 2HCl \tag{65}
$$

In fact, the main reaction is an allylic oxidation, yielding allyl alcohols:[169]

$$
\underset{H_3C}{\overset{H_3C}{\diagdown}} C{=}CH_2 + PdCl_2 + H_2O \longrightarrow \underset{H_3C}{\overset{HOH_2C}{\diagdown}} C{=}CH_2 + Pd + 2HCl \tag{66}
$$

These allyl alcohols can be isolated from the reaction mixture. However, they are easily subjected to further oxidation with aqueous palladium chloride, forming unsaturated carbonyl compounds through β-hydroxy carbonyl compounds,[172]

$$
\underset{\underset{H_3C}{|}}{\overset{\overset{HOH_2C}{|}}{C}}=CH_2 \xrightarrow[-Pd, -2HCl]{+PdCl_2 + H_2O} \underset{H_3C}{\overset{HOH_2C}{\diagdown}}CH-CHO \xrightarrow{H^+} \underset{H_3C}{\overset{H_2C}{\diagdown}}C-CHO \quad (67)
$$

Therefore, the description of the overall reaction (oxidation of branched olefins to unsaturated carbonyl compounds) as allylic oxidation[160] is correct only for the formation of the intermediate allylic alcohol. In this and the following examples,[160] it cannot be decided which one of the mechanisms governs the reaction. However, the following list shows by which mechanisms the oxidation products can be explained:

		Mechanism
Isobutene	α-Methacrolein	1, 2
2-Methyl-1-butene	α-Methylcrotonaldehyde	1
	β-Methylcrotonaldehyde	None
2-Methyl-2-butene	α-Methylcrotonaldehyde	1, 2
	β-Methylcrotonaldehyde	None
2-Methyl-1-pentene	Mesityl oxide	None
2-Methyl-2-pentene	Mesityl oxide	2
3-Methyl-2-pentene	3-Methyl-2-pentene-4-one	1, 2

In all cases a preceding isomerization of the olefins reacted (see Section IV-C) could be envisaged. However, since the π-allyl complexes that are exclusively formed from these olefins, e.g., (1,2-dimethyl-π-allyl PdCl)$_2$ from 2-methyl-1- and 2-butene, and (1-ethyl-2-methyl-π-allyl PdCl)$_2$ from 2-methyl-1- and 2-pentene yield the same products and even in higher yields isomerization of the starting olefins should be excluded. An isomerization mechanism that occurs before, or simultaneously with, the allyl oxidation yet unknown must be considered (cf. Sections III-D-4 and III-D-6). It must be mentioned that β-methylcrotonaldehyde is obtained preferably in a buffer solution. In no case have the intermediate allylic alcohols been isolated.

For the formation of α-methacrolein from both 1-chloro-2-methyl-1-propene and from 1-chloro-2-methyl-2-propene, an allylic oxidation mechanism can be formulated:

$$
\underset{H_3C}{\overset{H_3C}{\diagdown}}C=CHCl \xrightarrow{XPdOH} \underset{\underset{XPd}{|}}{\overset{H_3C}{\diagdown}}\underset{H_3C}{\diagup}C-CH\underset{CH}{\overset{Cl}{\diagdown}} \xrightarrow[HCl]{-XPdH} \underset{H_2C}{\overset{H_3C}{\diagdown}}C=C\underset{O}{\overset{H}{\diagup}} \quad (67a)
$$

$$\underset{\text{ClH}_2\text{C}}{\overset{\text{H}_3\text{C}}{>}}\text{C}=\text{CH}_2 \xrightarrow{\text{XPdOH}} \underset{\text{ClH}_2\text{C}}{\overset{\text{H}_3\text{C}}{>}}\underset{\overset{|}{\text{PdX}}}{\overset{|}{\text{C}}}-\text{CH}_2 \xrightarrow{-\text{XPdCl}}$$

$$\underset{\text{H}_2\text{C}}{\overset{\text{H}_3\text{C}}{>}}\text{C}-\text{CH}_2\text{OH} \xrightarrow[-\text{Pd, }-2\text{HX}]{\text{PdX}_2} \underset{\text{OHC}}{\overset{\text{H}_3\text{C}}{>}}\text{C}=\text{CH}_2 \qquad (67b)$$

(Cf. also Table IV formation of acrolein and crotonaldehyde from allyl chloride or 3-chloro-1-butene and crotyl chloride, respectively.)

3. Allylic Oxidation in Nonaqueous Media

Since products of allylic oxidation with palladium chloride and acetate in acetic acid solution have already been mentioned (Section III-B) and listed in Table V, only a short repetition is given here. Oxidation products are allylic esters. Lower olefins, e.g., propene, 1-butene, and 1-pentene give enol acetates (mainly secondary and only small amounts of primary isomers), as well as secondary and primary allylic esters, while from 2-olefins and higher 1-olefins mainly allylic acetates (primary and secondary) are obtained. (Examples and references are given in Table V).

Cyclohexene and cyclopentene upon oxidation with $PdCl_2$ in acetic acid give cyclohex- and cyclopent-2- and 3-enyl acetates, respectively.[6,122] A complete absence of enol acetates has been explained by the steric arrangement of the acetoxy group and the metal in *cis* position to each other in the intermediate σ-compound. Palladium is not able to abstract a hydrogen atom from the attacked carbon atom, which is in *trans* position[122] (see Section III-B-5).

In methylbenzenes, the carbon atom of the methyl group can be considered as allylic carbon atom, so that benzylic esters are produced from methylbenzenes. Toluene gives benzyl acetate with $Pd(OAc)_2$—$Sn(OAc)_2$—KOAc in acetic acid. At high conversions benzylidene diacetate is formed. Mesitylene, durene, and hexamethylbenzene give similar oxidation products. Xylenes undergo a selective diacetoxylation and yield α,α'-diacetates in preference to α,α-diacetates.[33,34] If the reaction is carried out with $PdCl_2$ instead of Pd-acetate as main products, e.g., bitolyls are obtained from toluene[149] (see Section III-E).

Electron-releasing groups such as the methoxy group in *o*- and *p*-position increase the yield, while electron-withdrawing groups, e.g., the nitro group, drastically decrease the yield of the corresponding benzyl acetate.[36b] In the course of the reaction to form benzylic esters, a complex of the hydrocarbon with the palladium salt must be assumed as intermediate. Two types of complexes known so far would fulfill the requirements to form benzylic esters on reaction with carboxylate anions. One is a π-allylic complex of the structure,[191]

The other one is a σ-benzyl compound of which stable prototypes [(PPh₃)₂ClPd—CH₂C₆H₅] and [(PPh₃)C₆H₅CH₂—PdCl]₂ have recently been obtained from Pd(PPh₃)₄ and benzyl chloride.[101a] They react with KOAc or AgOAc to give benzyl acetate; the difference in the reaction rate with KOAc and AgOAc (with the latter faster) suggests even a reaction of a coordinated acetate anion (formed by replacement of the chloride ion or cleavage of the chloro-bridge, respectively) with the benzyl group.

Allyl chloride has been used as an oxidation product[94] by passing propylene, HCl and O₂ over palladium metal or PdO₂ supported on pumice. Reaction products and the stereochemistry of the olefin oxidation with the acetates of metals other than palladium[308] do not seem to support a uniform mechanism for these oxidation reactions. With palladium salts the reaction is rather specific although the reason for the formation of enolic and allylic products has not yet been explained.

4. Reactions of π-Allyl Complexes

In reactions of π-allyl complexes with nucleophiles, allylic compounds are obtained. Since the allyl group in π-allyl complexes is in the same oxidation state as olefins, these reactions can also be considered as allylic-oxidation-type reactions. They would represent mechanism 1 (see Section III-D-1) with σ-allyl intermediates.

a. Reactions with Water. Bis-π-allyl palladium complexes are stable compounds and insoluble in water. Therefore, the reaction with water which is accompanied by the precipitation of metallic palladium proceeds very slowly at room temperature (Table VIII). Elevated temperatures accelerate. Reaction products, allylic alcohols, could be identified:[169]

$$\tfrac{1}{2}[\pi—C_3H_5PdCl]_2 + H_2O \longrightarrow H_2C{=}CH—CH_2OH + Pd + HCl \qquad (68)$$

The allyl alcohol can be further oxidized to an unsaturated carbonyl compound by another Pd^{II} from a complex releasing its π-allylic group as an olefin:[164,173]

$$[\pi—C_3H_5PdCl]_2 + H_2O \longrightarrow C_3H_6 + H_2C{=}CH—CHO + 2Pd + 2HCl \qquad (69)$$

Additional $PdCl_2$ or oxidants that regenerate bivalent palladium, e.g., CrO_3 or MnO_2 in sulfuric acid, increase the yield of unsaturated carbonyl compounds.[164,161]

Similarly, bis(1-methyl-π-allyl palladium chloride) gives crotyl alcohol and 1-methylallyl alcohol. The corresponding unsaturated carbonyl compounds, methylvinylketone and crotonaldehyde, respectively, are also obtained by further normal olefin oxidation. Since the allylic alcohols isomerize easily in acid medium, the exact origin of the carbonyl compound is ambiguous.[172]

Homologous π-allyl complexes give unsaturated carbonyl compounds,[160] probably by a similar route. However, it has already been mentioned (Section III-D-2) that particularly in a buffered solution abnormal products show up: from (1,2-dimethyl-π-allyl PdCl)$_2$ the abnormal β-methylcrotonaldehyde is obtained beside the expected α-methylcrotonaldehyde and methylisopropenyl ketone. (1-Ethyl-2-methyl-π-allyl PdCl)$_2$ leads to the abnormal mesityl oxide. (1,3-Dimethyl-2-ethyl-π-allyl PdCl)$_2$ gives under both conditions the expected product, 3-ethyl-2-penten-4-one.

b. Reaction with Other Nucleophiles. Sodium acetate in acetic acid medium attacks bis(π-allyl PdCl), yielding allyl acetate and allyl chloride in almost equivalent amount:[169]

$$[\pi-C_3H_5PdCl]_2 + NaOOCCH_3 \xrightarrow{\text{HOOCCH}_3} H_2C=CHCH_2-OOCCH_3$$
$$+ H_2C=CHCH_2Cl + 2Pd + NaCl \quad (70)$$

Bis(1-methyl-π-allyl palladium chloride) yields analogously crotyl- and 1-methylallyl acetates and crotyl and 1-methylallyl chlorides. Also, carbanions attack bis(π-allyl PdCl). Thus, with diethyl malonate and ethyl acetoacetate, allyl and bis-allyl derivatives of these esters are obtained[387] (see also oxidative coupling, Section III-E):

$$[\pi-C_3H_5PdCl]_2 + 2\,NaCHXCO_2Et \longrightarrow 2\,H_2C=CHCH_2CHXCO_2Et + 2\,Pd$$
$$+ 2\,NaCl^- + NaCHXCO_2Et \longrightarrow (H_2C=CHCH_2)_2CXCO_2Et$$
$$+ 2\,Pd + Nac + HCl \quad (71)$$

Furthermore, an enamine, 1-morpholino-1-cyclohexene, has been reacted with bis(π-allyl PdCl), yielding 2-allylcyclohexanone[387] after hydrolysis.

c. Thermal Decomposition of π-Allyl Complexes. Halogeno-bridged π-allyl palladium complexes give on heating above 160°C allylic halides,[164,419] e.g.,

$$[\pi-C_3H_5PdCl]_2 \longrightarrow 2H_2C=CH-CH_2Cl + 2Pd \quad (72)$$

Analogous examples are the formation of *trans*-crotyl chloride and 3-chloro-1-butene from bis(1-methyl-π-allyl PdCl) and of 3-chloro-2-methyl-1-propene from bis(2-methyl-π-allyl PdCl). Also, the formation of allyl bromide in the thermal decomposition of the corresponding bromo-bridged

TABLE VIII

Formation of π-Allyl Complexes from Olefins and PdCl₂ and Oxidative Reactions

Olefin	Solvent	Reaction temperature, °C	Reaction time, min	π-Allyl Complex and Other Products	Yield %	Description in Section	Example described	Refs.
a. Formation of π-allyl complexes								
Allyl alcohol	—	50	—	Propylene + ($H_2C{=}C{-}CH_2$ / H_2C $CH{-}CH_2OH$ / O)	Almost quantitative	III-D-5	VI-I-1	132,340
Allyl chloride	H_2O	20	ca. 60	[π-Allyl PdCl]₂	Almost quantitative	III-D-5	VI-I-2	173
	H_2O—HOAc 1:1	60	60	[π-Allyl PdCl]₂ + $H_3C{-}CO{-}CHO$	57			164
3-Chloro-1-butene / Crotyl chloride	H_2O	20	ca. 60	[1-Methyl-π-allyl PdCl]₂ + diacetyl	Almost quantitative	III-D-5		173
2-Methallyl chloride	H_2O—HOAc (1:1)	20 (100)	30 (120)	[2-Methyl-π-allyl PdCl]₂	60	III-D-5		164
1-Alkenes	DMF	20	30–180	[π-C_nH_{2n-1} PdCl]₂	30–35			255
	H_2O—HOAc 1:1	90	30–180	[π-C_nH_{2n-1} PdCl]₂	Quantitative	III-D-5	VI-I-3	159a
	$CHCl_3$, Na_2CO_3	RT	5 hr	[π-C_nH_{2n-1} PdCl]₂		III-D-5	VI-I-4	187
[Propene PdCl₂]₂	$CHCl_3$, Na_2CO_3	25	5 hr	[π-Allyl PdCl]₂		III-D-5		187
[Butene PdCl₂]₂	$CHCl_3$, Na_2CO_3	25	5 hr	[1-Methyl-π-allyl PdCl]₂		III-D-5		187
Isobutene	H_2O—HOAc	20 (90)	60	[2-Methyl-π-allyl PdCl]₂	27	III-D-5		160,173
2-Methyl-1-butene	H_2O—HOAc	20 (90)	60	[1,2-Dimethyl-π-allyl PdCl]₂	32	III-D		160
2-Methyl-2-butene	H_2O—HOAc	20 (90)	60	[1,2-Dimethyl-π-allyl PdCl]₂	43	III-D		160
2-Methyl-1-pentene	H_2O—HOAc	20 (90)	80	[1-Ethyl-2-methyl-π-allyl PdCl]₂	27	III-D		160
2-Methyl-2-pentene	H_2O—HOAc	20 (90)	80	[1-Ethyl-2-methyl-π-allyl PdCl]₂	24	III-D		160
2-Methyl-1-pentene	$CHCl_3$, Na_2CO_3	20	5 hr	[2-Propyl-π-allyl PdCl]₂		III-D		187
3-Methyl-2-pentene	H_2O—HOAc	20 (90)	60	[1,2,3-Trimethyl-π-allyl PdCl]₂	68	III-D		160
2,3-Dimethyl-2-butene	H_2O—HOAc	20 (90)	40	[1,1,2-Trimethyl-π-allyl PdCl]₂	90	III-D		160
2,3-Dimethyl-2-butene	H_2O—HOAc	20 (90)	40	[1,1,2-Trimethyl-π-allyl PdCl]₂	91	III-D		160
2-Methyl-2-hexene	H_2O—HOAc	20 (90)	60	[1-Propyl-2-methyl-π-allyl PdCl]₂	34	III-D		160
3-Ethyl-2-pentene	H_2O—HOAc	20 (90)	180	[1,3-Dimethyl-2-ethyl-π-allyl PdCl]₂	98	III-D		160
2,4-Dimethyl-2-pentene	H_2O—HOAc	20 (90)	50	[1-Isopropyl-2-methyl-π-allyl PdCl]₂	72	III-D		160
2,5-Dimethyl-2-hexene	H_2O—HOAc	20 (90)	60	[1-Isobutyl-2-methyl-π-allyl PdCl]₂	30	III-D		160
2,4,4-Trimethyl-1-pentene	H_2O—HOAc	20 (90)	120	[2-Neopentyl-π-allyl PdCl]₂	89	III-D		160
2,4,4-Trimethyl-2-pentene	H_2O—HOAc	20 (90)	180	[1-tert-Butyl-2-methyl-π-allyl PdCl]₂	90	III-D		160

π-Allyl complex	Solvent/nucleophile	Reaction temperature °C	time, min	Products	Yield %	Description in section	Refs.
[Cyclohexene PdCl₂]₂	H₂O—CH₂Cl₂	20		[1,3-Trimethylene-π-allyl PdCl]₂		III-D	161
Cycloheptene	H₂O—HOAc (1:1)	Reflux	60	[1,3-Tetramethylene-π-allyl PdCl]₂	59	III-D	161
1-Methyl-1-cycloheptene	H₂O—HOAc (1:1)	Reflux	60	[1,2-Pentamethylene-π-allyl PdCl]₂	23	III-D	161
1-Methyl-1-cyclooctene	H₂O—HOAc (1:1)	Reflux	180	[1,2-Hexamethylene-π-allyl PdCl]₂	90.5	III-D	161
α-Methylstyrene	H₂O—HOAc (1:1)	105	7 hr	[2-Phenyl-π-allyl PdCl]₂	37	III-D	164
β-Methylstyrene	H₂O—HOAc (1:1)	Reflux	60	[1-Phenyl-π-allyl PdCl]₂	11	III-D	164
α,β-Dimethylstyrene	H₂O—HOAc (1:1)	100	60	[α,β-Dimethylstyryl PdCl]₂	23.5	III-D	164
cis,trans-Cyclododecene	H₂O—HOAc (1:1)	Reflux	60	[1,3-Nonamethylene-π-allyl PdCl]₂	30–40	III-D	160a
1-Methylcyclododecene	H₂O—HOAc (1:1)	Reflux	7 hr	[1,2-Decamethylene-π-allyl PdCl]₂	76	III-D	160a

b. Solvolytic decomposition of bis-(π-allyl palladium chloride) complexes

π-Allyl complex	Solvent/nucleophile	Reaction temperature °C	time, min	Products	Yield %	Description in section	Refs.
[π-Allyl PdCl]₂	H₂O/OH⁻	100	120	Acrolein, propene + allyl chloride, acetone		III-D-4a	164, 169
[2-Methyl-π-allyl PdCl]₂	H₂O	100	120	α-Methacrolein, isobutyraldehyde isobutene	20		164
[1-Methyl-π-allyl PdCl]₂	H₂O/OH⁻	100		Vinyl methyl ketone			169
				Methyl ethyl ketone			169
				Crotonaldehyde			169
				Diacetyl			169
				Acrolein			169
				Acetone			169
[π-Allyl PdCl]₂	HOAc/NaOAc	100		Allyl chloride, allyl acetate (ca. 1:1)			169
[π-Allyl PdCl]₂	EtOH—DMSO / Na-ethyl malonate / Na-ethyl acetoacetate	RT		H₂C=CH—CH₂—CH₂—CHX—CO₂C₂H₅ (H₂C=CH—CH₂)₂CX—CO₂—C₂H₅ (X=CO₂C₂H₅, COCH₃)	High		387
[π-Allyl PdCl]₂	EtOH—DMSO / 1-Morpholino-1-cyclohexene $\begin{matrix} CH_2-CH_2 \\ O \quad N \\ CH_2-CH_2 \end{matrix}$ (HCl)	ca. 100		2-Allylcyclohexanone (O=cyclohexanone with CH₂—CH=CH₂ substituent)	High		387

(continued)

TABLE VIII (continued)

π-Allyl complex	Reaction temperature °C	time, min	Products	Yield %	Description in section	Refs.
c. Thermal (dry) decomposition of bis-(π-allyl palladium chloride) complexes						
[π-Allyl PdCl]₂	>160		Allyl chloride	High	III-D-4c	164
[2-Methyl-π-allyl PdCl]₂	>160		Methallyl chloride	58	III-D-4c	164
			1-Chloro-2-methyl-1-propene	15		
[1-Methyl-π-allyl PdCl]₂	>160		{ 3-Chloro-1-butene / trans-Crotyl chloride (1:1)	High		169
[2-Phenyl-π-allyl PdCl]₂	>220		3-Chloro-2-phenyl-1-propene	57		164
			α-Methylstyrene	12		

π-Allyl complex	Reaction temperature °C	Products	Yield %	Description in section	Ref.
d. Oxidation of bis-(π-allyl palladium chloride) complexes with CrO₃ or MnO₂ or PdCl₂ in aqueous solution (for example see Section VI-1-6)					
[π-Allyl PdCl]₂	100	Pyruvaldehyde, acetone (traces)	Low	III-D-4a	169
[2-Methyl-π-allyl PdCl]₂	100	Methacrolein	40	III-D-4a	160
[1,2-Dimethyl-π-allyl PdCl]₂	100	α- and β-Methylcrotonaldehyde (1:1) methyl isopropenyl ketone	84	III-D-4a	160
[1-Ethyl-2-methyl-π-allyl PdCl]₂	100	2-Methylpent-2-en-1-al / 2-Methylpent-1-en-3-one	20–25	III-D-4a	160
[1,2,3-Trimethyl-π-allyl PdCl]₂	100	3-Methylpent-2-en-4-one	30–40	III-D-4a	160
[1,3-Dimethyl-2-ethyl-π-allyl PdCl]₂	100	3-Ethylpent-2-en-4-one	74	III-D-4a	160
[1,1,2-Trimethyl-π-allyl PdCl]₂	100	2,3-Dimethylbut-2-en-1-al	13	III-D-4a	160
[2-Methyl-1-isopropyl-π-allyl PdCl]₂	100	2,4-Dimethylpent-2-en-1-al	28	III-D-4a	160
[2-Methyl-1-tert-butyl-π-allyl PdCl]₂	100	2,4,4-Trimethylpent-2-en-1-al	19	III-D-4a	160
[1,2-Pentamethylen-π-allyl PdCl]₂	100	1-Formylcyclohept-1-ene	6	III-D-4a	161
[1,2-Hexamethylene-π-allyl PdCl]₂	100	1-Formyl-1-cyclooctene	Low	III-D-4a	161

complexes has been described. The trinuclear complex $(\pi\text{-}C_3H_5)Pd(Br_2Pd)_2$-$(\pi\text{-}C_3H_5)$ evolves first allyl bromide and at higher temperatures (540–640°) bromine.[419]

A thermogravimetric study of the thermal decomposition of various bis(π-allyl) palladium halides was made by Zaitsev et al.[419] Further examples of the formation of allylic compounds from π-allyl complexes include the decomposition of bis(π-allyl)palladium, $(\pi\text{-}C_3H_5)_2Pd$, to yield biallyl[412,413] (see Section III-E). This specific formation of allylic compounds leads to assuming a uniform mechanism, at least for the decomposition of π-allyl complexes. Intermediate σ-allyl compounds are a reasonable explanation. In this connection the cyclooligomerization of butadiene catalyzed by nickel or palladium compounds[412,413] shall be mentioned. These reactions are also formulated through π-allylic intermediates, resulting in compounds in which the C—C links are established in allylic position to the double bond present in the final product. On the other hand, the formation of allyl chloride by the thermal decomposition of the propylene analogue of Zeise's salt, $K[C_3H_6\text{-}PtCl_3]$, beside isopropenyl chloride,[169] must not necessarily proceed through π- or σ-intermediates (cf. Section III-D-1 mechanism 2).

In the thermal decomposition of π-allyl complexes in which the allylic group contains more than 3 carbon atoms, conjugated dienes are also obtained.[88] The following mechanism has been proposed:

$$\text{(73)}$$

An example is the formation of 2,4- and 1,3-octadiene in the ratio 2:1 from bis(π-octenyl)palladium chloride when heated to 160°C at 10^{-2} mm Hg.

d. Further Reactions of π-Allyl PdCl Complexes.

For completeness, we shall mention a few reactions that do not fit into the classification of allylic oxidation given so far, e.g., the exchange of palladium by mercury.[129] The reaction takes place on shaking a solution of chloro-bridged bis(π-allyl)palladium chloride complexes in benzene with metallic mercury. In this reaction σ-allyl mercury compounds, accompanied by the precipitation of metallic palladium, are formed.

$$2R'CH{=}CR{-}CH_2{-}HgCl + 2Pd \quad \text{(74)}$$

The reaction seems to be initiated by cleavage of the chloro-bridges, since with $C_3H_5Pd(PPh_3)Cl$ no metal exchange takes place. This reaction shows that evidently π-allyl mercury compounds are not stable. A π-allyl complex has been assumed as intermediate in propylene oxidation by mercury salts leading to acrolein.[365] However, allylic oxidation by mercury salts has been formulated to proceed through σ-allylic intermediates so far,[308] and a route through allyl alcohol has been described for the oxidation with palladium chloride, so that a π-allylic intermediate must not necessarily be assumed. Ethyl diazoacetate is decomposed at low temperatures by bis(π-allyl palladium chloride), so that the resulting carbene can be added to double and triple bonds and diazirines.[8] The following mechanism for the decomposition has been proposed:

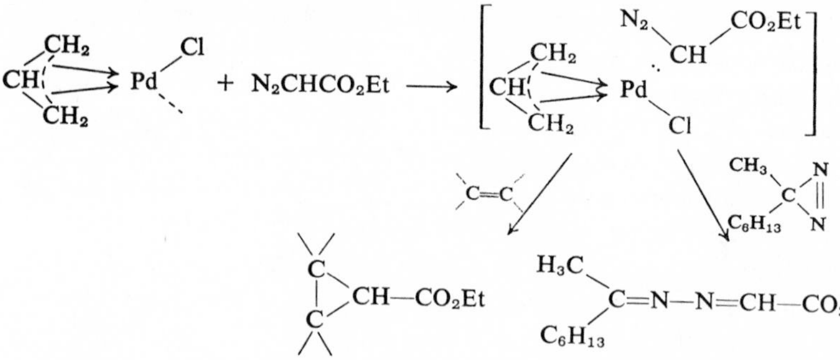

The carbene can also react otherwise, e.g., in 1,3-dipolar addition reactions. The following reactions have been carried out:

Substrate	Product
Cyclohexene	Ethyl bicyclo[4.1.0]heptane-2-carboxylate (47%)
2-Butyne	Ethyl 1,2-dimethyl-1-cyclopropene-3-carboxylate (24%)
Ethyl 1,2-dimethyl-1-cyclopropene-3-carboxylate	Diethyl fumarate
Acetonitrile	2-Methyl-5-ethoxyoxazole (16.3%)
Methyl-n-hexyldiazirine	Ethyl 2-methyl-3,4-diaza-2,4-undecadienoate

In an alkaline alcoholic solution, bis(π-allyl PdCl) complexes are reductively decomposed to give the corresponding olefin and palladium metal.[162]

5. Formation of π-Allyl Complexes

One of the two mechanisms discussed for allylic oxidation of olefins was described to proceed through intermediate π-allyl complexes. In this section only such methods for their preparation are listed, which are related to allylic oxidation.

Bis(π-allyl)palladium complexes are obtained from olefins branched at the double bond in the reaction with palladium chloride in 50% acetic acid buffered with sodium acetate.[163,164,340] (See Table IX.) An equilibrium between olefin complexes of Zeise's or Kharasch's type and π-allyl complexes has been discussed.[164]

$$[C_nH_{2n}\cdot PdCl_2]_2 \rightleftharpoons [\pi-C_nH_{2n-1}\cdot PdCl]_2 + 2HCl \qquad (76)$$

In the presence of sodium carbonate, π-allyl complex formation is favored but the reversibility of the reaction could not be confirmed[187] for bis(π-allyl palladium) complexes. It appears to be a function of the complex stability because $[L_2Pt-\pi-allyl]Cl$ (L = e.g., triphenylphosphine) was reported to evolve the corresponding olefin with HCl.[401] The formation of bis(π-allyl)PdCl complexes from straight-chain olefins is brought about in dimethylformamide.[255]

Bis(π-allyl) complexes are also formed in the reaction of $PdCl_2$ and $PdBr_2$ with anhydrous allyl alcohol,[254,340] as well as with allyl halides in aqueous medium.[164,173] Since the allyl group is a reduction product from these materials, an equivalent amount of oxidation products is also formed. By the interaction of allyl alcohol and $PdCl_2$ an alcohol $C_6H_{10}O_2$ (22) forms catalytically in large amounts, accompanied by propylene evolution:

$$3C_3H_5OH \xrightarrow{PdCl_2} C_3H_6 + C_6H_{10}O_2 + H_2O \qquad (77)$$
$$(22)$$

It is assumed that (22) is formed by a series of insertion reactions:[132]

It could be shown that the methylene species (23) is primarily formed and isomerizes successively into the methyl species (24):

This catalytic reaction (77) is more and more inhibited by the formation of the inactive π-allyl complex $[C_3H_5PdCl]_2$. By this reaction the first π-allyl complex was actually obtained.[340] The compound might be the above-mentioned oxidation product of allyl alcohol:

$$6C_3H_5OH + 2PdCl_2 \longrightarrow (\pi\text{---}C_3H_5PdCl)_2 + 2C_6H_{10}O_2 + 2HCl + 2H_2O \quad (79)$$

In the presence of H_2PtCl_6 and mineral acid, allyl alcohol gives rise to diallyl ether. If other alcohols are present, mixed allyl ethers are formed.[230] Compared with the acid-catalyzed etherification, the metal increases the reaction rate.

The following cyclic process has been suggested:

$$H[Pt(CH_2\!\!=\!\!CHCH_2OH)Cl_3] \; \rightleftharpoons \; Pt(CH_2\!\!=\!\!CHCH_2\overset{\overset{\displaystyle H}{|}}{O}H)Cl_3 \;\overset{-H_2O}{\rightleftharpoons}$$

$$Pt(CH_2\text{----}CH\text{----}CH_2)Cl_3 + \overset{ROH}{\underset{}{\rightleftharpoons}} Pt(CH_2\!\!=\!\!CHCH_2\overset{\overset{\displaystyle H}{|}}{O}R)Cl_3 \rightleftharpoons \quad (80)$$

$$H[Pt(CH_2\!\!=\!\!CHCH_2OR)Cl_3] \xrightarrow[-H_2C=CHCH_2OR]{+H_2C=CHCH_2OH} H[Pt(CH_2\!\!=\!\!CHCH_2OH)Cl_3]$$

With $RuCl_3$, allyl alcohol disproportionates to give propylene and acrolein besides propionaldehyde as isomerization product (see Section IV-C). $RuCl_2$ is assumed to be the catalytically active species.[265]

$$2CH_2\!\!=\!\!CH\text{---}CH_2OH \xrightarrow{RuCl_2} CH_2\!\!=\!\!CH\text{---}CH_3 + H_2C\!\!=\!\!CH\text{---}CHO \quad (81)$$

Similarly, 2-methylallyl alcohol has been converted to isobutene, α-methacrolein, and isobutyraldehyde. The different reactions of allyl alcohols with various metal salts is a good example of their different catalytic activity.

Allyl halides in aqueous medium yield α-hydroxy carbonyl compounds that are further oxidized under the same conditions to form α,β-dioxo compounds.[173] Thus 3-chloro-1-butene, as well as crotyl chloride, react with $PdCl_2$ in an aqueous medium:

$$2C_4H_7Cl + PdCl_2 + 2H_2O \longrightarrow$$

$$HC\!\!\overset{\displaystyle CH_2}{\underset{\displaystyle \underset{\displaystyle CH_3}{|}}{\overset{}{\diagup}}}\!\!\overset{}{\underset{\displaystyle CH}{}}\!\!Pd\!\!\overset{\displaystyle Cl}{\diagdown} + H_3C\text{---}CHOH\text{---}CO\text{---}CH_3$$

$$(C_4H_8O_2) + 3HCl \quad (82)$$

$$C_4H_7Cl + C_4H_8O_2 + PdCl_2 \longrightarrow$$

$$HC\!\!\overset{\displaystyle CH_2}{\underset{\displaystyle \underset{\displaystyle CH_3}{|}}{\overset{}{\diagup}}}\!\!\overset{}{\underset{\displaystyle CH}{}}\!\!Pd\!\!\overset{\displaystyle Cl}{\diagdown} + H_3C\text{---}CO\text{---}CO\text{---}CH_3$$

$$+ 2HCl \quad (83)$$

Therefore these products appear also in the oxidation of allylic compounds in aqueous solution, also at elevated temperatures, when π-allyl complexes cannot be isolated.

In an analogous manner allyl chloride forms pyruvaldehyde.[173,342] In this disproportionation reaction the electron transfer is assumed to proceed through the central Pd atom[173] similarly to the proposal[264] for the reduction of allyl chloride by carbon monoxide to form bis(π-allyl palladium) complexes:[84]

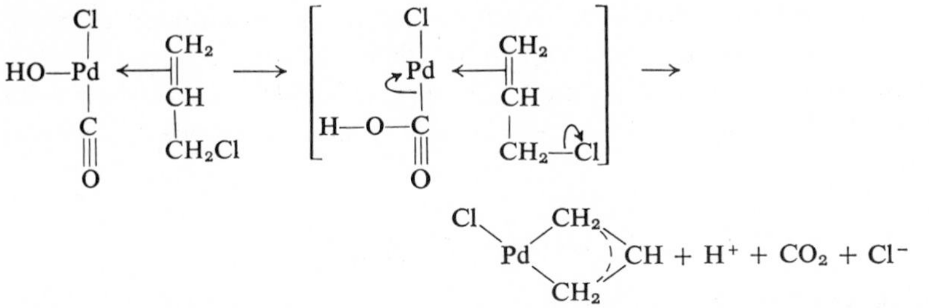

$$\text{Pd} \langle \begin{smallmatrix} \text{CH}_2 \\ \text{CH}_2 \end{smallmatrix} \rangle \text{CH} + \text{H}^+ + \text{CO}_2 + \text{Cl}^- \quad (84)$$

While these reactions occur in aqueous solutions, the oxidation in organic solvents in the presence of alkyl amines is quite similar. However, as oxidation products isocyanates corresponding to the amine used are formed instead of CO_2.[384]

A similar mechanism might govern the reaction of rhodiumcarbonyl chloride with allyl halides.[301]

$$[\text{RhCl(CO)}_2]_2 + 6\text{CH}_2{=}\text{CH}{-}\text{CH}_2\text{Cl} + 4\text{H}_2\text{O} \longrightarrow \quad (85)$$
$$[\text{RhCl}(\pi{-}\text{C}_3\text{H}_5)_2]_2 + 4\text{CO}_2 + 2\text{C}_3\text{H}_6 + 6\text{HCl}$$

6. Reactions of Allyl Halides with PdCl₂ in Aqueous Medium

Allyl halides show a variety of reactions with $PdCl_2$ in aqueous medium, shown in the following scheme:

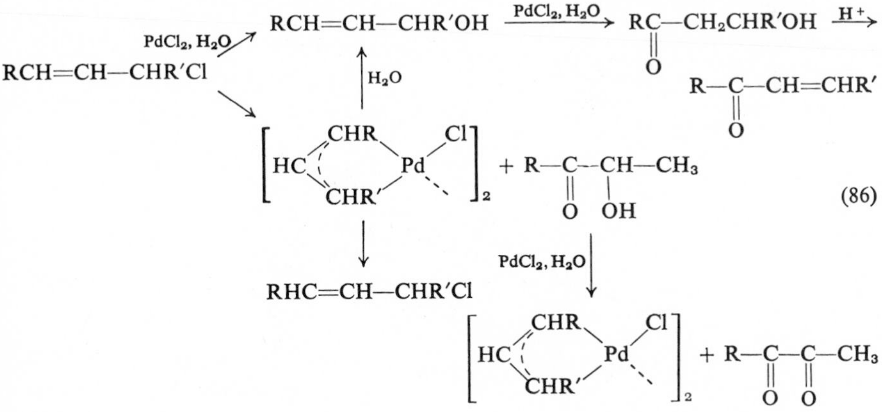

All the compounds shown in this scheme are formed in the reaction of allyl halides with $PdCl_2$ in aqueous solution. The scheme explains the formation of α,β-unsaturated carbonyl compounds from allyl halides through their hydrolysis (Section IV-A) and from the π-allyl complexes through allylic oxidation and, in both cases, the subsequent oxidation of the allylic alcohols formed.

There is no connection between the formation of unsaturated carbonyl compounds and α-dicarbonyl compounds, which has been assumed,[160] since acrolein does not give even traces of pyruvaldehyde on oxidation with aqueous $PdCl_2$; instead some acetaldehyde is formed, as described in Section III-A.

E. Oxidative Coupling

Oxidative coupling according to

$$\begin{array}{c}\diagdown\\C=C\\\diagup\quad\diagdown\end{array}^{H} + RH + PdX_2 \longrightarrow \begin{array}{c}\diagdown\\C=C\\\diagup\quad\diagdown\end{array}^{R} + 2HX + Pd \qquad (87)$$

is consistent with the oxidative formation of a C—C bond. It can be thought of as a reaction between an olefin complex and a carbanion as nucleophile, thus supplementing the reactions presented in Section III-B-4.

1. Reactions with Enolate Carbanions

Cyclooctadiene has been reacted with diethyl malonate and $PdCl_2$ in the presence of sodium carbonate. The isomers (25) and (26) have been obtained[386] via an intermediate σ-complex, according to

(25)   (26)

The isomer **(25)** can be considered as a reaction product of a carbene, while **(26)** corresponds to the normal oxidation product with accompanying isomerization. Similar reaction products are obtained with acetoacetates and methylsulfinylcarbanion.[372]

Acetylacetone has been reacted as a carbanion with styrene in the presence of palladium chloride and cupric chloride in acetic acid solution.[390] The formation of the two isomeric dihydrofuran derivatives has been explained to proceed through the two carbopalladation products possible followed by cleavage of the Pd—C bond and ring closure between an enolic oxygen and the free carbon atom (probably carbonium ion).*

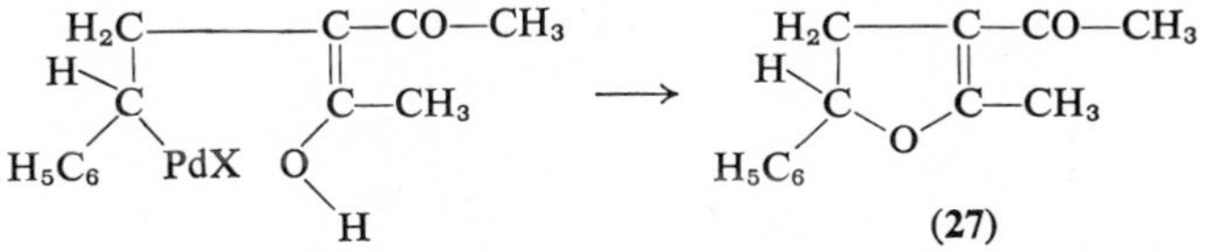

$$H_2C \overline{\quad\quad} C{-}CO{-}CH_3$$

(89a)

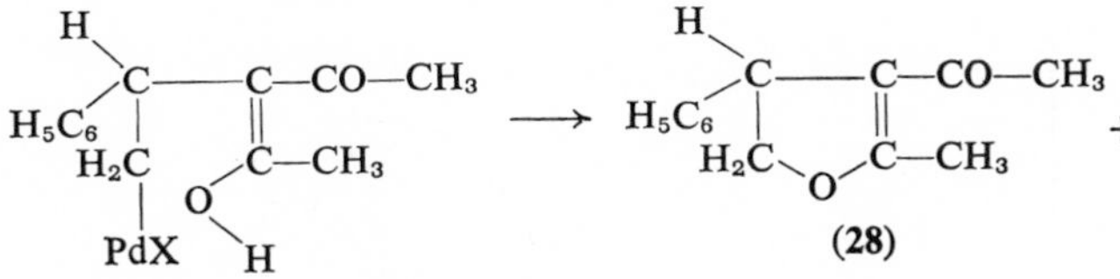

(27)

(89b)

(28)

2. Oxidative Coupling of Olefinic and Aromatic Compounds

Oxidative coupling of olefinic and aromatic compounds takes place at more elevated temperatures if the prerequisites are lacking for other reactions, such as normal olefin oxidation, allylic oxidation, or solvolytic reactions. Thus, in 50% acetic acid, from 1,1-diphenylethylene 33.3% 1,1,4,4-tetraphenylbutadiene are obtained beside 16% benzophenone (see Section III-F). Similarly, α-methylstyrene gives 2,5-diphenyl-2,4-hexadiene in a buffered aqueous solution of palladium chloride.[164] Other 1,1-disubstituted ethylenes and even styrene react in glacial acetic acid which contains alkali acetate with palladium acetate to yield butadiene derivatives (Table IX). Also, vinyl acetate undergoes oxidative coupling to form 1,4-diacetoxy-1,3-butadiene,[198] according to

$$2H_3CCOOCH{=}CH_2 + Pd(OAc)_2 \longrightarrow$$
$$H_3CCOOCH{=}CH{-}CH{=}CH{-}OOCCH_3 + Pd + 2HOAc \quad (90)$$

---

* 3-Acetyl-2-methyl-4,5-dihydrofuran and **(28)** have also been prepared from acetylacetone and ethylene or styrene, respectively, with $Tl(OAc)_3$.[165]

TABLE IX
Oxidative Coupling (formation of C—C bonds) (see Section III-E)

Reactants		Solvent	Oxidant	Reaction temperature °C	time, hr	Products	Yield %	Mechanism	Refs
Substrate	Nucleophile								

a. Reactions of olefins with enolate-carbanions

Substrate	Nucleophile	Solvent	Oxidant	°C	hr	Products	Yield %	Mechanism	Refs
1,5-Cyclooctadiene $PdCl_2$	$H_2C(COOEt)_2$	$DMSO—Na_2CO_3$	Substrate $PdCl_2$					ol, all.	386
		Benzene—Na_2CO_3						ol, iso	
Styrene	Acetylacetone	Acetic acid	$PdCl_2/CuCl_2$	75	18	3-Acetyl-2-methyl-4-phenyl-4,5-dihydrofuran	1.3	ol	390
						3-Acetyl-2-methyl-5-phenyl-4,5-dihydrofuran	2.2	ol	
						α-Acetoxyethylbenzene	12	ol	
Styrene	Acetylacetone	Acetic acid	$Tl(OAc)_3$			3-Acetyl-2-methyl-5-phenyl-4,5-dihydrofuran	69 Based Tl^{III}	ol	165
Ethylene	Acetylacetone	Acetic acid	$Tl(OAc)_3$			3-Acetyl-2-methyl-4,5-dihydrofuran	22 Based Tl^{III}	ol	

b. Oxidative dimerization of olefins

Substrate	Solvent	Oxidant	Reaction tempera-ture °C	time, hr	Products	Yield %	Example described	Refs.
Vinyl acetate	HOAc—NaOAc	Pd(OAc)$_2$	60	2.5	1,4-Diacetoxy-1,3-butadiene	30	VI-F-1	198
Vinyl chloride, fluoride	DMF	PtCl$_2$—Et$_4$NSnCl$_3$(CsF)	25	40	Butadiene	97	Cf. VI-F-3	177
Allyl chloride	DMF	PtCl$_2$—Et$_4$NSnCl$_3$(CsF)	25	72	1,5-Hexadiene	50	Cf. VI-F-3	177
		[C$_6$H$_5$CNPdCl$_2$]$_2$	3–5		1,5-Hexadiene-PdCl$_2$			420
			100		1,5-Hexadiene			420
Isobutene	HOAc—NaOAc	Pd(OAc)$_2$	85		2,5-Dimethyl-2,4-hexadiene	54	Cf. VI-F-2	397
Methyl methacrylate H$_3$COOC—C=CH$_2$ (with H$_3$C)	HOAc—NaOAc	Pd(OAc)$_2$	85		Dimethyl 2,5-dimethylmuconate: H$_3$COOC—C=CH—CH=C—COOCH$_3$ (with CH$_3$, H$_3$C)	20	Cf. VI-F-2	397
Dimethyl 2,5-dimethyl-muconate	HOAc—NaOAc	Pd(OAc)$_2$	85		Dimethyl terephthalate	34	Cf. VI-F-2	397
Styrene	HOAc	Pd(AcO)$_2$	95	4	trans,trans-1,4-Diphenyl-1,3-butadiene (57%); α-Acetoxystyrene (5%), cis-β-Acetoxystyrene (11%), trans-β-Acetoxystyrene (22%) } see Table V			391
	HOAc—NaOAc	PdCl$_2$	95	4	trans,trans-1,4-Diphenyl-1,3-butadiene (12%); α-Acetoxystyrene (1.9%); cis-β-Acetoxystyrene (22.9%); trans-β-Acetoxystyrene (49.2%); Acetophenone (3.8%)			391
α-Methylstyrene	HOAc—H$_2$O—NaOAc	PdSO$_4$ (see Table XII) PdCl$_2$	Reflux		2,5-Diphenyl-2,4-hexadiene	91	VI-F-2	164,

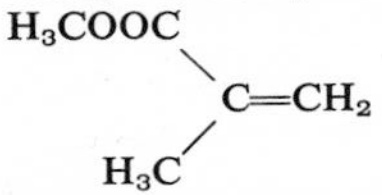

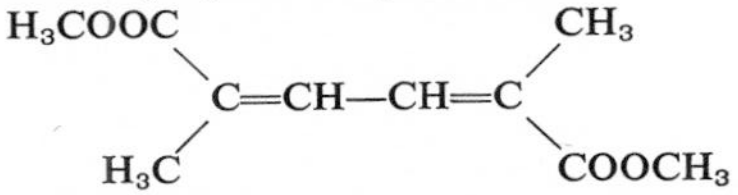

(continued)

87

TABLE IX (*continued*)

Substrate	Solvent	Oxidant	Reaction tempera-ture °C	time, hr	Products	Yield %	Example described	Refs.
C₆H₅\H₃C/C=CH₂	HOAc—NAOAc	Pd(OAc)₂	85		CH_3 C₆H₅—C=CH—CH=C—C₆H₅ with H₃C *trans,trans*-2,5-Diphenyl-2,4-hexadiene (41%), C₆H₅C(CH₂OAc) = CH₂			397 391
1,1-Diphenylethylene	HOAc—H₂O—NaOAc	PdSO₄ (see Table XII) PdCl₂	Reflux		1,1,4,4-Tetraphenylbutadiene	33		164
C₆H₅\C₆H₅/C=CH₂	HOAc—NaOAc	Pd(OAc)₂	85		C₆H₅—C=CH—CH=C—C₆H₅	84	Cf. VI-F-2	397
1,2-Diphenylpropene	HOAc—NaOAc	Pd(OAc)₂	85		2,3,4,5-Tetraphenyl-2,4-hexadiene	22	Cf. VI-F-2	397
2-Phenyl-1-butene	HOAc—NaOAc	Pd(OAc)₂	85		3,6-Diphenyl-3,5-octadiene	25	Cf. VI-F-2	397
C₆H₅\CH₃/CH—CH=CH₂	HOAc—NaOAc	Pd(OAc)₂	85		CH_3 C_6H_5 C₆H₅—CH—CH=CH—CH=CH—CH with H₃C	30		397
2,5-Diphenyl-2,4-hexadiene	HOAc—NaOAc	Pd(OAc)₂	85		*p*-Terphenyl	75		397
2,5-Diphenyl-1,5-hexadiene	DMF	PtCl₂—Et₄NSnCl₃	110	18	2,3-Diphenylbutadiene	11	Cf. VI-F-3	177
α-Chlorostyrene	DMF	PtCl₂—Et₄NSnCl₃	140	18	1,4-Diphenylbutadiene	25	VI-F-3	177
β-Bromostyrene								

c. Oxidative dimerization of aromatics

Substrate	Solvent	Oxidant	Reaction tempera-ture °C	time, hr	Products	Yield %	Example described	Refs.
Benzene	HOAc—NaOAc	Pd(OAc)₂	100	16	Biphenyl (Phenyl acetate, see Table V)		VI-F-4	74,76 149

Table (continued)

Substrate	Arylating (alkylating) agent	Solvent	Oxidant	Reaction temperature, °C	time, hr	Products	Yield %	Example described	Refs.
Toluene	H_2SO_4—H_2O		$PdSO_4$			Biphenyl	75		73
	HOAc—NaOAc		$Pd(OAc)_2$, $PdCl_2$	100–110	4–10	Bitolyls (p,p-bitolyl 10%)	58	Cf. VI-F-4	76,149
	HOAc—NaOAc		$PdCl_2$	90	6	Bitolyls: o,m' (12.4 mole%); o,p' (17.9); m,m' (14.5); m,p' (34.6); p,p' (20.4)		VI-G-8	391a
	HOAc—$HClO_4$		$Pd(OAc)_2$—$Hg(OAc)_2$	25	0.5	Bitolyls	95	Cf. VI-G-8	391a
	HOAc—$HClO_4$		H_2PtCl_6—$Hg(OAc)_2$	25	6	Bitolyls		Cf. VI-G-8	391a
	HOAc		$PtCl_4$	150		1,2-Diphenylethane			115
o-Xylene	HOAc—NaOAc		$PdCl_2$	118–130		3,4,3',4'-Tetramethylbiphenyl	22	Cf. VI-F-4	92
m-Xylene	HOAc—NaOAc		$PdCl_2$	100–110	4–10	Bixylyls	60	Cf. VI-F-4	149
Cumene	HOAc—NaOAc		$PdCl_2$	100–110	4–10	Bicumyls	81		149
m-Diisopropylbenzene	HOAc—NaOAc		$PdCl_2$	100–110	4–10	Tetraisopropylbiphenyls	25		149
Chlorobenzene	HOAc—NaOAc		$PdCl_2$	100–110	4–10	Dichlorobiphenyl(p,p'-dichlorobiphenyl 8%)	56		149
Anisole	HOAc—NaOAc		$PdCl_2$	100–110	4–10	Dimethoxybiphenyl(p,p'-derivative 10%)	60		149
Methyl benzoate	HOAc—NaOAc		$PdCl_2$	100–110	4–10	Dicarbomethoxybiphenyls	42		149
Phenyl pivalate	HOAc—NaOAc		$PdCl_2$	100–110	4–10	Dipivaloxybiphenyls	25		149
Biphenyl	HOAc—NaOAc		$PdCl_2$	100–110	4–10	Quaterphenyls (p,p'-derivative 6%) (3,4'-derivative 12%)	27		149
Diphenyl ether	HOAc—NaOAc		$PdCl_2$	100–110	4–10	Diphenoxybiphenyls	40		149

d. Arylation and alkylation of olefins

Substrate	Arylating (alkylating) agent	Solvent	Oxidant	Reaction temperature, °C	time, hr	Products	Yield %	Example described	Refs.
Propylene	C_6H_5MgBr/ether	Benzene	$PdCl_2$			β-Methylstyrene	3.8		278
						Allyl-, n-propenylbenzene	1.3		278
						α-Methylstyrene	2.4		278
						Isopropylbenzene	0.2		278
Styrene	Benzene	—	$Pd(OAc)_2$	Reflux		trans-Stilbene	90–97	VI-F-5	107
	Benzene	HOAc	Pd + AgOAc			Stilbene			108
	CH_3MgBr/ether	Benzene	$PdCl_2$			trans-β-Methylstyrene	3.2		278
						cis-β-Methylstyrene	0.1		278
						Ethylbenzene	6.7		278

(continued)

TABLE IX (*continued*)

Substrate	Arylating (alkylating) agent	Solvent	Oxidant	Reaction temperature, °C	time, hr	Products	Yield, %	Example described	Refs.
$[Styrene—PdCl_2]_2$	Benzene	HOAc	Substr. $PdCl_2$	Reflux		Stilbene (β-acetoxystyrene)	13		105,257
Styrene	Toluene		$Pd(OAc)_2$	Reflux		*trans*-*p*-Methylstilbene	58	Cf. VI-F-5	107
						trans-*o*-Methylstilbene	3		107
$[Styrene—PdCl_2]_2$	Toluene	HOAc	Substr. $PdCl_2$	Reflux		*trans*-*p*-Methylstilbene	47		105,257
Styrene	*p*-Xylene		$Pd(OAc)_2$	Reflux		*trans*-2,5-Dimethylstilbene	25		107
$[Styrene—PdCl_2]_2$	*p*-Xylene	HOAc	Substr. $PdCl_2$	Reflux		*trans*-2,5-Dimethylstilbene			105,257
1,1-Diphenylethylene	Benzene	HOAc	$Pd(OAc)_2$	Reflux		Triphenylethylene	72		106
trans-Stilbene	Benzene	HOAc	$Pd(OAc)_2$	Reflux		Triphenylethylene	28		106
Triphenylethylene	Benzene	HOAc	$Pd(OAc)_2$	Reflux		Tetraphenylethylene	13		106

e. Methylation and alkoxycarbonylation of olefinic compounds by means of mercurials[141] *(for example see Section VI-G-1)*

Olefin	Alkylating agent	Oxidant	Solvent	Product	Yield, %
Ethylene	$ClHgCOOCH_3$	Li_2PdCl_4	CH_3COOH	Methyl acrylate	50
Ethylene	$CH_3OCOHgCOOC_2H_5$	$LiPdCl_3$	CH_3CN	Ethyl acrylate	50
Propylene	$ClHgCOOCH_3$	$LiPdCl_3$	CH_3CN	Methyl crotonate	16
Styrene	CH_3HgCl	Li_2PdCl_4	CH_3OH	*trans*-1-Phenyl-1-propene	75
Styrene	$(CH_3)_4Sn$	Li_2PdCl_4	CH_3OH	*trans*-1-Phenyl-1-propene	95
Styrene	$(CH_3)_4Pb$	Li_2PdCl_4	CH_3OH	*trans*-1-Phenyl-1-propene	108
Styrene	$CH_3OCOHgCOOCH_3$	Li_2PdCl_4	CH_3OH	Methyl cinnamate	33
Styrene	$CH_3OCOHgCOOC_2H_5$	Li_2PdCl_4	C_2H_5OH	Ethyl cinnamate	13
Methyl acrylate	CH_3HgCl	Li_2PdCl_4	CH_3OH	Methyl crotonate	16
Methyl acrylate	$(CH_3)_4Sn$	Li_2PdCl_4	CH_3OH	Methyl crotonate	57
Methyl acrylate	$(CH_3)_4Pb$	Li_2PdCl_4	CH_3OH	Methyl crotonate	112

f. Arylation of olefinic compounds by means of mercurials (all reactions were carried out at room temperature for 15–24 hr)[141] *(for example see Sections VI-G-I, VI-G-2)*

Olefin	Arylating agent	Oxidant	Solvent	Product	Yield, %
Ethylene	Diphenylmercury	$LiPdCl_3$	CH_3CN	Styrene	63
Propylene	Diphenylmercury	$LiPdCl_3$	CH_3CN	Propenylbenzene	49 *trans*, 10 *cis*
Propylene	*p*-Chloromercurianisole	$LiPdCl_3$	CH_3CN	Anethole	26 *trans*, 6 *cis*

Olefin	Organometallic reagent	Catalyst	Solvent	Product	Yield (%)
Acrolein	Diphenylmercury	LiPdCl$_3$	CH$_3$CN	Cinnamaldehyde	30
Acrylonitrile	2-Chloromercurinaphthalene	LiPdCl$_3$	CH$_3$CN	3-(2-Naphthyl)acrylonitrile	64
1-Buten-3-one	Diphenylmercury	LiPdCl$_3$	CH$_3$CN	Benzalacetone	1
1-Buten-3-one	3,5-Bis(acetoxymercuri)salicylaldehyde	LiPdCl$_3$	CH$_3$CN	Salicylaldehyde-3,5-bis(1-buten-3-one)	88
Methyl acrylate	Diphenylmercury	LiPdCl$_3$	CH$_3$CN	Methyl cinnamate	53
Methyl acrylate	Phenylmercuric chloride	LiPdCl$_3$	CH$_3$CN	Methyl cinnamate	25
Methyl acrylate	Phenylmercuric chloride	RuCl$_3$	CH$_3$OH	Methyl cinnamate	60
Methyl acrylate	Phenylmercuric chloride	RhCl$_3$·3H$_2$O	CH$_3$OH	Methyl cinnamate	100
Methyl acrylate	Tetraphenyltin	Li$_2$PdCl$_4$	CH$_3$OH	Methyl cinnamate	82
Methyl acrylate	Tetraphenyllead	Li$_2$PdCl$_4$	CH$_3$OH	Methyl cinnamate	83
Methyl acrylate	Diphenyllead	Pd(NO$_3$)$_2$	CH$_3$OH	Methyl cinnamate	77
Methyl acrylate	Phenyltin trichloride	LiPdCl$_3$	CH$_3$OH	Methyl cinnamate	75
Methyl acrylate	Diphenyltin dichloride	Li$_2$PdCl$_4$	CH$_3$OH	Methyl cinnamate	8
Methyl acrylate	Phenylmagnesium bromide	LiPdCl$_3$	THF—CH$_3$CN	Methyl cinnamate	
Methyl acrylate	Di-2-naphthylmercury	Li$_2$PdCl$_4$	CH$_3$OH	Methyl 3-(2-naphthyl)acrylate	35
Methyl acrylate	p-Chloromercuridiethylaniline	Li$_2$PdCl$_4$	CH$_3$OH	Methyl p-diethylaminocinnamate	22
Methyl acrylate	p-Chloromercurinitrobenzene	Li$_2$PdCl$_4$	CH$_3$OH	Methyl m-nitrocinnamate	24
Methyl acrylate	m-Chloromercuribenzoic acid	Li$_2$PdCl$_4$	CH$_3$OH	Methyl m-methoxycarbonylcinnamate	54
Methyl acrylate	1-Chloromercuri-3,4-dichlorobenzene	Li$_2$PdCl$_4$	CH$_3$OH	Methyl 3,4-dichlorocinnamate	45
Methyl acrylate	2-Chloromercurithiophene	Li$_2$PdCl$_4$	CH$_3$OH	Methyl 3-(2-thienyl)acrylate	36
Methyl acrylate	p-Chloromercuriacetanilide	Li$_2$PdCl$_4$	CH$_3$OH	Methyl p-acetamidocinnamate	10
Methyl acrylate	o-Chloromercuriphenol	Li$_2$PdCl$_4$	CH$_3$OH	Methyl o-hydroxycinnamate	4
Methyl acrylate	4-Chloromercuribiphenyl	Li$_2$PdCl$_4$	CH$_3$OH	Methyl p-phenylcinnamate	2
Methyl acrylate	4-Chloro-2-chloromercuriphenol	Li$_2$PdCl$_4$	CH$_3$OH	Methyl 5-chloro-2-hydroxycinnamate	12,5
Methyl acrylate	2,4-Dichloro-5-chloromercuriphenol	Li$_2$PdCl$_4$	CH$_3$OH	Methyl 3,5-dichloro-2-hydroxycinnamate	11,4
Methyl acrylate	4-Chloromercuri-2-nitroanisole	Li$_2$PdCl$_4$	CH$_3$OH	Methyl 3-nitro-4-methoxycinnamate	40
Methyl acrylate	4-Chloromercuri-2-nitrochlorobenzene	Li$_2$PdCl$_4$	CH$_3$OH	Methyl 3-nitro-4-chlorocinnamate	3
Methyl acrylate	3,5-Bis(chloromercuri)nitrobenzene	Li$_2$PdCl$_4$	CH$_3$OH	Dimethyl 3-nitrobenzene-1,5-bis(3-acrylate)	18
Methyl acrylate	1-Chloromercuri-3-nitro-4,5-dichlorobenzene	Li$_2$PdCl$_4$	CH$_3$OH	Methyl 3-nitro-4,5-dichlorocinnamate	19
Methyl acrylate	Bis(acetoxymercuri)mesitylene	LiPdCl$_3$	CH$_3$CN	Dimethyl (1,3,5-trimethylbenzene-)2,4-bis(3-acrylate)	17
Methyl acrylate	3,5-Bis(acetoxymercuri)-salicylaldehyde	Li$_2$PdCl$_4$	CH$_3$OH	Dimethyl salicylaldehyde-3,5-bis(3-acrylate)	13
Methyl acrylate	3,3'-Bis(chloromercuri)-benzophenone	Li$_2$PdCl$_4$	CH$_3$OH	Dimethyl benzophenone-3,3'-bis(3-acrylate)	4
Allyl acetate	Phenylmercuric acetate	Pd(OAc)$_2$	CH$_3$COCH$_3$	Cinnamyl acetate	63
Styrene	4-Chloromercuritoluene	Li$_2$PdCl$_4$	CH$_3$OH	4-Methylstilbene	47,5
Styrene	4-Chloromercuricumene	Li$_2$PdCl$_4$	CH$_3$OH	4-Isopropylstilbene	42,4
Styrene	4-Chloromercuribenzoic acid	Li$_2$PdCl$_4$	CH$_3$OH	4-Methoxycarbonylstilbene	26
Styrene	2-Chloromercurithiophene	Li$_2$PdCl$_4$	CH$_3$OH	2-Styrylthiophene	16
Styrene	4-Chloromercuri-2-nitroanisole	Li$_2$PdCl$_4$	CH$_3$OH	4-Methoxy-3-nitrostilbene	17,5
Styrene	2,4-Dichloro-6-chloromercuriphenol	Li$_2$PdCl$_4$	CH$_3$OH	3,5-Dichloro-2-hydroxystilbene	14,5

(continued)

TABLE IX (continued)

Olefin	Arylating agent	Oxidant	Solvent	Product	Yield, %
Styrene	Pentamethylphenylmercuric chloride	Li_2PdCl_4	CH_3CN	2,3,4,5,6-Pentamethylstilbene	42
Styrene	3-Chloromercuribenzaldehyde	Li_2PdCl_4	CH_3OH	3-Formylstilbene	38
4-Vinylbiphenyl	4-Chloromercurianisole	Li_2PdCl_4	CH_3OH	4-Methoxy-4'-phenylstilbene	11
4-Vinylbiphenyl	4-Chloromercuri-2-nitroanisole	Li_2PdCl_4	CH_3OH	4-Methoxy-3-nitro-4'-phenylstilbene	17
Allylbenzene	2-Chloromercurinaphthalene	Li_2PdCl_4	CH_3OH	2-(2-Naphthyl)-1-phenyl-1-propene	18
1-Phenyl-1-propene	Phenylmercuric chloride	Li_2PdCl_4	CH_3OH	1,2-Diphenylpropene	21
1-Phenyl-1-propene	p-Chloromercurianisole	Li_2PdCl_4	CH_3OH	2-p-Anisyl-2-phenyl-1-propene	13
trans-Anethole	m-Chloromercurinitrobenzene	Li_2PdCl_4	CH_3OH	1-p-Anisyl-2-(m-nitrophenyl)-1-propene	7
Indene	4-Chloromercuri-2-nitroanisole	Li_2PdCl_4	CH_3COOH	2-(4-Methoxy-3-nitrophenyl)indene	10

g. Catalytic arylation in the presence of additional oxidants[141] (for example see Section VI-G-3)

Olefin	Arylating agent	Oxidant	Solvent	Reaction temperature °C	time, hr	Product	Yield %
Methyl acrylate	Phenylmercuric chloride	Li_2PdCl_4—$CuCl_2$	CH_3OH	RT	2	Methyl cinnamate	57
Methyl acrylate	Phenylmercuric chloride	Li_2PdCl_4—$CuCl_2$, NaCl, O_2, HCl	CH_3OH	RT	24	Methyl cinnamate	60
Methyl acrylate	Diphenyl mercury	$Pd(NO_3)_2$—$Fe(NO_3)_2 \cdot 9H_2O$	CH_3OH	RT	24	Methyl cinnamate	37
Methyl acrylate	Diphenyl mercury	$Pd(NO_3)_2$—$Hg(NO_3)_2 \cdot H_2O$	CH_3OH	RT	24	Methyl cinnamate	37
Methyl acrylate	p-Chloromercuribenzoic acid	Li_2PdCl_4—$CuCl_2$	CH_3OH	RT	24	Methyl p-methoxycarbonyl-cinnamate	20
Methyl acrylate	p-Acetoxymercurianisole	$Pd(OAc)_2$—$Hg(OAc)_2$	CH_3COOH	60	2	Methyl p-methoxycinnamate	27
Methyl crotonate	Phenylmercuric chloride	Li_2PdCl_4—$CuCl_2$	CH_3OH	RT	24	Methyl 3-methyl-3-phenyl-acrylate	24
Methyl methacrylate	Phenylmercuric chloride	Li_2PdCl_4—$CuCl_2$	CH_3OH	RT	24	Methyl 2-methyl-3-phenyl-acrylate	35
Acrolein	Di-2-naphthyl mercury	Li_2PdCl_4—$CuCl_2$	CH_3OH	RT	24	3-(2-Naphthyl)acrolein	8
Allylbenzene	Phenylmercuric acetate	$Pd(OAc)_2$—$Hg(OAc)_2$	CH_3COCH_3	RT	24	trans-1,3-Diphenylpropene	8
Crotyl acetate	Phenylmercuric chloride	$LiPdCl_3$—$CuCl_2$	CH_3CN	RT	4	3-Phenylbutenyl acetate	15
Allyl ethyl ether	Phenylmercuric acetate	$Pd(OAc)_2$—$Hg(OAc)_2$	CH_3COCH_3	RT	5	Cinnamyl ethyl ether	42

h. Formation of saturated aromatic halocoupling compounds[145] (Sections VI-G-4, VI-G-5)

Olefin	Arylating agent	Catalyst	Cupric halide	Salt added	Solvent	Product	Yield %
Ethylene	C_6H_5HgCl	Li_2PdCl_4	$CuCl_2$	LiCl	HOAc—H_2O (90:10)	$C_6H_5CH_2CH_2Cl$	76
						$C_6H_5CH=CH_2$	2
Ethylene	C_6H_5HgCl	$RhCl_3 \cdot 3H_2O$	$CuCl_2$	LiCl	HOAc—H_2O (90:10)	$C_6H_5CH_2CH_2Cl$	32
Ethylene	C_6H_5HgCl	$RuCl_3$	$CuCl_2$	LiCl	HOAc—H_2O (90:10)	$C_6H_5CH_2CH_2Cl$	25
Ethylene	C_6H_5HgCl	$FeCl_3$	$CuCl_2$	LiCl	HOAc—H_2O (90:10)	$C_6H_5CH_2CH_2Cl$	3
Ethylene	$C_6H_5SnCl_3$	Li_2PdCl_4	$CuCl_2$	LiCl	HOAc—H_2O (90:10)	$C_6H_5CH_2CH_2Cl$	5
Ethylene	$(C_6H_5)_4Sn$	Li_2PdCl_4	$CuCl_2$	LiCl	HOAc—H_2O (90:10)	$C_6H_5CH_2CH_2Cl$	34
Ethylene	$(C_6H_5)_4Pb$	Li_2PdCl_4	$CuCl_2$	LiCl	HOAc—H_2O (90:10)	$C_6H_5CH_2CH_2Cl$	23
Ethylene	C_6H_5HgBr	$Pd(NO_3)_2$	$CuBr_2$	LiBr	HOAc—H_2O (90:10)	$C_6H_5CH_2CH_2Br$	12
Ethylene	C_6H_5HgBr	$Pd(OAc)_2$	$CuBr_2$	LiBr	HOAc—H_2O (90:10)	$C_6H_5CH_2CH_2Br$	14
						C_6H_5Br	~50
Ethylene	$4\text{-}HOCOC_6H_4HgCl$	Li_2PdCl_4	$CuCl_2$	LiCl	HOAc—H_2O (90:10)	$4\text{-}HOCOC_6H_4CH_2CH_2Cl$	72
Ethylene	$4\text{-}(C_2H_5)_2NC_6H_4HgCl$	Li_2PdCl_4	$CuCl_2$	LiCl	HOAc—H_2O (90:10)	$4\text{-}(C_2H_5)_2NC_6H_4CH_2CH_2Cl$	20
Ethylene	$3\text{-}NO_2C_6H_4HgCl$	Li_2PdCl_4	$CuCl_2$	LiCl	HOAc—H_2O (90:10)	$3\text{-}NO_2C_6H_4CH_2CH_2Cl$	47
Ethylene	$2\text{-}C_{10}H_7HgCl$	Li_2PdCl_4	$CuCl_2$	LiCl	HOAc—H_2O (85:15)	$2\text{-}C_{10}H_7CH_2CH_2Cl$	30
Ethylene	$2\text{-}C_4H_3SHgCl$	Li_2PdCl_4	$CuCl_2$	LiCl	HOAc—H_2O (85:15)	$2\text{-}C_4H_3SCHCH_2Cl$	13
						$[2\text{-}C_4H_3S]_2$	13
Ethylene	$1,3,5\text{-}(CH_3)_3C_6H_2HgCl$	Li_2PdCl_4	$CuCl_2$	LiCl	HOAc—H_2O (90:10)	$1,3,5\text{-}(CH_3)_3C_6H_2CH_2CH_2Cl$	2
Ethylene	$1,3,5\text{-}(CH_3)_3C_6H(HgOCOCH_3)_2$	Li_2PdCl_4	$CuCl_2$	LiCl	HOAc—H_2O (85:15)	$1,3,5\text{-}(CH_3)_3C_6H(CH_2CH_2Cl)_2$	0.2
Propylene	C_6H_5HgCl	Li_2PdCl_4	$CuCl_2$	LiCl	HOAc—H_2O (90:10)	$C_6H_5CH_2CHClCH_3$	50
						$C_6H_5CH=CHCH_3$	30
Acrolein	C_6H_5HgCl	Li_2PdCl_4	$CuCl_2$	LiCl	HOAc—H_2O (90:10)	$C_6H_5CH_2CHClCHO$	63
Methyl acrylate	C_6H_5HgCl	Li_2PdCl	$CuCl_2$	LiCl	HOAc—H_2O (90:10)	$C_6H_5CH_2CHClCOOCH_3$	10
						$C_6H_5CH=CHCOOCH_3$	85
Crotonaldehyde	C_6H_5HgCl	Li_2PdCl_4	$CuCl_2$	LiCl	CH_3OH	$C_6H_5CH(CH_3)CHClCHO$	22
						$C_6H_5C(CH_3)=CHCHO$	19
1-Buten-3-one	C_6H_5HgCl	Li_2PdCl_4	$CuCl_2$	LiCl	HOAc—H_2O (85:15)	$C_6H_5CH_2CHClCOCH_3$	~80
						$C_6H_5CH=CHCOCH_3$	~20
1-Buten-3-one	$4\text{-}HOCOC_6H_4HgCl$	Li_2PdCl_4	$CuCl_2$	LiCl	HOAc—H_2O (85:15)	$4\text{-}HOCOC_6H_4CH_2CHCl\text{—}COCH_3$	5

(continued)

TABLE IX (continued)

i. Formation of 3-arylaldehydes and ketones from allylic alcohols at room temperature (DCHEA – dicyclohexylethylamine)[142] (for example see Section VI-G-6)

Allylic alcohol	Mercurial	Other Reagent	Oxidant	Solvent	Product	Yield %
$CH_2=CHCH_2OH$	C_6H_5HgCl	—	$LiPdCl_3$	CH_3CN	CH_2CH_2CHO	35
$CH_2=CHCH_2OH$	C_6H_5HgCl	—	$CuCl_2-Li_2PdCl_4$	CH_3COCH_3		27
$CH_2=CHCH_2OH$	C_6H_5HgCl	—	$CuCl_2-LiPdCl_3$	CH_3CN		53
$CH_2=CHCH_2OH$	$C_6H_5HgOCOCH_3$	—	$Hg(OAc)_2-Pd(OAc)_2$	CH_3CN		26
$CH_2=CHCH_2OH$	$3,4-(CH_3)_2C_6H_3HgCl$	—	$CuCl_2-LiPdCl_3$	CH_3CN	CH_2CH_2CHO	13.3
$CH_2=CHCH_2OH$	$3,4-Cl_2C_6H_3HgCl$	DCHEA	$CuCl_2-LiPdCl_3$	CH_3CN	CH_2CH_2CHO	10.5
$CH_2=CHCH_2OH$	$4-CH_3OC_6H_4HgCl$	DCHEA	$CuCl_2-LiPdCl_3$	CH_3CN	CH_2CH_2CHO	8.5

$CH_3CH=CHCH_2OH$	C_6H_5HgCl	DCHEA	$CuCl_2$—$LiPdCl_3$	CH_3CN	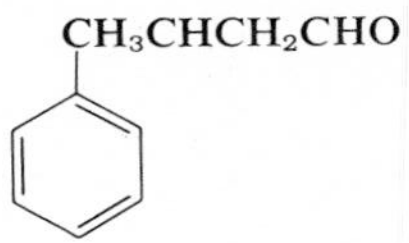 C_6H_5–CH_3CHCH_2CHO	14.2
$CH_2=C(CH_3)CH_2OH$	C_6H_5HgCl	DCHEA	$CuCl_2$—$LiPdCl_3$	CH_3CN	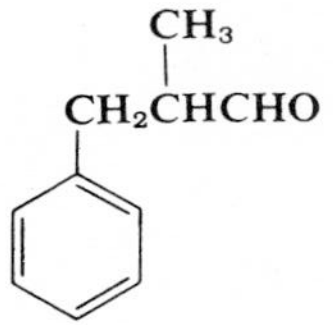 C_6H_5–$CH_2(CH_3)CHCHO$	47.5
$CH_2=C(CH_3)CH_2OH$	$3\text{-}OCHC_6H_4HgCl$	DCHEA	$CuCl_2$—$LiPdCl_3$	CH_3CN	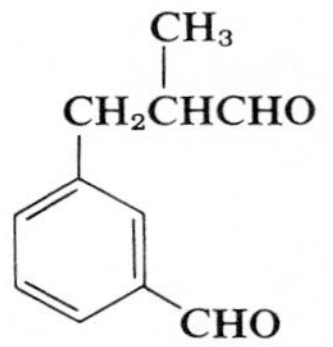 $3\text{-}CHO\,C_6H_4$–$CH_2(CH_3)CHCHO$	2.5
$CH_2=CHCH(OH)CH_3$	C_6H_5HgCl	DCHEA	$CuCl_2$—$LiPdCl_3$	CH_3CN	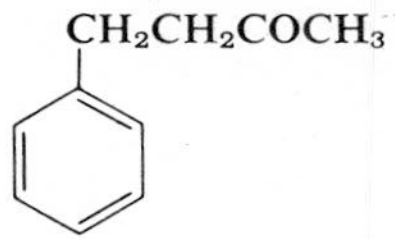 C_6H_5–$CH_2CH_2COCH_3$	46
$CH_2=CHCH(OH)CH_2CH_3$	C_6H_5HgCl	DCHEA	$CuCl_2$—$LiPdCl_3$	CH_3CN	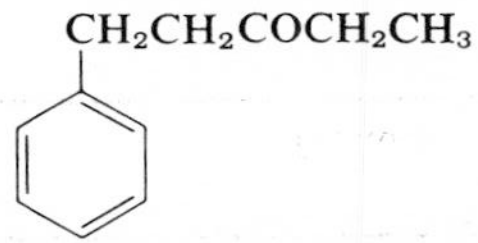 C_6H_5–$CH_2CH_2COCH_2CH_3$	32

(continued)

95

TABLE IX (*continued*)

Allylic alcohol	Mercurial	Other reagent	Oxidant	Solvent	Product	Yield %
$CH_3CH=CHCHCH_3$ with OH	C_6H_5HgCl	DCHEA	$CuCl_2-LiPdCl_3$	CH_3CN	$CH_3CHCH_2COCH_3$–phenyl	12.5
$CH_2=CHCHCH_2CH_3$ with OH	$3\text{-}CH_3OCOC_6H_4HgCl$	DCHEA	$CuCl_2-LiPdCl_3$	CH_3CN	$CH_2CH_2COCH_2CH_3$–phenyl ($COOCH_3$)	6.6
$CH_2=CHCHCH_2CH_3$ with OH	$HgCl$, aryl with NO_2, Cl, Cl	—	$CuCl_2-LiPdCl_3$	CH_3CN	$CH_2CH_2COCH_2CH_3$–aryl with NO_2, Cl, Cl	15.7
2-cyclohexenol (OH)	C_6H_5HgCl	DCHEA	$CuCl_2-LiPdCl_3$	CH_3CN	3-phenylcyclohexanone	45.5

j. Arylation reaction of enol esters, ethers, and halides with organomercury compounds in the presence of palladium salts[144] (see Sections IV-A-3, VI-G-8 VI-G-7, VI-J-9)

Enol compound	Mercurial	Solvent	Catalyst	Products	Yield %
$CH_2=CHOAc$	C_6H_5HgCl	HOAc	$Li_2PdCl_4—CuCl_2$	$trans\text{-}C_6H_5CH=CHC_6H_5$	34
				$C_6H_5CH_2CHO$	33
				$C_6H_5CH=CHOAc$	30
				$C_6H_5CH=CH_2$	3
$CH_2=CHOAc$	C_6H_5HgOAc	HOAc	$Pd(OAc)_2—Hg(OAc)_2$	$trans\text{-}C_6H_5CH=CHC_6H_5$	13
				$C_6H_5CH_2CHO$	Trace
$CH_2=CHOAc$	C_6H_5HgCl	CH_3CN	$LiPdCl_3—CuCl_2$	$trans\text{-}C_6H_5CH=CHC_6H_5$	20
				$C_6H_5CH_2CHO$	8
				$C_6H_5CH=CH_2$	2
$CH_2=CHOAc$	C_6H_5HgCl	CH_3COCH_3	$Li_2PdCl_4—CuCl_2$	$trans\text{-}C_6H_5CH=CHC_6H_5$	31
				$C_6H_5CH_2CHO$	10
				$C_6H_5CH=CH_2$	3
$CH_2=CHOAc$	$3\text{-}NO_2C_6H_4HgCl$	CH_3COCH_3	$Li_2PdCl_4—CuCl_2$	$(3\text{-}NO_2C_6H_4)CH=CH(3\text{-}NO_2C_6H_4)$	9
$CH_2=CHOAc$	$3\text{-}CH_3OCOC_6H_4HgCl$	CH_3CN	$LiPdCl_3—CuCl_2$	$(3\text{-}CH_3OCOC_6H_4)CH=CH(3\text{-}CH_3OCOC_6H_4)$	9
$CH_2=CHOCOCF_3$	C_6H_5HgCl	CH_3CN	$LiPdCl_3—CuCl_2$	$trans\text{-}C_6H_5CH=CHC_6H_5$	26
				Styrene	Trace
$CH_2=CHCl$	C_6H_5HgCl	HOAc	$Li_2PdCl_4—CuCl_2$	$trans\text{-}C_6H_5CH=CHC_6H_5$	35
$CH_2=CHOC_4H_9$	C_6H_5HgCl	CH_3CN	$LiPdCl_3—CuCl_2$	$trans\text{-}C_6H_5CH=CHC_6H_5$	11
				$C_6H_5CH_2CHO$	Trace
				$(C_6H_5)_2$	48
				C_6H_5Cl	31
$CH_3CH=CHOAc$	C_6H_5HgCl	HOAc	$LiPdCl_4—CuCl_2$	$CH_3CH(C_6H_5)CHO$	21
				$C_6H_5CH=C(C_6H_5)CH_3$	66
$CH_3CH=CHOAc$	C_6H_5HgCl	CH_2COCH_3	$Li_2PdCl_4—CuCl_2$	$CH_3CH(C_6H_5)CHO$	29
				$C_6H_5CH=C(C_6H_5)CH_3$	18
$CH_3CH=CHOAc$	C_6H_5HgCl	CH_3CN	$LiPdCl_3—CuCl_2$	$CH_3CH(C_6H_5)CHO$	11
				$C_6H_5CH=C(C_6H_5)CH_3$	39
$CH_3CH=CHOAc$	$4\text{-}CH_3OC_6H_4HgCl$	HOAc	$Li_2PdCl_4—CuCl_2$	$CH_3CH(4\text{-}CH_3OC_6H_4)CHO$	18
				$(4\text{-}CH_3OC_6H_4)CH=C(4\text{-}CH_3OC_6H_4)CH_3$	3
$CH_3CH=CHOAc$	$3\text{-}NO_2C_6H_4HgCl$	HOAc	$Li_2PdCl_4—CuCl_2$	$(3\text{-}NO_2C_6H_4)CH=C(3\text{-}NO_2C_6H_4)CH_3$	1

(continued)

(TABLE IX *continued*)

Enol compound	Mercurial	Solvent	Catalyst	Products	Yield %
CH₃CH=CHBr	C₆H₅HgCl	CH₃CN	LiPdCl₃—CuCl₂	C₆H₅CH=C(C₆H₅)CH₃	14
				C₆H₅Cl	46
(CH₃)₂C=CHOAc	C₆H₅HgCl	7:1 HOAc—H₂O	Li₂PdCl₄—CuCl₂	(CH₃)₂C(C₆H₅)CHO	7
CH₃C(OAc)=CH₂	C₆H₅HgCl	7:1 HOAc—H₂O	Li₂PdCl₄—CuCl₂	C₆H₅CH₂COCH₃	50
				C₆H₅Cl	40
CH₃CH(OAc)=CH₂	4-HOCOC₆H₄HgCl	19:1 HOAc—H₂O	Li₂PdCl₄—CuCl₂	4-HOCOC₆H₄CH₂COCH₃	4
C₆H₅C(OCOC₆H₅)=CH₂	C₆H₅HgCl	CH₃COCH₃	Li₂PdCl₄—CuCl₂	C₆H₅CH₂COC₆H₅	40
C₆H₅C(OAc)=CH₂	3-NO₂C₆H₄HgCl	19:1 CH₃OH—H₂O	Li₂PdCl₄	3-NO₂C₆H₄CH₂COC₆H₅	9
4-CH₃OC₆H₄C(OAc)=CH₂	3,4-Cl₂C₆H₃HgCl	25:1 CH₃OH—H₂O	Li₂PdCl₄	3,4-Cl₂C₆H₃CH₂CO(4-CH₃OC₆H₄)	8

Some of these butadiene derivatives undergo further oxidation with $Pd(OAc)_2$ in acetic acid—sodium acetate medium and yield aromatics, e.g.[225]

$$2C_6H_5-C\underset{CH_3}{\overset{CH_2}{\big\langle}} \longrightarrow C_6H_5-C\underset{CH_3}{\overset{CH-CH}{\big\langle}}\underset{CH_3}{\big\rangle}C-C_6H_5 \longrightarrow$$

$$C_6H_5-C\underset{CH_2}{\overset{CH_2-CH_2}{\big\langle}}\underset{CH_2}{\big\rangle}C-C_6H_5 \longrightarrow C_6H_5-C\underset{CH-CH}{\overset{CH_2-CH_2}{\big\langle}}\big\rangle C-C_6H_5 \longrightarrow$$

$$C_6H_5-C\underset{CH=CH}{\overset{CH-CH}{\big\langle}}\big\rangle C-C_6H_5 \quad (91)$$

It is assumed that this reaction is brought about after the 1,4-alkyl-substituted butadiene derivatives are isomerized to the 1,5-hexadiene derivatives, since 2,5-diphenyl-1,5-hexadiene gives a higher yield of p-terphenyl than the 2,5-diphenyl-2,4-hexadiene. Another example is the formation of dimethyl terephthalate from dimethyl 2,5-dimethylmuconate.

As experimental evidence for a possible mechanism, it could be shown that the hydrogen atom which is abstracted in this reaction originates from the terminal double-bonded carbon atom. There is no loss of deuterium when α-trideuteriomethyl styrene is converted to the deuterated 2,5-diphenyl-2,4-hexadiene. For the coupling reaction

$$2C_6H_5-C\underset{CD_3}{\overset{CH_2}{\big\langle}} \longrightarrow C_6H_5-C\underset{CD_3}{\overset{CH-CH}{\big\langle}}\underset{CD_3}{\big\rangle}C-C_6H_5 \quad (92)$$

Volger[397] proposed an acetato-bridged, binuclear, bis-olefin complex as an intermediate in which the olefins are parallel to each other and the vinylic CH_2-groups are situated very close. At this position the hydrogen abstraction should be facilitated. The intermediate complex proposed would simultaneously explain the necessity of the acetate ions and the acetic acid as solvent.

Another coupling reaction takes place with aromatics, which form biphenyl derivatives by oxidation with $PdCl_2$ in acetic acid-sodium acetate[149] or by palladium sulfate in sulfuric acid.[73] Monosubstituted benzenes, such as toluene, chlorobenzene, and methyl benzoate give, slightly depending on the substituent, o-, m-, p-, or mixed biphenyl derivatives.[149] Acetoxylation of the aromatic nucleus or the side chain[73] in the presence of sodium acetate is a side reaction in the dimerization of benzene or toluene, yielding 40–45%

phenyl and benzyl acetate, respectively (see Section III-D). The formation of phenyl acetate can be prevented by carrying out the reaction under 50 atm of oxygen.[74]

(Styrene·$PdCl_2$)$_2$ gives on treatment with aromatics and acetic acid stilbene and its alkyl-substituted derivatives, and as a by-product α-methylbenzyl acetate.[105,107,108,257] If palladium acetate and styrene are reacted, instead of the styrene palladium chloride complex, the yield of stilbene is almost quantitative (90–97%). Toluene and xylene form *trans-p*-methylstilbene and *trans*-2,5-dimethylstilbene, respectively. By-product β-acetoxystyrene is obtained only in traces. Phenyl-substituted ethylenes such as 1,1-diphenylethylene, *trans*-stilbene or triphenylethylene react similarly to form styrene in both $Pd(OAc)_2$ and $PdCl_2$—NaOAc systems.[106]

For the aromatic coupling a complex between the palladium salt and an aromatic hydrocarbon of the type

has been proposed as an intermediate that should be attacked by the nucleophile, the acetate ion, to form an enyl complex from which the biphenyl is obtained via coupling of the allyl ends.[149]

Evidence for the possibility of complex formation of platinum metal compounds with aromatic hydrocarbons has been given by deuterium exchange with these hydrocarbons catalyzed by platinum compounds.[112] A complex $[Pd(C_6H_6)(H_2O)ClO_4]_n$ has been described by Davidson and Triggs.[75]

Thermal decomposition of bis(π-allyl)palladium yields biallyl[412,413]

$$(C_3H_5)_2Pd \longrightarrow CH_2{=}CH{-}CH_2{-}CH_2{-}CH{=}CH_2 + Pd \qquad (93)$$

under formation of a new C—C bond.

If the complex $[(tol)_2PtCl_2]_n$ that forms in the reaction of toluene with $PtCl_4$ in HOAc is heated to 150°C, 1,2-diphenylethane is obtained.[115] The structure of this complex has not yet been established but two types of complexes known so far, a π-allyl complex of the type[191]

and a benzyl complex[101a] (a prototype is e.g., $(PPh_3)_2ClPd{-}CH_2C_6H_5$) would fulfill the requirements for this coupling reaction similarly to benzylic oxidation (see Section III-D-3).

A further coupling reaction leads from vinyl halides to the corresponding 1,3-dienes.[177] It is a reductive coupling carried out by stannous chloride in the presence of $PtCl_2$ and CsF in dimethylformamide solution. Vinyl chloride and vinyl fluoride give butadiene in an almost quantitative yield.

$$2CH_2{=}CHCl \xrightarrow[\text{DMF}]{\text{(Et}_4\text{N)SnCl}_3,\ \text{PtCl}_2,\ \text{CsF}} CH_2{=}CH{-}CH{=}CH_2 \qquad (94)$$

Similarly, β-bromostyrene, α-chlorostyrene and allyl chloride are reacted to give, respectively, 1,4-diphenylbutadiene, 2,3-diphenylbutadiene and biallyl. The fact that $PtCl_2$-$SnCl_2$ complexes are active in hydride transfer reactions (see Section IV-C) suggests a mechanism similar to oxidative coupling, considering the instability of Hal^+-ions in the presence of the reducing Sn^{II}-halide.

Allyl chloride undergoes a similar reaction with bis(benzonitrile $PdCl_2$) to form dichloro-1,5-hexadiene-palladium, which dissociates above 100°C to liberate the hydrocarbon,[420]

3. Reactions with Carbanions from Organo-Pd Compounds

Another type of coupling reaction comprises the reactions of olefins with carbanions from allyl- or aryl-palladium compounds as assumed intermediates in the reactions of organometallics with olefins in the presence of palladium salts. Normally, such organometallics, e.g., those of mercury, tin, lead, lithium, magnesium, etc., are too stable to react directly with olefins. In the presence of palladium salts, however, R. F. Heck assumed a transfer of the organic group from the metal to the palladium e.g., according to

$$R{-}HgX + PdY_2 \longrightarrow R{-}PdY + HgXY \qquad (95)$$

and reported numerous reactions with mercury compounds in polar organic solvents.[141,142,144,146] They are easily available in general, particularly those of aromatics that form directly from the hydrocarbon with mercuric salt:

$$\langle\!\!\!\text{—}\rangle{-}CH_3 + Hg(OAc)_2 \longrightarrow CH_3\langle\!\!\!\text{—}\rangle{-}HgOAc + HOAc \qquad (96)$$

The reactions reported follow the general scheme:

$$R{-}HgX + \overset{H}{\underset{}{\underset{}{\diagup}}}C{=}C\overset{}{\underset{}{\diagdown}} + PdCl_2 \longrightarrow R{-}\overset{H}{\underset{|}{C}}{-}\overset{|}{\underset{|}{C}}{-}PdCl + HgXCl \qquad (97)$$

$$\begin{array}{c} H \\ | \quad | \\ R-\overset{|}{\underset{|}{C}}-\overset{|}{\underset{|}{C}}-PdCl \longrightarrow R-C{=}C\diagup \quad + \ Pd \ + \ HCl \hspace{2cm} (98) \\ \qquad\qquad\qquad\qquad | \quad \diagdown \end{array}$$

In the presence of $CuCl_2$ the palladium can be reoxidized to make the reaction catalytic.

Table VIII lists the reactions performed. Typical examples for the reaction of aromatic mercury compounds with olefinics are the formation of styrene from diphenylmercury with ethylene and the formation of methyl cinnamate from phenylmercuric chloride and methyl acrylate. With methylmercuric chloride and methyl acrylate, methyl crotonate is formed; $ClHgCOOCH_3$ with ethylene gives methyl acrylate.[141]

a. Note

The elimination of a hydrido palladium species from the addition product of the proposed alkylpalladium intermediate to the olefin proceeds in analogy to the same reaction step in normal olefin oxidation (Section III-A and III-B). However, the addition of the "alkylpalladium" species to the olefin remarkably takes place in an "anti-Markovnikov" route, that is, the alkyl group enters the least substituted carbon atom of the double bond.[146a] Thus in the reaction of C_6H_5HgOAc, $Pd(OAc)_2$, and propylene in methanol the mixture of the reaction products contains 60% trans-1-phenyl-1-propene, 9% cis-1-phenyl-1-propene, and only 16% 2-phenyl-1-propene (α-methylstyrene) as well as 15% allylbenzene. Chloride ions favor the "anti-Markovnikov" route: with C_6H_5HgCl and $PdCl_2$ the composition of the product mixture is (in the same order) 87, 4, 7, and 0.5%. Similarly methylmercuric acetate, $Pd(OAc)_2$ and styrene form mainly trans-1-phenyl-1-propene.

The reaction is stereospecific. The product composition obtained from trans-1-phenyl-1-propene, C_6H_5HgOAc and $Pd(OAc)_2$ in methanol solution (98% trans-1,2-diphenyl-1-propene) and from cis-1-phenyl-1-propene (65% cis-1,2-diphenyl-1-propene) suggests a cis-addition of the aryl palladium intermediate to the double bond followed by a cis-elimination of the hydrido palladium species after rotation around the C–C axis of the original double bond according to the scheme on p. 103.

A detailed description of analogous stereospecific cis-addition elimination routes is given in Sections IV-A-2 and IV-C on transalkenylation and isomerisation mechanisms. Unexpected products, for example, 1,2-diphenyl-2-propene and other isomeric products, probably arise from a readdition of the intermediate hydridopalladium compound as shown in the scheme.

Solvents and aryl or alkyl sources (e.g., tin, lead in place of mercury compounds) influence the product composition to some extent.

Row 1:

C_6H_5 / H_3C C=C H / H $\quad$ + [C$_6$H$_5$PdOAc] $\longrightarrow$
$$\left[\begin{array}{c} C_6H_5 \\ H-C-C_6H_5 \\ \quad | \\ CH_3 \; H \\ \text{—C—PdOAc} \end{array} \right]$$
$\rightleftharpoons$
$$\left[\begin{array}{c} H \quad C_6H_5 \\ C=C \\ C_6H_5 \; H_3C \;\; Pd\text{—}OAc \\ H \end{array} \right]$$
$\xrightarrow{-\,[HPdOAc]}$
$$C_6H_5 \quad H \\ C=C \\ H_3C \quad C_6H_5$$

Row 2:

C_6H_5 / H C=C H / CH_3 $\quad$ + [C$_6$H$_5$PdOAc] $\longrightarrow$
$$\left[\begin{array}{c} C_6H_5 \\ H-C-CH_3 \\ C_6H_5 \; H \\ \text{—C—PdOAc} \end{array} \right]$$
$\rightleftharpoons$
$$\left[\begin{array}{c} H \quad H \\ C=C \\ C_6H_5 \; C_6H_5H_2C \;\; Pd\text{—}OAc \\ H \end{array} \right]$$
$\xrightarrow{-\,[HPdOAc]}$
$$C_6H_5 \quad H \\ C=C \\ C_6H_5H_2C \quad H$$

Row 3:

H_3C / H C=C H / C_6H_5 $\quad$ + [C$_6$H$_5$PdOAc] $\longrightarrow$
$$\left[\begin{array}{c} CH_3 \; C_6H_5 \\ C_6H_5-C-H \\ \quad | \\ \text{—C—PdOAc} \end{array} \right]$$
$\rightleftharpoons$
$$\left[\begin{array}{c} H \quad C_6H_5 \\ C=C \\ H_3C \; C_6H_5 \;\; Pd\text{—}OAc \\ H \end{array} \right]$$
$\xrightarrow{-\,[HPdOAc]}$
$$H_3C \quad H \\ C=C \\ C_6H_5 \quad C_6H_5$$

Allylic alcohols react with aromatic mercurials to yield phenyl-substituted aldehydes:[142]

$$C_6H_5-HgCl + CH_2=CH-CH_2OH + PdCl_2 \longrightarrow$$

$$C_6H_5-CH_2-CH_2-CHO + HgCl_2 + Pd + HCl \quad (99)$$

which can be thought of as the isomerized coupling product.

Further examples of reacted olefins comprise enol esters, ethers and halides,[144] and conjugated dienes.[146] With high $CuCl_2$ concentrations, saturated β-halo-coupling products are obtained:[145]

$$C_6H_5-HgCl + C_2H_4 + 2CuCl_2 \xrightarrow{PdCl_2}$$

$$C_6H_5-CH_2-CH_2Cl + HgCl_2 + 2CuCl \quad (100)$$

analogous to the formation of ethylenechlorohydrin[357] or β-chloroethyl acetate[153] as by-products in olefin oxidations.

We consider the aforesaid coupling reactions as intramolecular insertion reactions between a carbanion and an olefin both complexed on palladium. Such reactions should, therefore, also be brought about if one reacts a palladium-olefin complex with an organometallic. In fact, it was reported[278] that [(styrene)PdCl₂]₂ reacts with Grignard or lithium compounds, i.e., with methylmagnesium bromide to yield β-methylstyrene.

A further reaction has been described with toluene and mercuric acetate in the presence of acetic acid, perchloric acid, and Pd^{II} or Pt^{IV} compounds to form bitolyls.[391a] Since the palladium salt is added after the mercurial has been formed from toluene and the mercuric salt, this example shows that mercurials also add to aromatics in the presence of platinum metal compounds (see Table IXc).

F. Oxidative Degradation of Olefins by PdCl₂; forming Carbonyl Compounds

In all olefin and allylic oxidation reactions with $PdCl_2$, oxidative degradation occurs as a side reaction to various extents, especially if the normal course of the oxidation is obstructed by substituents at the double bond. The reaction has not been very thoroughly investigated so far. It seems to be a cleavage of the double bond,[343] in most cases, similar to the oxidative cleavage of double bonds by OsO_4, RuO_4, permanganate, and the like, since saturated aldehydes are formed from α-olefins with one carbon atom less than the original olefin, e.g., propionaldehyde from 1-butene, acetaldehyde from 2-butene. The degradation takes place preferably if the β-carbon atom in an α-olefin is substituted by an alkyl or an aryl group. Examples are isobutene, α-methylstyrene,[164] 1,1-diphenylethylene,[164,342] β,β-dimethylacrylic acid. Acetone is also a product of oxidation of branched allylic compounds with four carbon atoms, but also the unbranched γ-methylallylamine and -iso-cyanate form acetone in relatively high yields (see Table III).

IV. CATALYTIC REACTIONS WITH GROUP VIII METAL SALTS
A. Solvolytic Reactions

1. Hydrolysis

Negative groups, such as halide, alkoxy, or carboxy groups attached to a double-bonded carbon atom are easily hydrolyzed in aqueous $PdCl_2$ solution[342] and carbonyl compounds are formed (see Table X).

$$CH_2{=}CHX + H_2O \xrightarrow{\ PdCl_2\ } CH_3{-}CHO + HX \qquad (101)$$
$$(X = \text{halide, alkoxy, carboxy.})$$

Kinetic investigations of the hydrolysis of vinyl chloride and 1-chloro-1-propene revealed the same rate law as was found for the olefin oxidation (see Eq. (9), Section III-A-1). Therefore, the same rate-determining step and the same preequilibria can be assumed, suggesting a *cis*-ligand insertion reaction.

Formally, the reaction appears as a simple replacement of the negative substituent by an OH group to form an enol which is then tautomerized to the carbonyl compound. However, such simplification would not explain, for instance, the formation of acetone from 1-chloro-1-propene or generally the formation of methylketones from 1-halo-olefins.[342] Attempts to explain these experimental results[174] started from the fact that the energy content of the transition state governs the position of the entering OH ligand. In the case of 1-chloro-1-propene, e.g., a transition or intermediate state like (29) is more stabilized than structure (30) by the electron-releasing effect of the methyl group:

(29) (30)

The 2,1-hydrogen transfer may proceed as in the olefin oxidation (see Section III-A-1), accompanied by a 1,2 transfer of the metal, which finally leaves with the chloride ion.

Stabilization of the transition state as mentioned may be the reason that formation of aldehydes instead of ketones from hydrolysis of 1-halo-olefins is limited as in the oxidation of α-olefins (see Section III-A-5). It is remarkable that the hydrolysis of 2-chloropropene proceeds much slower than that of 1-chloro-1-propene to form acetone. From 1-chloro-2-methyl-1-propene isobutyraldehyde is formed only to a minor extent. The main reaction is an allylic oxidation (see Section III-D). Even allyl chloride forms acetone to some extent with aqueous PdCl$_2$ beside allyl alcohol and the oxidation products described (cf. Section III-D-6).[173] For the hydrolysis of allyl halides, the role of the palladium salt can be formulated according to:

$$H_2C{=}CH{-}CH_2Cl \xrightarrow{\text{XPdOH}} HOH_2C{-}\underset{\underset{PdX}{|}}{CH}{-}CH_2Cl \xrightarrow{-\text{PdXCl}} HOH_2C{-}CH{=}CH_2 \qquad (101a)$$

Proof for this change of the position of the functional group cannot be derived from the reaction of homologous allylic compounds, since the alcohols formed are easily isomerized into each other (see Section III-D-2, Eq. (67b)).

In all of these reactions the negative charge brought in by the OH$^-$ ion is removed from the molecule by the desertion of the halide ion, whereas in the olefin oxidation it is taken up by the palladium. The same mechanism can be assumed for the reaction of α-halo-α,β-unsaturated carboxylic acids with aqueous PdCl$_2$, which yields methyl ketones with one carbon atom less than the original acid. (See Table XI.) The reaction might proceed through hydrolysis of the α-halo atom by a mechanism probably involving a σ-compound like structure (**29**) mentioned above and subsequent hydrogen transfer to form the β-oxo-carboxylic acid that decarboxylates. (Compare the oxidation of α,β-unsaturated carboxylic acids by aqueous PdCl$_2$ in Section III-A-5.)

Alkoxy, aroxy, and carboxylate groups at double-bonded carbon atoms are likewise hydrolyzed to yield the appropriate carbonyl compounds, e.g., acetone from α-methoxy-crotonic acid.[342]

Allylamines are hydrolyzed to form saturated aldehydes and ketones beside other products such as methyl ethyl ketone from α- and γ-methylallylamines, propionaldehyde from allylamine and allylurea,[342] and n-butyraldehyde from crotylamine. This formation of aldehydes is remarkable. The reaction might proceed through a shift of the double bond by isomerization (see Section IV-C) caused by an effect of the cleaved amino group on the palladium complex.

2. Transalkenylation

In nonaqueous solutions solvolysis reactions are transvinylation reactions. They are reversible reactions that lead to equilibria. Thus vinyl esters are converted with carboxylic acids to an equilibrium mixture of the corresponding esters and acids in the presence of palladium salts[343]

$$RCOOCH{=}CH_2 + R'COOH \xrightarrow[]{PdCl_2} R'COOCH{=}CH_2 + RCOOH \qquad (102)$$

The rate of achieving equilibrium is accelerated by alkali carboxylates.[323] By this reaction, e.g., vinyl esters of higher carboxylic acids can be prepared from vinyl acetate. Examples are given in Table XI. Analogously, iso- and n-propenyl groups and even the allyl group can be transferred (Table XI), but the reaction rates decrease in the same order.[323] Because of the accelerating influence of carboxylate anions, a nucleophilic attack of these ions has been assumed for the initiating step of the reaction.[343] This could be proved by the reaction of vinyl propionate with [18]O tagged acetic acid. By mass spectroscopy of the products in the resulting equilibrium mixture, it could be shown that the tagged atoms remain in the acetate group.[323]

A transvinylation mechanism could also be proved in the mercuric salt-catalyzed reaction by the use of tagged substrates[309] and by characterization of an oxymercuration intermediate by NMR spectroscopy.[215,216,338]

Therefore, the mechanism of the palladium salt-catalyzed transvinylation (also by analogy to other noble metal salt-catalyzed reactions, e.g., oxidation) has been assumed to proceed through oxypalladation intermediates:

$$H_2C{=}CHOCOCH_3 + HOCOR + [PdX_4]^{2-} \rightleftharpoons$$

$$\left[\begin{array}{c} OCOCH_3 \\ / \\ X_3Pd{-}CH_2{-}CH \\ \backslash \\ OCOR \end{array} \right]^{2-} + HX \rightleftharpoons$$

$$H_2C{=}CHOCOR + [PdX_4]^{2-} + HOCOCH_3 \qquad (103)$$

$$(R = alkyl; X = hal^-, carboxylate.)$$

Catalysis with salts of either palladium or mercury differs in the reaction medium. Mercuric salt catalysis occurs only in the presence of strong acids, while in the palladium salt catalysis an alkaline (carboxylate) medium is preferred. This may be the reason why no isopropenyl interchange between carboxylic acids has been described with mercuric salts. These esters are unstable in acidic medium and are hydrolyzed.

Alkenyl halides react under similar conditions in the presence of solutions of palladium and alkali metal salts in carboxylic acid medium to give the corresponding alkenyl esters, e.g., from vinyl chloride and acetic acid in the presence of $PdCl_2$ and disodium hydrogen phosphate or sodium acetate vinyl acetate is formed:[199,334,360]

$$H_2C{=}CHCl + OCOCH_3^- \xrightarrow[AcOH]{PdCl_2} H_2C{=}CH{-}OCOCH_3 + Cl^- \qquad (104)$$

TABLE X

Reactions of Olefinic Compounds Carrying Hydrolysable Functional Groups in Vinylic and Allylic Position with Aqueous $PdCl_2$
(Section VI-A-8)

Substrate	$PdCl_2$ concentration moles/l	Reaction temperature °C	time, min	Products	Yield % (conversion)	Description in Section	Mechanism	Refs.
a. Vinylic compounds								
Vinyl ethyl ether	0.1	20	30	Acetaldehyde	Quantitative	IV-A-1	hy	169
Vinyl acetate	0.1	20	60	Acetaldehyde	(73)	IV-A-1	hy	342
Isopropenyl acetate	0.1	25	5	Acetone	(94)	IV-A-1	hy	342
Vinyl chloride	0.1	20		Acetaldehyde	Quantitative	IV-A-1	hy	174,342
Vinyl bromide	0.1	10	15	Acetaldehyde	98	IV-A-1	hy	342
1-Chloro-1-propene	0.05	20		Acetone Propionaldehyde		IV-A-1	hy	174
1-Bromo-1-propene	0.1	30	15	Acetone	65	IV-A-1	hy	342
2-Chloro-1-propene	0.1	20	120	Acetone	32	IV-A-1	hy	342
1-Bromo-1-butene	0.1	30	15	Methyl ethyl ketone	67	IV-A-1	hy	342
1-Chloro-2-methyl-1-propene	0.1	40	30	α-Methacrolein Isobutyraldehyde	30 15	}IV-A-1	hy all. hy	342
1-Bromo-1-pentene	0.1	50	15	Pentan-2-one	61	IV-A-1	hy	342
1-Bromo-1-hexene	0.1	50	45	Hexan-2-one	88	IV-A-1	hy	342
1-Bromo-1-heptene	0.1	50	45	Heptan-2-one	85	IV-A-1	hy	342
α-Chlorostyrene	0.1	40	30	Acetophenone	55	IV-A-1	hy	342
β-Bromostyrene	0.1	40	20	Acetophenone Acetaldehyde	55 5	IV-A-1 III-F	hy hy, degr	342
α-Chloro-β-methylstyrene	0.1	70	120	Propiophenone	47	IV-A-1	hy	342
1-Chloro-3-phenyl-1-propene	0.1	70	10 hr	Benzyl methyl ketone	25	IV-A-1	hy	342
2-Chloro-3-phenyl-1-propene	0.1	70	10 hr	Benzyl methyl ketone	22	IV-A-1	hy	342
α-Bromoacrylic acid	0.1	25	60	Acetaldehyde	60	IV-A-1	hy, dec	342
α-Chlorocrotonic acid	0.1	50	60	Acetone	70	IV-A-1	hy, dec	342
α-Methoxycrotonic acid	0.1	50	120	Acetone	82	IV-A-1	hy, dec	342
α-Bromo-α,β-pentenoic acid	0.1	80	60	Methyl ethyl ketone	62	IV-A-1	hy, dec	342
α-Bromo-α,β-hexenoic acid	0.1	80	60	Pentan-2-one	57	IV-A-1	hy, dec	342

Compound				Products				Ref
α-Bromo-α,β-heptenoic acid	0.1	50	60	Hexan-2-one	70	IV-A-1	hy, dec	342
α-Bromo-α,β-octenoic acid	0.1	50	60	Heptan-2-one	65	IV-A-1	hy, dec	342
α-Bromocinnamic acid	0.1	70	120	Acetophenone	64	IV-A-1	hy, dec	342
b. Allylic Halides								
Allyl chloride	0.1	20	*ca.* 60	$[\pi\text{—}C_3H_5PdCl]_2$	Almost quant.	III-D-5	disprop	173
				Pyruvaldehyde	High	III-D-5		173
				Acrolein	Low	III-D-2, III-A-5	hy, ol	173
				Allyl alcohol	Traces	IV-A-1	hy	173
Allyl bromide	0.1	50	30	Pyruvaldehyde	65	III-D-5	ox	342
2,3-Dibromo-1-propene	0.1	50	30	Pyruvaldehyde	80	III-D-5	ox	342
1,3-Dichloro-1-propene	0.1	50	120	Pyruvaldehyde	40		ox	342
1-Chloro-2-methyl-2-propene	0.1	50	6 hr	Pyruvaldehyde	32		ox	342
3-Chloro-1-butene	0.1	50	60	α-Methacrolein	65	III-D-2	hy, ol	173
1-Chloro-2-butene(crotyl chloride)	0.1	20	*ca.* 60	$[\pi\text{-Crotyl—}PdCl]_2$	Almost quant.	III-D-5	disprop	173
				Diacetyl,	High	III-D-5		
				Acetoin	Low	III-D-5		
				Crotonaldehyde, vinyl methyl ketone			hy, ol	173
				Methyl ethyl ketone, crotyl alcohol			hy	173
				Acrolein, acetone	Traces		degr	173
c. Allylic Nitrogen Compounds								
1-Methallyl isothiocyanate	0.1	20		Methyl ethyl ketone	⎫ Decreasing		hy	169
				Vinyl methyl ketone	⎬		hy, ol	169
				Acetone	⎭		degr	169
3-Methallyl isothiocyanate	0.1	20		Acetone	⎫ Traces		degr	169
				Methyl ethyl ketone	⎬ Decreasing		hy	169
				Vinyl methyl ketone	⎭		hy, ol	169
				Diacetyl			ox	169
Allyl amine	0.1	25	60	Pyruvaldehyde			ox	349
				Propionaldehyde			hy, iso	349
				Acetaldehyde			degr	349
1-Methylallylamine	0.1	50	45	Methyl ethyl ketone	45		hy	349
				Diacetyl			ox	349
				Acetone	13		degr	349
3-Methylallylamine (crotylamine)	0.1	50		Methyl ethyl ketone, butyraldehyde			hy	169
				Acetone(acetaldehyde)			degr	169
N-Diethyl-3-methylallylamine	0.1	50	45	Methyl ethyl ketone	36		hy	349
Allylurea	0.1	50	10	Propionaldehyde	24		hy, iso	349

TABLE XI

Transalkenylation (see Sections IV-A-2 and IV-A-3)

a. Trans-alkenylation between alkenyl esters (and -halides) and acids (for examples see Sections VI-J-1, VI-J-2, VI-J-3)

Alkenylating agent	alk. ag./acid	Acid-alkali metal salt-solvent	Catalyst (mol cat. 10^2/mol acid)	Reaction temperature °C	time, hr	Products	Yield %	Example described	Refs.
Vinyl acetate	(3)	Propionic-NaOAc	PdCl₂ (0.5)	76-80	3	Vinyl propionate	45	VI-J-1	323,343
Vinyl acetate	(3)	Propionic-NaOAc	PtCl₂ (0.5)	75-80	5	Vinyl propionate	38	VI-J-1	323,343
Vinyl acetate	(3)	α-Chloropropionic-NaOAc	PdCl₂ (0.5)	76-80	2	Vinyl α-chloropropionate	65	VI-J-1	323,343
Vinyl acetate	(3)	Butyric-DMF	PdCl₂—NaCl/C	60-65	4	Vinyl butyrate		VI-J-1	109,111
Vinyl acetate	(3)	Crotonic-NaOAc	PdCl₂ (0.8)	76-80	5	Vinyl crotonate	55	VI-J-1	323,343
Vinyl acetate	(6.5)	e-Phthalimidocapric	PdCl₂ (0.8)	76-80	4	Vinyl e-phthalimidocaproate	53	VI-J-1	323,343
Vinyl acetate	(3)	Sorbic-NaOAc	PdCl₂ (1.0)	76-80	4	Vinyl sorbate	39	VI-J-1	323,343
Vinyl acetate	(3)	Lauric-NaOAc	PdCl₂ (1.4)	76-80	5	Vinyl laurate	77	VI-J-1	323,343
Vinyl acetate	(6)	Lauric-NaOAc	PdCl₂ (1.4)	25	8	Vinyl laurate	55	VI-J-1	323,343
Vinyl acetate	(3)	Lauric-NaOAc	RhCl₃ (1.3)	76-80	5	Vinyl laurate	28	VI-J-1	323,343
Vinyl acetate		Palmitic-DMF (1:3)	PdCl₂ (0.8)	60-65	4	Vinyl palmitate		VI-J-1	109,111
Vinyl acetate	(6)	Stearic-NaOAc	PdCl₂ (1.4)	76-80	3.5	Vinyl stearate	70	VI-J-1	323,343
Vinyl acetate	(6)	Stearic-DMF (1:3)	PdCl₂—NaCl/C	60-65	4	Vinyl stearate	85	VI-J-1	109,111
Vinyl acetate	(3)	Oleic-NaOAc	PdCl₂ (1.6)	76-80	5.5	Vinyl oleate	70	VI-J-1	323,343
Vinyl acetate	(4.5)	Adipic	PdCl₂ (1.0)	80-90	2.5	(Mono) vinyl adipate / divinyl adipate	38 / 42	VI-J-1	323,343
Vinyl acetate		Dicarboxylic monoalkylesters	PdCl₂—NaCl	30-150		Alkyl vinyl esters of dicarboxylic acids		VI-J-1	110
Vinyl acetate		Benzoic-NaOAc	PdCl₂ (1.2)	76-80	3	Vinyl benzoate	53		323,343

TABLE XI (continued)

Alkenylating agent	Acid-alkali metal salt-solvent	Catalyst	Reaction temperature °C	time, hr	Products	Yield %	Example described	Refs.
Vinyl chloride (2 atm)	HOAc—Na_2HPO_4—i-C_8H_{18}	$PdCl_2$	20	48	Vinyl acetate	27		360
Vinyl chloride (atm pressure)	Acetic-NaOAc, (DMF)	$PdCl_2$	65	1.25	Vinyl acetate	94	VI-J-2	199
Vinyl chloride	Pivalic-Na-pivalate	$PdCl_2$	75	1.3	Vinyl pivalate	97	Cf. VI-J-2	199
Vinyl chloride	Di(tri-n-butylammonium)-adipate-1,2-dimethoxyethane	$PdCl_2$	60	0.75	Divinyl adipate	20	VI-J-3	199
Vinyl chloride	Tri-n-butylammonium-benzoate-1,2-dimethoxyethane	$PdCl_2$	60	0.75	Vinyl benzoate	36	Cf. VI-J-3	199
Vinyl chloride	HF—MF-organic solvent M = alkali, alkali earth metal	PdF_2	100	2	Vinyl fluoride	ca. 1	VI-J-4	374,375
Vinyl bromide (6 atm)	KCl—DMF	$PdCl_2$	75	4.5	Vinyl chloride	83.5 (16.5% conversion)		199

Alkenylating agent	Acid-alkali metal salt (mole/mole acid)		Catalyst (mole/mole acid)		Reaction temperature °C	time, hr	Products	Yield %	Example described	Refs.
Isopropenyl acetate	Propionic-Na-propionate	3.0	$PdCl_2$—NaCl	0.008	Reflux	1	Isopropenyl propionate	30.4	VI-J-1	323
Isopropenyl propionate	Isobutyric-Na-isobutyrate	3.0	$PdCl_2$—NaCl	0.008	Reflux	1	Isopropenyl butyrate	35.0	VI-J-1	323
Isopropenyl acetate	Crotonic-NaOAc	2.0	$PdCl_2$—NaCl	0.008	60	1	Isopropenyl crotonate	21.5	VI-J-1	323
Isopropenyl acetate	Pivalic-NaOAc	3.0	$PdCl_2$—NaCl	0.008	90	1	Isopropenyl pivalate	7	VI-J-1	323
Isopropenyl acetate	Caproic-LiOAc	2.5	$PdCl_2$—NaCl	0.012	60	3	Isopropenyl caproate	30	VI-J-1	323
Isopropenyl acetate	ε-Phthalimido caproic-NaOAc	3.0	$PdCl_2$—NaCl	0.008	Reflux	1	Isopropenyl ε-phthalimido caproate	23.1	VI-J-1	323
Isopropenyl acetate	2-Ethylcaproic-LiOAc	2.5	$PdCl_2$—NaCl	0.012	60	4	Isopropenyl 2-ethylcaproate	26.3	VI-J-1	323
Isopropenyl acetate	Lauric-NaOAc	3.0	$PdCl_2$—NaCl	0.011	Reflux	1.5	Isopropenyl laurate	31.6	VI-J-1	323
Isopropenyl acetate	Adipic-NaOAc	3.0	$PdCl_2$—NaCl	0.016	80	2	Di-isopropenyl adipate	11.1	VI-J-1	323

(continued)

111

TABLE XI (*continued*)

Alkenylating agent	Acid-alkali metal salt (mole/mole Pd)	Catalyst (mole/mole acid)	Reaction temperature °C	time, hr	Products	Yield %	Example described	Refs.
Isopropenyl acetate	Hexahydrobenzoic-NaOAc 3.0	PdCl₂—NaCl 0.008	Reflux	1	Isopropenyl hexahydro-benzoate	20.8	VI-J-1	323
Isopropenyl acetate	Benzoic-Na-benzoate 3.0	PdCl₂—NaCl 0.008	80	1	Isopropenyl benzoate	25.5	VI-J-1	323
n-Propenyl acetate	Propionic-Na-propionate	PdCl₂—NaCl	50–80	20	n-Propenyl propionate	8	VI-J-1	323
Allyl acetate	Propionic-Na-propionate	PdCl₂—NaCl	Reflux	4	Allyl propionate	3	VI-J-1	323
2-Chloropropene	Acetic-NaOAc	PdCl₂	50	6.5	Isopropenyl acetate	Low	VI-J-2	199
1-Chloro-1-propene	Acetic-NaOAc-THF	PdCl₂ or Pd(OAc)₂	20	2	n-Propenyl acetate	ca. 10	VI-J-2	175,361

b. Reactions of alkenyl compounds with alcohols and amines.

Alkenylating Agent	Alcohol(amine)-solvent	Catalyst	Reaction temperature °C	time, hr	Products	Yield %	Example described	Refs.
Vinyl acetate	Methanol-dinonyl phthalate	Li₂PdCl₄	70	6	Methyl vinyl ether	ca. 20	VI-J-5	53
					Acetaldehyde dimethylacetal	ca. 7		
Vinyl acetate	Isopropanol	Li₂PdCl₄	20		Isopropyl vinyl ether		Cf. VI-J-5	53
Vinyl acetate	Isobutanol	Li₂PdCl₄	0		Iso-butyl vinyl ether		Cf. VI-J-5	53
Vinyl acetate	Ethyleneglycol	PdCl₂, CuCl₂	70	5	2-Methyl-1,3-dioxolane	ca. 35	Cf. VI-D-2	323,98a
					Glycol monoacetate	ca. 60		
Methyl vinyl ether	Isobutanol, DMSO	Li₂PdCl₄	25	1	Isobutyl vinyl ether	ca. 10		54,166
					Acetaldehyde diisobutylacetal			
Ethyl vinyl ether	Ethyleneglycol	PdCl₂, CuCl₂	80		2-Methyl-1,3-dioxolane		Cf. VI-D-2	323,383a
Vinyl chloride	Methanol-MeONa	PdCl₂	35–40	3.5	Acetaldehyde dimethylacetal	55	Cf. VI-J-6	199
					Acetaldehyde	10		
Vinyl chloride	Ethanol-EtONa	PdCl₂	40	5.5	Acetaldehyde diethylacetal	62	VI-J-6	199
					Acetaldehyde	7		
Vinyl chloride	Ethanol	PdCl₂/carrier	190		Vinyl ethyl ether			360
Vinyl chloride (2 atm)	Isopropanol-isooctane	PdCl₂—Na₂HPO₄	RT	48	Isopropyl acetal	37.5		360
Vinyl chloride (7 atm)	Ethyleneglycol	PdCl₂, CuCl₂	75	0.70	2-Methyl-1,3-dioxolane		Cf. VI-D-2	323,383a

Allylic compound	Solvent	Catalyst				Product	Ref.
Vinyl chloride	n-Butylamine–THF	$PdCl_2$—Na_2HPO_4	RT	168		After hydrogenation of the mixture: ethylbutylamine	360
Isopropenyl acetate	Methanol	Li_2PdCl_4		20		Isopropyl methyl ether	53
Allyl acetate	Methanol	Li_2PdCl_4		40	Low	Allyl methyl ether	53
Allyl chloride	Methanol	$PdCl_2$		100	19	Allyl methyl ether	Cf. VI-J-7 — 330
Allyl chloride	Ethanol (tenfold excess)	Na_2PdCl_4		55	50	Allyl ethyl ether	VI-J-7 — 330

c. Arylation reactions of allylic halides with organomercury compounds in the presence of palladium salts[143] (see Sections IV-A-3, VI-J-10, VI-J-11)

Allylic compound	Mercurial	Solvent	Catalyst	Products	Yield %
$CH_2{=}CHCH_2Cl$	C_6H_5HgCl	CH_3CN	$LiPdCl_3$	$C_6H_5CH_2CH{=}CH_2$	61
$CH_2{=}CHCH_2Cl$	C_6H_5HgOAc	CH_3CN	$Pd(OAc)_2$—$Hg(OAc)_2$	$C_6H_5CH_2CH{=}CH_2$	30
$CH_2{=}CHCH_2Cl$	C_6H_5HgCl	CH_3OH	Li_2PdCl_4—$CuCl_2$	$C_6H_5CH_2CH{=}CH_2$	6
$CH_2{=}CHCH_2Cl$	C_6H_5HgCl	CH_3COCH_3	Li_2PdCl_4—$CuCl_2$	$C_6H_5CH_2CH{=}CH_2$	17
$CH_2{=}CHCH_2Cl$	$3,4\text{-}Cl_2C_6H_3HgCl$	CH_3CN	$LiPdCl_3$—$CuCl_2$	$3,4\text{-}Cl_2C_6H_3CH_2CH{=}CH_2$	28
$CH_2{=}CHCH_2Cl$	$3\text{-}OCHC_6H_4HgCl$	CH_3CN	$LiPdCl_3$—$CuCl_2$	$3\text{-}OCHC_6H_4CH_2CH{=}CH_2$	43
$CH_2{=}CHCH_2Cl$	$2\text{-}C_4H_3SHgCl$	CH_3CN	$LiPdCl_3$—$CuCl_2$	$2\text{-}C_4H_3SCH_2CH{=}CH_2$	12
$CH_2{=}CHCH_2Cl$	$1,3,5\text{-}(CH_3)_3C_6H(HgOCOCH_3)_2$	CH_3CN	$LiPdCl_3$—$CuCl_2$	$1,3,5\text{-}(CH_3)_3C_6H(CH_2CH{=}CH_2)_2$	49
$CH_2{=}CHCH_2Cl$	$4\text{-}(C_2H_5)_2NC_6H_4HgCl$	CH_3CN	$LiPdCl_3$—$CuCl_2$	$4\text{-}(C_2H_5)_2NC_6H_4CH_2CH{=}CH_2$	33
$CH_2{=}CHCH_2Cl$	$4\text{-}CH_3OCOC_6H_4HgCl$	CH_3CN	Li_2PdCl_4—$CuCl_2$	$4\text{-}CH_3OCOC_6H_4CH_2CH{=}CH_2$	31
$CH_2{=}CHCH_2Cl$	$4\text{-}CH_3OC_6H_4HgCl$	CH_3CN	$LiPdCl_3$—$CuCl_2$	$4\text{-}CH_3OC_6H_4CH_2CH{=}CH_2$	47
$CH_2{=}CHCH_2Br$	C_6H_5HgOAc	CH_3CN	$Pd(OAc)_2$—$CuBr_2$	$C_6H_5CH_2CH{=}CH_2$	33
$CH_3HC{=}CHCH_2Cl$	C_6H_5HgCl	CH_3CN	$LiPdCl_3$	$C_6H_5CH_2CH{=}CHCH_3$	15
$CH_2{=}CHCHClCH_3$	C_6H_5HgCl	CH_3CN	$LiPdCl_3$	$C_6H_5CH_2CH{=}CHCH_3$	50
$CH_2{=}\underset{CH_3}{C}CH_2Cl$	C_6H_5HgCl	CH_3CN	$LiPdCl_3$	$C_6H_5CH_2\underset{CH_3}{C}{=}CH_2$	74
$CH_2{=}\underset{Cl}{C}CH_2Cl$	$4\text{-}CH_3OC_6H_4HgCl$	CH_3CN	$LiPdCl_3$—$CuCl_2$	$4\text{-}CH_3OC_6H_4CH_2\underset{Cl}{C}{=}CH_2$	35
$CH_2{=}\underset{Cl}{C}CH_2Cl$	C_6H_5HgCl	CH_3CN	$LiPdCl_3$	$C_6H_5CH_2\underset{Cl}{C}{=}CH_2$	68
$CH_2{=}CCH_2Cl$	$3\text{-}NO_2C_6H_4HgCl$	CH_3CN	$LiPdCl_3$—$CuCl_2$	$3\text{-}NO_2C_6H_4CH_2C{=}CH_2$	87

113

At temperatures higher than 80° side reactions take place such as the formation of ethylidene diacetate by the addition of acetic acid to vinyl acetate and the
formation of acetaldehyde and acetic anhydride (see Section III-B-2., Eq. (57))[55]
and presumably 1,4-diacetoxybutadiene (see Section III-E-2., Eq. (90)).[198] The
latter reaction accounts for palladium metal precipitation.

The formation of vinyl acetate from vinyl chloride is first order with respect to
both sodium acetate and palladium salt concentrations at constant vinyl chloride
pressure.[199]

This rate law differs from the one found for the formation of vinyl acetate from
ethylene (see Section III-B-1, Eq. (56)), which shows a higher reaction order with
respect to the acetate ion concentration. For the analogous reactions in aqueous
medium, i.e., the oxidation of ethylene and the hydrolysis of vinyl chloride to
form acetaldehyde, the same rate law has been found (see Section IV-A).

Halide ions decrease the catalytic ability of the palladium salt by complexing
and impede the formation of a vinyl halide palladium(II) complex that is assumed
to be an intermediate. Dimethylformamide used as a solvent instead of acetic
acid increases the reaction rate, probably due to the higher nucleophilicity of
acetate ions in this medium.

Also, ferric acetate increases the transvinylation reaction with vinyl chloride
considerably. It is assumed that the complexed vinyl halide is more activated by
the electron-withdrawing influence of the ferric ions across the chloro-bridge of a
binuclear $PdCl_2$-ferric acetate complex.

If cupric acetate is used instead of sodium acetate, the reaction rate decreases
because of the lower degree of dissociation of the cupric salt into free acetate ions.
The above-mentioned side reactions become more important. With high palladium chloride concentration, glycolaldehyde triacetate is obtained as a consecutive reaction product of vinyl acetate, according to

$$CH_2{=}CH{-}OAc + PdCl_2 + Cu(OAc)_2 \longrightarrow$$
$$CuCl_2 + Pd + AcO{-}CH_2{-}CH(OAc)_2 \quad (105)$$

This reaction is quite analogous to the formation of glycol derivatives formed
from ethylene, e.g., ethylene glycol and chlorohydrin in an aqueous medium (see
Section III-A-1, Eqs. (28) and (29)[357] and glycol mono- and diacetate and β-
chloroethyl acetate in acetic acid medium (see Section III-B-1[153]), all reactions
occurring in the presence of high amounts of cupric salts.[199]

Analogous reactions with other carboxylates include the replacement of the
chloro atom in 2-chloro-1-propene by acetate ion to form isopropenyl acetate and
are listed in Table XI.

1-Halo-1-alkenes react with carboxylic acids in the presence of palladium
salts to give 1-carboxy-1-alkenes.[361] This replacement is in contrast to the
hydrolysis of 1-halo-1-alkenes, where the nucleophile enters position 2 (see
Section IV-A-1).

Also, vinyl and even allyl ethers can be formed by an analogous reaction of vinyl and allyl acetate, respectively,[53,138] as well as of vinyl halides[360] and allyl halides[330] with alcohols in the presence of group VIII metal salts. However, vinyl ethers are only formed at elevated temperatures, e.g., vinyl ethyl ether by passing vinyl chloride and ethanol over supported $PdCl_2$ at 190°,[360] while at lower temperatures acetals resulting from addition of the alcohols to the vinyl ether are obtained.[199,323,360]

Similarly, vinyl exchange has been carried out between vinyl ethers and alcohols in the presence of group VIII metal compounds to form other vinyl ethers.[54,166] Also, a halogen exchange has been observed when vinyl halides are reacted with alkali or alkaline earth halides in the presence of palladium halides in an organic solvent. Thus vinyl bromide has been converted into vinyl chlorde[199] and vinyl chloride into vinyl fluoride,[374] which is also obtainable from vinyl acetate.[375] Vinyl acetate also forms vinyl chloride but only in traces, since the reaction is impeded by chloride ions that are necessary for the reaction. Other alkenyl chlorides are also obtained from the corresponding acetates, e.g., 2-chloro-1-propene from isopropenyl acetate. These reactions indicate that at least most of the transalkenylation reactions are reversible.

Stereochemical aspects of transvinylation reactions can start from the observation that the substrate ion always enters the molecule at the carbon atom that carried the leaving group, e.g., isopropenyl and n-propenyl acetates or chlorides give exclusively isopropenyl and n-propenyl derivatives, respectively.[199,323,361] Also, in the reaction of deuterio-labeled vinyl chloride with acetate ion, the label remains in the original 2-position.[398] Another aspect of the stereochemistry of transvinylation reactions is the geometric configuration with regard to the double bond. *Cis*- or *trans-n*-propenyl acetate yield the inverse geometric isomers when exchanged with propionate, i.e., *cis-n*-propenyl acetate gives *trans-n*-propenyl propionate, while *trans-n*-propenyl acetate gives *cis-n*-propenyl propionate.[323]

The reaction is accompanied by *cis,trans* isomerization of the starting materials and the products. It is assumed that isomerization of the n-propenyl esters proceeds by the same mechanism and the same rate as propenyl interchange does; it is an interchange between the same carboxylate anions accompanied by the inversion of the geometrical configuration.

These results can be explained by a *cis* addition of a Pd—X′ species to the alkenyl compound to form a palladium-σ-compound and consecutive *cis* elimination (see scheme, Eq. (106)) after rotation of the σ-compound around the axis of the original double bond:

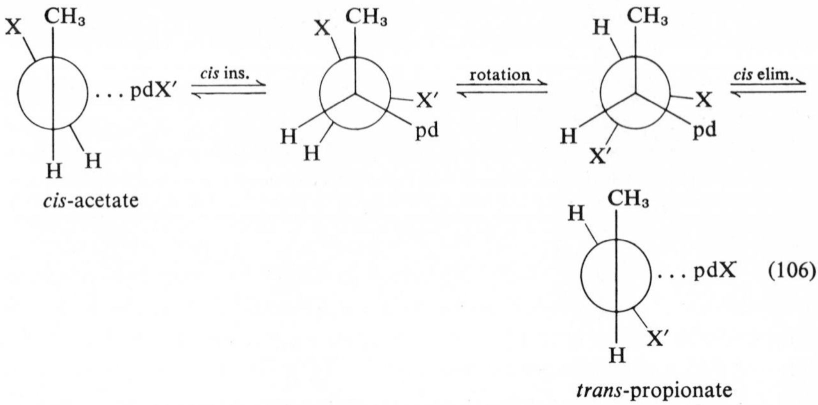

cis-acetate

trans-propionate

if X = CH$_3$COO$^-$ and X' = C$_2$H$_5$COO$^-$.

In analogy to the olefin oxidation reactions (see Sections III-A and III-B), a *cis*-ligand insertion reaction was assumed for the palladation step (*cis* addition).

cis-Isomers of *n*-propenyl carboxylates are thermodynamically preferred and prevail in the equilibrium mixture after sufficient reaction time because of the simultaneously occurring isomerization of starting and product esters. If *n*-propenyl chloride is reacted with sodium acetate in the presence of palladium salt in acetic acid, also the *cis* isomers of the chloride and the *n*-propenyl acetate obtained prevail after sufficient time.[323]

Primary products in this reaction, however, have been found to retain their original configuration, e.g., *trans*-1-chloro-1-propene yielded *trans*-1-acetoxy-1-propene[361] and the appropriate *cis* compound yielded *cis*-acetoxy-1-propene. There are two possible courses of reactions *cis* addition, followed by *trans* elimination or *trans* addition followed by *cis* elimination.

The latter route would be consistent with the attack of a carboxylate anion from the solution on the coordinated alkenyl-halide, followed by a *cis*-β-abstraction according to an inverse ligand-insertion reaction after rotation around the C—C axis.[175,361]

Isomerization of the products then leads to a mixture containing mainly the thermodynamically preferred *cis* isomer. Also, the starting propenyl halides are isomerized but with considerably lower rate than the esters.

In the reaction of *trans*-2-deuterio-1-chloroethylene with sodium acetate in the presence of PdCl$_2$ in acetic acid, *cis*- and *trans*-2-deuterio-1-acetoxy-ethylene were formed in equal amounts,[398] possibly due to an appropriate position of the corresponding equilibrium.

3. Transfer of Alkenyl Groups to Carbanions

In analogy to the coupling reactions with mercurials mentioned in Section III-E-3, vinyl and allyl compounds were reacted with mercurials in the presence of $PdCl_2$. The catalytic replacement of the negative group by carbanions gives poor yields with vinyl compounds but good yields with allyl halides, e.g.,[143]

$$C_6H_5-HgCl + ClCH_2-CH{=}CH_2 \xrightarrow{PdCl_2}$$

$$C_6H_5-CH_2-CH{=}CH_2 + HgCl_2 \quad (107)$$

B. Oligomerization and Polymerization

1. Dimerization of Olefins

Dimerization of olefins in the presence of $PdCl_2$ was first observed by Smidt, et al.[342,344] In nonaqueous, e.g., acetic acid solution of $PdCl_2$ ethylene is absorbed very rapidly. On heating the solution the olefin evolves; to some extent, according to the residence time, butenes are formed.[113,342] Similarly, propylene is dimerized.[342] Oligomerization can also be carried out in other solvents. Suspensions of $PdCl_2$ in nonpolar solvents such as benzene or other aromatics, n-pentane, CCl_4, etc., have been used for the dimerization of ethylene[260] and propylene[261] to form 1- and 2-butenes and C_6-olefins, respectively. Yields of dimerization products decrease in the following order of solvents used: acetic acid, 1,2-dichloroethane, perchloroethylene, benzene, chlorobenzene, triethyleneglycol, ethyl acetate, chloroform, and cyclohexane.[181]

Ethylene and propylene are also dimerized in the presence of $RhCl_3 \cdot 3H_2O$ in methanol or ethanol.[3] There are different yields of 1- and 2-olefins with different temperatures, e.g., rather high amounts of 1-butene form at 30°, while at 45° only low yields of this isomer are found. With still increasing temperature the yields of 1-butene increase again due to the thermodynamic equilibrium. It is, therefore, assumed that two reactions concur: the 1-olefin is formed in the primary olefin dimerization. At increasing temperatures the secondary isomerization is competing, which leads to the thermodynamic equilibrium mixture.

As catalysts for the dimerization of propene, mixtures of $C_2H_5AlCl_2$ and halides of platinum, palladium, rhodium, and iridium in the presence of triphenylphosphine, arsine, and stibine have been reported.[296] $RhCl_3 \cdot 3H_2O$ has been used for the dimerization of mixed olefins. From a mixed feed of ethylene and propylene, a mixture of isomeric C_4, C_5, and C_6 olefins has been obtained.[3] Likewise, 2-phenyl-2-butene was obtained by the reaction of ethylene with styrene in the presence of rhodium chloride. The same catalyst was also used for the addition of monoolefins such as ethylene or propylene to 1,3-dienes, yielding 1,4-dienes, e.g., 1,4-hexadiene from butadiene and ethylene as the almost exclusive product under mild conditions.[3] Isomerization takes place at elevated temperatures and longer contact times. Further examples for the addition of olefins to dienes are listed in Table XIII.

An unusual course of the oligomerization of ethylene with palladium chloride was observed in the presence of sodium fluoride in benzonitrile, adipodinitrile, or nitrobenzene as a solvent at 100°C[69] and in the presence of hydrogen chloride in acetic acid–acetic anhydride as a solvent at 80°C.[2a] Propylene is thereby formed as the major product. The reaction does not take place with other olefins or vinyl fluoride in the first case or in the absence of $PdCl_2$, acetic anhydride, or when the hydrochloric acid is neutralized with lithium acetate in the latter reaction.

2. Mechanisms

The Pd^{II}-catalyzed dimerization of olefins probably involves an olefin-palladium complex as a first intermediate, since Kharasch's complex $[C_2H_4PdCl_2]_2$ yields butenes on heating.[113,260] Also, solutions of such complexes in various solvents act as catalysts in olefin oligomerization reactions.[113,188] Since complexes with two molecules of ethylene coordinated to one palladium atom have been made probable by NMR analysis of catalytically active solutions,[188] such species can be considered.*

A plausible mechanism for the dimerization of ethylene in the presence of $RhCl_3 \cdot 3H_2O$ was suggested by Cramer.[63,66] He could demonstrate that an induction period in the dimerization of ethylene occurs if $RhCl_3 \cdot 3H_2O$ is used as a catalyst, while the reaction immediately starts if diethylene complexes of Rh^I are used:

$$[(C_2H_4)_2Rh \cdot Cl]_2 \quad \text{or} \quad [acac\ Rh(C_2H_4)_2]$$

which form from $RhCl_3 \cdot 3H_2O$ and ethylene.[61] Furthermore, he found a linear dependence of the reaction rate on the concentrations of H^+, Cl^-, rhodium ion, and ethylene, which suggests an oxidative addition of HCl to the Rh^I complex to form a hydrido-Rh^{III} complex. The existence of an ethyl complex of rhodium could be demonstrated by NMR analysis of the reaction mixture at low temperatures.† On heating the solution the NMR spectrum

---

* Evidence for the existence of palladium complexes with two molecules of ethylene was also deduced from the rate of absorption of ethylene in the oxidation reaction in the absence of Cl^- ions but in the presence of sulfuric acid.[343]

† An ethyl rhodium complex could be isolated as cesium salt from such solutions[63]: $Cs[C_2H_5RhCl_3(H_2O)]$.

changes at temperatures when dimerization starts. This leads to the assumption that an insertion reaction between the two ligands $\sigma\text{-}C_2H_5$ and $\pi\text{-}C_2H_4$ takes place as the rate-determining step* to form a σ-butyl complex. Presumably, via β-hydrogen abstraction a butene-hydrido complex is formed and butene is liberated through replacement by ethylene, which closes the catalytic circle:

$$[Cl_2Rh^I(C_2H_4)_2]^- \underset{HCl}{\overset{HCl}{\rightleftharpoons}} [Cl_3HRh^{III}(C_2H_4)_2]^- \rightleftharpoons$$

$$[C_2H_5Rh^{III}(C_2H_4)Cl_3]^- \xrightarrow{\text{rate-determining}} [\sigma\text{-}C_4H_9Rh^{III}Cl_3]^- \rightleftharpoons$$

$$[\pi\text{-}C_4H_8Rh^{III}HCl_3]^- \overset{-HCl}{\rightleftharpoons} [C_4H_8Rh^ICl_2]^- \xrightarrow[+2\,C_2H_4]{-C_4H_8}$$

$$[Cl_2Rh^I(C_2H_4)_2]^- \quad (108)$$

Insertion reactions have been described so far as equilibrium reactions. In the case of the formation of the butyl complex, the reason why the reaction is not reversible may be that the cleavage of a C—H bond is easier compared to the cleavage of a C—C bond. Acids other than hydrogen halides fail to act as cocatalysts in 1-butene synthesis. This is in accordance with the fact that hydrido complexes are preferably formed from hydrogen halides. It should be noted that in other reactions also, in which hydrido complexes are possible intermediates, e.g., hydrogenation, olefin isomerization, and carbonylation hydrogen halides are preferred cocatalysts, whereas other acids often exert only low activity. In addition, molecular hydrogen can be used as a cocatalyst in olefin oligomerization.

For the codimerization of olefins and 1,3-diolefins, Cramer[65] also suggested a mechanism based on the following observations:

1. No induction period with a rhodium(I) compound as catalyst and HCl in methanol as reaction medium.

2. First-order dependence of the rate of reaction on C_2H_4, Rh, H^+, and Cl^- concentration and dependence on butadiene concentration by an order varying with temperature between zero and one.

3. Formation of the complex

(32)

---

* Rate constants for ethylene dimerization with $Cl_2Rh(C_2H_4)_2$ follow.

T °C	$k \cdot 10^4$, (sec^{-1})
10	0.35, 0.371
30	2.67, 2.79
50	16.8, 16.9, 17.9

by interaction of butadiene with an ethylrhodium(III) species formed by oxidative addition of HCl to an ethylenerhodium(I) complex (see Eq. (108) above).

4. Ready replacement of the coordinated butadiene by ethylene.

From this mechanism the formation of catalytic species (33) has been inferred, according to the following sequence of equilibria and reactions, or by direct reaction of the hydridorhodium(III) complex with butadiene:

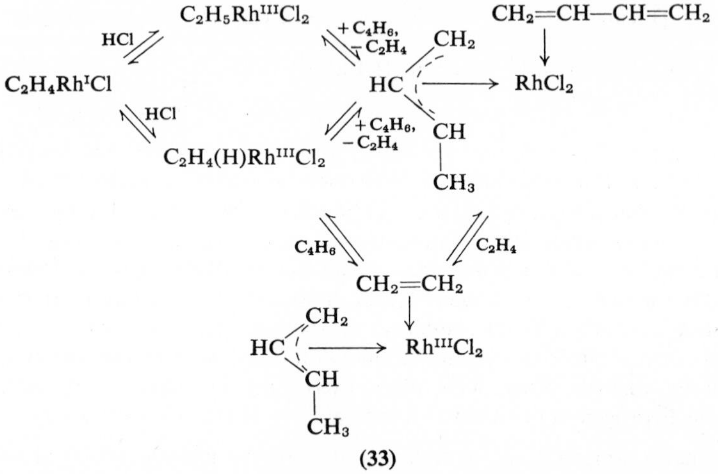

$$
\text{(109)}
$$

(33)

The interaction of the coordinated olefin and π-crotyl group proceeds as a ligand-insertion reaction in which the crotyl group attacks the coordinated

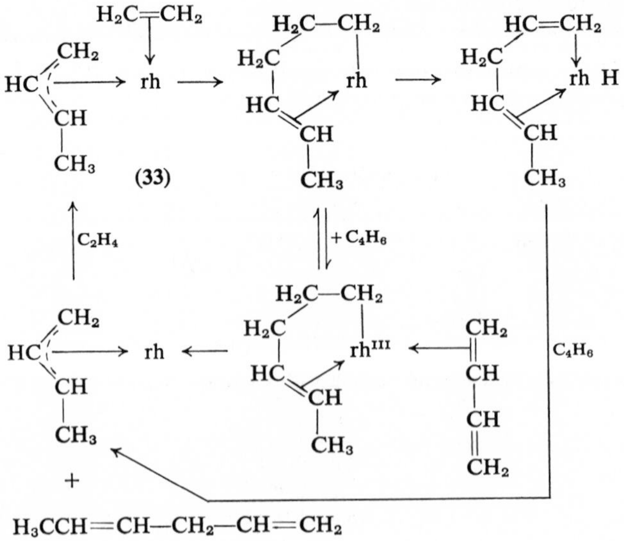

$$
\text{(110)}
$$

$$H_3CCH=CH-CH_2-CH=CH_2$$

olefin or the olefin is formally inserted between the metal and that carbon atom on which a certain σ-character is preformed by the unsymmetry of the π-allylic bond (see Sections II and III-D). The hexadiene is formed by β-hydrogen abstraction. The cycle closes by addition of butadiene (to form the π-crotyl species) and ethylene.

The preferred formation of hexenes (instead of butenes) may be caused by the relative stability of complex (33). The hexene $H_2C{=}CHCH(CH_3)CH{=}CH_2$, which is obtained only to a minor extent, originates from the formal insertion of the olefin between the metal and the other outer carbon atom of the allylic group. Higher 1,3-dienes react similarly; the products obtained can be derived from the most stable π-allyl complexes possible, e.g., the following complexes from $1,3$-C_5H_8 and isoprene: see table XII

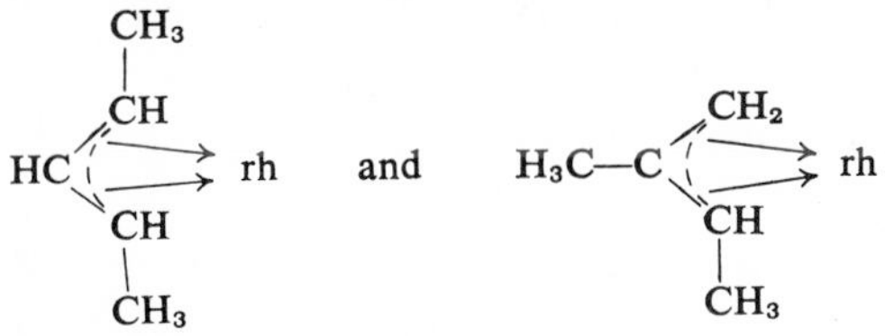

$$
\begin{array}{c}
CH_3 \\
| \\
CH \\
HC \overset{\displaystyle\nearrow}{\underset{\displaystyle\searrow}{}} rh \\
CH \\
| \\
CH_3
\end{array}
\quad \text{and} \quad
\begin{array}{c}
CH_2 \\
H_3C{-}C \overset{\displaystyle\nearrow}{\underset{\displaystyle\searrow}{}} rh \\
CH \\
| \\
CH_3
\end{array}
$$

3. Dimerization of Substituted Olefins

Olefins carrying a substituent with a double bond conjugated to the olefinic double bond, such as

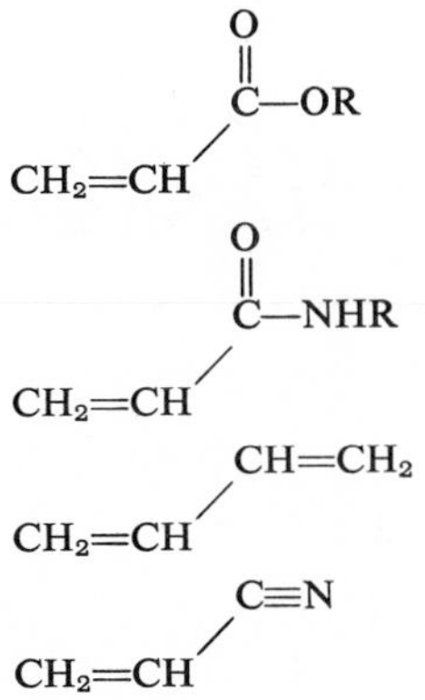

$$
\begin{array}{c}
\overset{\displaystyle O}{\underset{\displaystyle \|}{}} \\
CH_2{=}CH{-}C{-}OR
\end{array}
$$

$$
\begin{array}{c}
\overset{\displaystyle O}{\underset{\displaystyle \|}{}} \\
CH_2{=}CH{-}C{-}NHR
\end{array}
$$

$$
CH_2{=}CH{-}CH{=}CH_2
$$

$$
CH_2{=}CH{-}C{\equiv}N
$$

surprisingly yield end-to-end dimerization products, i.e., 1,4-substituted butenes.

Methyl acrylate has been dimerized to form dimethyl 2-hexenedioate.[3] The addition of ethylene to methyl acrylate gave a small amount of methyl pent-3-enoate.

TABLE XII

Oligomerization and Polymerization of Olefinic Compounds (see Section IV-B)

Substrate olefin	Solvent	Catalyst	Reaction temperature, °C	pressure, atm	time, hr	Products	Yield % (conversion)	Example described	Refs.
a. Dimerization of aliphatic mono- and diolefins									
Ethylene	Acetic acid, methyl ethyl ketone	$PdCl_2$—HCl($NaCl$)	90	55	10	1- and 2-Butenes	ca. 50	VI-K-1	342,344
	Benzene, n-pentane, CCl_4, $CHCl_3$, C_6H_5Cl, Cyclohexane	$PdCl_2$	25	0	—	1- and 2-Butenes			181,260
	$CHCl_3$—ROH, CH_2Cl_2	$PdCl_2$	50	10	—	1- and 2-Butenes			188
	Nitropropane	$PdCl_2$	40–45	—	—	1- and 2-Butenes			200
	Benzene	Pd-halide-sulfolan	75	50	18	1- and 2-Butenes			195
	Benzene, dioxane	$[C_2H_4PdCl_2]_2$	25	—	—	1- and 2-Butenes	(80)		113,181b
	$CHCl_3$—ROH, CH_2Cl_2	$[C_2H_4PdCl_2]_2$	25	—	—	1- and 2-Butenes	90–100		188
	C_6H_5CN, $C_6H_5NO_2$	$PdCl_2$ + NaF	160	1.4	4	1- and 2-Butenes	90–100		69
	Acetic acid-acetic anhydride	$PdCl_2$—HCl	80	0	10	Propene!	ca. 20		2a
						Propene!	ca. 15		2a
						Butenes	ca. 6		2a
	CH_2Cl_2	$Pd(CN)_2$	50	10	10 min	1- and 2-Butenes, trace of polyethylene			188
	$CHCl_3$, CCl_4	$[RhCl_3(H_2O)_3]$	25	10	—	2-Butene			188
	CH_3OH, C_2H_5OH	$[RhCl_3(H_2O)_3]$, $[RuCl_3(H_2O)_3]$, H_2PtCl_6	45	400–1000	6	1- and 2-Butenes	(>80)	VI-K-2	3
Propene	Acetic acid	$PdCl_2$—HCl($NaCl$)	80	26	3	Isomeric methylpentenes		VI-K-1	342,344
	Benzene, CCl_4, CH_2Cl_2	$PdCl_2$	25	0	—	C_6-Olefins			188,261

Reactant	Solvent	Catalyst	Temp. (°C)		Ratio	Products	Yield (%)	Section	Ref.
	Acetic acid	PdCl$_2$	—	—	—	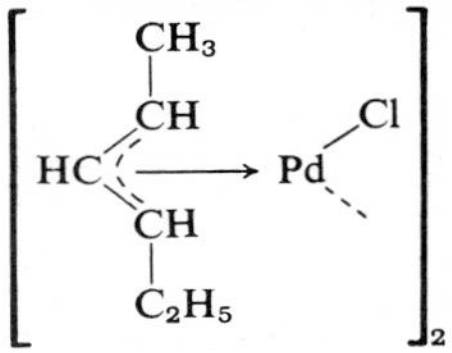	—		239
	CH$_3$OH, C$_2$H$_5$OH	[RhCl$_3$(H$_2$O)$_3$], [RuCl$_3$(H$_2$O)$_3$], Halides of Rh, Pd, Ir, Pt + C$_2$H$_5$AlCl$_2$	30–50	50–1000	16	n-Hexenes, methylpentenes	—		3
Isobutene			40			n-Hexenes, methylpentenes	78		296
	CHCl$_3$, CH$_2$Cl$_2$, C$_2$H$_5$NO$_2$, C$_6$H$_5$NO$_2$	[C$_2$H$_4$PdCl$_2$]$_2$	20–30	5–10	—	2,5-Dimethyl-1-hexene 2,5-Dimethyl-2-hexene		VI-K-3	185
Butadiene	CH$_3$OH, C$_2$H$_5$OH	[RhCl$_3$(H$_2$O)$_3$]—KOAc	100	16	16	2,4,6-Octatriene	70	VI-K-3	3
	Benzene, acetone, THF	(PPh$_3$)$_2$Pd(MA) MA = maleic anhydride	115	—	8	1,3,7-Octatriene			352,367, 368,369, 370
	Alcohols	(PPh$_3$)$_2$Pd(MA)	115	—	8	1-Alkoxy-2,7-octadiene 3-Alkoxy-1,7-octadiene		VI-K-4 VI-K-4	368
	Phenol	(PPh$_3$)$_2$Pd(MA), (pyridine)$_2$PdCl$_2$	115	—	8	1-Phenoxy-2,7-octadiene		Cf. VI-K-4	352,368
	R$_2$NH (e.g., morpholine, piperidine, diisopropylamine)	(PPh$_3$)$_2$Pd(MA)	115	—	8	1-Amino-2,7-octadienes		Cf. VI-K-4	368
	RNH$_2$ (e.g., butylamine)	(PPh$_3$)$_2$Pd(MA)	115	—	8	RNH-(2,7-C$_8$H$_{13}$), RH-(2,7-C$_8$H$_{13}$)$_2$		Cf. VI-K-4	368
	2-Methoxyethanol	RuCl$_3$	90			Dichloro(dodeca-2,6,10-trien-1,12-diyl)Ru(IV) 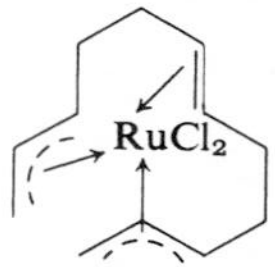			267

(continued)

123

TABLE XII (continued)

Substrate olefin	Solvent	Catalyst	Reaction temperature °C	pressure atm	time, hr	Products	Yield % (conversion)	Example described	Refs.
Isoprene	Ethanol	$RuCl_3$				(2,7-Dimethyl-octa-2,6-dien-1,8-diyl)Ru(IV)Cl₂ $\xrightarrow[CH_2Cl_2]{H_2}$ 2,7-Dimethyl-2,6-octadiene			298

$$\left[\begin{array}{c} CH_3 \\ H_2C-CH \\ \\ H_2C-CH_2 \end{array} \underset{\substack{Cl \\ Cl}}{\overset{\displaystyle Ru}{\longrightarrow}} \begin{array}{c} CH_2 \\ C \\ CH_2 \\ C-CH_3 \end{array} \right]_2$$

b. Dimerization of alicyclic and aromatic olefins

Substrate olefin	Solvent	Catalyst	Reaction temperature °C	pressure atm	time, hr	Products	Yield % (conversion)	Example described	Refs.
Norbornadiene		Rh/C	110			Dimers: A, B	23, 53	VI-K-5	258
						Trimer:	13		258

Ph—CH=CH—CH—CH—Ph
            |
           CH₃

Substrate olefin	Solvent	Catalyst	Reaction temperature °C	time, hr		Products	Yield % (conversion)	Example described	Refs.
α-Methylstyrene	HOAc—NaOAc—H₂O	PdCl₂	105		3	2,4-Diphenyl-4-methyl-2-pentene; PhC(Me)=CHCPh(Me)₂; Acetophenone; 2,5-Diphenyl-2,4-hexadiene (see Table VIII)	(30)	Cf. VI-F-2	164,397
	Acetic acid	PdSO₄	95		4	2,4-Diphenyl-4-methyl-2-pentene			391
α,β-Dimethylstyrene	HOAc—NaOAc—H₂O	PdCl₂	100		1	2,4-Diphenyl-3,4-dimethyl-2-hexene			164
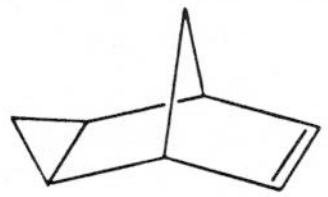 Exo-tricyclo[3,2,1,0²,⁴]-octene	—	Rh/C	90				15		181a

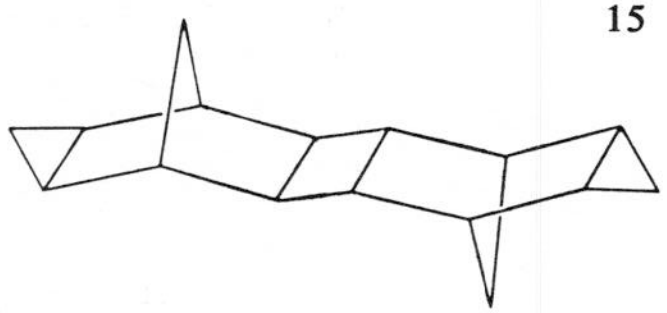

c. Dimerization of olefinic compounds carrying functional groups

Substrate olefin	Solvent	Catalyst	Reaction temperature °C	time, hr	Products	Yield % (conversion)	Example described	Refs.
Acrylonitrile (AN)	C₂H₅OH	RuCl₃(H₂O)₃—H₂ / RuCl₂(AN)₃₋₄—H₂ (30 atmg H₂)	170	0.5	*cis*-1,4-Dicyano-1-butene (18%), *trans*-1,4-Dicyano-1-butene (22%), Propionitrile (51%), Adiponitrile (4%)	(94)	VI-K-6	233,234,235,310
Acrylonitrile	N-Methylpyrrolidine	RuCl₂(AN)₄—H₂ (10–40 atm)			1,4-Dicyanobutene, adiponitrile	65		226
Methyl acrylate	CH₃OH (hydroquinone)	[RhCl₃(H₂O)₃] / [RuCl₃(H₂O)₃]	140 / 210	10 / 10	Dimethyl α-hydromuconate, H₃COOC—CH=CH—CH₂—CH₂—COOCH₃	31 (low) / 44 (low)		3

(*continued*)

125

TABLE XII (continued)

Substrate olefin	Solvent	Catalyst	Reaction temperature °C	time, hr	Products	Yield % (conversion)	Example described	Refs.
Acrylamides								
H₂C=CH—C(=O)—NHR	n-C₄H₉OH	RhCl₃ (anhydrous)	Reflux	24	trans-α-Hydromuconamides	24	VI-K-7	196
(R=H, CH₃, C₂H₅, cyclohexyl, phenyl)		+ p-Benzoquinone			RHNOC—CH=C(H)—CH₂—CH₂—CONHR			
d. Codimerization of olefinic compounds								
C₂H₄ + C₃H₆ (50–1000 atm)	CH₃OH, C₂H₅OH	[RhCl₃(H₂O)₃] [RuCl₃(H₂O)₃]	30–50	16	C₄, C₅, C₆-Olefins			3
C₂H₄ + styrene (1000 atm)	C₂H₅OH	[RhCl₃(H₂O)₃]	50	16	2-Phenyl-2-butene			3
C₂H₄ + methyl acrylate	CH₃OH	[RuCl₃(H₂O)₃]	150	16	Methyl 3-pentenoate (5%) Dimethyl 2-hexenedioate (56%)		Cf. VI-K-8	3 3
C₂H₄ + butadiene	C₂H₅OH	[RhCl₃(H₂O)₃]	50	16	1,4-Hexa- and 2,4-hexadiene, octadienes		VI-K-8	3,65
C₂H₄ + chloroprene	C₂H₅OH	[RhCl₃(H₂O)₃]	50	16	Conjugated chlorinated C₆-dienes		Cf. VI-K-8	3
C₂H₄ + 1,3-pentadiene	C₂H₅OH	[RhCl₃(H₂O)₃]	50	16	3-Methyl-1,4-hexadiene		Cf. VI-K-8	3
C₂H₄ + isoprene	C₂H₅OH	[RhCl₃(H₂O)₃]	50	16	Various C₇-dienes		Cf. VI-K-8	3
C₂H₄ + 2,4-hexadiene	C₂H₅OH	[RhCl₃(H₂O)₃]	50	16	Various C₈-dienes		Cf. VI-K-8	3
C₃H₆ + butadiene	C₂H₅OH	[RhCl₃(H₂O)₃]	50	16	2-Methyl-1,4-hexadiene		Cf. VI-K-8	3
C₃H₆ + isoprene	C₂H₅OH	[RhCl₃(H₂O)₃]	50	16	C₈-Dienes		Cf. VI-K-8	3
e. Polymerization of unsaturated compounds (see Section IV-B-4)								
Ethylene (10 atmg)	CH₂Cl₂	Pd(CN)₂	50		Polyethylene Butenes (see Table XIIa)	Trace		188

126

Reactant	Solvent	Catalyst	Temp.		Product			Ref.
Ethylene (2.8 atmg)	Benzene	Chloro(azobenzene-2-C,N')-carbonyl platinum(II) 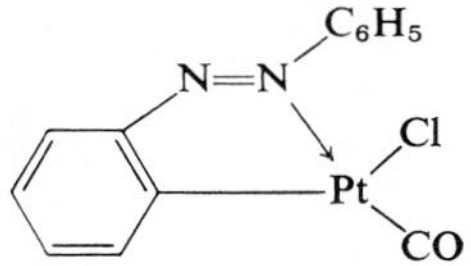	RT	13	C_{20}—C_{22} hydrocarbons			58a
Propene (10 atmg)		$Pd(CN)_2$	50		Low molecular weight polypropylene	Low		188
Propene (3.5 atm)	CH_3OH	$Pd(CN)_2$	50		1,3-Polypropylene (polyethylene)			186
Butadiene	H_2O, C_2H_5OH, DMF	$RhCl_3$—$3H_2O$ $Rh(NO_3)_3$—$2H_2O$	50		trans-1,4-Polybutadiene	ca. 20g/hr	VI-K-9	72,87, 314,315, 380
Butadiene, isoprene	Saturated alcohols	$Rh(NO_3)_3$	50		Polybutadiene, polyisoprene			36a
Norbornene (subst.)	2-Ethylenic alcohols	$PdCl_2$	95	6	Polynorbornene	20	VI-K-10	326

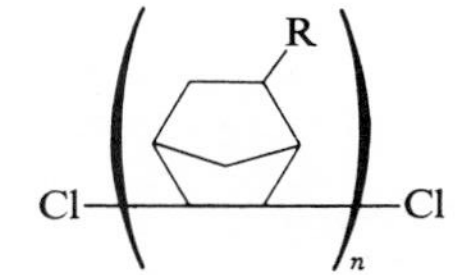

R = CH_2OH, CH_2OCH_3, CH_2OAc

| | Ru^{3+}, Os^{3+}, Ir^{3+} salts | ROH, H^+ | | | | | | 229,313 |

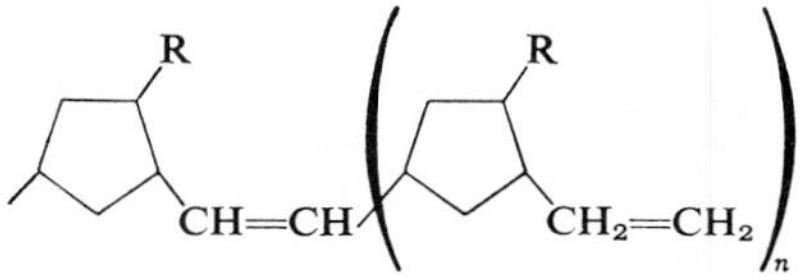

R = H, CH_2, CN

R = COOH

| | $PdCl_2$ | | | | | | | 326 |

(continued)

127

TABLE XII (*continued*)

Substrate olefin	Solvent	Catalyst	Reaction temperature °C	time, hr	Products	Yield % (conversion)	Example described	Refs.
Allene	C_2H_5OH, CH_2Cl_2	[RhCl(CO)$_2$]$_2$ + xPPh$_3$ [RhCl(C$_2$H$_4$)$_2$]$_2$ + xPPh$_3$ [RhCl(PPh$_3$)$_3$] RuCl$_3$ + nH$_2$O RuCl$_{2-3}$ PPh$_3$		5	1,2-Polyallene 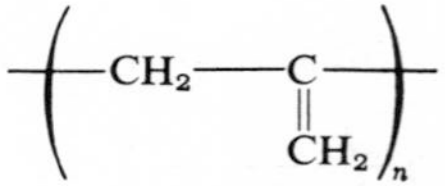 $\left[\text{CH}_2-\underset{\underset{\text{CH}_2}{\|}}{\text{C}}\right]_n$	(100)		284,285
	H_3CCOOH	Pd(NO$_3$)$_2$ + P(aryl)$_3$ As(aryl)$_3$			Low molecular weight 1,2,2,1-Polyallene 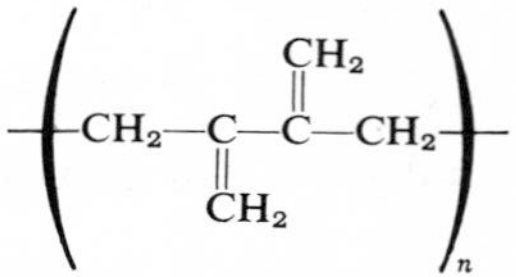			336

128

The dimerization of acrylonitrile was effected under hydrogen pressure with an ethanolic solution of $RuCl_3 \cdot 3H_2O$ obtaining a mixture of *cis-* and *trans-*1,4-dicyano-1-butene as main products.[235] Hydrogen acts as a co-catalyst to form the hydrido intermediate necessary for the dimerization, according to Cramer's mechanism[63] (see IV-B-2). Two possible inter-mediates that also catalyze the dimerization of acrylonitrile gave further evidence for the mechanism: one of them is identified and has the formula:[226]

$$[RuCl_2(NC—CH=CH_2)_{3-4}(H_2O)_{1-0}]$$

with the acrylonitrile groups bonded through the lone electron pairs of the nitrogen. The other one, prepared under hydrogen pressure, whose composition has not been determined, carries a cyanoethyl group (probably σ-bonded) and yields propionitrile and acrylonitrile on dry heating.[233] By-products of the dimerization of acrylonitrile are propionitrile and adipodinitrile, resulting from the hydrogenation of acrylonitrile and 1,4-dicyanobutene, respectively.

In the absence of hydrogen the Ru catalysts are inactive.

Amines, e.g., *N*-methylpyrrolidine, have also been used as solvents for the reaction, as well as other Ru^{III} and Ru^{II} compounds (some of them with aryl phosphine, arsine, and stibine ligands) as catalysts.[226,234,310]

Anhydrous $RhCl_3$ in *n*-butanol was used as a catalyst for the dimerization of acrylamide and mono-*N*-substituted acrylamides[196]

$$2CH_2=CH—\overset{\overset{\displaystyle O}{\|}}{C}\cdot NHR \xrightarrow[\text{in R·OH}]{RhCl_3} \quad (111)$$

to form *trans-α*-hydromuconamides. As the Rh salt is reduced to the metal by side reactions, the addition of *p*-benzoquinone increased the acrylamide conversion.

N,N-Disubstituted acrylamides are not dimerized, possibly due to a change in coordination: *N*-coordination instead of olefin coordination. An analogous product, 1,4-diacetoxybutene, is a by-product in the oxidative dimerization of vinyl acetate, which leads to 1,4-diacetoxybutadiene (see Section III-E).

The dimerization of butadiene is carried out with palladium catalysts. Although with $PdCl_2$ in EtOH only oily low molecular weight polymers are obtained,[273] with palladium complexes such as bis(triphenylphosphine)(maleic anhydride)-Pd^0 or Pd complexes with PPh_3 and other dienophiles butadiene dimerizes to yield 85% 1,3,7-octatriene in aprotic solvents like benzene, tetrahydrofuran, or acetone.[367,370] This dimer is also formed in high yield with other palladium catalysts, such as π-allylic complexes, e.g., $[(\pi\text{-allyl})PdCl]_2$, and the butadiene-$\pi$-allylic complex of Pd^{II},[318,332] or bis(benzonitrile)palladium chloride in the presence of triphenylphosphine.[352]

1,3,7-Octatriene is also probably the primary product in the dimerization of butadiene with $RhCl_3$-potassium acetate catalyst followed by an isomerization to yield the more stable conjugated 2,4,6-octatriene.[3]

If the dimerization of butadiene is carried out in the presence of protic compounds such as phenol[352] or pyridine and the above-mentioned palladium catalysts or the pyridine complex py_2PdCl_2, phenol adds in a formal 1,4-addition to the conjugated grouping of the 1,3,7-octatriene to yield 1-phenoxy-2,7- or 3-phenoxy-1,7-octadiene.

In the presence of alcohols or acetic acid and triphenylphosphine palladium complexes coordinated with dienophiles as catalysts,[367–370] the protic compounds add to form 1-alkoxy- or 1-acetoxy-2,7-octadiene or the appropriate 3-substituted 1,7-dienes. Amines as solvents also add to the triene similarly.[368]

Surprisingly, 1-methoxy-6-deuterio-2,7-octadiene was obtained with MeOD, so that π-allyl complexes were postulated as intermediates[370] in the addition reactions of protic compounds on 1,3,7-octatriene.

With $RuCl_3$ in 2-methoxyethanol, butadiene forms a complex at 90° with the following structure:[217,267]

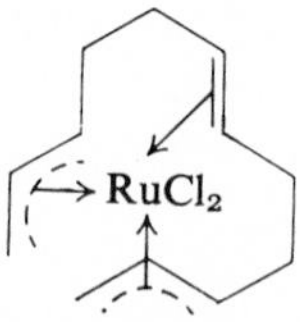

On pyrolysis it gives *trans,trans,trans-* and *trans,trans,cis*-cyclo-1,5,9-dodecatriene.[267] Similar intermediates have been postulated by Wilke et al.[413] in nickel-catalyzed cyclooligomerization of butadiene to yield cyclododecatrienes. These compounds are also formed from butadiene with bis(π-allyl)-palladium, $(C_3H_5)_2Pd$ as catalyst.[413]

Isoprene forms the following complex with $RuCl_3$ in ethanol. On treatment with hydrogen it gives 2,7-dimethyl-2,6-octadiene.[298]

In the reaction of ethylene at 30 atm with $PdCl_2$ in *n*-butyl acetate, the formation of *tert*-butyl chloride was observed.[11]

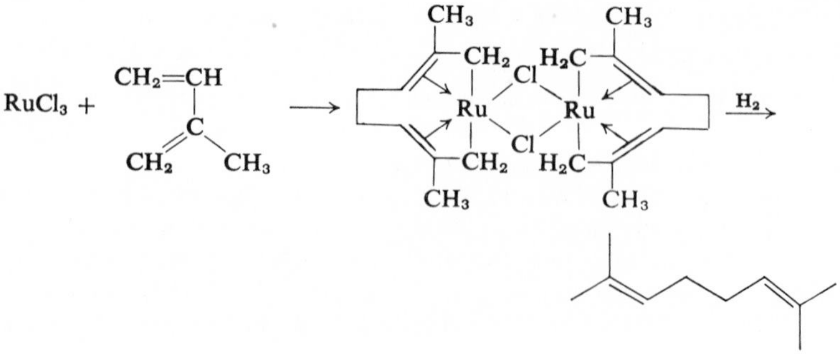

(112)

4. Polymerization

A highly crystalline polyethylene was obtained as white coating of the $Pd(CN)_2$ catalyst during ethylene dimerization.[188] With propylene and $Pd(CN)_2$ in methanol at 50-psi propylene pressure a polymer was obtained, the structure of which follows from a 1,3-propylene polymerization mechanism, since it was determined as a formal copolymer containing 93% ethylene and only 7% propylene. Ethylene was completely absent in this reaction. As the catalyst is insoluble in the reaction medium, the catalysis was assumed to occur at the surface of the salt. The following mechanism has been proposed:[186]

With Rh^{III} salts, such as chloride, nitrate, or chloro complexes in water, ethanol, or dimethylformamide, a stereoregular trans-1,4-polybutadiene has been obtained.[72,87,314,380] The reaction occurs in water with and without emulsifier.[314,315]

Norbornene derivatives give two types of polymers with noble metal salts. With $PdCl_2$[326] the reaction resembles the oligomerization of ethylene. The first insertion step, however, has been described as an insertion of a norbornene molecule between the palladium and a chloro ligand, instead of an insertion between a palladium hydrido bond:

$R = CH_2OH, CH_2OCH_3, CH_2OAc$ (114)

With ruthenium, osmium, and iridium salts, products are formed that derive from a ring opening.[229,313] Michelotti assumes an attack of a solvent molecule, e.g., EtOH in the allylic position, to explain this type of reaction.

(115)

If $R = COOH$, this reaction also proceeds with $PdCl_2$.[326]

The polymerization of allene is catalyzed by Rh^I and Ru^{III} complexes to form highly crystalline 1,2-polyallene. It takes place in polar solvents such as ethanol or methylene chloride. Catalysts are $[RhCl(CO)_2]_2$; $[RhCl(C_2H_4)_2]_2$ in the presence of triphenylphosphine; and $[RhCl(PPh_3)_3]$, $RuCl_3 \cdot n \, H_2O$, and $RuCl_{2-3}PPh_3$.[284,285]

With $Pd(NO_3)_2$ in glacial acetic acid and in the presence of triarylphosphines or arsines, allene polymerizes to give a low molecular weight, 1,2,2,1-polyallene of the structure:[336]

In addition, acetylene can be polymerized by solutions of palladium salts to form vinylacetylene and polymers of uncertain structures.[348] Substituted acetylenes form mainly cyclic oligomers such as benzene derivatives[36] or cyclobutadiene palladium complexes, for which a summarized description has been given by P. M. Maitlis.[221]

For the polymerization of phenylacetylene, $RhCl(Ph_3P)_3$ has been described[184] as a catalyst.

C. Isomerization of Olefinic Compounds

1. Mechanisms

Most reactions of olefinic compounds with noble metal compounds are accompanied by a shift of double bonds, i.e., olefin isomerization. This was demonstrated in olefinic and allylic oxidations, in aqueous as well as in non-aqueous medium. Olefin oligomerization is also followed by the equilibration of the double bonds in the products formed.

If olefins are contacted with catalytically active compounds for a sufficient time, a thermodynamically favored mixture of the olefins is obtained.[354]

Strong complexing agents, such as halide ions, tertiary phosphines, and olefins inhibit the reaction by coordinating with the metal, indicating that in this reaction also olefin complexes are formed in an initial equilibrium. Even if such agents are necessary to stabilize intermediate steps, e.g., hydrides in the presence of halide ions, tertiary phosphines, or the like, they block the reaction when used in excess.

The proposal for a mechanism with the most compelling experimental arguments implies insertion-abstraction equilibria of a hydride ion between a metal hydride acting as a catalyst and the olefin analogous to the hydride transfer in olefin oxidation and oligomerization.

$$R—CH_2—CH{=}CH_2 \;\rightleftharpoons\; R—CH_2—CH—CH_3 \;\rightleftharpoons\; R—CH{=}CH—CH_3 \qquad (116)$$
$$\downarrow \qquad\qquad\qquad\quad \downarrow \qquad\qquad\qquad\qquad \downarrow$$
$$mH \qquad\qquad\qquad m \qquad\qquad\qquad\qquad mH$$

Such a course was first proposed by T. A. Manuel[222] for the iron carbonyl-catalyzed and by Harrod and Chalk[136] for the palladium salt-catalyzed olefin isomerization. It is characterized by an exchange of a hydrogen between olefin and the catalyst or cocatalyst, and between different olefin molecules (via the hydrido form of the catalyst). Strong acids, particularly hydrogen halides, molecular hydrogen, and alcohols (as solvents) act as cocatalysts, since they form hydrido complexes with noble metal salts. These hydrido complexes are the catalytically active species in the mechanism in question.

Proof of this mechanism has been given by R. Cramer[64] for butene isomerization with rhodium catalysts.

1. The reaction rate is proportional to the concentration of the olefin. H^+, Cl^-, and Rh concentrations affect the reaction rate similarly to olefin dimerization (see Section IV-B), so that an analogous hydrido catalyst is suggested.

2. In 1-butene isomerization with CH_3OD as the reaction medium, mono-deuterated butenes are obtained. Isomerization and deuteration occur in the same reaction and, therefore, with the same rate and are simultaneously inhibited by the same means.

3. In 1-butene isomerization-deuteration the over-all amounts of isomerized and deuterated products are nearly equal.

4. In the reaction mixture of 1-butene isomerization, the deuterium atoms are found preferably in 1-butene at the secondary carbon atom.

5. In *cis*-2-butene isomerization (at low conversion), deuterium is not incorporated in *cis*-2-butene. 1-Butene, however, is highly deuterated. Deuterated and nondeuterated *trans*-2-butene are obtained in nearly equal amounts.

6. Isomerization of $CH_3CD_2CH{=}CH_2$ gives mainly monodeuterated 2-butenes; the deuterium loss shows up in higher deuterated isomerized butenes.

These results can only be explained by the addition-elimination mechanism. The catalytic species may be a hydrido rhodium(III) species that is formed by oxidative HCl addition to a Rh^I compound e.g., to $[(C_2H_4)_2RhCl]_2$ or $[acacRh(C_2H_4)_2]$, according to

$$L_3Rh^ICl + HCl \rightleftharpoons L_3(H)Rh^{III}Cl \qquad (117)$$

For 1-butene isomerization the favored reaction cycle accounting for the above-mentioned results (1–4) has been formulated as*

$$(118)$$

Different deuterated products are obtained from competing reactions of intermediates.

2-Butene isomerization and deuteration has been formulated as

---

* Normally, the hydrogen atom enters at the 2-position (Markovnikov addition). This accounts for the deuteration without isomerization. The latter requires the less-favored, anti-Markovnikov addition of the metal hydride to the double bond.

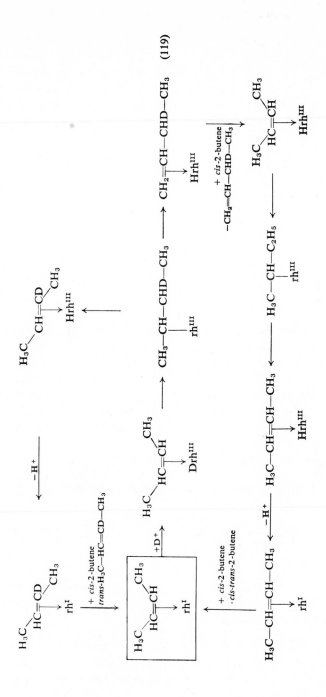

(119)

135

One of the most important results for the explanation of the insertion reactions is the formation of *trans*-2-*D*-2-butene in the reaction of *cis*-2-butene with a deuterio-Rh catalyst. It also explains the hydrido route in olefin isomerization, as well as the stereospecificity of such reactions, which is evident for a *cis*-ligand insertion reaction, since by this term *cis* addition and elimination can best be explained:

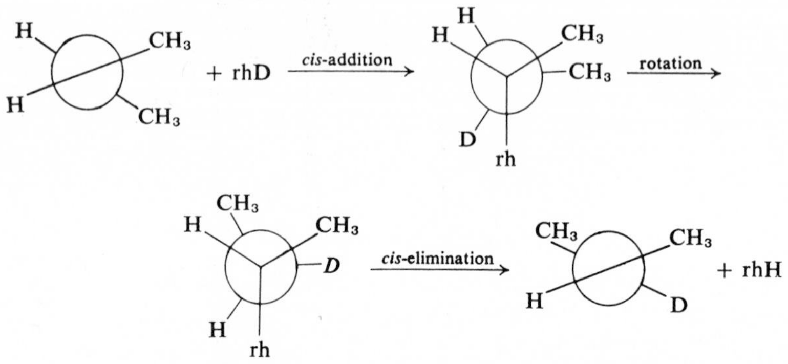

This mechanism has also been suggested for other catalyst systems,[68] e.g., H_2PtCl_6—$SnCl_2$—H_2 and Li_2PdCl_4—CF_3COOH. Other strong support for the hydrido conception can be derived from the fact that many hydrogenation catalysts[159,220,378] in the presence of H_2, as well as transition metal hydrides, isomerize alkenes (see also Table XIII). Even supported metals such as palladium, rhodium, iridium, osmium, platinum, nickel, and ruthenium[1,40,117,220] isomerize olefins to thermodynamic equilibria in the presence of molecular hydrogen.

A different mechanism that involves the abstraction of a hydrogen atom from the allylic position of an olefinic ligand in a metal complex to form a hydrido-π-allyl intermediate has also been discussed:[78,222]

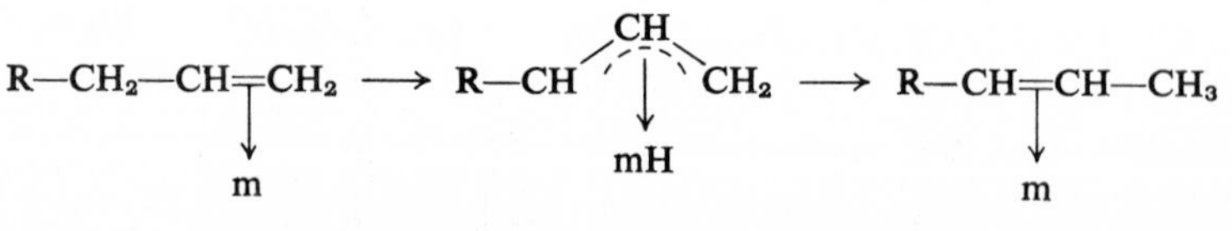

Support was predominantly presented from the observation[137] that 3,3-di-deuterio-1-heptene yielded 1,3-di-deuterio-2-heptene on reaction with bis(benzonitrile $PdCl_2$) as catalyst.

$$C_3H_7—CH_2—CD_2—CH=CH_2 \xrightarrow{Pd^{2+}} C_3H_7—CH_2—CD=CH—CH_2D \quad (122)$$

Such a pronounced 3,1-hydrogen shift with 3,3-di-deuterio-1-alkenes could not be observed by Cramer[68] and by Davies.[77] Moreover, it can also be explained by the hydrido route:[79]

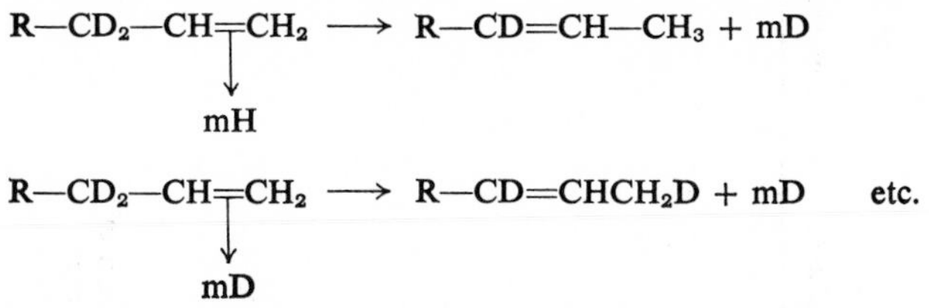

$$R—CD_2—CH{=}CH_2 \longrightarrow R—CD{=}CH—CH_3 + mD$$

mH   (123)

$$R—CD_2—CH{=}CH_2 \longrightarrow R—CD{=}CHCH_2D + mD \quad etc.$$

mD

On the other hand, the validity of the hydrido route conception could be doubted because isomerization of olefins with $PdCl_2$ was observed in the absence of any solvent[354] or with $PdCl_2$ or bis(benzonitrile $PdCl_2$) in benzene,[27,40,135,137] which normally would not give rise to the formation of a hydrido species. Furthermore, CH_3COOD as the reaction medium for isomerization of 1-octene in the presence of $PdCl_2$ did not yield deuterated olefinic material.[77,78]

There are, however, contrasting results: on repeating the latter experiment with CH_3COOD,[68] it was claimed that a small but significant amount of D was found in the products. As to the above-mentioned experiments Moiseev[241-243] could not observe any isomerization in the strict absence of protic material.

Moiseev further observed an inhibition of isomerization in the presence of oxidants such as p-benzoquinone or $CuCl_2$ and noted the rate of isomerization to be proportional to the square of the Pd^{II} concentration. He concluded a modified π-allylic route with a binuclear hydrido Pd^I-π-allyl-Pd^I-intermediate:

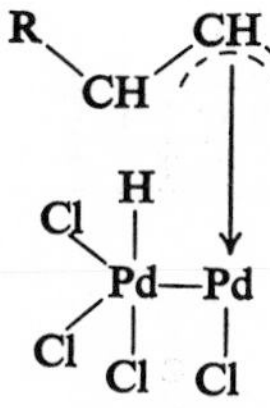

His observations can also be interpreted if the hydrido intermediate (see Sections III-A and III-B) that forms on reduction of Pd^{II} by olefins in the presence of protic material is taken into account. Therefore, they do not necessarily contradict Cramer's conception.

An indication that different mechanisms do exist for the isomerization of olefins by palladium and rhodium catalysts seems to be the stepwise shift of the double bond in olefins with rhodium compounds,[266] which has not been observed with palladium compounds.[354] But differences in isomerization-deuteration products may arise from the different stabilities of olefin- and hydrido–metal complexes and different reaction rates of olefin complex

TABLE XIII
Isomerization of Olefinic Compounds (see Sections IV-C; VI-L-1)

Catalyst	Solvent (cocatalyst)	Substrate olefin used	Reaction temperature °C	time, hr	Isomerization products	Conversion	Refs.
Ru, Rh, Pd, Os, Ir, Pt, Ni/C—H₂ (1 atmg)	C₂H₅OH	1-Hexene 2-Methyl-1-pentene 3-Methyl-1-pentene 2,4-Dimethyl-1-butene	40	—	Isomeric hexenes		1,117
5% Rh/Al₂O₃—H₂ 5% Rh/SiO₂—H₂	—	1-Butene	−20 to 80	—	1-Butene, 2-butenes		220
RhCl₃—3H₂O	i-C₃H₇OH	1-Pentene-1,2-d₂ 1-Heptene-3-d₂			Isomers Isomers		137
	C₂H₅OH, i-C₃H₇OH, tert-C₄H₉OR	1-Hexene 1-Heptene			1-, 2-, 3-Hexenes 1-, 2-, 3-Heptenes		135 135
a[acac Rh(C₂H₄)₂]—CH₃OH—HCl	ROH	1-Butene	> −33		1- and 2-Butenes		64,68
[(C₂H₄)₂RhCl]₂—ROH—HCl	ROH	cis- and trans-1-Butene					
RhCl₃—3H₂O—PPh₃—H₂ (Rh:P = ca. 1:3)	Benzene-ethanol (2:1)	1-Pentene	24	4	1-(2-)Pentenes (equil.) pentane		159
Pd/Al₂O₃		1-Butene	160–240		Isomeric butenes		40
PdCl₂—Cl⁻—HClO₄	H₂O	1-Butene	50		cis-2-Butene		245
PdCl₂	—	1-Butene 1-Pentene	50	24	Olefin complexes [CₙH₂ₙPdCl₂]₂ of 1- and 2-butenes and pentenes		304
PdCl₂	Benzene, ethyl acetate, methyl ethyl ketone	1-Pentene, cis-2-pentene	70		Isomeric pentenes		27
PdCl₂		4-Methyl-1-pentene n-1-Octene			Isomeric methylpentenes (n-hexenes) 2-Octene		354,355
PdCl₂		n-C₅H₁₁—CD₂—CH=CH₂					77,78

138

Catalyst	Solvent	Temperature	Substrate	Isomers without change of the carbon skeleton		Reference
PdCl₂	H₂O, H⁺	RT	1-Hexene, 4-methylpentene 2-Methyl-1-pentene	Isomers without change of the carbon skeleton		242
PdCl₂—(1–3M)LiCl	(1–3M)HClO₄—H₂O	25	1-Butene	cis,trans-2-Butenes		242,243 244
Li₂PdCl₄—CF₃COOH	—	25	1- and 2-Butenes	Isomeric butenes		68
Li₂PdCl₄—H₂	CH₃OH	25	1- and 2-Butenes	Isomeric butenes		68
[C₆H₅CNPdCl₂]₂	Benzene, ethyl acetate, methyl ethyl ketone	70	1-Pentene, cis-2-pentene	Isomeric pentenes		27
[C₆H₅CNPdCl₂]₂	C₂H₅OH	65	1-Hexene	1-, 2-, and 3-Hexenes		135
ᵃ(acac)₂Pd/SiO₂		61.5	1- and 2-Butenes	Isomeric butenes		232
[IrHCl₂(PEt₂Ph)₃] trans-[IrH₃(PPh₃)₃]	Benzene	80–85	1-Octene	Isomeric n-octenes		57
trans-[IrCl(CO)(PPh₃)₂]—H₂	Organic solvents		1-Butene	Isomeric butenes		91
[C₂H₄PtCl₂]₂—H₂	CH₃OH	>50	1- and 2-Butenes	Isomeric butenes		68
[C₂H₄PtCl₂]₂—C₂H₅OH	C₂H₅OH	25	1-Hexene	Isomeric hexenes		135
H₂PtCl₆—SnCl₂—H₂	CH₃OH, CF₃COOH	25	1-Butene	cis,trans-2-Butenes		68
	CH₃OH	25	1-Pentene	cis,trans-2-Pentenes		28,29

b. Double-bond migration in substituted olefinic compounds

Catalyst	Solvent	Temperature	Substrate	Product		Reference
RuCl₃(RhCl₃)	Allyl alcohol-H₂O (1:1)	Reflux	Allyl alcohol	Propionaldehyde (propene, acrolein)		265
RuCl₃	H₂O (1:1)	Reflux	2-Methylallyl alcohol	Isobutyraldehyde (isobutene, methacrolein)		265
RuCl₃	H₂O (1:1)	Reflux	2-Buten-1-ol	Methyl ethyl ketone (n-butenes)		265
RuCl₃	H₂O (1:1)	Reflux	cis-2-Buten-1,4-diol	Crotonaldehyde (ethylene, CO)		265
Ru, Pd, Ru-salts, Pd-salts	Benzene, hexane	50–300	Allylic alcohols	Saturated carbonyl compounds		381
Pd (0.1–2%)	—	160 (6)	2-Methyl-1-hepten-6-one	2-Methyl-2-hepten-6-one	96.5, 81	259
PdCl₂ (0.1–2%)	—	150 (4)				
PdCl₂—2C₆H₅CN	—	Reflux (10 min.)	3,4-Dichloro-1-butene	1,4-Dichloro-2-butene	Equil.	281

(continued)

TABLE XIII (*continued*)

Catalyst	Solvent (cocatalyst)	Substrate olefin	Reaction temperature °C	time, hr	Products	Conversion	Refs.
c. Conjugation of diolefins and araliphatic olefins							
RhCl$_3$—3H$_2$O	C$_2$H$_5$OH	1,5-Cyclooctadiene	78		1,3-Cyclooctadiene (1,4-cyclooctadiene)	Quant.	266
IrCl$_3$—3H$_2$O	C$_2$H$_5$OH	1,5-Cyclooctadiene	78		1,3-Cyclooctadiene (1,4-cyclooctadiene)		
[IrHCl$_2$(PEt$_2$Ph)$_3$]	—	1,5-Cyclooctadiene	130		1,3-Cyclooctadiene (1,4-cyclooctadiene)		
[IrCl$_3$(PEt$_2$Ph)$_3$]	—	1,5-Cyclooctadiene	130		1,3-Cyclooctadiene (1,4-cyclooctadiene)		
[PtCl$_2$(PPh$_3$)$_2$]—SnCl$_2$—H$_2$ (34 atm)	CH$_2$Cl$_2$, benzene-CH$_3$OH	1,5-Cyclooctadiene	20		1,4- and 1,3-Cyclooctadiene	—	377
RhCl(PPh$_3$)$_3$—H$_2$	C$_2$H$_5$OH	Damsin			Isodamsin		24
RhCl(PPh$_3$)$_3$ (1% by weight)	CHCl$_3$, benzene	1-Methoxy-1,4-cyclohexadiene	Reflux	2	1-Methoxy-1,3-cyclohexadiene	80	25

140

Catalyst	Solvent	Substrate	Conditions	Product		
RhCl(PPh$_3$)$_3$	CHCl$_3$, benzene	1-Methoxy-3-methylcyclo-1,4-hexadiene 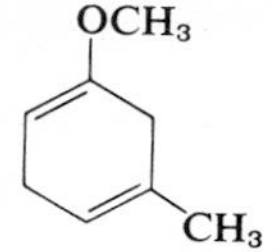	Reflux	1-Methoxy-3-methylene-1-cyclohexene 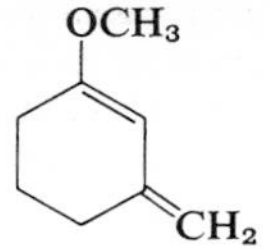		25
RhCl(PPh$_3$)$_3$	CHCl$_3$	6-Methoxy-1,2,3,4,5,8-hexahydronaphthalene 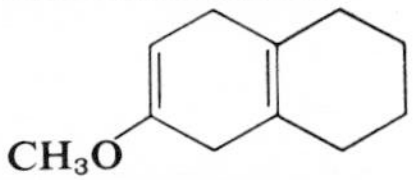	Reflux 5 min	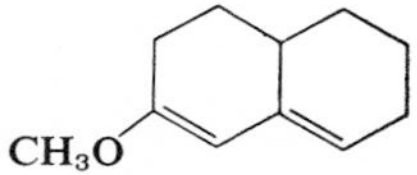		25
RhCl(PPh$_3$)$_3$	CHCl$_3$	1,4-Dihydroestrone methyl ether ethylene ketal 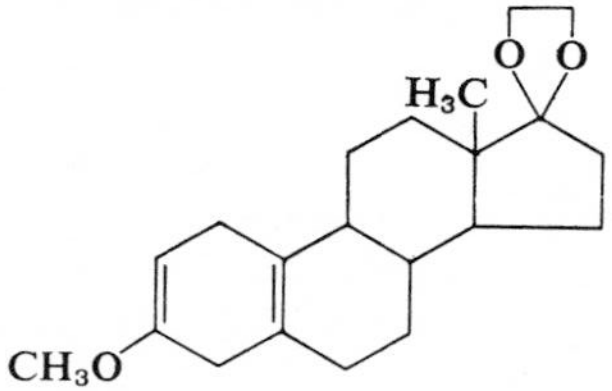	Reflux			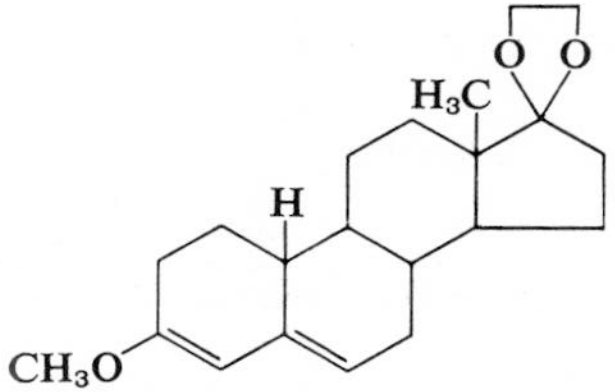 25
RhCl(PPh$_3$)$_3$	CHCl$_3$	Safrol 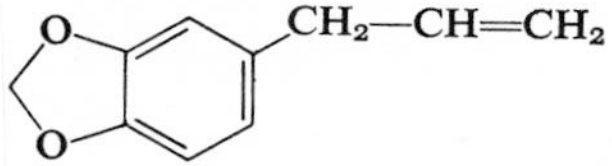	Reflux	2 cis-Isosafrol trans-Isosafrol 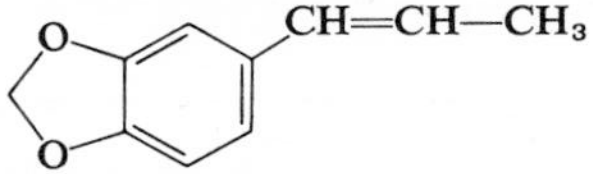	40 60	25
RhCl(PPh$_3$)$_3$	Benzene	Safrol	Reflux	2 cis-Isosafrol (only)	60	25
[C$_6$H$_5$CNPdCl$_2$]$_2$	Benzene	Safrol	Reflux	3 cis,trans-Isosafrol		25
	—	4-Phenyl-1-butene	—	1-Phenyl-1-butene		80

(continued)

141

TABLE XIII (continued)

Catalyst	Solvent (cocatalyst)	Substrate olefin	Reaction temperature °C	time, hr	Isomerization products	Conversion	Refs.
d. Double-bond migration to form stable diene complexes							
$RhCl_3 \cdot 3H_2O$	C_2H_5OH	1,3-Cyclooctadiene	50	24	[1,5-Cyclooctadiene)Rh(Ir)Cl]$_2$	66	312
$IrCl_3 \cdot 4H_2O$	C_2H_5OH	1,3-Cyclooctadiene	50	Several days			
$PdCl_2$ $PtCl_2$	—	1,3-Cyclooctadiene	50		(1,5-Cyclooctadiene)Pd(Pt)Cl$_2$		103
$RhCl_3 \cdot 3H_2O$	C_2H_5OH	1,5-Cyc'odecadiene			[(1,6-Cyclodecadiene)RhCl]$_2$		383
e. Valence-isomerization (change of the carbon skeleton)							
$PdCl_2$		4-Methyl-1-pentene			*n*-Hexenes (isomeric methylpentenes, see Table XIIIa)	low	354 355
$[C_6H_5CNPdCl_2]_2$	Benzene	4-Vinylcyclohexene	RT	ca. 15	(1,5-Cyclooctadiene)PdCl$_2$	35	104
$[C_6H_5CNPdBr_2]_2$	Benzene	4-Vinylcyclohexene	RT	0.25	(1,5-Cyclooctadiene)PdBr$_2$	35	104

(continued)

Catalyst	Solvent (cocatalyst)	Substrate olefin used	Reaction temperature °C	time, hr	Isomerization products	Conversion	Refs.
[(C₂H₄)₂RhCl]₂ [Norbornadiene—RhCl]₂ [1,5-Cyclooctadiene—PdCl₂] [π-Methallyl—PdCl]₂ [Norbornadiene PtCl₂]₂ } $CHCl_3$		Quadricyclene 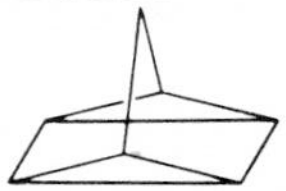	26	0.75	Norbornadiene 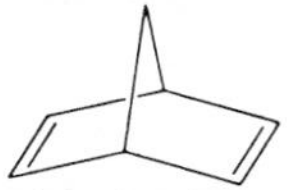	Quant.	156
[C₆H₅CN—PdCl₂]₂	Benzene	cis,trans-1,5-Cyclodecadiene 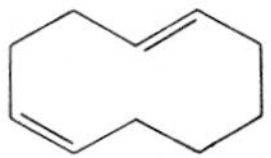	RT	3	 [1,2-Divinylcyclohexane-PdCl₂]		382
Na_2PtCl_4—$4H_2O$	n-Propanol	cis,trans-1,5-Cyclodecadiene	RT	2 weeks	[1,2-Divinylcyclohexane-PtCl₂]		382
[(Hexamethyl-Dewar-benzene)—PdCl₂]	—	—	79	—	Hexamethylbenzene		86
[(Hexamethyl-Dewar-benzene)—PtCl₂]	—	—	75 (vac)	—	Hexamethylbenzene		14
[(Hexamethyl-Dewar-benzene)—RhCl]₂	—	Hexamethyl-Dewar-benzene	60–75	—	Hexamethylbenzene		399
RhCl₃—3H₂O	H₂O	Hexamethyl-Dewar-benzene	90		(Pentamethylcyclopentadienyl-Rh^III Cl₂) + acetaldehyde	25	179
RhCl₃—3H₂O	CH₃OH	Hexamethyl-Dewar-benzene	60 RT	4 days	[Pentamethylcyclopentadienyl-Rh^III Cl₂]	91 52	29a
IrCl₃—4H₂O	CH₃OH	Hexamethyl-Dewar-benzene	65		Hexamethylbenzene [C₆Me₆IrCl₂]₂	High	180

143

TABLE XIII (*continued*)

Catalyst	Solvent (cocatalyst)	Substrate olefin	Reaction temperature °C	time, hr	Isomerization products	Conversion	Refs.
$RhCl_3$—$3H_2O$ $IrCl_3$—$4H_2O$	CH_3OH CH_3OH	(pentamethylcyclopentadiene, CHX—Me, Me substituents)	65		$[C_8Me_6Rh(Ir)Cl_2]_2$ (Rh(Ir)Cl₂ structure)		180
		X = Cl, OMe			$+ CH_3$—$CH(OCH_3)_2$		14
K_2PtCl_6—$SnCl_2$—HCl	CH_3OH	Hexamethyl-Dewar-benzene	65		Pentamethylcyclopentadiene-$PtCl_2$		
$[C_2H_4PdCl_2]_2$	CH_2Cl_2	Spiropentane	25	5–10 min	[2-(2-Chloroethyl-π-allyl-PdCl]₂		187a
					$ClCH_2$—CH_2—$C\langle{}^{CH_2}_{CH_2}\rangle \rightarrow Pd \cdots Cl]_2$		
$PdCl_2$	H_2O	Phenylcyclopropane (PhC_3H_5:Pd = 4:1)	75	2	*trans*-Propenylbenzene	15	285a

Catalyst	Solvent	Substrate	Temp.	Product	Yield	Ref.
$[(C_6H_5\text{—}CN)PdCl_2]_2$		Bullvalene	RT	Bicyclo[4,2,2]deca-2,4,7,9-triene		396
H_2PtCl_6	Acetic anhydride or acetic acid	Cyclopropane	RT	24 Dichlorotrimethylene-platinum(IV)	50–70	24a
[Norbornadiene-RhCl]$_2$	$CHCl_3$	Hexamethyltetracyclo[2,2,0,0^{2,6},0^{3,5}]-hexane (hexamethylprismane)	<0	Dewar-hexamethylbenzene hexamethylbenzene (1:0.05)	Quant.	156a
$Rh(CO)_2Cl_2$	$CDCl_3$	exo-Tricyclo[3,2,1,0^{2,4}]-6-octene	RT	Tetracyclo[3,3,0,0^{2,8},0^{4,6}]octane		399a
$IrCl(CO)(PPh_3)_2$	Benzene	exo-Tricyclo[3,2,1,0^{2,4}]-6-octene	130	5-Methylenebicyclo[2,2,1]2-heptene	Quant.	399b

(continued)

TABLE XIII (*continued*)

Catalyst	Solvent (cocatalyst)	Substrate olefin	Reaction temperature °C	time, hr	Isomerization products	Conversion	Refs.
	Benzene	exo,exo-Tetracyclo-[3,3,1,0^{2,4},0^{6,8}]-nonane	130		exo-6-Methylenetricyclo[3,2,1,0^{2,4}]-octane	Quant.	399b
(PPh$_3$)$_3$RhCl		exo-Tricyclo[3,2,1,0^{2,4}]6-octene	90	2		62(25)	
With Rh/C (yields in parenthesis)						32(55) 6(20)	181a

(Dimerization product, see Table XII)

^{a} acac = acetylacetonyl.

formation and hydrogen insertion and abstraction reactions. Though more aspects of possible routes for the reactions in question have been presented by several authors (see [12,79,137]), we feel that not enough experimental facts have been collected yet to make a final decision on the allylic mechanism.

Two different mechanistic proposals shall be mentioned. The one involves an equilibrium between an olefin- and a π-allylic complex, according to [79]

$$[C_nH_{2n}\cdot PdCl_2]_2 \rightleftharpoons [\pi\text{-}C_nH_{2n-1}\cdot PdCl]_2 + 2HCl \qquad (76)$$

which, however, is improbable, since π-allylic complexes are too stable to be easily reconverted to the olefin complex.

The other implies formation of a carbene complex intermediate:[78]

$$R\cdot CH_2\cdot CH{=\!\!=}CH_2 \rightleftharpoons R\cdot CH_2{-}C{-}CH_2 \rightleftharpoons R\cdot CH{=\!\!=}CH{-}CH_3 \qquad (124)$$

$$\underset{Pd}{|} \qquad\qquad \underset{Pd}{\|} \qquad\qquad \underset{Pd}{|}$$

postulated from the observation of a 2,1-hydrogen shift, which, however, can also be explained by the hydrido conception.[136] Furthermore, carbene complexes of this sort have not yet been obtained.

Isomerization according to hydrido mechanism through insertion-abstraction equilibria of a hydride ion that leads to the thermodynamically most stable mixture also comprises *cis,trans* isomerization. Cramer has shown with labeled reactants that this isomerization involves hydrogen transfer. We have always considered the insertion-abstraction reactions to be reversible. Therefore, groups other than hydrogen should also be transferable. An indication is given by Oshima,[281] who studied the equilibrium of 3,4-dichloro-1-butene and 1,4-dichloro-2-butene in the presence of palladium compounds. Furthermore, we have demonstrated *cis, trans* isomerization of the alkenyl esters and chlorides in Section IV-A, which accompanies *trans* vinylation reactions.

2. Double Bond Migration

Table XIII lists the isomerization reactions reported with group VIII noble metal compounds. In all cases the olefinic substrate isomerizes to yield mixtures according to the thermodynamically favored equilibria.

If diolefins are isomerized, conjugated systems are normally obtained; e.g., 1,4-dienes yield 1,3-dienes with $[RhCl(PPh_3)_3]$.[25] The conjugated system is so preferred that, in some instances, almost quantitative yields are obtained or, in alkylated benzenes with unsaturated side chains, the molecule isomerizes to place the double bond of the side chain into conjugation with the benzene ring.[319] For example, allylbenzene gives propenylbenzene; safrole yields *cis*- and *trans*-isosafrole[25], and 4-phenyl-1-butene gives 1-phenyl-1-butene.[80]

$$\underset{H_2C}{\overset{O}{\diagdown}}\underset{O}{\diagup} \text{---} CH_2\text{---}CH\text{=}CH_2 \longrightarrow \underset{H_2C}{\overset{O}{\diagdown}}\underset{O}{\diagup} \text{---}CH\text{=}CH\text{---}CH_3 \qquad (125)$$

4-Phenyl-1-butene gives 1-phenyl-1-butene.[80]

1,5-Cyclooctadiene reacted with a $RhCl_3$ or $IrCl_3$ catalyst gives 1,3-cyclooctadiene, but the reaction stops when the competing complex formation of, e.g., $[RhCl(1,5\text{-}C_8H_{12})]_2$, has blocked all the rhodium. The latter complex is stable enough to be obtained from $RhCl_3$ and 1,3-cyclooctadiene. Therefore, 1,5-cyclooctadiene can also be obtained from the more stable 1,3-diene[266,312] by liberation of the hydrocarbon with strong complexing agents e.g., KCN. $PdCl_2$, and $PtCl_2$[103] show a similar behavior.

Allyl alcohol and 2-methylallyl alcohol are isomerized to propionaldehyde and isobutyraldehyde[265] in the presence of a palladium catalyst. The reaction can be considered as a shift of the double bond to form the enol of the respective aldehydes. Allyl alcohols are reported to form saturated aldehydes and ketones under isomerization conditions with ruthenium or palladium chlorides or nitrates.[381,*]

Allyl amines also give aldehydes and ketones with aqueous $PdCl_2$-solutions.[342] This reaction can be considered as an isomerization reaction with subsequent hydrolysis.

3. Valence Isomerization

The examples of isomerization reactions reported so far comprised the transfer of hydride or other negative groups in reversible insertion-abstraction reactions under preservation of the carbon skeleton. There are also examples of isomerizations that involve changes in the carbon skeleton (see Table XIII); e.g., in the reaction of 4-methyl-1-pentene with $PdCl_2$, some n-hexenes are found in the isomer mixture that can have formed only by transfer of an alkyl group, i.e., by cleavage of a C—C-bond. Such cleavage requires higher energies than the cleavage of a C—H-bond, for instance.†

Other examples of valence isomerization known so far are reactions that lead to stable compounds under high energy release. From Table XIV we cite here the formation of hexamethylbenzene from hexamethyl-Dewar-benzene:[14,86,179,399]

---

* Such reactions have also been described with catalysts such as $Fe(CO)_5$[71] and $Co_2(CO)_8$.[218]

† In the rhodium-catalyzed dimerization of ethylene, we have not considered reversible the formation of the butyl group (see Section IV-B).

(126)

and the formation of the $PdCl_2$ complex of 1,5-cyclooctadiene from vinyl-cyclohexene.[104]

(127)

V. CONCLUSION

Screening the multitude of reactions reported in this chapter has revealed the capability of palladium and other group VIII noble metal salts to bring about oxidations of olefins, as well as a wide variety of related reactions through organometallic intermediates. The mechanism of olefin oxidation with $PdCl_2$ was treated in great detail to demonstrate the role of these intermediates within a general principle of homogeneous catalysis that comprises ligand substitution equilibria on the metal (complexing of the reactants), insertion-abstraction equilibria (intramolecular rearrangements, including hydride transfer), heterolytic cleavage of metal σ-compounds (liberation of the oxidation product) in a series of reversible and irreversible reactions, followed by or including the regeneration of the catalytic species. The courses of the reactions reported combine all or part of these steps.

This principle has generally been used to describe transition metal salt-catalyzed reactions of unsaturated compounds: carbonylation and decarbonylation with palladium and rhodium compounds,[385] the homogeneous hydrogenation of olefinic and carbonyl compounds with noble metal salts,[26,133,280] the platinum salt catalyzed addition of H—Si[20,45,356] and H—Ge[101] compounds on olefins, as well as catalytic reactions with other transition metal compounds such as Ziegler polymerization, hydroformylation,[41,140,147] and a number of other insertion reactions reviewed in [139].

The term *insertion reaction* as used in this chapter should be considered as a reaction within the complex sphere of the transition metal in which the nucleophile changes its site to add onto the unsaturated ligand. This migration of the nucleophile could be demonstrated in CO insertion reactions.[37,38,227,228,270] For olefins the over-all reaction could also be thought of as *cis*-addition of the nucleophile-metal compound to the double bond.

In homogeneous catalysis, activation of the reactants through complexing with the catalytic metal salt corresponds to activation by adsorption in heterogeneous catalysis. Since most of the reactions mentioned have first been carried out by heterogeneous catalysis, the work summarized in this chapter enabled a clarification of the mechanisms of a wide range of catalytic reactions by kinetic and synthetic methods and can, therefore, be considered as a contribution not only for a new field of organometallic chemistry but also for a better understanding of catalytic reactions.

ACKNOWLEDGMENT

We are indebted to Drs. W. Hafner and F. Sedlmeier for valuable discussions.

VI. EXPERIMENTAL PREPARATIONS

A. Reactions of Olefinic Compounds with Aqueous Solutions of Noble Metal Salts in the Absence of Additional Oxidants

See Table III.

1. Conversion of Gaseous Olefins

Reactions of gaseous olefins with aqueous $PdCl_2$ solutions are easily performed. The olefins are bubbled through the solution or absorbed in the solution charged in a shaking flask, which may be heated and which is connected to a gas burette to control the amount of gas absorption. Products are isolated by distillation. To prevent secondary reactions in the first case higher temperatures, e.g., $90-95°$, can be used to remove products out of the reaction mixture with the gas stream after they have formed. Products are isolated from the gas stream by cooling or extraction.

Palladium chloride solution used in most examples of Table III is prepared by dissolving solid $PdCl_2$ in water by heating and adding a minimum amount of hydrochloric acid. The ratio $Pd:Cl^-$ is mostly about $1:2.3$.

2. Conversion of Liquid Material

Liquid substrates are usually reacted with $PdCl_2$ solutions under stirring at reflux temperature. The products are isolated by normal or steam distillation or by extraction. To increase the solubility of the higher olefinic compounds, organic solvents miscible with water such as acetic acid, dimethylformamide, or the like can be added.

3. Preparation of Acetaldehyde

One liter of an aqueous solution containing 17.8 g $PdCl_2$ is charged into a flask connected with a gas burette filled with ethylene and heated up to

50°. After shaking for a few minutes 2.6 liters of ethylene are absorbed and palladium metal is precipitated. Acetaldehyde is isolated by distillation (yield 96%).

4. Preparation of Aldehydes and Ketones from α-Olefins[130a]

Propylene is reacted in a flask at 70° with a solution containing 0.05 mole K_2PdCl_4 and 1 mole $HClO_4$ per liter. The carbonyl compounds isolated consist of 15% propionaldehyde and 85% acetone. The reaction rate is much less than with the solution described for the general conversion of gaseous olefins.

With the molar $HClO_4$ solution containing 0.05 mole of K_2PdCl_4 higher α-olefins give different proportions of aldehydes:

Olefin:	propene	1-butene	1-pentene	1-hexene
% aldehyde:	15.3	8.9	20.0	3.8
Olefin:	1-heptene	1-octene	styrene	
% aldehyde:	5.0	28.0	75	

(with respect to total carbonyl compounds).

5. Conversion of 2-Methyl-1- and -2-butene[160]

2-Methyl-1-butene (5.5 g) are shaken with a solution of 14 g $PdCl_2$ in 50% acetic acid at 90° for 4 hr. After filtration α-methylcrotonaldehyde (18%) and 2-methylbutanol (2%) are removed by steam distillation (total yield 20%). At pH 3 (by neutralization with NaOH) β-methylcrotonaldehyde forms in 8.5–9.5% yield.

6. Conversion of 1,5-Hexadiene[176]

This conversion has been carried out with a mole ratio of $PdCl_2$: diene = 2:1. The mixture is refluxed for 4–5 hr and the palladium metal is filtered after cooling. Reaction products are extracted with ether and separated by preparative gas chromatography. Main products: 3-methylcyclopentanone (yield 13%) and hexan-2,5-dione (yield 5%)

7. Conversion of Cyclohexene and 1-Methyl-1-cyclohexene[164]

A solution of 2.5 g cyclohexene is shaken with a solution of 6 g finely powdered $PdCl_2$ in 350 ml, 50% acetic acid for 2 hr at room temperature. After filtration from palladium metal the solution is diluted with 150 ml H_2O and extracted with ether after addition of NaCl. The ether is then evaporated and the residual liquid distilled. The first fraction contains benzene (75%) and cyclohexane (25%); the second fraction is cyclohexanone (yield 60%) boiling at 150–153°. If 1-methyl-1-cyclohexene is shaken for 24 hr with the same $PdCl_2$ solution, only toluene and methylcyclohexane but no methyl-cyclohexanone is obtained.

8. Hydrolytic Reactions of Olefinic Compounds

The reactions are carried out analogously to those generally described in Sections VI-A-1 and VI-A-2 respectively. Only a small amount of metallic palladium precipitates by oxidative side reactions. The reaction rate decreases mostly because of the inhibiting influence of the hydrolyzed groups. This effect is pronounced in the case of halide ions.

B. Reactions of Olefins with Aqueous PdCl$_2$—CuCl$_2$ Solutions

1. Continuous Preparation of Acetaldehyde

An aqueous solution containing 1.78 g PdCl$_2$, 150 g CuCl$_2 \cdot 2H_2O$, and 24 g Cu(OAc)$_2 \cdot H_2O$ per liter is charged in a vertical, heatable glass pipe filled with Raschig rings. At 90–95° a gas mixture of 84% per volume C$_2$H$_4$ and 16% per volume oxygen is passed through the solution with a rate of about 50 liters/hr·liter catalyst. Acetaldehyde is separated from the unreacted gas by cooling and/or scrubbing with water. The space-time yield under these conditions is 10–15 = $\frac{g}{l \cdot h}$ The initial muddy (by basic copper salts) solution becomes clear during the reaction, and a constant oxidation degree is reached. This procedure represents the model for the commercial "one-stage process."

The procedure of the "two-stage process" can be carried out with the same solution if ethylene and air (or oxygen) are introduced alternatively. Ethylene is replaced by air when cuprous chloride begins to precipitate and it is fed again when the solution becomes slurried by copper oxychloride. If the reaction is carried out for a longer time the water removed by the unreacted gas must be compensated for by continuous feeding.

After several days of reaction an insoluble precipitate of copper oxalate accumulates. It is formed via chlorinated by-products. In this reaction low amounts of mono-, di- and trichloroacetaldehyde, ethylene chlorohydrin, and others can be observed. Similar side reactions take place with higher olefins. Under certain conditions chlorinated products can be obtained as main products, e.g., ethylene chlorohydrin and 3-chlorobutan-2-one in butene oxidation.

2. Formation of Ethylene Chlorohydrin[357]

A solution that is prepared by dissolving 700 g CuCl$_2 \cdot 2H_2O$, 57 g CaCl$_2$ and 1.78 g PdCl$_2$ in 1 liter of water is charged into a tantalum-lined autoclave with a volume at least 10 times as large as the liquid fed and is vigorously shaken with a gas mixture of 50 atm C$_2$H$_4$ and 5 atm oxygen. After a pressure drop of about 4–5 atm, 3 atm oxygen are added. This is repeated once more. After about 4 hr total reaction time, the pressure is released and the products separated by distillation. Per liter catalyst solution, about 45 g ethylene-chlorohydrin and 18 g acetaldehyde are obtained.

3. Formation of 3-Chlorobutan-2-one[201]

A mixture of n-butenes is reacted with an aqueous solution of 142 g $CuCl_2 \cdot 2H_2O$ and 3 g $PdCl_2$ at 115° and 17 atm in an autoclave under vigorous shaking. If after several minutes reaction time there is still enough butene indicated by no pressure drop, about 4 atm oxygen can be added to continue the reaction. This can be done once or twice more if a pressure drop now shows oxygen consumption. (Caution should be used because of explosive mixtures.) After pressure release the ketones are separated by distillation from the solution; 70% of the total ketone content consists of 3-chlorobutan-2-one beside methylethylketone and 3,3-dichlorobutan-2-one.

4. Formation of Dodecan-2-one- and 10-Ketoundecanoic Acid[56]

The reaction was brought about with a solution of 0.02 mole $PdCl_2$, 0.02 mole $CuCl_2 \cdot 2H_2O$ in 50 ml dimethylformamide and 7 ml H_2O in a cylindrical 250-ml glass reactor that has a gas dispersion inlet tube affixed to the bottom. The reactor is equipped with a stirrer and a condenser. After heating to 60–70°, 0.2 mole 1-dodecene is fed by drop within 2.5 hr through a dropping funnel (whose outlet is well below the liquid surface) under stirring and feeding of 3.3 liter/hr oxygen. The products are separated by distillation. The yield of dodecan-2-one is about 85%.

Similarly, 27.5 g of 10-undecenoic acid is fed within a period of 2 hr. The mixture is poured into excess cold dilute hydrochloric acid, the precipitated solid taken up in benzene, filtered, and after removal of benzene extracted with cold pentane to leave 18 g 10-ketoundecanoic acid, which can be recrystallized from ethyl acetate.

C. Oxidation of Olefins in Acetic Acid Medium

See Table V.

1. Preparation of Vinyl Acetate from Ethylene with PdCl₂[250]

A solution of 8.88 g anhydrous $PdCl_2$ and 8.2 g anhydrous sodium acetate in 60 ml glacial acetic acid is treated with ethylene at 20° for 16 hr. The solution is then filtered from palladium metal and distilled to separate first a fraction boiling between 96 and 118° (24 ml), from which a fraction boiling between 72 and 86° is isolated by a further distillation. This is treated with water to remove acetic acid and dried with magnesium sulfate and again distilled. The yield is 0.84 g.

2. Preparation of Vinyl Acetate from Ethylene with PdCl₂ and Benzoquinone

To a solution of 0.178 g anhydrous $PdCl_2$ and 8.2 g anhydrous sodium acetate in 125 ml glacial acetic acid, 27 g benzoquinone are added; the mixture is treated with ethylene at 18° for 63 hr. The solution is treated as described in Section VI-C-1. The yield of vinyl acetate is 3.27 g.

3. Preparation of Vinyl Acetate from Ethylene and Oxygen in the Presence of PdCl₂ and CuCl₂[356a]

First 0.2 g $PdCl_2$, 10 g $Cu(OAc)_2 \cdot H_2O$, 3.8 g KCl, and 30 g KOAc are dissolved or suspended in 250 ml glacial acetic acid, the mixture charged into a 1-liter, titanium-lined autoclave and heated up to 120° under shaking. Then ethylene is pressured into the autoclave up to 40–45 atm under continued shaking. The pressure drops because of the dissolution of ethylene. Alternating charging of ethylene and shaking of the autoclave is repeated until the pressure of 40 atm remains constant. Then 5 atm of oxygen are charged and the autoclave is agitated. The pressure drops within 2 min by about 6–7 atm. Four atmospheres of oxygen are again charged and this repeated two to three times after every pressure drop with decreasing amount (4, 3, 2 atm). Vinyl acetate and acetaldehyde are obtained from the mixture by distillation after cooling and releasing the pressure. The yields are about 20 g vinyl acetate and 3–4 g acetaldehyde.

4. Preparation of Vinyl Acetate[158]

In this example a catalyst carrier is used. The carrier is prepared from alumina and bentonite (92:8) from which pellets of a diameter of 4 mm are formed and calcined at 1500°. The internal surface is 10 m²/g. The carrier is treated with an aqueous $PdCl_2$ solution and metallic palladium is precipitated with an alkaline solution of hydrazine hydrate. The palladium content of the catalyst is 4% by weight. Next, 500 ml of this catalyst are charged into a tube of a diameter of 30 mm and a length of 100.0 cm. A solution of 2 moles of potassium acetate in glacial acetic acid is fed down from the top of the tube over the fixed bed catalyst at a rate of 3 liters/hr, together with a mixture of ethylene and oxygen (80:20 v/v) at a rate of 20 liters/hr. The reaction is carried out at 100° and atmospheric pressure. The yield of vinyl acetate is 90% with respect to carbon converted.

5. Formation of Glycol Diacetate and β-Chloroethyl Acetate[153]

In a 500-ml, titanium-lined autoclave, a mixture containing 0.01 mole of $PdCl_2$, 2 moles of $CuCl_2$, and 4 moles of an alkali metal acetate per liter, acetic acid is charged, heated, pressured with ethylene to 33 atm and agitated for 1 hr at 100° and 0.5 hr at 120°. With different alkali metal acetates the ratios of the products formed are:

Metal acetate	Product formation: moles/1·hr	Ratio vinyl acetate/ satd. acetates	Ratio diacetate/ chloro acetate
Li	< 1.0	0.01	0.12
Na	0.63	0.86	2.2
K	0.06	5.0	9.0

In the reactions with propene and butene the amount of olefin charged is weighed and transferred to the bomb at room temperature.

6. Preparation of Glycol Monoacetate[373]

One millimole of $PdCl_2$, 50 mM $LiNO_3$ in 100 ml acetic acid were stirred at 50° and ethylene was led into the solution at the rate of 5 liters/hr; after 2 hr the mixture contained 72.1 mM glycol monoacetate, 4.8 mM glycol diacetate, and 2.3 mM acetaldehyde.

Similarly, propene and 1-butene give the appropriate monoacetates $R—CH(OH)—CH_2(OAc)$ and $R—CH(OAc)—CH_2OH$, respectively (R = CH_3, C_2H_5).

7. Preparation of Hexenyl Acetates. Examples for the Conversion of Higher Olefins[327]

a. Conversion of 1-Hexene in the Absence of Copper(II). A mixture of palladium(II) acetate (1.00 g, 4.46 mM), sodium acetate (0.73 g, 8.92 mM; or AcO/Cl/Pd ratio = 4/0/1), and glacial acetic acid (50 ml) is stirred at 25° for 30 min in a 250 ml round-bottomed flask. Then 5 ml of hexene (3.37 g, 40 mM) are added, and the stirring is continued for 1 hr. (Within 15 min of the addition, extensive palladium precipitation occurs.) The mixture is then filtered to remove the palladium precipitate, and 100 ml of water are added to the dark brown filtrate, giving a further palladium precipitate. The acetic acid-water mixture is extracted with three 50-ml portions of benzene; the combined benzene extracts are washed with water, dilute aqueous sodium bicarbonate, and water again and are then dried over sodium sulfate. Evaporation of the yellow-brown benzene solution to small volume caused additional palladium metal to precipitate and a dark red solution formed from which a mixture of hexenyl acetates could be isolated by distillation.

When this sample is hydrogenated (diluted to 7 ml with heptane), using 150 mg 5% platinum on carbon catalyst at 25° and atmospheric pressure, an uptake of hydrogen of 70 ml equivalent to a yield of 64.1% of vinylation products based on palladium(II) acetate is found. The reduction products from the hexenyl acetates consist of 38.2% 1-hexyl acetate, 60.6% 2-hexyl acetate, and 1.2% 3-hexyl acetate (by gas chromatography).

The reaction of 1-hexene with a solution of 0.79 g palladium(II) chloride and 2.92 g sodium acetate in 50 ml glacial acetic acid at 100° with stirring is completed within 1 min. The yield of hexenyl acetates (1-, 2-, and 3-acetates) is about 77% when the mixture is worked up as described above.

b. *Conversion of 1-Hexene in the Presence of Copper(II).* A 300-ml autoclave is charged with 0.364 g (2.06 mM) palladium chloride, 5.0 g (37.4 mM) anhydrous cupric chloride, 14.5 g (177 mM) anhydrous sodium acetate, and 100 ml glacial acetic acid under nitrogen (AcO/Cl ratio, 2.25). The autoclave is heated to 115° with stirring (500 rpm). Hexene (10 ml, 6.73 g, 80 mM) is injected through a septum assembly attached to the reactor head. (In studies at higher temperatures a nitrogen-pressured vessel is used to charge the olefin into the reactor.) After 15 min the heating is stopped, and the reactor is cooled rapidly to 25° by immersion in an ice bath. Those reactions studied at "zero" time are cooled to 25° immediately upon adding the olefin. The rate of vinylation is found to be negligible at 25° under these reaction conditions.

The cooled reaction mixture is filtered, diluted with 300 ml of water, and extracted with three 50-ml portions of benzene. Water dilution effectively stops any further vinylation. The combined benzene extracts are washed with water, dilute aqueous sodium bicarbonate, and with water and dried over sodium sulfate. Benzene is then removed by distillation at atmospheric pressure; the residue (containing products and benzene) is examined by gas chromatography. The organic products are found to consist only of hexenyl acetates, no high boiling products being found. Hydrogenating a portion of this crude sample, using the procedure described above, shows 72.0% 1-hexyl acetate, 24.8% 2-hexyl acetate, and 3.2% 3-hexyl acetate in the product. The reaction can also be carried out in a round-bottomed flask at reflux temperature. Hexene is added through the reflux condenser.

8. Preparation of Benzyl Acetate

a. *Reaction in solution.*[34] A solution of 482.0 g (8.04 mole) of acetic acid, 107.9 g (1.10 mole) of potassium acetate, 92.0 g (1.00 mole) of toluene, 14.2 g (0.06 mole) of stannous acetate, 3.6 g (0.016 mole) Pd^{II} acetate, and 33.6 g of charcoal is charged to an appropriately sized flask, fitted with a stirrer, a condenser, a thermometer, and an air-inlet tube, and stirred at 100° for 9 hr, while air is blown over its surface at a rate of 500 ml/min.

The cooled reaction mixture is filtered through diatomaceous silica. The filtrate is then diluted with an equal volume of water and extracted with 1:1 Et$_2$O-pentane. The extracts are combined, washed successively with saturated NaHCO$_3$ solution, water, saturated NaCl solution, and then dried (MgSO$_4$). Distillation gives 66.0 g of a liquid, bp 103–105° (20 mm) containing 4.5 g (4.2%) of benzaldehyde and 61.5 g (41.0%) of benzyl acetate. Trituration of the distillation residue (4.9 g) with petroleum ether (bp 60–70°) gives 1.3 g of crude solid. Recrystallization gives 1.0 g (0.5%) of benzylidene diacetate, mp 44–45°.

Similarly, other alkyl benzenes (see Table V) are converted to give the appropriate benzylic esters.

b. Heterogeneous Catalytic Reactions.[206]   Benzyl acetate is prepared by treating PhMe with HOAc and O in the presence of a palladium catalyst at 50–250°. Thus Al_2O_3-bentonite (92:8) carrier is formed into 4-mm rods, and calcined at 1500° to give a carrier with 25% water adsorption capacity and 10 m²/g surface area. The carrier is impregnated with $PdCl_2$, which is precipitated with $N_2H_4 \cdot H_2O$ to give 2% palladium content. The catalyst (250 cm³) in a wire tube is placed in a horizontal tubular reactor and 200 ml $1M$ KOAc in HOAc and 69 g PhMe under 50 atm air reacted at 120° for 10 min by the trickling process by rotating the catalyst. $AcOCH_2Ph$ is obtained in 92.6% yield with 19% conversion of the PhMe.

9. Preparation of Glycolaldehyde Triacetate from Vinyl Chloride[199]

A 300-ml rocking autoclave is charged with acetic acid (1.67 mole), cupric acetate (0.088 mole), palladium chloride (0.028 mole), and vinyl chloride (1.2 mole).

The reaction mixture is heated to 75°, whereupon the vinyl chloride pressure in the autoclave rises to 7.5 atm. After shaking for 3 hr at 75°, the autoclave is cooled to room temperature and excess vinyl chloride released in a cold trap ($-70°$). The reaction product is diluted with pentane (200 ml) and the precipitated metal salts and metallic palladium are removed by filtration. Fractional distillation of the filtrate yields 3 g of a fraction (bp 60–70°/0.15 mm Hg), which solidifies at room temperature (mp 47–48°). After recrystallization from petroleum ether (boiling range: 60–80°) the crystalline compound (1.2 g) melts at 51–52°.

D. Oxidation of Olefins in Alcoholic Medium

See Table VI.

1. Preparation of Acetaldehyde Diethylacetal[250]

To a solution of 0.5 g (2.81 mM) anhydrous $PdCl_2$ in 29 ml absolute ethanol are added 25 ml of absolute ether and 54 g (0.5 mole) benzoquinone. The mixture is shaken in an atmosphere of dry ethylene for 6 hr at 10°. After 5.5 liters ethylene are absorbed, 50 ml ether are added, the mixture filtered, and the filtrate washed with 10% aqueous KOH. The ether layer is then dried with magnesium sulfate and distilled. The yield of acetaldehyde diethylacetal is 19.9 g (72.4% with respect to the ethylene converted).

2. Preparation of 2-Methyl-1,3-dioxolane from Ethylene[212]

One hundred ml ethylene glycol, 0.7 g $PdCl_2$ and 1.7 g cupric chloride dihydrate are heated in a stirred, stainless steel autoclave of 250-ml capacity. The autoclave is pressured 14 atm with ethylene and with 3 atm of oxygen (caution: explosive mixture). The water content of the charge is about 3% by volume. The autoclave is heated to 100° and maintained at this temperature until the pressure decreases to 10 atm (about 2 hr). After cooling the product is analyzed by gas chromatography. The yield of 2-methyl-1,3-dioxolane is about 91%, based on the ethylene converted.

3. Preparation of 2-Cyanomethyl-1,3-dioxolane from Acrylonitrile[212]

A 250-ml, stainless steel bomb is charged with a mixture of 0.35 g $PdCl_2$, 0.85 g $CuCl_2 \cdot 2H_2O$, 10 ml acrylonitrile, and 50 ml ethylene glycol; the mixture is purged with oxygen and then pressured with 2 atm oxygen. The bomb is then heated, while shaken, to 85° and is so maintained for 2 hr, during which time a pressure drop of 1 atm is recorded. After cooling the clear liquid is decanted from a precipitate of inorganic salts. The yield of 2-cyanomethyl-1,3-dioxolane is nearly quantitative (25% conversion), as determined by gas chromatography.

Similarly, other olefinic compounds listed in Table VI can be converted to the appropriate acetals.

E. Oxidative Reactions with Other Nucleophiles

See Table VII.

1. Preparation of Acrylonitrile[274]

Thirty milliliters of benzonitrile and 0.03 mole of $Pd(CN)_2$ are charged in an autoclave, pressured to 55 atm with ethylene, heated to 150°, and maintained at this temperature for 5 hr. After cooling, the products are isolated by distillation. Based on the amount of $Pd(CN)_2$ used, the yield of acrylonitrile is 50.8% (6.9% propionitrile are also obtained).

2. Preparation of Allyl Chloride[155a]

A solution of 18 g $PdCl_2$ in aqueous hydrochloric acid is adsorbed by 200 ml granular pumice and reduced to metallic Pd by hydrogen at 100° for 8 hr. The catalyst is washed with water, dried, and treated with oxygen at 800° for 8 hr to oxidize the palladium metal to PdO. It is then charged in a tube and a gas mixture containing propylene (60), oxygen (20), and hydrogen chloride (20% by volume) passed over it at 250°. The effluent gas mixture contains, apart from nonreacted gas, 3% by volume allyl chloride, 0.8% 2-chloropropane, 0.05% 1-chloropropane, and 0.08% carbon dioxide.

F. Oxidative Formation of C—C Bonds

See Table IX.

1. Preparation of 1,4-Diacetoxybutadiene from Vinyl Acetate[198]

A mixture of vinyl acetate (14 moles) and palladium acetate (0.320 mole) is charged to a three-necked, round-bottom flask, equipped with a mechanical stirrer, thermowell, and a reflux condenser to which a $CaCl_2$ tube is attached. The mixture is vigorously stirred for $2\frac{1}{2}$ hr at 60–65°. Hydroquinone (0.1% w based on vinyl acetate) is added as polymerization inhibitor. Precipitation of metallic palladium starts after 5–10 min. The reaction mixture is filtered to remove metallic palladium (66 at. % based on $Pd(OAc)_2$). Excess vinyl acetate and most of the acetic acid produced are removed by distillation at reduced pressure. The remaining product is extracted five times with 750 ml petroleum ether (boiling range: 60–80°), and the extract is fractionated on a Vigreux column yielding 42.5 g of a fraction of bp 75–120°/0.1 mm and 6 g of high-boiling residue. Fractional distillation yields:

Fraction 1, bp 75– 83°/0.3 mm, 5.4 g
Fraction 2, bp 83– 95°/0.3 mm, 11.2 g
Fraction 3, bp 95–105°/0.1 mm, 12.0 g
Fraction 4, bp 105–120°/0.1 mm, 11.6 g

On cooling to room temperature 4.2 g of a product with mp 85–91° separate from fractions 1 and 2. Additional amounts (10.2 g) of impure product are obtained when the remainder of fractions 1 and 2 is repeatedly diluted with petroleum ether and allowed to stand at 0° to −15°. Recrystallization from petroleum ether (twice), and subsequently from methanol, affords 7.6 g of 1,4-diacetoxybutadiene (mp 97–99°).

2. Preparation of 2,5-Diphenyl-2,4-hexadiene from α-Methylstyrene[397]

A solution of 1.46 g of α-methylstyrene dissolved in glacial acetic acid is added to a solution of palladium acetate (2.83 mM) and sodium acetate (5.65 mM) in glacial acetic acid at 85°. After precipitation of palladium metal, the reaction mixture is poured into ice water and extracted with ether. After several washings (H_2O, 5% aqueous $NaHCO_3$) the ether is removed by distillation and the above product purified by recrystallization.

Liquid products listed in Table VIIIb are purified by distillation under reduced pressure.

3. Preparation of trans,trans-1,4-Diphenyl-1,3-butadiene from β-Bromostyrene[177]

A mixture of 2.0 g (7.5 mM) of platinous chloride, 8.0 g (0.0226 mole) of tetraethylammonium trichlorostannite, 8.3 g (0.045 mole) of β-bromostyrene, about 5 g of cesium fluoride, a trace of hydroquinone, and 25 ml of anhydrous dimethylformamide is stirred in a nitrogen atmosphere at 135–140° for 18 hr. The solvent is distilled at 60° and 0.1 mm. The residue is extracted with ether. The extract is concentrated and recrystallized from a mixture of benzene and ethanol to give, in two crops, 1.14 g (25%) of trans,trans-bistyrene, mp 151–152°.

4. Preparation of Biphenyl from Benzene[149]

A mixture of 4.0 g (0.049 mole) of sodium acetate, 10.0 g (0.128 mole) benzene, 1.80 g (0.010 mole) of $PdCl_2$, and 40 g acetic acid is heated for 5.5 hr at 90° with stirring and then cooled to room temperature. The palladium metal formed is removed by filtration and the filtrate diluted with water; the upper layer is separated, washed with $1N$ NaOH and water, and dried over Na_2SO_4. After removal of benzene by distillation, 1.1 g of biphenyl is obtained as a residue (71% on $PdCl_2$ used, mp 60–65°). Recrystallization from ethanol gives a product mp 69°.

5. Preparation of trans-Stilbene from Styrene and Benzene[107]

In a solution of 3.36 g of styrene (equal molar equivalent to palladium acetate), 340 ml of dry benzene, and 80 ml of acetic acid, 7.21 g of palladium acetate is dissolved, and the mixture refluxed with continued stirring for 8 hr. The precipitated palladium metal is filtered and the filtrate washed with water and then dried over sodium sulfate. Evaporation of the benzene gives 5.24 g of crude crystalline stilbene, mp. 115–120° (90% yield based on styrene) and 0.052 g of liquid β-acetoxystyrene, bp 118–121° at 10 mm (1%). Recrystallization of the crude stilbene from ethanol gives 5.11 g of white crystals of trans-stilbene, mp 122–123° (88%). The crude β-acetoxystyrene is distilled carefully to give 0.046 g of pure product, bp 119–121° at 10 mm.

G. Oxidative Coupling of Olefins with Carbanions Derived from Organomercury Compounds

1. General Procedure for Alkylation or Arylation of Olefins with Organomercury, and Lead and Tin Compounds[141]

Mixtures of the organometallic compound, the olefin in equivalent amount (or better, twofold or more excess), and solvent are stirred and the group VIII metal compound is added as a solid or as a solution. Stirring is continued overnight at room temperature. Generally, enough organometallic reagent is added to produce a concentration between 0.1 and $1.0M$. A more concentrated solution could not be used because the slurries obtained could not be stirred effectively. Gaseous olefins are added under pressure; usually 2 atm. are sufficient. Methanol, acetic acid, ethanol, or acetonitrile is usually the solvent. The products (if soluble) are isolated by filtering to remove precipitate and distilling under reduced pressure to remove the solvent. The product may be distilled directly from the residue or taken up in a solvent that does not dissolve the salts such as methylene chloride, filtered, and then distilled or recrystallized.

In catalytic reactions, a slight excess of the oxidizing salt was added initially, and the group VIII metal compound was generally added in an amount between 0.01 and 1.0% of the oxidizing salt.

2. Preparation of Cinnamyl Acetate from Allyl Acetate[141]

A mixture of 31.8 g of phenylmercuric acetate, 100 ml of allyl acetate, and 0.10 mole of palladium(II) acetate is stirred at room temperature overnight and then at 40–50° for 1 hr. The solution is then diluted with water and pentane and filtered through celite. The solids are extracted thoroughly with pentane and combined with the original filtrate. The pentane layer is separated and the aqueous phase is extracted four more times with pentane. The combined pentane extracts are washed with water, aqueous sodium bicarbonate, and water again. After drying over anhydrous magnesium sulfate, the product is distilled under reduced pressure. There is obtained 11.0 g cinnamyl acetate, bp 104–110° (3 mm), which is about 95% pure by gas chromatographic analyses.

3. Preparation of Methyl Cinnamate from Methyl Acrylate in the Presence of $PdCl_2$, $CuCl_2$, and $Oxygen$[141]

In a 500-ml, three-necked flask provided with a condenser with a mercury-sealed gas outlet tube at the top, a stirrer, and a gas inlet tube that reaches nearly to the bottom of the flask, is placed 62 g of phenylmercuric chloride, 20 g of sodium chloride, 2.0 g of cupric chloride, 120 ml of methanol, 20 ml of methyl acrylate, and 40 ml of $0.1M$ Li_2PdCl_4 in methanol. The solution is stirred and kept at 40° in a thermostatted bath, and a slow stream of oxygen is bubbled through. At 15-min intervals, 10-ml portions of freshly prepared $3M$ HCl in methanol are added. After five additions (50 ml), two more additions are made at 1-hr intervals.

After being stirred at room temperature overnight, about $^3/_4$ of the solvent is evaporated under reduced pressure at room temperature. The residue is diluted with water and the product extracted with five portions of pentane. The extracts are washed once with water, dried over anhydrous magnesium sulfate, filtered, and distilled under reduced pressure. The yield is 22.4 g of colorless product, bp 110–113° (6 mm).

4. Preparation of 2-Phenylethyl Chloride from Ethylene[145]

A mixture of 15.70 g (50 mM) of phenylmercuric chloride, 2.10 g (50 mM) of lithium chloride, and 13.40 g (100 mM) of anhydrous cupric chloride is placed in a heavy-walled Pyrex pressure bottle with a magnetic stirring bar. The bottle is then capped with a rubber-lined metal cap with two small holes in the metal for hypodermic injections. The air is replaced with ethylene by evacuating and filling the bottle with ethylene several times through a hypodermic needle inserted through the rubber liner of the cap. Then 40 ml of acetic acid, 5 ml of water, and 5 ml of $0.1M$ Li$_2$PdCl$_4$ in acetic acid are injected. The mixture is stirred and the pressure of ethylene in the bottle is kept at 2 atmg overnight.

After about 20 hr the reaction mixture is poured into a mixture of water and pentane, and filtered. The solids are extracted with fresh pentane, and the aqueous layer extracted three more times with pentane. The combined pentane extracts are washed with water, dried over anhydrous magnesium sulfate, and distilled under reduced pressure to give 6.6 g of product, bp 105–115° (41 mm), which consists of more than 95% 2-phenylethyl chloride.

5. Preparation of 3-Phenyl-2-chloropropionaldehyde[145]

A reaction mixture containing 15.7 g (5 mM) of phenylmercuric chloride, 26.8 g (200 mM) of cupric chloride, 2.1 g (50 mM) of lithium chloride, 35 ml of acetic acid, 5 ml of acrolein, 5 ml of water, and 5 ml of $0.1M$ Li$_2$PdCl$_4$ in acetic acid is stirred, initially by ice cooling until the temperature no longer rises spontaneously, and then at room temperature overnight.

The product from three such reactions is isolated by diluting the reaction mixture with water and methylene chloride. Insoluble material is removed by filtration, and the methylene chloride layer is separated. The insoluble material and the aqueous phase are extracted three more times with methylene chloride. The combined methylene chloride extracts are then washed twice with water, dried over anhydrous magnesium sulfate, and evaporated at room temperature under reduced pressure. Distillation gives two fractions: bp 80–100° (8 mm) (1.5 g) and bp 100–101.5° (7.5 mm) (4.5 g). The first fraction is about 50% the desired product (yield 63.5%).

Purification is accomplished by converting the crude product into its sodium bisulfite addition product, washing it with ether, regenerating the aldehyde with aqueous sodium bicarbonate, and redistilling.

6. Preparation of 3-Phenylpropionaldehyde[142]

A reaction mixture of 0.20 mole of phenylmercuric chloride, 0.20 mole of cupric chloride, 0.25 mole of allyl alcohol, 390 ml of acetonitrile and 10 ml of $0.1M$ LiPdCl$_3$ in acetonitrile is stirred at room temperature for 3 hr. The solution is now $0.15M$ in 3-phenylpropionaldehyde. The product is isolated by diluting the reaction mixture with water and pentane, filtering to remove insoluble material, and separating the pentane layer. The insoluble material and the aqueous solution are extracted several times more with pentane, and the combined extracts are washed twice with water and dried over anhydrous magnesium sulfate. Pentane is distilled from the product through a long Vigreux column, and the residue is distilled under reduced pressure to give 2.7 g of colorless liquid, bp 81–120° (4.5 mm), which is about 90% 3-phenyl-propionaldehyde.

7. Preparation of Phenylacetaldehyde [144]

A mixture of 50 mM of phenylmercuric chloride, 50 mM of lithium chloride, 50 mM of cupric chloride, 37 ml of acetic acid, 2.5 ml of water, 5 ml of vinyl acetate, and 5 ml of $0.1M$ Li_2PdCl_4 in acetic acid is stirred at room temperature for 2 hr. The products of three such reaction mixtures are then combined, diluted with water, and extracted with four portions of methylene chloride. The combined extracts are washed with water, dried over anhydrous magnesium sulfate, and distilled under reduced pressure. The result is 5.2 g of colorless product, bp 71–80° (7 mm), which is about 85% phenylacet-aldehyde.

8. Coupling of Toluene with $PdCl_2$ through an Organomercury Intermediate [391a]

Mercuric acetate (3.1 g, 0.01 mole) is added at 25° to a mixture of 9.2 g (0.1 mole) of toluene and 6 g (0.1 mole) of acetic acid. On the addition of 1.25 ml of $HClO_4$ the mercuration takes place rapidly and is complete in 5 min. Then 0.44 g (0.0025 mole) of $PdCl_2$ is added. After 30 min the palladium metal is filtered, washed, and dried. About 95% of the theoretical amount can be obtained. The mixture consists of 1.6% o,m'-, 3.2% o,p'-, 2.3% m,m'-, 35.2% m,p'-, and 60% p,p'-bitolyl. Using excess mercuric acetate, close to theoretical yields of 1 mole of bitolyl for 1 mole of palladium acetate can be obtained.

H. σ-Complexes of Palladium(II) and Platinum(II)

See Table IV

1. General Procedure for Oxymetallation of Cyclic Dienes [363]

Equimolar amounts of the metal halide or the lithium halide complex salt and the diene or allylamine are reacted in the appropriate solvent to form the complex of the type [diene·MX_2] while the color turns from red-brown to yellow. Oxymetallation takes place in the presence of sodium carbonate (in MeOH) or sodium acetate (in acetic acid or methanol) during refluxing for about 0.5 to 1 hr. After hot filtration the solvent is evaporated to dryness and the residue recrystallized from methylene chloride. The yield is almost quantitative.

I. Formation and Reactions of π-Allyl Complexes

See Table X.

1. Reaction of $PdCl_2$ with Allyl Alcohol. Formation of 4-Methylenetetrahydrofurfuryl Alcohol and 4-Methyl-2,5-dihydrofurfuryl Alcohol[132]

In a 250-ml, three-necked flask (equipped with stirrer, condenser, and thermometer) 2 g $PdCl_2$ and 150 g freshly distilled allyl alcohol are charged. The mixture is heated to 42° over a period of 30 min and for an additional 30 min up to 45°. The main amount of propylene is evolved. Within 1 hr the temperature is increased to 75° and maintained for 15 min. During the reaction the color changes from brown to orange to pale yellow. Unreacted allyl alcohol and some low-boiling by-products are evaporated at 50 torr. For the separation of bis(π-allyl palladium chloride) the solution is cooled to 0°C when about $\frac{4}{5}$ of the liquid is removed. About 1.6 g of the yellow complex precipitates. If about 20 ml ether are added and cooled further, 0.3–0.4 g bis(π-allyl PdCl) are obtained. The solution is liberated from ether and distilled in the presence of some hydroquinone in vacuo. About 15 g of a mixture of the dihydrofurfuryl alcohols are obtained, bp 30–31° (15 mm).

2. Formation of Bis(π-allyl PdCl) Complexes from Allyl Halides

An aqueous solution of $PdCl_2$ is shaken with excess allyl chloride, 3-chloro-1-butene or crotyl chloride at room temperature until the initial brown color disappears completely. The hydrophobic precipitates of the corresponding π-allyl complexes are filtered from the solution and are only slightly contaminated by metallic palladium. It is recrystallized from benzene, acetone, ethanol, etc. From the residual solution α,α-dioxo compounds can be isolated by distillation. The yield of the complexes is almost quantitative with respect to the palladium salt used.

3. Formation of Bis(π-allyl palladium) Complexes from Olefins[159a]

Twenty-five grams of finely powdered $PdCl_2$ are dissolved in 1 liter of 50% acetic acid under stirring and boiling for 0.5 hr. Nondissolved $PdCl_2$ is filtered off. One-half liter of the solution is shaken with the olefin at room temperature, whereby the brown olefin complex $[C_nH_{2n}PdCl_2]_2$ precipitates. The suspension is then heated to 90° until the solid is dissolved, while the color changes to yellow. About 0.5–3 hr are needed for this procedure. On cooling the solution the π-allyl complex crystallizes. By diluting with water and extraction with benzene, more of the complex can be obtained. It is recrystallized from ethanol-water (4:1).

4. Formation of Bis(π-allyl PdCl) Complexes from Olefins in the Presence of Na_2CO_3[187]

A solution of 2 g $PdCl_2$, 10 g Na_2CO_3 and 7 ml 2-methyl-1-pentene is stirred at room temperature for 5 hr in 25 ml of $CHCl_3$ and yields quantitatively bis-(2-propyl-π-allyl palladium chloride).

5. Hydrolytic Decomposition of Bis(π-allyl PdCl) Complexes[164]

One gram of the complex is completely decomposed in 100 ml boiling H_2O within 2 hr. After filtering from metallic palladium, the products can be isolated by usual methods. The reaction is not uniform. Several products are simultaneously obtained. Therefore, only three typical examples are listed in Table VIII. The decomposition in water is accelerated by OH^- ions and inhibited by acid.

6. Oxidation of Bis(π-allyl PdCl) Complexes[160]

Oxidation with $PdCl_2$ in the mole ratio of complex:Pd::1:2 is carried out under shaking and boiling in 50% acetic acid for 1.5 hr. After filtration from metallic palladium the products are separated by distillation.

Oxidation with $Na_2Cr_2O_7$ is carried out at boiling temperature in 25% acetic acid. A solution of 0.33 mM $Na_2Cr_2O_7$ and 0.833 mM H_2SO_4/ml is added dropwise to 0.5 mM of complex during a period of 10 min. The products are simultaneously distilled, together with water vapor. Distillation is continued for 10 min.

Oxidation with MnO_2 is carried out in 25% acetic acid in which the complex and MnO_2 are charged; H_2SO_4 is added dropwise during boiling of the solution. The products together with water vapor are then distilled.

J. Catalytic Transalkenylation

See Table XI.

1. General Procedure for the Preparation of Vinyl and Isopropenyl Esters from the Acetates[323]

Molar amounts of vinyl or isopropenyl acetate, respectively, and a carboxylic acid are heated to reaction temperature, generally reflux temperature, together with 0.005–0.01 mole $PdCl_2 \cdot NaCl$ (or $PdCl_2 \cdot LiCl$) per mole carboxylic acid. An excess of alkenyl acetate increases the yield of the new alkenyl ester. After 3–6 hr the reaction mixture is cooled and active carbon is added to precipitate the palladium salt. This catalyst "coal" can be used for further transvinylations. The activity, however, decreases, since palladium salt is reduced to the metal by side reactions. The reduction is almost complete in the case of transisopropenylation, so that the palladium salt can be used as a catalyst for one run only.

The volatile portion (acids and esters) of the reaction mixture can also be separated from the catalyst by vacuum distillation. The reaction can also be carried out in the presence of inert solvents, as THF, DMF, DMSO, or dimethoxyethane. The reaction products are isolated by fractional distillation.

2. Preparation of Vinyl Acetate from Vinyl Chloride [199]

The reaction vessel, equipped with a bulb agitator, gas inlet tube, reflux condenser and thermowell, is charged with a solution of sodium acetate (0.2 mole) in glacial acetic acid (2.2 moles). The apparatus is flushed with vinyl chloride and the acetic acid solution saturated with vinyl chloride, at 65° ± 0.5°, under atmospheric pressure, with vigorous stirring. The gas inlet tube is then connected to a calibrated vinyl chloride storage vessel and palladium chloride (0.028 mole) added. The absorption of vinyl chloride starts after a short induction period. The reaction is stopped after 74 min by disconnecting the olefin supply. The amount of vinyl chloride consumed is 0.190 mole (95% on intake of sodium acetate). The reaction mixture is fractionated under reduced pressure.

The yield of vinyl acetate based on vinyl chloride consumed is 94%.

3. Preparation of Divinyl Adipate [199]

The reaction of di(tri-n-butyl)ammonium adipate (0.2 mole) in 1,2-dimethoxyethane (1.67 moles) as solvent, with vinyl chloride (atm pressure) at 60°, in the presence of palladium chloride (0.022 mole), is complete after 45 min, 0.196 mole of vinyl chloride being consumed. The reaction mixture is freed from the solvent by vacuum distillation and the residual product extracted with 300 ml of ether. The ether solution is washed at 0–5°, first with 2N HCl to remove tri-n-butylamine, next with 5% aqueous NaHCO$_3$, and then dried over calcium chloride. After removing the solvent by distillation, the ether extract (8.4 g) is fractionated on a short Vigreux column, which yields 3.4 g (20% mole on olefin consumed) of divinyl adipate (bp 69–72°/ 0.1 mm Hg.).

4. Preparation of Vinyl Fluoride from Vinyl Chloride [374]

Vinyl chloride is passed through a solution of 1 g palladium acetate and 1.5 g lithium fluoride in 60 ml acetic acid at 100°C at the rate of 1.5 liters/hr for 2 hr. Vinyl fluoride is removed with unreacted gas and collected. It is formed at a rate of 1.2 mM/hr.

5. Preparation of Vinyl Methyl Ether from Vinyl Acetate [53]

A mixture of 20 g (0.23 mole) of vinyl acetate, 80 g (0.19 mole) dinonyl phthalate, and 0.001 mole lithium chloropalladite is charged in a round-bottomed flask fitted with stirrer, reflux condenser, and thermowell. Vinyl acetate and methanol are added continuously at the rate of 28 g (0.33 mole) and 7 g (0.22 mole), respectively, per hour. Argon is passed through the mixture with a rate of 45 liters/hr while stirring at 70°. The products are removed by the argon stream and condensed in a cold trap. After 1 hr 0.07 mole methyl vinyl ether and 0.02 mole acetaldehyde dimethylacetal are formed.

6. Preparation of Acetaldehyde Diethylacetal from Vinyl Acetate[199]

Absolute ethanol (2.5 mole) is saturated with vinyl chloride at 40° under atmospheric pressure. Then palladium chloride (0.056 mole) is added and a solution of sodium ethanolate (0.522 mole) is added dropwise over a reaction period of 5.5 hr, while vinyl chloride is passed through the vigorously stirred reaction mixture at such a rate that the amount of exhaust gases is about 2 liters/hr. The exhaust gases are cooled in a cold trap. The reaction mixture is distilled under reduced pressure.

The following products are obtained:

Acetaldehyde diethyl acetal	0.300 mole (62%)
Acetaldehyde	0.034 mole (7%)
Paraldehyde	<0.010 mole (<2%)

7. Preparation of Allyl Ethyl Ether from Allyl Chloride[330]

A mixture of 19.1 g of allyl chloride, 115 g methanol and 1 g Na_2PdCl_4 is kept at 50° for 5 hr. The volatile components are removed by vacuum distillation. The distillate contains 10.5 g allyl ethyl ether.

8. Phenylation of Vinyl Acetate[144]

A mixture of 10 mM of phenylmercuric chloride, 10 mM of cupric chloride, 8 ml of acetic acid, 2 ml of vinyl acetate, and 1 ml of $0.1M$ Li_2PdCl_4 in acetic acid is stirred at room temperature overnight. The solution is then $0.15M$ in *trans*-stilbene, $0.30M$ in phenylacetaldehyde, $0.27M$ in phenylacetaldehyde enol acetate, and $0.03M$ in styrene. Other reactions listed in Table XIc are carried out similarly.

8. Preparation of 2-Phenylpropionaldehyde and 1,2-Diphenyl-1-propene[144]

A mixture of 50 mM of phenylmercuric chloride, 50 mM of cupric chloride, 50 mM of lithium chloride, 5 ml of propenyl acetate, 35 ml of acetic acid, 5 ml of water, and 5 ml of $0.1M$ Li_2PdCl_4 in acetic acid is stirred at room temperature overnight. Four similar reaction mixtures are then combined, diluted with water, and extracted with methylene chloride several times. After being washed with water and dried over anhydrous magnesium sulfate, the extracts are distilled under reduced pressure. The yield is 5.4 g of colorless liquid, bp 60–70° (4 mm), which is about 95% 2-phenylpropionaldehyde.

A second fraction from the distillation of the extracts, bp 120–160° (4 mm), solidifies on cooling. Several recrystallizations from aqueous methanol give 0.63 g of colorless plates, mp 88.5–89.0°, which are *trans*-1,2-diphenyl-1-propene.

9. Preparation of Benzyl Methyl Ketone [144]

A reaction mixture containing 10 mM of phenylmercuric chloride, 10 mM of lithium chloride, 10 mM of cupric chloride, 7 ml of acetic acid, 1 ml of water, 1 ml of isopropenyl acetate, and 1 ml of $0.1M$ Li_2PdCl_4 in acetic acid is stirred at room temperature overnight. The reaction mixture is $0.5M$ in benzyl methyl ketone and about $0.4M$ in chlorobenzene.

10. Preparation of 1-Phenyl-2-butene, 2-Phenyl-2-butene, and 1-Phenyl-1-butene [143]

A reaction mixture containing 50 mM (15.65 g) of phenylmercuric chloride, 10 mM (1.34 g) of $CuCl_2$, 10 ml of crotyl chloride, 25 ml of acetonitrile, and 5 ml of $0.1M$ $LiPdCl_3$ in acetonitrile is stirred at room temperature overnight.

The products are isolated by adding 25 ml of water and 100 ml of pentane. Insoluble material is removed by filtration, and the solids are extracted several times with fresh pentane. The pentane layer is separated and the water layer is extracted four more times with pentane. The combined pentane extracts are washed twice with water, dried over anhydrous magnesium sulfate and distilled under reduced pressure. The yield obtained is 1.9 g of colorless liquid product, bp 95–125° (47 mm). At least seven compounds are detected in the product by gas chromatography. Three of the products are tentatively identified as 2-phenyl-2-butene ($\sim 34\%$), 1-phenyl-1-butene ($\sim 29\%$), and 1-phenyl-2-butene (15%).

11. Preparation of Methyl 4-Allylbenzoate [143]

In a 500-ml flask, fitted with a stirrer, a thermometer, and a calcium chloride-filled drying tube, is placed 0.090 mole (34.4 g) of methyl 4-chloromercuric benzoate, 30 mM of $CuCl_2$, 20 ml of allyl chloride, 50 ml of acetonitrile, and, with stirring, 10 ml of $0.1M$ $LiPdCl_3$ in acetonitrile. Cooling with ice water is necessary initially to keep the temperature below 28°. After 3 hr of stirring at room temperature, the reaction is complete.

The product is isolated by adding 300 ml of hexane and 300 ml of water. The mixture is filtered and the solids are extracted several times with fresh hexane. The hexane layer is separated and the aqueous phase is extracted twice more with hexane; the combined extracts are washed with water, dried over anhydrous magnesium sulfate, and distilled under reduced pressure to give 4.9 g of colorless product, bp 87–93° (2.5 mm), mainly 90–92° (2.5 mm), which is about 95% methyl 4-allylbenzoate. A lower boiling fraction of 1–2 g is 75% of this product also. A higher boiling fraction of about 2 g solidified, mp 92–94°. It is probably dimethyl 3,3′-diphenyldicarboxylate.

K. Oligomerization and Polymerization

See Table XII.

1. Preparation of Butenes from Ethylene [344]

A solution of 2 g $PdCl_2$ in 2 ml concentrated hydrochloric acid is added to 60 ml of glacial acetic acid. The mixture is charged into a 500-ml, titanium-lined autoclave, pressured with 55 atm ethylene and heated to 90° for 10 hr. After cooling, the residual pressure is about 25 atm. The pressure is released and the gas mixture passed through a trap cooled to −78° for collecting the butenes formed. Finally, the reaction mixture is heated to 80–90° to remove dissolved gas. For purification the liquified gas collected is distilled. About 12–15 g of product is obtained.

2. Dimerization of Ethylene with Rhodium Chloride Catalyst [3]

A 400-ml, silver-lined pressure vessel is charged with 100 ml of methanol and 3 g of rhodium chloride ($RhCl_3 \cdot 3H_2O$). The temperature is raised to 45°, agitation commenced, and ethylene is injected to a pressure of approximately 400 atm. The pressuring is accompanied by a 10° rise in temperature. When the pressure has fallen to 200 atm, the vessel is repressured to 400 atm. The mixture is maintained at 45° over a 6-hr period, while the pressure is gradually increased to 1,000 atm. Over 80% of the ethylene absorption occurs during the first four hours. The reaction vessel is cooled, and the product (178 g) condensed in a trap cooled with solid carbon dioxide. The product contains 2% 1-butene, 78% trans-2-butene, and 20% cis-2-butene.

3. Dimerization of Butadiene in an Aprotic Solvent to Octa-1,3,7-triene [368]

A 100-ml, stainless steel autoclave is charged with 30 ml of acetone and 219 mg (0.3 mM) of bis(triphenylphosphine) (maleic anhydride) palladium. Butadiene (20 g) is then condensed into the autoclave. The reaction mixture is heated to 115° and held there for 8 hr while being stirred. In order to separate the reaction product from the catalyst, the yellow reaction mixture is distilled into a cold trap at ∼60° under reduced pressure. Fractional distillation under nitrogen afforded 14 g (70% yield) of 1,3,7-octatriene (bp 124–125°). The distillate also contains a small amount (ca. 5%) of 4-vinyl-1-cyclohexene. The infrared spectrum of octa-1,3,7-triene shows bands at 1638 (C=C), 1600 (conjugated C=C) and 1002, 912, and 898 cm^{-1} (—CH=CH$_2$). The NMR spectrum shows complex bands at 3.5–4.8 (=CH—), 4.8–5.4 (=CH$_2$) and centered at 8.0 τ (—CH$_2$—).

4. Dimerization of Butadiene in Methanol[368]

The autoclave described above is charged with 30 ml of methanol, 73 mg (0.1 mM) of bis(triphenylphosphine) (maleic anhydride) palladium, and 20 g of butadiene. The reaction mixture is heated to 70° and held there for 2 hr while being stirred. The yellow reaction mixture is distilled into a cold trap at ~70° under reduced pressure to give 20 g (77% yield) of 1-methoxy-2,7-octadiene (bp 103–105°/83 mm). The distillate contains a small amount (ca. 3%) of 3-methoxy-1,7-octadiene (bp 145–146°).

The infrared spectrum of 1-methoxy-2,7-octadiene shows bands at 1670 (internal C=C), 1638 (terminal C=C), 1115 (CH$_3$—O—), 970 (*trans*-CH=CH—), and 991 cm^{-1} (—CH=CH$_2$). Its NMR spectrum shows bands at 4.0–4.7 (multiplet, =CH—), 4.7–5.2 (multiplet, =CH$_2$), 6.22 (doublet, $J = 3$ cps, O—CH$_2$—C=), 6.78 (singlet, O—CH$_3$), 7.7–8.2 (multiplet, =C—CH$_2$—C—CH$_2$—C=), and 8.2–8.7 τ (multiplet, —C—CH$_2$—C—).

5. Dimerization and Trimerization of Norbornadiene with Rhodium on Carbon

Norbornadiene (20 g) and 5% rhodium on charcoal (3.0 g) are stirred and heated (bath temperature 110°) in an argon atmosphere for 23 hr. Pentane (150 ml) is added; the mixture is filtered; and the solvent is evaporated at reduced pressure. Distillation of the residue gives 10.52 g (53% yield) of a mixture of norbornadiene dimers, bp 76–77° (0.8 mm), which consists of three isomers in the ratio 4:84:12. They are isolated by preparative gas chromatography at 190°. The dimer in the lowest concentration is *A* (see Table XIIb), the other two are stereoisomers of *B*.

The pot residue from the distillation of the dimers solidifies on cooling to room temperature. It is washed from the distillation flask with ethanol. Filtration and recrystallization from ethanol affords 2.52 g (13% yield) of the trimer white crystals, mp 176–178°.

6. Dimerization of Acrylonitrile[235]

A 100-ml, stainless-steel autoclave is charged with 20 ml of ethanol, 10 ml of acrylonitrile, and 0.200 g of ruthenium trichloride trihydrate under hydrogen. The mixture is then heated to 150° and kept at that temperature for 0.5 hr. The reaction products are propionitrile (51%), adiponitrile (4%), *cis*-1,4-dicyano-1-butene (18%), and *trans*-1,4-dicyano-1-butene (22%). The conversion of acrylonitrile is 94%.

7. Dimerization of Acrylamide[196]

Acrylamide (5.01 g), RhCl$_3$·3H$_2$O (0.42 g), hydroquinone (0.51 g) and *p*-benzoquinone (1.00 g) are dissolved in 1-butanol (100 ml). The solution is refluxed for 24 hr. The color of the solution changes from red-brown to dark brown with formation of a rhodium mirror. The rhodium metal is precipitated and filtered from the hot solution. The filtrate is evaporated to dryness *in vacuo*. About 20 ml of ethanol is added to the residue and the insoluble *trans*-α-hydromuconamide is obtained by filtration, 1.24 g (24.8% based on acrylamide), mp 216–218.5°.

N-Methylacrylamide is precipitated from the reaction mixture by the addition of $CHCl_3$ and then acetone: yield 15.0%. *N*-Ethylacrylamide is precipitated by the addition of ligroin: yield 20%.

8. Addition of Ethylene to Butadiene[3]

A 400-ml pressure vessel is charged with 0.5 g of rhodium chloride, 1 ml of ethanol, 175 g (2.34 moles) of butadiene, and 75 g (2.68 moles) of ethylene. The temperature is raised to 50° and held there for 16 hr, while the pressure vessel is agitated. At the end of this time the vessel is cooled to room temperature and vented through a trap to obtain 30 ml of liquid condensate that is principally butadiene. The pressure vessel contains 295 ml of clear orange liquid that is distilled to a pot temperature of 50° (5 mm) to leave a residue of 7 g. The distillate, 270 ml (189 g), contains 8% butadiene, 67% 1,4-hexadiene, and 22% 2,4-hexadiene.

9. Polymerization of Butadiene by Rhodium Chloride[314,315]

A mixture of 1 g of $RhCl_3 \cdot 3H_2O$, 100 g of butadiene, 200 ml H_2O and 5 g sodium dodecylbenzenesulfonate are charged in an autoclave heated to 80° and stirred. 1,4-Polybutadiene (21 g/hr) with a *trans* content of more than 98% is formed. The reaction can also be carried out without emulsifier.

10. Polymerization of Hydroxymethylnorbornene with Palladium Chloride[326]

A suspension of 100 mg palladium chloride in 23 g of 2-hydroxymethyl-5-norbornene is heated and stirred at 95° for 6 hr. Partial solution of $PdCl_2$ occurs. The viscous red-brown solution is then poured into 250 ml of acetone; a white precipitate results. The solid is filtered, washed with acetone, and air dried, yielding 4.61 g (20% of monomer charged) of polymer (average molecular weight: 2130).

L. Isomerization of Olefinic Compounds

See Table XIII.

1. General Procedure

From 0.1 to a few percent of catalyst (with respect to the substrate) is dissolved in an inert solvent, together with the substrate olefin or directly in the substrate. In some cases higher amounts of catalyst are used because of side reactions, which consume or inactivate the catalyst. Liquid gases are condensed into the reaction vessel, which must be sealed if the reaction is carried out at temperatures higher than the boiling point of the substrate. The mixture is then brought to the reaction temperature and stirred or shaken. Isomerization often takes place even at room temperature and leads to the thermodynamically favored mixture of the isomers. They are separated from the catalyst by distillation or extraction and the content of each isomer is determined by gas chromatography or any other analytical method.

REFERENCES

1. M. Abubaker, I. V. Gostunskaya, and B. A. Kazanskii, *Vestn. Mosk. Univ. Ser. II*, 23, 105 (1968), 148 (1968); *Chem. Abstr.*, 68, 113,961 (1968), 69, 86,227 (1968).
2. A. Aguilò, *Advances in Organometallic Chemistry*, Vol. 5 (1967) Academic Press, New York, p. 321.
2a. A. Aguilò and L. Stautzenberger, *Chem. Commun.*, 1969, 406.
3. T. Alderson, E. L. Jenner, and R. V. Lindsey, Jr., *J. Amer. Chem. Soc.*, 87, 5638 (1965).
4. C. B. Anderson and B. J. Burreson, *J. Organomet. Chem.*, 7, 181 (1967).
5. C. B. Anderson and B. J. Burreson, *Chem. Ind.* (London), 1967, 620.
6. C. B. Anderson and S. Winstein, *J. Org. Chem.*, 28, 605 (1963).
7. J. S. Anderson, *J. Chem. Soc.*, 1934, II, 971.
8. R. K. Armstrong, *J. Org. Chem.*, 31, 618 (1966).
9. Asahi Chemical Industry Co., Japanese Patent Appl 12,606/65.
10. Asahi Chemical Industry Co., Belgian Patent 670,276.
11. Asahi Chemical Industry Co., Electro Chemical Co., Kurashiki Rayon Co., Nippon Synthetic Chemical Co., Shin-Etsu Chemical Co., Toa Gosei Chemical Co., and Yawata Chemical Co., Japanese Patent Appl. 19,623/64.
12. F. Asinger, B. Fell, and P. Krings, *Tetrahedron Lett.*, 1966, 633.
13. W. C. Baird, Jr., *J. Org. Chem.*, 31, 2411 (1966).
14. P. V. Balakrishnan and P. M. Maitlis, *Chem. Commun.*, 1968, 1303.
15. Cf. F. Basolo and R. G. Pearson, "The trans-Effect in Metal Complexes" in *Progress in Inorganic Chemistry*, Vol. 4, F. A. Cotton, Ed., Interscience, New York, 1962, p. 381.
16. A. P. Belov and I. I. Moiseev, *Izv. Akad. Nauk SSSR*, Ser. Khim., 1966, 139.
17. A. P. Belov, I. I. Moiseev, and N. G. Uvarova, *Izv. Akad. Nauk SSSR, Ser. Khim.*, 1965, 2224.
18. A. P. Belov, I. I. Moiseev, and N. G. Uvarova, *Izv. Akad. Nauk SSSR, Ser. Khim.*, 1966, 1642.
19. A. P. Belov, G. Yu. Pek, and I. I. Moiseev, *Izv. Akad. Nauk SSSR, Ser. Khim.*, 1965, 2204.
20. R. A. Benkeser, St. Dunny, G. S. Li, P. G. Nerlekar, and St. D. Work, *J. Amer. Chem. Soc.*, 90, 1871 (1968).
21. M. A. Bennet, "Metal π-Complexes Formed by Seven-membered and Eight-membered Carbocyclic Compounds," in *Advances in Organometallic Chemistry*, Vol. 4, F. G. A. Stone and R. West, Eds., Academic Press, New York, 1966, p. 353.
22. M. A. Bennet, "Olefin and Acetylene Complexes of Transition Metals," *Chem. Rev.*, 62, 611 (1962).

23. R. Berger and R. Mittag, *Erdoel Kohle Erdgas, Petrochem*, **15**, 699 (1962).
24. J. F. Biellmann and M. J. Jung, *J. Amer. Chem. Soc.*, **90**, 1673 (1968).
24a. S. E. Binns, R. H. Cragg, R. D. Gillard, B. T. Heaton, and M. F. Pilbrow, *J. Chem. Soc., A*, **1969**, 1227.
25. A. J. Birch and G. S. R. Subba Rao, *Tetrahedron Lett.*, **1968**, 3797.
26. C. W. Bird, *Transition Metal Intermediates in Organic Synthesis*, Logos Press, London, 1967, p. 248.
27. G. C. Bond and M. Hellier, *J. Catal.*, **4**, 1 (1965).
28. G. C. Bond and M. Hellier, *J. Catal.*, **7**, 217 (1967).
29. G. C. Bond and M. Hellier, *Chem. Ind.* (London), **1965**. 35.
29a. B. L. Booth, R. N. Haszeldine, and M. Hill, *J. Chem. Soc., A*, **1969**, 1299.
30. A. R. Brause, F. Kaplan, and M. Orchin, *J. Amer. Chem. Soc.*, **89**, 2661 (1967).
31. British Celanese, Netherlands Patent Appl. 6,506,734.
32. J. Broichard, B. Brossard, M. Gay, and R. Janin, Rhône-Poulenc, French Patent, 1,457.618.
33. D. R. Bryant, J. E. McKeon, and B. C. Ream, *Tetrahedron Lett.*, **1968**, 3371.
34. D. R. Bryant, J. E. McKeon, and B. C. Ream, *J. Org. Chem.*, **33**, 4123 (1968).
35. D. R. Bryant, J. E. McKeon, and P. S. Starcher, Abstracts, Second Intern. Symp. on Organomet. Chem., Madison, Wis., Aug. 1965, p. 94.
36. D. Bryce-Smith, *Chem. Ind.* (*London*), **1964**, 239.
36a. J. E. Burleigh and S. R. Collins, Phillips Petroleum Co., U.S. Patent 3,296,227.
36b. C. H. Bushweller, *Tetrahedron Lett.*, **1968**, 6123.
37. F. Calderazzo and F. A. Cotton, *Inorg. Chem.*, **1**, 30 (1962).
38. F. Calderazzo and F. A. Cotton, *Chim. Ind.* (Milan), **46**, 1165 (1964).
39. C. W. Capp, G. W. Godin, R. F. Neale, J. B. Williamson, and B. W. Harries, Distillers Co., German Patent 1,216,288.
40. S. Carrà and V. Ragaini, *J. Catal.*, **10**, 230 (1968).
41. A. J. Chalk and J. Harrod, *Advances in Organometallic Chemistry*, Vol. 6, Academic Press, New York, 1968, p. 119.
42. S. B. Chandalia, *Indian J. Technol.*, **4**, 260 (1966).
43. S. B. Chandalia, *Indian J. Technol.*, **5**, 218 (1967).
44. S. B. Chandalia, *Indian J. Technol.*, **6**, 88 (1968).
45. F. de Charentenay, J. A. Osborn, and G. Wilkinson, *J. Chem. Soc., A*, **1968**, 787.
46. J. Chatt, R. S. Coffey, A. Gough, and D. T. Thompson, *J. Chem. Soc., A*, **1968**, 190.
47. J. Chatt and L. A. Duncanson, *J. Chem. Soc.*, **1953**, 2939.
48. J. Chatt and B. L. Shaw, *J. Chem. Soc.*, **1962**, 5075.
49. J. Chatt, L. M. Vallarino, and L. M. Venanzi, *J. Chem. Soc.*, **1957**, 2496.
50. J. Chatt, L. M. Vallarino, and L. M. Venanzi, *J. Chem. Soc.*, **1957**, 3413.
51. I. I. Chernyaev and A. D. Gel'man, *Izv. Sektora Platina*, **14**, 96 (1937).
52. D. Clark and P. Hayden, Amer. Chem. Soc., Div. Petrol. Chem. Preprints, **11**, D5 (1966).
53. D. Clark and P. Hayden, Imperial Chemical Industries, Netherlands Patent Appl. 6,703,724, German Patent 1,273,525.
54. D. Clark and P. Hayden, Imperial Chemical Industries, German Patent 1,275,532.
54a. D. Clark, P. Hayden, and R. D. Smith, *Discussions Faraday Soc.*, No. 46, 98 (1967).
55. W. H. Clement and C. M. Selwitz, *Tetrahedron Lett.*, **1962**, 1081.
56. W. H. Clement and C. M. Selwitz, *J. Org. Chem.*, **29**, 241 (1964).
57. R. S. Coffey, *Tetrahedron Lett.*, **1965**, 3809.
58. A. C. Cope, J. M. Kliegman, and E. C. Friedrich, *J. Amer. Chem. Soc.*, **89**, 287 (1967).

58a. A. C. Cope, R. W. Siekman, Massachusetts Institute of Technology, U.S. Patent 3,424,739; *Chem. Abstr.*, **70**, 68,529 (1969).

59. P. Cossee, *Rec. Trav. Chim. Pays-Bas*, **85**, 1151 (1966).

60. F. A. Cotton, J. W. Faller, and A. Musco, *Inorg. Chem.*, **6**, 179 (1967).

60a. D. R. Coulson, *J. Amer. Chem. Soc.*, **91**, 200 (1969).

61. R. Cramer, *Inorg. Chem.*, **1**, 722 (1962).

62. R. Cramer, *J. Amer. Chem. Soc.*, **86**, 217 (1964).

63. R. Cramer, *J. Amer. Chem. Soc.*, **87**, 4717 (1965).

64. R. Cramer, *J. Amer. Chem. Soc.*, **88**, 2272 (1966).

65. R. Cramer, *J. Amer. Chem. Soc.*, **89**, 1633 (1967).

66. R. Cramer, *Accounts Chem. Res.*, **1**, 186 (1968).

67. R. D. Cramer and F. N. Jones, Du Pont de Nemours, U.S. Patent 3,356,748.

67a. R. Cramer, J. B. Kline, and J. D. Roberts *J. Amer. Chem. Soc.*, **91**, 2519 (1969).

68. R. Cramer and R. V. Lindsey, Jr., *J. Amer. Chem. Soc.*, **88**, 3534 (1966).

69. J. C. Crano, E. K. Fleming, and G. M. Trenta, *J. Amer. Chem. Soc.*, **90**, 5036 (1968).

70. R. J. Cross, *Organomet. Chem. Rev.*, **2**, 97 (1967).

71. R. Damico and T. J. Logan, *J. Org. Chem.*, **32**, 2356 (1967).

72. R. Dauby, F. Dawans, and P. Teyssié, *J. Polym. Sci., Part C*, Polym. Symposia **16**, 1989 (1967)

73. J. M. Davidson and C. Triggs, *Chem. Ind. (London)*, **1966**, 457.

74. J. M. Davidson and C. Triggs, *Chem. Ind. (London)*, **1967**, 1361.

75. J. M. Davidson and C. Triggs, *J. Chem. Soc.*, A, **1968**, 1324 .

76. J. M. Davidson and C. Triggs, *J. Chem. Soc.*, A, **1968**, 1331.

77. N. R. Davies, *Aust. J. Chem.*, **17**, 212 (1964).

78. N. R. Davies *Nature*, **201**, 490 (1964).

79. N. R. Davies, *Rev. Pure and Appl. Chem.*, **17**, 83 (1967).

80. N. R. Davies, A. D. DiMichiel, and V. A. Pickles, *Aust. J. Chem.*, **21**, 385 (1968).

81. F. Dean, Imperial Chemical Industries, British Patent, 879,197.

82. H. C. Dehm and J. C. W. Chien, *J. Amer. Chem. Soc.*, **82**, 4429 (1960).

83. J. N. Dempsey and N. C. Baenziger, *J. Amer. Chem. Soc.*, **77**, 4984 (1955).

84. W. T. Dent, R. Long, and A. J. Wilkinson, *J. Chem. Soc.*, **1964**, 1585.

85. M. J. S. Dewar, Bull. Soc. Chim. Fr., **18**, 71 (1951).

86. H. Dietl and P. M. Maitlis, *Chem. Commun.*, **1967**, 759.

87. B. A. Dolgoplosk, I. I. Moiseev, and E. I. Tinyakova, *Dokl. Akad. Nauk SSSR*, **173**, 1087 (1967).

88. M. Donati and F. Conti, *Tetrahedron Lett.*, **1966**, 4953.

89. T. Dozono and T. Shiba, *Bull. Japan Petr. Inst.*, **5**, 8 (1963). (In English.)

90. H. A. Droll, B. P. Block, and W. C. Fernelius, *J. Phys. Chem.*, **61**, 1000 (1957).

91. G. G. Eberhardt and L. Vaska, *J. Catal.*, **8**, 183 (1967).

92. A. F. Ellis, Gulf Research, U.S. Patent 3,294,484; Chem. Abstr., **66**, 104,799 (1967).

93. Farbwerke Hoechst AG, Belgian Patent 662,098.

94. Farbwerke Hoechst AG, Belgian Patent 665,073.

95. Farbwerke Hoechst, Netherlands Patent Appl. 6,503,492.

96. Farbwerke Hoechst, Netherlands Patent Appl. 6,505,608.

97. Farbwerke Hoechst, Netherlands Patent Appl. 6,802,462.

98. A. B. Fasman, V. A. Golodov, *Kinetika i Kataliz*, **6**, 956 (1965).

98a. K. Fichtel, Consortium für elektrochemische Industrie, unpublished experiments.

99. E. O. Fischer and H. Werner, "Metall-π-Komplexe mit di- und oligo-olefinischen Liganden," Verlag Chemie Weinheim, 1963.

100. E. O. Fischer and H. Werner, "Metal-π-Complexes with di- and oligo-olefinic ligands," Elsevier Publishing Co., Amsterdam, 1966.
101. R. H. Fish and H. G. Kuivila, *J. Org. Chem.*, **31**, 2445 (1966).
101a. P. Fitton, J. E. McKeon, and B. C. Ream, *Chem. Commun.*, **1969**, 370.
101b. P. François and Y. Trambouze, *Bull. Soc. Chim. Fr.*, **1969**, 51.
102. H. P. Fritz, K. E. Schwarzhans, and D. Sellmann, *J. Organomet. Chem.*, **6**, 551 (1966).
103. H. Frye, E. Kuljian, and J. Viebrock, *Inorg. Chem.*, **4**, 1499 (1965).
104. H. Frye, E. Kuljian, and J. Viebrock, *Inorg. Nucl. Chem. Lett.*, **2**, 119 (1966).
105. Y. Fujiwara, T. Moritani, and M. Matsuda, *Tetrahedron*, **24**, 4819 (1968).
106. Y. Fujiwara, J. Moritani, R. Asano, and S. Teranishi, *Tetrahedron Lett.*, **1968**, 6015.
107. Y. Fujiwara, I. Moritani, M. Matsuda, and S. Teranishi, *Tetrahedron Lett.*, **1968**, 633.
108. Y. Fujiwara, I. Moritani, M. Matsuda, and S. Teranishi, *Tetrahedron Lett.*, **1968**, 3863.
109. K. A. Galutkina, B. A. Kravchenko, and N. Y. Salivon, *Zh. Prikl. Khim.*, **41**, 456 (1968); *Chem. Abstr.*, **69**, 58,799 (1968).
110. K. A. Galutkina, N. Y. Salivon, and B. A. Kravchenko, USSR Patent 196,806; *Chem. Abstr.*, **68**, 68,481 (1968).
111. K. A. Galutkina, N. Y. Salivon, and B. A. Kravchenko, *Zh. Prikl. Khim.*, **41**, 381 (1968); *Chem. Abstr.*, **68**, 114,004 (1968).
112. J. L. Garnett and R. J. Hodges, *Chem. Commun.*, **1967**, 1220.
113. J. T. van Gemert and P. R. Wilkinson, *J. Phys. Chem.*, **68**, 645 (1964).
114. H. R. Gerberich and W. Keith Hall, *Nature*, **213**, 1120 (1967).
115. R. D. Gillard, Private communication.
116. *Gmelin's Handbuch der Anorganischem Chemie Platin*, (Syst. Nr. 68), Teil D, Verlag Chemie, Weinheim, 1957.
117. I. V. Gostunskaya, V. S. Petrova, A. I. Leonova, V. A. Mironova, M. Abubaker, and B. A. Kazanskii, *Neftekhimiya*, **7**, 3 (1967); *Chem. Abstr.*, **67**, 21,276 (1967).
118. E. S. Gould, "Mechanismus und Struktur in der Organischen Chemie," Verlag Chemie, Weinheim, 1962.
119. G. Gourlay, Imperial Chemical Industries, British Patent 1,130,760.
120. A. S. Gow, Jr., and H. Heinemann, *J. Phys. Chem.*, **64**, 1574 (1960).
121. M. Green and R. I. Hancock, *J. Chem. Soc.*, A, **1967**, 2054.
122. M. Green, R. N. Haszeldine, and J. Lindley, *J. Organomet. Chem.*, **6**, 107 (1966).
123. M. L. H. Green and P. L. I. Nagy, *Proc. Chem. Soc. (London)*, **1962**, 74.
124. M. L. H. Green and P. L. I. Nagy, "Allyl Metal Complexes," in *Advances in Organometallic Chemistry*, Vol. 2, F. G. A. Stone and R. West, Eds., Academic Press, New York, 1964, p. 325.
125. W. P. Griffith, J. Lewis, and G. Wilkinson, *J. Inorg. Nucl. Chem.*, **7**, 38 (1958).
126. A. A. Grigor'ev, M. Y. Klimenko, and I. I. Moiseev, USSR Patent 189,415; *Chem. Abstr.*, **67**, 63,795 (1967).
127. M. J. Grogan and K. Nakamoto, *J. Amer. Chem. Soc.*, **88**, 5454 (1966).
128. M. C. Grogan and K. Nakamoto, *J. Amer. Chem. Soc.*, **90**, 918 (1968).
129. S. P. Gubin, A. Z. Rubezhov, L. I. Denisovich, and A. N. Nesmeyanov, *Izv. Akad. Nauk SSSR, Ser. Khim.*, **1966**, 1680.
130. R. G. Guy and B. L. Shaw, "Olefin, Acetylene and π-Allylic Complexes of Transition Metals," in *Advances in Inorganic Chemistry and Radiochemistry*, Vol. 4, H. J. Eméleus and A. G. Sharpe, Eds., Academic Press, New York, 1962, p. 77.

130a. W. Hafner, Consortium für elektrochemische Industrie, unpublished experiments.
131. W. Hafner, R. Jira, J. Sedlmeier, and J. Smidt, Chem. Ber., 95, 1575 (1962).
132. W. Hafner, H. Prigge, and J. Smidt, Liebigs Ann. Chem., 693, 109 (1966).
133. J. Halpern, Proc. Intern. Congr. Catalysis, 3rd, Amsterdam, 1964, p. 146. (Published 1965.)
134. B. W. Harris, Distillers Co., French Patent 1,397,054.
135. J. F. Harrod and A. J. Chalk, J. Amer. Chem. Soc., 86, 1776 (1964).
136. J. F. Harrod and A. J. Chalk, Nature, 205, 280 (1965).
137. J. F. Harrod and A. J. Chalk, J. Amer. Chem. Soc., 88, 3491 (1966).
138. P. Hayden, Imperial Chemical Industries, British Patent 1,119,657.
138a. P. Hayden and D. Clark, Imperial Chemical Industries, British Patent 140,105; Chem. Abstr., 70, 67,647 (1969).
139. R. F. Heck, Advan. Chem. Ser., 49, Washington, D.C., 181 (1965).
140. R. F. Heck, Advances in Organometallic Chemistry, Vol. 4, Academic Press, New York, 1966, p. 243.
141. R. F. Heck, J. Amer. Chem. Soc., 90, 5518 (1968).
142. R. F. Heck, J. Amer. Chem. Soc., 90, 5526 (1968).
143. R. F. Heck, J. Amer. Chem. Soc., 90, 5531 (1968).
144. R. F. Heck, J. Amer. Chem. Soc., 90, 5535 (1968).
145. R. F. Heck, J. Amer. Chem. Soc., 90, 5538 (1968).
146. R. F. Heck, J. Amer. Chem. Soc., 90, 5542 (1968).
146a. R. F. Heck, J. Amer. Chem. Soc., 91, 6707-14 (1969).
147. R. F. Heck and D. S. Breslow, J. Amer. Chem. Soc., 83, 4023 (1961).
148. R. van Helden, C. F. Kohll, D. Medema, G. Verberg, and T. Jonkhoff, Rec. Trav. Chim. Pays-Bas, 87, 961 (1968).
149. R. van Helden and G. Verberg, Rec. Trav. Chim. Pays-Bas, 84, 1263 (1965).
150. P. M. Henry, J. Amer. Chem. Soc., 86, 3246 (1964).
151. P. M. Henry, J. Amer. Chem. Soc., 87, 4423 (1965), and cited literature.
152. P. M. Henry, J. Amer. Chem. Soc., 88, 1595 (1966).
153. P. M. Henry, J. Org. Chem., 32, 2575 (1967).
154. P. M. Henry, Abstr. Papers, 154th meeting Am. Chem. Soc., Sept. 1967, p. 78.
155. P. M. Henry, Advan. Chem. Ser., 70, Washington, D.C., 126 (1968).
155a. L. Hörnig, L. Hirsch, G. Mau, and T. Quadflieg, Fw. Hoechst, German Patent 1,222,913.
156. H. Hogeveen and H. C. Volger, J. Amer. Chem. Soc., 89, 2486 (1967).
156a. H. Hogeveen and H. C. Volger, Chem. Commun., 1967, 1133.
157. J. R. Holden and N. C. Baenziger, J. Amer. Chem. Soc., 77, 4987 (1955).
158. H. Holzrichter, W. Krönig, and B. Frenz, Farbenfabriken Bayer, German Patents 1,185,604; 1,196,644.
159. L. Horner, H. Büthe, and H. Siegel, Tetrahedron Lett., 1968, 4023.
159a. R. Hüttel and H. Christ, Chem. Ber., 96, 3101 (1963).
160. R. Hüttel and H. Christ, Chem. Ber., 97, 1439 (1964).
160a. R. Hüttel and H. Dietl, Chem. Ber., 98, 1753 (1965).
161. R. Hüttel, H. Dietl, and H. Christ, Chem. Ber., 97, 2037 (1964).
162. R. Hüttel and P. Kochs, Chem. Ber., 101, 1043 (1968).
163. R. Hüttel and J. Kratzer, Angew. Chem., 71, 456 (1959).
164. R. Hüttel, J. Kratzer, and M. Bechter, Chem. Ber., 94, 766 (1961).
165. K. Ichikawa, S. Uemura, and T. Sugita, Tetrahedron Lett., 22, 407 (1966).
166. Imperial Chemical Industries, Netherlands Patent Appl. 6,514,991.
167. B. R. James and G. L. Rempel, Can. J. Chem., 46, 571 (1968).

168. Japanese Geon Co., Japanese Patent Appl. 20,250/65.
169. R. Jira, Unpublished results.
170. R. Jira, European Chemical News, Survey, 1965, 58.
171. R. Jira, "Direct Oxidation of Ethylene to Acetaldehyde," in Ethylene and Its Industrial Derivatives, S. A. Miller, Ed., Ernest Benn, London, 1969.
172. R. Jira, Tetrahedron Lett., 1971, 1225.
173. R. Jira and J. Sedlmeier, Tetrahedron Lett., 1971, 1227.
174. R. Jira, J. Sedlmeier, and J. Smidt, Liebigs Ann. Chem., 693, 99 (1966).
175. R. Jira and H. Prigge, to be published.
176. R. Jira and H. Prigge, to be published.
177. F. N. Jones, J. Org. Chem., 32, 1667 (1967).
178. J. R. Joy and M. Orchin, Z. Anorg. Allg. Chem., 305, 236 (1960).
179. J. W. Kang and P. M. Maitlis, J. Amer. Chem. Soc., 90, 3259 (1968).
180. J. W. Kang, K. Mosley, and P. M. Maitlis, Chem. Commun., 1968, 1304.
181. Y. Kasunoki, R. Katsuno, N. Hasegawa, S. Kurematsu, Y. Nagao, K. Ishii, and S. Tsutsumi, Bull. Chem. Soc. Jap., 39, 2021 (1966). (In English.)
181a. T. J. Katz and St. Cerefice, J. Amer. Chem. Soc., 91, 2405 (1969).
181b. K. Kawamoto, T. Imanaka, and S. Teranishi, Bull. Chem. Soc. Jap., 89, 639 (1968).
182. C. Kemball and W. R. Patterson, Proc. Roy. Soc., A, 270, 219 (1962).
183. R. D. W. Kemmitt and D. W. A. Sharp, J. Chem. Soc., 1963, 2567.
184. R. J. Kern, Chem. Commun., 1968, 706.
185. A. D. Ketley, (W. R. Grace & Co.), French Patent 1,499,833.
186. A. D. Ketley and J. A. Braatz, J. Polym. Sci., Part B, Polym. Lett., 6, 341 (1968).
187. A. D. Ketley and J. Braatz, Chem. Commun., 1968, 169.
187a. A. D. Ketley and J. A. Braatz, Chem. Commun., 1968, 959.
187b. A. D. Ketley and L. P. Fischer, J. Organomet. Chem., 13, 243 (1968).
188. A. D. Ketley, L. P. Fisher, A. J. Berlin, C. R. Morgan, E. H. Gorman, and T. R. Steadman, Inorg. Chem., 6, 657 (1967).
189. S. F. A. Kettle and R. Mason, J. Organomet. Chem., 5, 573 (1966).
190. M. S. Kharasch, R. C. Seyler, and F. R. Mayo, J. Amer. Chem. Soc., 60, 882 (1938).
191. R. B. King and A. F. Fronzaglia, J. Amer. Chem. Soc., 88, 709 (1966).
192. S. Kiryu and T. Shiba, Lecture Annual Meeting Japan Petr. Inst., Sept. 1961, Tokyo. (Cited in Ref. 89.)
193. W. Kitching, Z. Rappoport, S. Winstein, and W. G. Young, J. Amer. Chem. Soc., 88, 2054 (1966).
194. D. L. Klass, Union Oil Co., U.S. Patent 3,245,890.
195. H. S. Klein, Shell Oil Co., U.S. Patent 3,354,236.
196. Y. Kobayashi and S. Taira, Tetrahedron Lett., 24, 5763 (1968).
197. J. K. Kochi, Science, 155, 415 (1967).
198. C. F. Kohll and R. van Helden, Rec. Trav. Chim. Pays-Bas, 86, 193 (1967).
199. C. F. Kohll and R. van Helden, Rec. Trav. Chim. Pays-Bas, 87, 481 (1968).
200. C. F. Kohll and R. van Helden, Shell Oil Co., U.S. Patent 3,361,840.
201. H. Kojer, R. Rüttinger, R. Sieber, and J. Smidt, Consortium für elektrochemische Industrie, German Patent, 1,138,755.
202. B. L. Kozik, S. V. Pestrikov, and A. P. Savelev, Khim. Tekhnol. Topl. Masel, 8, 11 (1963).
203. B. L. Kozik, S. V. Pestrikov, and A. P. Savelev, Tr. Bashkirsk. Naukhn.-Issled. Inst. Pererabotk Nefti, 7, 74 (1964).
204. H. Krekeler and W. Krönig, Report on the 7th World Petroleum Congress, Mexico City, April 1967, Panel Discussion 18(5).

205. H. Krekeler and H. Schmitz, *Chem. Ing. Tech.*, **40**, 785 (1968).
206. W. Kroenig and B. Frenz, Farbenfabriken Bayer, German Patent 1,262,992; *Chem. Abstr.*, **69**, 35,774 (1968).
207. J. Kummer, Dow Chemical Corp., U.S. Patents 3,202,715; 3,202,717.
208. Kurashiki Rayon, British Patent 1,124,862.
209. W. M. Latimer, *Oxidation Potentials*, 2nd ed., Prentice Hall, Englewood Cliffs, N.J., 1959.
210. I. Leden and J. Chatt, *J. Chem. Soc.*, **1955**, 2936.
210a. O. G. Levanda and I. I. Moiseev, *Zh. Org. Khim.*, **4**, 1533 (1968).
210b. O. G. Levanda, I. I. Moiseev, and M. N. Vargaftik, *Izv. Akad. Nauk SSSR, Ser. Khim.*, **1968**, 2368; *Chem. Abstr.*, **70**, 23,588 (1969).
211. J. Lewis, R. J. Irving and G. Wilkinson, *J. Inorg. Nucl. Chem.*, **7**, 32 (1958).
212. W. G. Lloyd, Lummus Co., Belgian Patent 668,601. *J. Org. Chem.*, **34**, 3949 (1969).
213. W. G. Lloyd, *J. Org. Chem.*, **32**, 2816 (1967).
214. H. Lucas, F. Hepner, and S. Winstein, *J. Amer. Chem. Soc.*, **61**, 3102 (1939).
215. H. Lüssi, *Helv. Chim. Acta,* **49**, 1684 (1966).
216. H. Lüssi, *Chimia*, **21**, 82 (1967).
217. I. E. Lyden, J. K. Nicholson, B. L. Shaw, and M. R. Truter, Proc. Chem. Soc. (London), **1964**, 421.
218. W. V. Macho, M. Polyefka, and L. Komora, *Chem. Zvesti*, **21**, 170 (1967).
219. A. F. MacLean and A. L. Stautzenberger, Celanese Corp., U.S. Patent 3,384,669.
220. J. I. MacNab and G. Webb, *J. Catal.*, **10**, 19 (1968).
221. P. M. Maitlis, *Advances in Organometallic Chemistry*, Vol. 4, Academic Press, New York, 1966, p. 95.
222. T. A. Manuel, *J. Org. Chem.*, **27**, 3941 (1962).
223. R. Mason and D. R. Russell, *Chem. Commun.*, **1966**, 26.
224. K. I. Matveev, A. M. Osipov, B. F. Odyakov, Y. V. Suzdal'nitskaya, I. F. Bukhtoyarov, and O. A. Emel'yanova, *Kinet. Katal.*, **3**, 661 (1962).
225. K. I. Matveev, I. F. Bukhtoyarov, N. N. Shulz, and O. A. Emel'yanova, *Kinet. Katal.*, **5**, 649 (1964).
226. J. D. McClure, R. Owyang, and L. H. Slaugh, *J. Organomet. Chem.*, **12**, 8 (1968).
227. R. J. Mawby, F. Basolc, and R. G. Pearson, *J. Amer. Chem. Soc.*, **86**, 3994 (1964).
228. R. J. Mawby, F. Basolo, and R. G. Pearson, *J. Amer. Chem. Soc.*, **86**, 5043 (1964).
229. F. W. Michelotti and W. P. Keaveney, *J. Polymer Sci.*, A3, 895 (1965).
230. J. Milgrom and W. H. Urry, Proc. 7. Intern. Conference on Coordination Chemistry, Stockholm, 1962, p. 264.
231. S. A. Miller " Manufacture of Vinyl Acetate," in *Ethylene and its Industrial Derivatives*," S. A. Miller, Ed., Ernest Benn, London, p. 946.
232. M. Misono, Y. Saito, and Y. Yoneda, *J. Catal.*, **10**, 200 (1968).
233. A. Misono, Y. Uchida, M. Hidai, and H. Kanai, *Chem. Commun.*, **1967**, 357.
234. A. Misono, Y. Uchida, M. Hidai, and I. Inomata, *Chem. Commun.*, **1968**, 704.
235. A. Misono, Y. Uchida, M. Hidai, H. Shinohara, and Y. Watanabe, *Bull. Chem. Soc. Japan*, **41**, 396 (1968). (In English.)
236. Mitsui Toatsu, Chem. Co., Japanese Patent Appl. 4541/69.
237. A. Mitsutani and K. Tanaka, *Shokubai Kondan-Kai*, **4**, 388 (1962). (In Japanese.)
238. A. Mitsutani, K. Tanaka, and M. Yano, *Kogyo Kagaku Zasshi*, **68**, 1219 (1965). (In Japanese.)
239. I. I. Moiseev, A. P. Belov, V. A. Igoshchin, and Y. K. Syrkin, *Dokl. Akad. Nauk SSSR*, **173**, 863 (1967).
240. I. I. Moiseev, A. P. Belov, and G. Y. Pek, *Zh. Neorg. Khim.*, **10**, 336 (1965).

241. I. I. Moiseev, A. P. Belov, and Y. K. Syrkin, *Izv. Akad. Nauk SSSR, Ser. Khim.*, **1963**, 1527.
242. I. I. Moiseev, A. A. Grigor'ev, and S. V. Pestrikov, *Zh. Org. Khim.*, **4**, 354 (1968).
243. I. I. Moiseev and S. V. Pestrikov, *Izv. Akad. Nauk SSSR, Ser. Khim.*, **1965**, 1717.
244. I. I. Moiseev and S. V. Pestrikov, *Dokl. Akad. Nauk SSSR*, **171**, 151 (1966).
245. I. I. Moiseev, S. V. Pestrikov, and L. M. Sverzh, *Izv. Akad. Nauk SSSR, Ser. Khim.*, **1966**, 1866.
246. I. I. Moiseev, M. N. Vargaftik, *Izv. Akad. Nauk SSSR, Ser. Khim.*, **1965**, 759.
247. I. I. Moiseev and M. N. Vargaftik, *Dokl. Akad. Nauk SSSR*, **166**, 370 (1966).
248. I. I. Moiseev, M. N. Vargaftik, S. V. Pestrikov, O. G. Levanda, T. N. Romanova, and Y. K. Syrkin, *Dokl. Akad. Nauk SSSR*, **171**, 1365 (1966).
249. I. I. Moiseev, M. N. Vargaftik, and Y. K. Syrkin, *Dokl. Akad. Nauk SSSR*, **130**, 820 (1960).
250. I. I. Moiseev, M. N. Vargaftik, and Y. K. Syrkin, *Dokl. Akad. Nauk SSSR*, **133**, 377 (1960).
251. I. I. Moiseev, M. N. Vargaftik, and Y. K. Syrkin, *Dokl. Akad. Nauk SSSR*, **152**, 147 (1963).
252. I. I. Moiseev, M. N. Vargaftik, and Y. K. Syrkin, *Dokl. Akad. Nauk SSSR*, **153**, 140 (1963).
253. I. I. Moiseev, M. N. Vargaftik, and Y. K. Syrkin, *Izv. Akad. Nauk SSSR, Otd. Khim. Nauk*, **1963**, 1144.
254. I. I. Moiseev, M. N. Vargaftik, and Y. K. Syrkin, *Izv. Akad. Nauk SSSR, Ser. Khim.*, **1964**, 775.
255. D. Morelli, R. Ugo, F. Conti, and M. Donati, *Chem. Commun.*, **1967**, 801.
256. R. A. Morgan, Dissertation, University of Iowa, 1966, Univ. Microfilms, Ann Arbor, Mich., Order No. 66,682.
257. I. Moritani and Y. Fujiwara, *Tetrahedron Lett.*, **1967**, 1119.
258. J. J. Mrowca and T. J. Katz, *J. Amer. Chem. Soc.*, **88**, 4012 (1966).
259. H. Müller, H. Köhl, and H. Pommer, Badische Anilin-und Sodafabrik AG, German Patent 1,267,682.
260. M. Nakamura and K. Gunji, *J. Japan. Petr. Inst.*, **5**, 720 (1962). (In Japanese.)
261. M. Nakamura and K. Gunji, *J. Japan. Petr. Inst.*, **6**, 191 (1963). (In Japanese.)
262. M. Nakamura and K. Gunji, *J. Japan. Petr. Inst.*, **6**, 695 (1963). (In Japanese.)
263. M. Nakamura and K. Gunji, *J. Japan. Petr. Inst.*, **7**, 555 (1964). (In Japanese.)
264. J. K. Nicholson, J. Powell, and B. L. Shaw, *Chem. Commun.*, **1966**, 174.
265. J. K. Nicholson and B. L. Shaw, Proc. Chem. Soc. (London), **1963**, 282.
266. J. K. Nicholson and B. L. Shaw, *Tetrahedron Lett.*, **1965**, 3533.
267. J. K. Nicholson and B. L. Shaw, *J. Chem. Soc., A*, **1966**, 807.
268. A. V. Nikiforova, I. I. Moiseev, and Y. K. Syrkin, *Zh. Obshch. Khim.*, **33**, 3239 (1963).
269. R. Ninomiya, M. Sato, and T. Shiba, *Bull. Japan. Petr. Inst.*, **7**, 31 (1965).
270. K. Noack and F. Calderazzo, *J. Organomet. Chem.*, **10**, 101 (1967).
271. R. S. Nyholm, Proc. 3rd Intern. Congr. on Catalysis, Amsterdam, July 1964, pp. 25, 68.
272. W. E. Oberhansli and L. F. Dahl, *J. Organomet. Chem.*, **3**, 43 (1965).
273. E. Ochiai, T. Miyairi, H. Hirai, and S. Makishima, *J. Polym. Sci., Part B, Polym. Lett.*, **5**, 387 (1967).
274. Y. Odaira, T. Oishi, T. Yukawa, and S. Tsutsumi, *J. Amer. Chem. Soc.*, **88**, 4105 (1966).
275. Y. Odaira, T. Yoshida, and S. Tsutsumi, *Technol. Rep., Osaka Univ.*, **16**, 737 (1966); *Chem. Abstr.*, **67**, 90,334 (1967).

276. S. C. Ogburn, Jr., and W. C. Brastow, *J. Amer. Chem. Soc.*, **55**, 1308 (1933).
277. H. Okada and H. Hashimoto, *Kogyo Kagaku Zasshi*, **69**, 2137 (1966); *Chem. Abstr.*, **66**, 85242r (1967).
278. H. Okada and H. Hashimoto, *Kogyo Kagaku Zasshi*, **70**, 2152 (1967); *Chem. Abstr.*, **68**, 95,407 (1968).
279. H. Okada, T. Noma, Y. Katsuyama, and H. Hashimoto, *Bull. Chem. Soc. Jap.*, **41**, 1395 (1968); *Chem. Abstr.*, **69**, 85,936 (1968).
280. J. A. Osborn, F. H. Jardine, J. F. Young, and G. Wilkinson, *J. Chem. Soc.*, *A*, **1966**, 1711.
281. A. Oshima, *Nippon Kagaku Zasshi*, **89**, 92 (1968); *Chem. Abstr.*, **69**, 58,685 (1968).
282. A. M. Osipov and K. I. Matveev, *Katal. Reacts. Zhidk. Faze, Tr. Vses. Conf.*, *2nd Alma-Ata Kaz. SSSR*, 1966; *Chem. Abstr.*, **69**, 43,203 (1968).
283. A. M. Osipov, K. I. Matveev, and N. N. Shul'ts, *Zh. Neorg. Khim.*, **12**, 1886 (1967) (Engl. transl., p. 993).
284. S. Otsuka and A. Nakamura, *J. Polym. Sci., Part B, Polym. Lett.*, **5**, 973 (1967).
285. S. Otsuka, A. Nakamura, and K. Tani, *Kogyo Kagaku Zasshi*, **70**, 2007 (1967).
285a. R. J. Ouelette and C. Levin, *J. Amer. Chem. Soc.*, **90**, 6889 (1968).
286. G. Paiaro, A. DeRenzi, and R. Palumbo, *Chem. Commun.*, **1967**, 1150.
287. S. V. Pestrikov, *Zh. Fiz. Khim.*, **39**, 428 (1965).
288. S. V. Pestrikov and B. L. Kozik, *Neftepererabotka Neftekhim., Naukhn. Tekhn. Sb.*, **1965**, 35.
289. S. V. Pestrikov and B. L. Kozik, *Neftepererabotka Neftekhim.*, **1965**, 39.
290. S. V. Pestrikov, B. L. Kozik, and N. Z. Nasrtdinova, *Neftepererabotka Neftekhim.*, **1966**, 26; *Chem. Abstr.*, **66**, 28,321 (1967).
291. S. V. Pestrikov and I. I. Moiseev, *Izv. Akad. Nauk SSSR, Ser. Khim.*, **1965**, 349.
292. S. V. Pestrikov, I. I. Moiseev, and T. N. Romanova, *Zh. Neorg. Khim.*, **10**, 2203 (1965).
293. S. V. Pestrikov, I. I. Moiseev, and L. M. Sverzh, *Zh. Neorg. Khim.*, **11**, 2081 (1966).
294. S. V. Pestrikov, I. I. Moiseev, and B. A. Tsvilikhovskaya, *Zh. Neorg. Khim.*, **11**, 1742 (1966).
295. F. C. Phillips, *Amer. Chem. J.*, **16**, 255 (1894).
296. Nhu-Hung Phung and G. Lefebvre, *C. R. Acad. Sci., Paris*, **C265**, 519 (1967).
297. R. Platz and W. Fuchs, Badische Anilin-und Sodafabrik AG, German Patent 1,166,173.
298. L. Porri, M. C. Gallazzi, A. Colombo, and G. Allegra, *Tetrahedron Lett.*, **1965**, 4187.
299. J. Powell, S. D. Robinson, and B. L. Shaw, *Chem. Commun.*, **1965**, 78.
300. J. Powell and B. L. Shaw, Proc. 9th Intern. Conf. on Coord. Chemistry, Sept. 1966, St. Moritz-Bad, Switzerland, p. 184.
301. J. Powell and B. L. Shaw, *Chem. Commun.*, **1966**, 236.
302. J. Pradilla-Sorzano and J. P. Fackler, *J. Mol. Spectrosc.*, **22**, 80 (1967).
303. G. Pregaglia, *Chim. Ind. (Milan)*, **49**, 1277 (1967).
304. G. Pregaglia, M. Donati, and F. Conti, *Chim. Ind. (Milan)*, **49**, 1277 (1967).
305. Prévost, *Ann. Chim.*, **10**, [10] 152; Beilstein I, 2. Erg., p. 480.
306. K. C. Ramey, D. C. Lini, and W. B. Wise, *J. Amer. Chem. Soc.*, **90**, 4275 (1968).
307. K. C. Ramey and G. L. Statton, *J. Amer. Chem. Soc.*, **88**, 4387 (1966).
308. Z. Rappoport, P. D. Sleezer, S. Winstein, and W. G. Young, *Tetrahedron Lett.*, **1965**, 3719, and quoted literature.
309. A. F. Rekasheva and L. A. Kiprianova, *Kinet. Katal.*, **5**, 299 (1966). (English ed., p. 266.)
310. Rhône-Poulenc S. A., British Patent 1,102,460.

311. W. Riemenschneider, W. Schmidt, and L. Hörnig, Farbwerke Hoechst, German Patent 1,136,685.

312. R. E. Rinehart and J. S. Lasky, *J. Amer. Chem. Soc.*, **86**, 2516 (1964).

313. R. E. Rinehart and H. P. Smith, *J. Polymer Sci.*, **B3**, 1049 (1965).

314. R. E. Rinehart, H. P. Smith, H. S. Witt, and H. Romeyn, Jr., *J. Amer. Chem. Soc.*, **83**, 4864 (1961).

315. R. E. Rinehart, H. P. Smith, H. S. Witt, and H. Romeyn, Jr., *J. Amer. Chem. Soc.*, **84**, 4145 (1962).

316. R. E. Robinson, National Distillers, U.S. Patent 3,190,912.

317. R. E. Robinson, National Distillers, U.S. Patent 3,379,780.

318. S. D. Robinson and B. L. Shaw, *J. Chem. Soc.*, **1963**, 4806.

319. L. Roos and M. Orchin, *J. Amer. Chem. Soc.*, **87**, 5502 (1965).

320. M. Rossberg and H. Schmitz, Farbwerke Hoechst, German Patent 1,143,807.

321. J. M. Rowe, Proc. Chem. Soc. (London), **1962**, 66.

322. C. K. Rule and V. K. La Mer, *J. Amer. Chem. Soc.*, **60**, 1974 (1938).

323. A. Sabel, J. Smidt, R. Jira, and H. Prigge, *Chem. Ber.*, **102**, 2939 (1969).

324. G. N. Schrauzer, *J. Amer. Chem. Soc.*, **81**, 5310 (1959).

325. R. G. Schultz, *J. Organomet. Chem.*, **6**, 435 (1966).

326. R. G. Schultz, *J. Polymer Sci.*, **B4**, 541 (1966).

327. R. G. Schultz and D. E. Gross, "Homogeneous Catalysis," *Advan. Chem. Ser.*, **70**, Washington, D.C., 1968, p. 97.

328. R. G. Schultz and P. R. Rony, *Amer. Chem. Soc., Div., Petrol. Chem., Preprints*, **12**, 139 (1967).

329. W. Schwerdtel, *Chem.-Ing.-Tech.*, **40**, 781 (1968).

330. J. Sedlmeier and A. Treiber, Consortium für elektrochemische Industrie, German Patent 1,269,613.

331. K. Sennewald, W. Vogt, and H. Glaser, Knapsack AG, German Patent 1,244,766.

332. B. L. Shaw, *Chem. Ind.* (*London*), **1962**, 1190.

333. B. L. Shaw, *Chem. Commun.*, **1968**, 464.

334. Shell Internationale Research Maatschappij N.V., British Patent 1,010,024.

335. Shell Internationale Research Maatschappij N.V., French Patent 1,419,966.

336. G. D. Shier, *Polymer Preprints*, **9**, 176 (1968).

338. G. Slinckx and G. Smets, *Tetrahedron*, **22**, 3163 (1966).

339. J. Smidt, *Chem. Ind.* (*London*), **1962**, 54.

340. J. Smidt and W. Hafner, *Angew. Chem.*, **71**, 284 (1959).

341. J. Smidt, W. Hafner, and R. Jira, Consortium für elektrochemische Industrie, U.S. Patent 3,080,425.

342. J. Smidt, W. Hafner, R. Jira, J. Sedlmeier, R. Sieber, R. Rüttinger, and H. Kojer, *Angew. Chem.*, **71**, 176 (1959).

343. J. Smidt, W. Hafner, R. Jira, R. Sieber, J. Sedlmeier, and A. Sabel, *Angew. Chem.*, **74**, 93 (1962); *Angew. Chem. Intern. Ed.*, **1**, 80 (1962).

344. J. Smidt, W. Hafner, and J. Sedlmeier, Consortium für elektrochemische Industrie, German Patent 1,193,934.

345. J. Smidt, W. Hafner, J. Sedlmeier, R. Jira, and R. Rüttinger, Consortium für Elektrochemische Industrie, German Patent 1,049,845.

345a. J. Smidt and R. Jira, *Angew. Chem.*, **71**, 651 (1959).

346. J. Smidt and R. Jira, *Chem. Ber.*, **93**, 162 (1960).

347. J. Smidt and H. Krekeler, *Erdoel Kohle, Erdgas, Petrochem.*, **16**, 560 (1963).

348. J. Smidt, J. Sedlmeier, and R. Jira, Consortium für elektrochemische Industrie, German Patent 1,077,662.

182   REINHARD JIRA AND WERNER FREIESLEBEN

349. J. Smidt and R. Sieber, *Angew. Chem.*, **71**, 626 (1959).
350. J. Smidt, R. Sieber, W. Hafner, R. Jira, Consortium für elektrochemische Industrie, U.S. Patent 3,153,083.
351. A. E. Smith, *Acta Cryst.*, **18**, 331 (1965).
352. E. J. Smutny, *J. Amer. Chem. Soc.*, **89**, 6793 (1967).
353. Souk Kwon Choi, *Chem. Abstr.*, **67**, 116,938 (1967).
354. M. B. Sparke, L. Turner, and A. J. M. Wenham, *J. Catal.*, **4**, 332 (1965).
355. M. B. Sparke, A. J. Wenham, and L. Turner, British Petroleum, Belgian Patent 612,300.
356. L. Spialter and D. H. O'Brien, *J. Org. Chem.*, **32**, 222 (1967).
356a. H. Stangl, Consortium für elektrochemische Industrie, unpublished experiments.
357. H. Stangl and R. Jira, *Tetrahedron Lett.*, **1970**, 3589.
358. G. L. Statton and K. C. Ramey, *J. Amer. Chem. Soc.*, **88**, 1327 (1966).
359. E. W. Stern, *Proc. Chem. Soc. (London)*, **1963**, 111.
360. E. W. Stern, *J. Catal.*, **6**, 152 (1966).
361. E. W. Stern, *Catal. Rev.*, **1**, 73,125 (1967).
362. E. W. Stern and M. L. Spector, *Proc. Chem. Soc. (London)*, **1961**, 370.
363. J. K. Stille and R. A. Morgan, *J. Amer. Chem. Soc.*, **88**, 5135 (1966).
364. J. K. Stille, R. A. Morgan, D. D. Whitehurst, and J. R. Doyle, *J. Amer. Chem. Soc.*, **87**, 3282 (1965).
365. J. C. Strini and J. Metzger, *Bull. Soc. Chim. Fr.*, **1966**, 3150.
366. A. Sucevanu and C. Fordea, *Rev. Chim. (Bucharest)*, **16**, 499 (1965).
367. S. Takahashi, T. Shibano, and N. Hagihara, *Tetrahedron Lett.*, **1967**, 2451.
368. S. Takahashi, T. Shibano, and N. Hagihara, *Bull. Chem. Soc. Jap.*, **41**, 454 (1968).
369. S. Takahashi, H. Yamazaki, and N. Hagihara, *Mem. Inst. Sci. Ind. Res., Osaka Univ.*, **25**, 125 (1968); *Chem. Abstr.*, **69**, 26,464d (1968).
370. S. Takahashi, H. Yamazaki, and N. Hagihara, *Bull. Chem. Soc. Jap.*, **41**, 254 (1968).
371. M. Takahashi and T. Yanagira, *Denki Kagaku*, **34**, 139 (1966).
372. H. Takahashi and J. Tsuji, *J. Amer. Chem. Soc.*, **90**, 2387 (1968).
373. M. Tamura and T. Yasui, *Chem. Commun.*, **1968**, 1209.
374. M. Tamura and T. Yasui, Kurashiki Rayon, Japanese Patent 8241/68,9525/68.
375. M. Tamura and T. Yasui, Kurashiki Rayon, Japanese Patent 8243/68.
375a. M. Tamura and T. Yasui, *Kogyo Kagaku Zasshi*, **71**, 1855 (1968); *Chem. Abstr.*, **70**, 61,532 (1969).
375b. M. Tamura and T. Yasui, *Kogyo Kagaku Zasshi*, **71**, 1859 (1968); *Chem. Abstr.*, **70**, 61,533 (1969).
376. H. Taube, "Mechanisms of Redox Reactions," in *Advances in Inorganic Chemistry and Radiochemistry*, Vol. 1, H. J. Emeléus and J. G. Sharpe, Eds., Academic Press, New York, 1959.
377. H. A. Tayim and J. C. Bailar, Jr., *J. Amer. Chem. Soc.*, **89**, 3420 (1967).
378. H. A. Tayim and J. C. Bailar, Jr., *J. Amer. Chem. Soc.*, **89**, 4330 (1967).
379. K. Teramoto, T. Oga, S. Kikuchi, and M. Ito, *Yuki Gosei Kagaku Kyokai Shi*, **21**, 288 (1963).
380. P. Teyssie and R. Dauby, *Bull. Soc. Chim. Fr.*, **1965**, 2842.
380a. T. Tisue and W. J. Downs, *Chem. Commun.*, **1969**, 410.
381. Toyo Rayon, Japanese Patent Appl. 5377/66.
382. J. C. Trebellas, J. R. Olechowski, and H. B. Jonassen, *J. Organomet. Chem.*, **6**, 412 (1966).
383. J. C. Trebellas, J. R. Olechowski, H. B. Jonassen, and D. W. Moore, *J. Organomet. Chem.*, **9**, 153 (1967).

383a. A. Treiber, Consortium für elektrochemische Industrie, unpublished experiments.
384. J. Tsuji and N. Iwamoto, *Chem. Commun.*, **1966**, 328.
385. J. Tsuji and K. Ohno, "Homogeneous Catalysis," *Advan. Chem. Ser.* **70**, Washington, D.C., 1968, p. 155.
386. J. Tsuji and H. Takahashi, *J. Amer. Chem. Soc.*, **87**, 3275 (1965).
387. J. Tsuji, H. Takahashi, and M. Morikawa, *Tetrahedron Lett.*, **1965**, 4387.
388. S. Tsurugi, J. Hayasaki, and M. Sakai, *Kogyo Kagaku Zasshi*, **68**, 1809 (1965).
389. S. Uemura and K. Ichikawa, *Nippon Kagaku Zasshi*, **88**, 893 (1967).
390. S. Uemura and K. Ichikawa, *Bull. Chem. Soc. Jap.*, **40**, 1016 (1967).
391. S. Uemura, T. Okada, and K. Ichikawa, *Nippon Kagaku Zasshi*, **89**, 692 (1968); *Chem. Abstr.*, **70**, 19678 (1969).
391a. M. O. Unger and R. A. Fouty, *J. Org. Chem.*, **34**, 18 (1969).
392. M. N. Vargaftik, I. I. Moiseev, and Y. K. Syrkin, *Dokl. Akad. Nauk SSSR*, **139**, 1396 (1961).
393. M. N. Vargaftik, I. I. Moiseev, and Y. K. Syrkin, *Dokl. Akad. Nauk SSSR*, **147**, 399 (1962).
394. M. N. Vargaftik, I. I. Moiseev, Y. K. Syrkin, and V. V. Yakshin, *Izv. Akad. Nauk SSSR, Otd. Khim. Nauk*, **1962**, 930.
395. M. N. Vargaftik, I. I. Moiseev, and Y. K. Syrkin, *Izv. Akad. Nauk, Otd. Khim. Nauk SSSR*, **1963**, 1147.
396. E. Vedejs, *J. Amer. Chem. Soc.*, **90**, 4751 (1968).
397. H. C. Volger, *Rec. Trav. Chim. Pays-Bas*, **86**, 677 (1967).
398. H. C. Volger, *Rec. Trav. Chim. Pays-Bas*, **87**, 501 (1968).
399. H. C. Volger and H. Hogeveen, *Rec. Trav. Chim. Pays-Bas*, **86**, 830 (1967).
399a. H. C. Volger, H. Hogeveen, and M. M. P. Gaasbeek, *J. Amer. Chem. Soc.*, **91**, 218 (1969).
399b. H. C. Volger, H. Hogeveen, and M. M. P. Gaasbeek, *J. Amer. Chem. Soc.*, **91**, 2137 (1969).
400. H. C. Volger and K. Vrieze, *J. Organomet. Chem.*, **6**, 297 (1966).
401. H. C. Volger and K. Vrieze, *J. Organomet. Chem.*, **13**, 495 (1968).
402. K. Vrieze, P. Cossee, C. W. Hilbers, and A. P. Praat, *Rec. Trav. Chim. Pays-Bas*, **86**, 769 (1967).
403. K. Vrieze, P. Cossee, G. MacLean, and C. W. Hilbers, *J. Organomet. Chem.*, **6**, 672 (1966).
404. K. Vrieze, P. Cossee, A. P. Praat, and C. W. Hilbers, *J. Organomet. Chem.*, **11**, 353 (1968).
405. K. Vrieze, C. MacLean, P. Cossee, and C. W. Hilbers, *Rec. Trav. Chim. Pays-Bas*, **85**, 1077 (1966).
406. K. Vrieze, A. P. Praat, and P. Cossee, *J. Organomet. Chem.*, **12**, 533 (1968).
407. K. Vrieze and H. C. Volger, *J. Organomet. Chem.*, **9**, 537 (1967).
408. R. Wakasa, N. Kominami, and K. Ishii, Asahi Chem. Ind., Japanese Patent 68/07205; *Chem. Abstr.*, **69**, 51,629 (1968).
409. E. D. Weed, Dissertation, Ohio State University, Columbus, Ohio, Univ. Microfilms, Ann Arbor, Mich., Order No. 64-9598. Diss. Abstr., **25**, 795 (1965).
410. F. H. Westheimer, Chem. Rev., **61**, 265 (1961).
411. W. A. Whitla, H. M. Powell, and L. M. Venanzi, *Chem. Commun.*, **1966**, 310.
412. G. Wilke, *Angew. Chem.*, **75**, 10 (1963).
413. G. Wilke, B. Bogdanović, P. Hardt, P. Heimbach, W. Keim, M. Kröne, W. Oberkirch, K. Tanaka, E. Steinrücke, D. Walter, and H. Zimmermann, *Angew. Chem.*, **78**, 157 (1966).

414. J. A. Wunderlich and D. P. Mellor, *Acta Cryst.*, **7**, 130 (1954).
415. W. F. K. Wynne-Jones, *Trans. Faraday Soc.*, **32**, 1397 (1936).
416. S. Yamamoto and R. Konaka, *Kogyo Kagaku Zasshi*, **71**, 945 (1968); *Chem. Abstr.*, **69**, 86,285 (1968).
417. M. Yano, A. Mitsutani, and K. Tanaka, *Kogyo Kagaku Zasshi*, **68**, 1620 (1965); *Chem. Abstr.*, **63**, 17,824 (1965).
418. W. G. Young, K. Nozaki, R. Warner, *J. Amer. Chem. Soc.*, **61**, 2564 (1939).
419. L. M. Zaitsev, A. P. Belov, M. N. Vargaftik, and I. I. Moiseev, *Zh. Neorg. Khim.*, **12**, 396 (1967).
420. I. A. Zakharova, G. A. Kukina, T. S. Kuli-Zade, I. I. Moiseev, G. Y. Pek, and M. A. Porai-Koshits, *Zh. Neorg. Khim.*, **11**, 2543 (1966).
421. W. C. Zeise, *Pogg. Ann.*, **21**, 497 (1831).
422. G. Zöllner and L. Ruszinkò, *M.T.A. Kémiai, Oszt. Közl.*, **25**, 50 (1966).

Addendum List of Literature 1969 and 1970

1. D. M. Adams and A. Squire, *J. Chem. Soc.* (*London*), *Sect. A*, **1970**, 1808. "Vibrational Spectra of the Chloro- and Bromo-π-allylpalladium Dimers and of the π-2-Methylallyl Analogues."
2. U. Belluco, B. Crociani, R. Pietropaolo, and P. Uguagliati, *Inorg. Chimica Acta Rev.*, **3**, 19 (1969). "Complexes of Platinum(II) with Unsaturated Hydrocarbons."
3. D. R. Gee and J. K. S. Wan, *Chem. Commun.*, **1970**, 641. "The Nature of Bonding in Silver-olefin Complexes: An Electron Spin Resonance Study."
4. F. R. Hartley, *J. Organomet. Chem.*, **21**, 1 (1970). "The Ultraviolet and Visible Spectra of π-Allylpalladium Complexes."
5. F. R. Hartley, *Chem. Rev.*, **69**, 799 (1969). "Olefin and Acetylene Complexes of Platinum and Palladium."
6. J. W. Faller and M. J. Incorvia, *J. Organomet. Chem.*, **19**, P 13 (1969). "Organometallic Conformational Equilibria. VII. On the Planar Rotation of π-Allyl Ligands in Metal Complexes."
7. P. W. N. M. van Leeuwen, K. Vrieze, and A. P. Praat, *J. Organomet. Chem.*, **20**, 219 (1969). "Nuclear Magnetic Resonance Study in Coordination Chemistry. X. The Reactions of (π-Methallyl)palladium Chloride Containing Various Phosphines with 1,5-Cyclooctadiene-rhodium Chloride Dimer."
8. P. W. N. M. van Leeuwen and A. P. Praat, *Chem. Commun.*, **1970**, 365. "New Methods for Studying the Mechanism of the π, σ-Reaction in Allylic Metal Complexes."
9. K. S. Wheelock, J. H. Nelson, L. C. Cusachs, and H. B. Jonassen, *J. Amer. Chem. Soc.*, **92**, 5110 (1970). "The Barrier to Rotation in Platinum Acetylene and Olefin Complexes."
10. P. Francois and Y. Trambouze, *Bull. Soc. Chim. Fr.*, **1969**, 51. "Kinetic Study of the Direct Oxidation of Ethylene in Aqueous Medium."
11. P. Francois, *Ann. Chim.* (*Paris*), **4**, 371 (1969). "Kinetics and Mechanisms of Oxidation of Ethylene in Aqueous and Methanolic Media, Catalysed by Palladium(II) Chloride."
12. I. I. Moiseev, *Kinetika i Kataliz*, **11**, 342 (1970). "Kinetics and Mechanism of the Oxidation of Olefins with Palladium Salts."
13. M. N. Vargaftik, O. G. Levanda, A. P. Belov, L. M. Zakharova, and I. I. Moiseev, *Kinetika i Kataliz*, **10**, 1016 (1969). "Studying the Kinetics of Olefin Oxidation by Palladium(II) Salts."

14. A. R. Blake, J. G. Sunderland, and A. T. Kuhn, *J. Chem. Soc. (London), Sect. A,* **1969**, 3015. "The Partial Anodic Oxidation of Ethylene on Palladium."
15. G. Gourlay (Imp. Chem. Industries, Ltd.) U.S. Patent 3,471,567. "Glyoxal."
16. Société des Usines Chimiques Rhone-Poulenc, Fr. Patent 1,457,618; Fr. Addn. 89,997; *Chem. Abstr.,* **72**, 21,368 (1970). "Glyoxylic acid."
17. L. M. Zakharova, M. N. Vargaftik, I. I. Moiseev, and L. A. Katsman, *Izv. Akad. Nauk SSSR, Ser. Khim.,* **1970**, 700. "Selectivity of Styrene Oxidation by Palladium Chloride in Water."
18. M. E. D. Hillman and W. C. Overhults (W. R. Grace and Co.) Ger. Offen. 1,905,880; *Chem. Abstr.,* **72**, 42,825 (1970). "Triacetin."
19. R. G. Schultz and P. R. Rony, *J. Catalysis,* **16**, 133 (1970). "The Chemistry of Palladium Complexes. VI. Studies on the Palladium(II)-catalyzed Decomposition of Vinyl Acetate."
20. K. Shimizu and N. Ohta, *Kogyo Kagaku Zasshi,* **72**, 1773 (1969); *Chem. Abstr.,* **72**, 2,783 (1970). "Vinyl Acetate Synthesis from Ethylene in Acetic Acid. I. Activated Catalysts in Vinyl Acetate Synthesis from Ethylene and Acetic Acid."
21. M. Tamura and T. Yasui, *Kogyo Kagaku Zasshi,* **71**, 1855 (1968); *Chem. Abstr.,* **70**, 61,532 (1969). "Catalytic Properties of Palladium(II) Salts in Acetic Acid. II. Reactions between Palladium Salts and Various Metal Salts."
22. M. Tamura and T. Yasui, *Kogyo Kagaku Zasshi,* **71**, 1859 (1968); *Chem. Abstr.,* **70**, 61,533 (1969). "III. Oxidation of Metallic Palladium by Cupric Salt."
23. M. Tamura and T. Yasui, *Kogyo Kagaku Zasshi,* **72**, 557 (1969); *Chem. Abstr.,* **70**, 118,495 (1969). "IV. Reactions of Cuprous and Cupric Salts with Alkali Metal Salts and Oxidation of Cuprous Salt with Oxygen in Acetic Acid."
24. M. Tamura and T. Yasui, *Kogyo Kagaku Zasshi,* **72**, 561 (1969); *Chem. Abstr.,* **71**, 2,928 (1969). "V. Synthesis of Vinyl Acetate from Ethylene in Liquid Phase."
25. M. Tamura and T. Yasui, *Kogyo Kagaku Zasshi,* **72**, 568 (1969); *Chem. Abstr.,* **71**, 12,252 (1969). "VI. Synthesis of Ethylene Glycol Monoacetate from Ethylene with Palladous Salt—Cupric Salt System."
26. M. Tamura and T. Yasui, *Kogyo Kagaku Zasshi,* **72**, 605 (1969); *Chem. Abstr.,* **71**, 12,253 (1969). "VIII. Reactions of Palladous Salt with Metal Salts and Ethylene in *N,N*-Dimethylformamide."
27. M. Tamura and T. Yasui, *Kogyo Kagaku Zasshi,* **72**, 575 (1969); *Chem. Abstr.,* **71**, 12,254 (1969). "IX. Behavior of Various Nitrogen-containing Oxidants in Acetic Acid."
28. M. Tamura and T. Yasui, *Kogyo Kagaku Zasshi,* **72**, 578 (1969); *Chem. Abstr.,* **71**, 12,260 (1969). "X. Reaction of Ethylene with Palladous Salt-Nitrate Catalyst in Acetic Acid."
29. M. Tamura and T. Yasui, *Kogyo Kagaku Zasshi,* **72**, 581 (1969); *Chem. Abstr.,* **71**, 12,255 (1969). "XI. Rate and Mechanism of Glycol Monoester Formation."
30. M. Tamura, M. Tsutsumi, and T. Yasui, *Kogyo Kagaku Zasshi,* **72**, 585 (1969); *Chem. Abstr.,* **71**, 12,256 (1969). "XII. Synthesis of Ethylene Glycol Monoacetate from Ethylene in Presence of Oxygen."
31. H.-J. Arpe and L. Hörnig, *Erdöl und Kohle, Brennstoffchemie,* **23**, 79 (1970). "The Acetoxylation of Benzene."
32. W. G. Lloyd and B. J. Luberoff, *J. Org. Chem.,* **34**, 3949 (1969). "Oxidations of Olefins with Alcoholic Palladium(II) Salts."
33. H. Hirai, H. Sawai, and Sh. Makishima, *Bull. Chem. Soc. Japan,* **43**, 1148 (1970) (in English). "Reaction of Olefin-palladium(II) Chloride Complexes with *n*-Butylamine."

34. H. Hirai and H. Sawai, *Bull. Chem. Soc. Japan*, **43**, 2208 (1970) (in English). "Reaction of Chlorolefin-palladium(II) Complexes with Amides."
35. E. Weingaertner, (Deutsche Erdöl AG), German Patent 1,267,683. "Vinylcyanide."
36. K. Fujimoto, T. Kunugi, *Kogyo Kagaku Zasshi*, **72**, 1760 (1969); *Chem. Abstr.*, **72**, 42,688 (1970). "Synthesis of Vinyl Acetate with Palladium Activated Carbon as Catalyst."
37. K. Fujimoto, Y. Negami, and T. Kunugi, *Kogyo Kagaku Zasshi*, **73**, 1822 (1970). "Synthesis of Acetaldehyde from Ethylene using Palladium Chloride-Activated Charcoal Catalyst."
38. K. Fujimoto, H. Takeda, H. Arai, S. Mizuo, and T. Kunugi, *Kogyo Kagaku Zasshi*, **73**, 2168 (1970). "Oxidation of Ethylene on Platinum Metal Salt/Charcoal Catalysts."
39. H. R. Gerberich and W. K. Hall, U.S. Patent 3,534,093; *Chem. Abstr.*, **73**, 130,605 (1970). "Ethylene Oxidation in the Presence of Palladium Metal to form Acetaldehyde, Acetic acid, and Acetic Anhydride."
40. T. Kunugi, H. Arai, and K. Fujimoto, *Bull. Jap. Petr. Inst.*, **12**, 97 (1970), (in English); *Chem. Abstr.*, **73**, 65,703 (1970). "Acetoxylation of Olefins over Supported Palladium Metal and Salt Catalysts."
41. S. Nakamura and T. Yasui, *J. Catalysis*, **17**, 366 (1970). "Mechanism of the Palladium-catalyzed Synthesis of Vinyl Acetate from Ethylene in a Heterogenous Gas Reaction."
42. A. P. Belov, I. I. Moiseev, and Y. K. Syrkin, *Izv. Akad. Nauk SSSR, Ser. Khim.*, **1970**, 46. "Decomposition of π-Allyl Complexes of Palladium in Alkaline Aqueous and Alcoholic Solutions."
43. A. Bright, B. L. Shaw, and G. Shaw, *Amer. Chem. Soc., Div. Petrol. Chem., Prepr.*, **14**, B 81 (1969). "Allylic Palladium Complexes."
44. T. Kajimoto, H. Takahashi, and J. Tsuji, *J. Organomet. Chem.*, **23**, 275 (1970). "Organic Syntheses by Means of Noble Metal Compounds. XLI. Reaction of Isocyanides with π-Allylpalladium Chloride."
45. A. D. Ketley, J. A. Braatz, J. Craig, and R. Cole, *Amer. Chem. Soc., Div. Petrol. Chem., Prepr.*, **14**, B 142 (1969). "Reactions of π-Alkene-palladium Chloride Complexes with Cyclopropane Derivatives."
46. See ref. 8.
47. R. Pietropaolo, P. Uguagliatti, T. Boschi, B. Crociani, and U. Belluco, *J. Catal.*, **18**, 338 (1970). "Mechanism of formation of palladium(II) allyl complexes."
48. T. A. Schenach and F. F. Caserio, Jr., *J. Organomet. Chem.*, **18**, P 17 (1969). "The Hydrolysis of π-Allylpalladium Complexes in Dilute Base—Evidence for Disproportionation of the Allyl Group."
49. W. Thielebeule (Deutsche Erdöl AG) German Patent 1,300,930; *Chem. Abstr.*, **72**, 42,730 (1970). "Catalyst for the Manufacture of Allyl Chloride from Propene."
50. H. C. Volger, *Rec. Trav. Chim. Pays-Bas*, **88**, 225 (1969). "Synthesis of β-Alkyl and β-Aryl π-Allylpalladium Halide Complexes and Its Mechanistic Aspects."
51. H. C. Volger, *Ind. Eng. Chem.*, **1970**, 311. "Synthesis of π-Allylpalladium Halide Complexes."
52. M. J. Wriglesworth (Brit. Petr. Co., Ltd.), Brit. Patent 1,184,494; *Chem. Abstr.* **73**, 14,505 (1970). "Benzyl Acetate."
53. R. Asano, I. Moritani, Y. Fujiwara, and S. Teranishi, *Chem. Commun.*, **1970**, 1293. "Aromatic Substitution of Olefins. The Reaction of Ferrocene with Styrene in the Presence of Palladium(II) Acetate."
54. A. J. Bingham, L. K. Dyall, R. O. C. Norman, and C. B. Thomas, *J. Chem. Soc*

(*London*), *Sect. C*, **1970**, 1879. "Reactions of Palladium(II) with Organic Compounds. I. Oxidative Cyclization of 3-Methyl-3-phenyl-1-butene and 3,3,3-Triphenylpropene."

55. S. Danno, I. Moritani, and Y. Fujiwara, *Tetrahedron*, **25**, 4809 (1969). "Aromatic Substitution of Olefins. VII. Reactions of Lower Olefins with Benzene in the Presence of Palladium Acetate."

56. S. Danno, I. Moritani, and Y. Fujiwara, *Chem. Commun.*, **1970**, 610. "Aromatic Substitution of Olefins. Reaction of [^{2}H$_2$] Styrene with Benzene in the Presence of Palladium(II) Acetate."

57. Y. Fujiwara, I. Moritani, S. Danno, R. Asano, and S. Teranishi, *J. Amer. Chem. Soc.*, **91**, 7166 (1969). "Aromatic Substitution of Olefins. VI. Arylation of Olefins with Palladium(II) Acetate."

58. K. Garves, *J. Org. Chem.*, **35**, 3273 (1970). "Coupling, Carbonylation, and Vinylation Reactions of Aromatic Sulfinic Acids via Organopalladium Intermediates."

59. N. F. Goldshleger and M. L. Chidekel, *Izv. Akad. Nauk SSSR, Ser. Khim.*, **1969**, 675. "Oxidative Coupling of Aromatic Compounds on Systems with Ruthenium Complexes."

60. R. P. Hughes and J. Powell, *J. Organomet. Chem.*, **20**, P 17 (1969). "The Reaction of Allene with Acetylacetonato-π-allylpalladium(II): Formation of 2,2′-Bi-π-allyl Complexes of Palladium."

61. O. L. Kaliya, O. N. Temkin, R. M. Flid, and L. G. Volkova, *Zh. Neorg. Khim.*, **15**, 2562 (1970); *Chem. Abstr.*, **73**, 109,884 (1970). "Synthesis and Reactions of β-Chlorovinylpalladium Chloride."

62. T. Matsuda and Y. Nakamura, *Kogyo Kagaku Zasshi*, **72**, 1766 (1969); *Chem. Abstr.*, **72**, 42,694 (1970). "Reaction of Palladium Acetate with Aliphatic Unsaturated Compounds. II. Products from the Reaction of Some Unsaturated Esters and Nitriles with Palladium Acetate."

63. O. H. Mattsson, *Tetrahedron Lett.*, **1969**, 2489. "Oxidation of 1,2-Bis(2,6-diketo-4,4-dimethylcyclohexyl)ethane with Oxygen over Palladium."

64. I. Moritani, Y. Fujiwara, S. Teranishi, H. Itatani, and M. Matsuda, Amer. Chem. Soc., Div. Petr. Chem., Prepr., **14**, B 172 (1969). "Aromatic Substitution of Olefin by Palladium Salts."

65. T. Sakakibara, T. Teramoto, and Y. Odaira, *Chem. Commun.*, **1970**, 1563. "Reaction of Palladium(II) Salts and Aromatic Compounds with Malonic Acids."

66. Y. Takahashi, K. Tsukiyama, S. Sakai, and Y. Ishii, *Tetrahedron Lett.*, **1970**, 1913. "The Anchimeric Assistance in the Ligand-coupling Reactions of π-Allylicpalladium Acetate Complexes."

67. P. M. Treichel and R. W. Hess, *J. Amer. Chem. Soc.*, **92**, 4731 (1970). "Insertion Reactions Involving Isocyanide Ligands in Platinum Alkyl and Aryl Complexes."

68. J. Tsuji, *Accounts Chem. Research*, **2**, 144 (1969). "Carbon-Carbon Bond Formation via Palladium Complexes."

69. A. A. Adamov, G. N. Freidlin and N. A. Fillipova U.S.S.R. 272,282; *Chem. Abstr.*, **73**, 124,006 (1970). "Preparation of a Transvinylation Catalyst."

70. K. E. Atkins, W. E. Walker, and R. M. Manyik, *Tetrahedron Lett.*, **1970**, 3821. "Palladium-catalysed Transfer of Allylic Groups."

71. D. G. Brady, *Chem. Commun.*, **1970**, 434. "Palladium(II) Catalysed Synthesis of Allylic Esters."

72. G. Hata, K. Takahashi, and A. Miyake, *Chem. Commun.*, **1970**, 1392. "Palladium-catalysed Exchange of Allylic Groups of Ethers and Esters with Active-hydrogen Compounds."

73. J. E. Lloyd (Imp. Chem. Industries, Ltd.) Brit. Patent 1,200,730; *Chem. Abstr.*, **73**, 109,251 (1970). "Catalytic Production of Olefin Derivatives from Vinyl or Allyl Esters."

74. M. Tamura and T. Yasui, *Kogyo Kagaku Zasshi*, **72**, 572 (1969); *Chem. Abstr.*, **71**, 12,259 (1969). "Catalytic Properties of Palladous Salts in Glacial Acetic Acid. VII. Synthesis of Vinyl Acetate from Vinyl Chloride by Means of Palladous Salt Catalyst."

75. M. Yamaji, Y. Fujiwara, T. Imanaka, and S. Teranishi, *Bull. Chem. Soc. Japan*, **43**, 2659 (1970) (in English). "Catalytic Diacetoxylation of *cis*- and *trans*-Dichloroethylenes by Means of Palladium(II) Chloride."

76. K. Kawamoto, T. Imanaka, and S. Teranishi, *Nippon Kagaku Zasshi (J. Chem. Soc. Japan)*, **89**, 639 (1968); *Chem. Abstr.*, **69**, 105,565 (1968). "Dimerisation of Ethylene Catalyzed by an Ethylene-Palladium(II) Chloride Complex. Kinetics and Effect of Bidentate Ligands."

77. K. Kawamoto, T. Imanaka, and S. Teranishi, *Bull. Chem. Soc. Japan*, **42**, 2688 (1969) (in English). "Reaction Intermediate in the Dimerisation of Ethylene Catalyzed by a Palladium(II) Complex. NMR Spectral Evidence for the Formation of the π-Bonded Chloro-acetylacetonato-(1-butene)palladium(II) Complex."

78. K. Kawamoto, T. Imanaka, and S. Teranishi, *Nippon Kagaku Zasshi (J. Chem. Soc. Japan)*, **91**, 39 (1970) (in English). "Effects of Solvents on Dimerization of Ethylene Catalyzed by Ethylenepalladium(II) Chloride Complex."

79. M. G. Barlow, M. J. Bryant, R. N. Haszeldine, and A. G. Machie, *J. Organometal. Chem.*, **21**, 215 (1970). "Organic Reactions Involving Transition Metals. III. Palladium(II)-catalyzed Dimerisation of Olefinic Compounds."

80. D. A. Cornforth and D. Williams (Imp. Chem. Ind.) U.S. Patent 3,484,475. "Dimerization and Hydrodimerization of α,β-Olefinically Unsaturated Compounds."

81. G. Hata, K. Takahashi, and A. Miyake, *Chem. and Ind.*, **51**, 1836 (1969). "Palladium-catalyzed Reactions of 1,3-Dienes with Active Methylene Compounds."

82. K. Kawamoto, T. Imanaka, and S. Teranishi, *Bull. Chem. Soc. Japan*, **43** 2512 (1970) (in English). "The Codimerization of Styrene with Ethylene Catalyzed by Olefin-palladium(II) Chloride Complexes."

83. R. M. Manyik, W. E. Walker, K. E. Atkins, and E. S. Hammack, *Tetrahedron Lett.*, **1970**, 3813. "Palladium Complex-catalyzed Reactions of Conjugated Dienes. I. Reactions of Butadiene with Aldehydes."

84. P. Mushak and M. A. Battiste, *Chem. Commun.*, **1969**, 1146. "A Novel Palladium(II) Chloride-Promoted Addition-Rearrangement Reaction of Terminal Olefins with Diphenylacetylene."

85. S. Otsuka, K. Tani, and A. Nakamura, *J. Chem. Soc. (London), Sect. A.*, "Allene and Cyclic Allene Pentamer-complexes of Monovalent Rhodium."

86. G. D. Shier (Dow Chemical Corp.) U.S. Patent 3,458,562; *Chem. Abstr.*, **71**, 80,641 (1969). "Palladium Catalyzed Reactions of 1,2-Alkadienes with 1-Alkynes."

87. E. J. Smutny (Shell Oil Co.) U.S. Patent 3,499,042; *Chem. Abstr.*, **73**, 132,047 (1970). "Alkadienyl Ethers."

88. W. E. Walker, R. M. Manyik, K. E. Atkins, and M. L. Farmer, *Tetrahedron Lett.*, **1970**, 3817. "Palladium Complex-catalyzed Reactions of Conjugated Dienes. II. Solvent and Ligand Effects of the Reaction of Butadiene with Acetic Acid."

89. F. J. Weigert, R. L. Baird, and J. R. Shapley, *J. Amer. Chem. Soc.*, **92**, 6630 (1970). "The Palladium Chloride-Catalyzed Cyclodimerization of 1-Methylcyclopropene."

90. A. D. Ketley (W. R. Grace and Co.) German Ausl. 1,810,122; *Chem. Abstr.*, **71**,

61,552 (1969). "Palladium-π-Allyl Complexes as Catalysts for the Polymerization of Butadiene."

91. F. Mikeš and J. Kálal, *Chem. Prumysl*, **20**, 218 (1970). "Polymerization of Butadiene by Rhodium Trichloride in Aqueous Medium."

92. R. L. Augustine and J. F. van Peppen, *Chem. Commun.*, **1970**, 495. "Olefin Isomerization over Tris(triphenylphosphine)chlororhodium."

93. W. H. Clement and T. Speidel, *Ind. Eng. Chem.*, **9**, 220 (1970). "Ligand Factors in the Isomerization of Olefins by Palladium Complexes."

94. K. Mosley, J. W. Kang, and P. M. Maitlis, *Chem. Commun.*, **1969**, 1155. "π-Cyclooctenyl-rhodium and -iridium Complexes as Intermediates in the Isomerisations of Cyclo-octadienes."

95. H. A. Tayim and A. Vassilian, *Chem. Commun.*, **1970**, 630. "Rearrangement of Coordinated Cyclo-octadienes in Palladium(II) and Platinum(II) Complexes."

96. L. Cassar, P. E. Eaton, and J. Halpern, *J. Amer. Chem. Soc.*, **92**, 6366 (1970). "Silver(I)- and Palladium(II)-catalyzed Isomerizations of Cuban. Synthesis and Characterization of Cuneane."

97. L. Cassar and J. Halpern, *Chem. Commun.*, **1970**, 1082. "Oxidative Addition of Quadricyclene to Di-μ-chlorotetracarbonyldirhodium(I) and the Mechanism of the Rhodium(I)-catalyzed Isomerization of Quadricyclene to Norbornadiene."

98. D. Duffin and J. K. Sutherland, *Chem. Commun.*, **1970**, 626. "Silver Ion Catalysis in the Cyclopropyl-allyl Rearrangement."

99. P. E. Eaton and S. A. Cerefice, *Chem. Commun.*, **1970**, 1494. "Rhodium(I)-catalysed Isomerization of Cyclobutane Cage Compounds: Synthesis of *cis,syn,cis*-Tricyclo(5,3,0,0^{2,6})deca-4,8-diene-3,10-dione and of *exo*-Dicyclopentadienone."

100. J. W. Kang, K. Moseley, and P. M. Maitlis, *J. Amer. Chem. Soc.*, **91**, 5970 (1969). "Pentamethylcyclopentadienylrhodium and Iridium Halides. I. Synthesis and Properties."

101. T. J. Katz and S. A. Cerefice, *Tetrahedron Lett.*, **1969**, 2561. "Rhodium-catalysed Isomerization of Tricyclo(3,2,2,0^{2,4})nonatriene."

102. T. J. Katz and S. A. Cerefice, *J. Amer. Chem. Soc.*, **91**, 6519 (1969). "The Mechanism of a Metal-catalyzed Cycloaddition Reaction."

103. A. D. Ketley, J. A. Braatz, and J. Craig, *Chem. Commun.*, **1970**, 1117. "Reactions of Dicyclopropyl Compounds with Di-μ-chlorodichlorobis(ethylene)dipalladium."

104. J. A. Roth, *J. Amer. Chem. Soc.*, **92**, 6658 (1970). "Ring-opening of Cyclopropanes over Palladium Metal."

Summarizing reports:

105. R. Hüttel, Brennstoff-Chemie, **50**, 281, 331 (1969). "Palladium Salts and Palladium Complexes in Organic Chemistry."

106. R. Hüttel, *Synthesis*, **1970**, 225. "Palladium Salts and Palladium Complexes in Preparative Organic Chemistry."

107. P. R. Brookes and R. S. Nyholm, *Chem. Commun.*, **1970**, 169. "Cyclic Compounds with a Pt—C σ-Bond formed by Olefin Insertion Reactions."

108. A. J. Cheney, B. E. Mann, B. L. Shaw, and R. M. Slade, *Chem. Commun.*, **1970**, 1176. "Intramolecular Platinum-carbon Bond Formation Promoted by Steric Hindrance."

109. A. Kasahara, K. Tanaka, and T. Izumi, *Bull. Chem. Soc. Japan*, **42**, 1702 (1969) (in English). "Formation of Complexes with a σ-Bond between 2-Vinyl-pyridine and Palladium(II) or Platinum(II) Chloride."

110. W. Keim, *J. Organomet. Chem.*, **14**, 179 (1968). "New σ-Bonded Rhodium(I) Complexes Containing a Metal-carbon Bond."

111. R. Palumbo, A. De Renzi, A. Panunzi, and G. Paiaro, *J. Amer. Chem. Soc.*, **91**, 3874 (1969). "Addition Reactions on Coordinated Olefinic Ligands. I. The Reactions of Amines with Diene Complexes of Platinum(II) and Palladium(II)."

112. A. Panunzi, A. De Renzi, R. Palumbo, and G. Paiaro, *J. Amer. Chem. Soc.*, **91** 3879 (1969). "II. The Reaction between Amines and Monoolefins Coordinated in *cis*-Dichloro(olefin)(*t*-phosphine) platinum(II) Complexes."

113. G. W. Parshall, *Accounts Chem. Res.*, **3**, 139 (1970). "Intramolecular Aromatic Substitution in Transition Metal Complexes."

114. J. K. Stille and D. B. Fox, *J. Amer. Chem. Soc.*, **92**, 1274 (1970). "The Stereospecific Addition of Carbon and Nitrogen Nucleophiles to Dicyclopentadieneplatinum and -palladium Complexes."

115. J. K. Stille, D. B. Fox, L. F. Hines, R. W. Fries, and R. D. Hughes, *Amer. Chem. Soc.*, *Div. Petrol. Chem., Prepr.*, **14**, B 149 (1969). "Synthesis and Reactions of Palladium-carbon Sigma-Bonded Complexes."

Cleavage Reactions of the Carbon–Silicon Bond

VÁCLAV CHVALOVSKÝ

Institute of Chemical Process Fundamentals,
Czechoslovak Academy of Science, Prague, Czechoslovakia

Translated by J. Hetflejš

I. INTRODUCTION

During the last 25 years, research in the field of organosilicon chemistry has gone through an intense development, especially in connection with the expansion of the production of organosilicon commercial products—silicones. These products have been widely applied because of their resistance toward thermal oxidation decomposition. Their resistance toward chemical reagents is, however, relatively lower. Silicon is markedly less electronegative than carbon (in Pauling's scale, silicon:1.8; carbon:2.5). For this reason the silicon–carbon bond has a 12% ionic character and undergoes relatively ready heterolytic fission by ionic reagents with an attack of either the electrophilic particle on carbon or of the nucleophilic particle on silicon. This comparatively ready splitting can sometimes be utilized for both synthetic and analytical purposes.

It is still more important however, to know how reaction conditions and the structure of the types of compounds concerned affect the course of these fission reactions, in order to avoid undesirable reactions. Therefore, in this chapter the possibility of undesirable side reactions, characterized by the Si—C bond cleavage, will be stressed more than the synthetic exploitation of this type of reaction itself. The danger of these decompositions has to be taken into account not only in the preparation of organosilicon compounds but also in their further treatment, purification, and storage, especially in the presence of imperceptible amounts of acid-base catalysts.

II. GENERAL CONSIDERATIONS

A. Homolytic Fission of the Si—C Bond

Since this type of reaction is always accompanied by considerable energy consumption, it can be most often detected in pyrolytic, photolytic, and radiation reactions and during the action of electric discharges.

The relationships between the structure of organosilicon compounds and their resistance toward homolytic fission have been studied in detail in the case of pyrolytic reactions. It was found that the thermal stability of alkyl-silicon compounds decreases with the increasing length of the alkyl group. Whereas tetramethylsilane decomposes at 660–720°,[1] the decomposition of tetraethylsilane and tetra-n-propylsilane takes place at temperatures about 100° lower.[2] Accurate values of dissociation energies of the silicon–alkyl bonds have not until now been unambiguously determined, and the data available in the literature frequently vary substantially.[3–6] However, it seems evident that the bond energy of the same silicon–alkyl bond is lower in alkylsilicon hydrides[3] than in tetraalkylsilanes or alkylchlorosilanes.[4,7–9]

In the pyrolysis of tetramethylsilane a radical fission of the silicon–methyl bond is generally assumed[1] to be the primary reaction. According to some authors,[10] the trimethylsilyl radical thus formed further decomposes to give elementary silicon.[2] The reaction performed in static equipment results in the formation of gaseous products consisting mostly of methane (60%) and hydrogen (40%), and a small amount of ethylene and acetylene. Of course, in such an arrangement not only the pyrolysis of the starting tetramethylsilane, but also that of primary formed products, proceeds.

In the pyrolysis of tetramethylsilane in a flow reactor at a holding time of several minutes, the formation of elementary silicon for all practical purposes does not take place. Beside gaseous products and $C_6H_5Si(CH_3)_3$, complex organosilicon compounds with the $SiCH_2Si$ skeleton are formed, e.g.,

$(CH_3)_3SiCH_2Si(CH_3)_3$ $(CH_3)_3SiCH_2SiH(CH_3)_2$ $(CH_3)_3SiCH_2SiH(CH_3)(C_2H_5)$
         (1)   **(2)**   **(3)**

(4)   **(5)**   **(6)**

(7)   **(8)**

At higher temperatures and longer reaction times a larger amount of high molecular weight products is formed.[11,12]

Similar products are found in the pyrolysis of tetraethylsilane. The reaction yields the compounds with linear (1, 2, 3), cyclic (4, 5, 6), and polycyclic (7, 8) chains having alternating silicon atoms and methylene groups. In all cases the fission of the C—H and C—C bonds in alkyl groups takes place. Thus average bond energies of reacting compounds (Si—C 69–76 kcal/mole, C—H 99 kcal/mole, and C—C 83 kcal/mole) do not give a sufficient clue for an appreciation of their reactivity in pyrolytic reactions.

In studying the pyrolysis of α,ω-disilaalkanes of type $R_3Si(CH_2)_nSiR_3$ in a flow apparatus[13] at 600°, it was found that the $SiCH_2Si$ skeleton is extraordinarily stable, since in $(CH_3)_3SiCH_2Si(CH_3)_3$ only the fission of the Si—CH_3 bond occurs. However, in the hexaalkyldisilethylenes the homolytic fission of the R_3Si—$CH_2CH_2SiR_3$ bond was observed. The fission of the C—C bonds has not been detected. In compounds with three or more methylene groups between silicon atoms, not only the Si—C bond but also the C—C bonds are split.

High stability of the $SiCH_2Si$ skeleton is obviously the reason that products of the pyrolysis of tetramethylsilane[11,14,15] consist predominantly of silmethylene units. Thus it seems that the grouping in which silicon atoms are separated from each other by a higher number of methylene units does not possess necessary thermal stability. On the other hand, it is of interest that, during the decomposition of tetramethylsilane in an electric discharge,[16] the formation of the $SiCH_2CH_2Si$ does occur and the mass spectra of the compounds $(CH_3)_3Si(CH_2)_nSi(CH_3)_3$ ($n = 1$–6) show the $SiCH_2CH_2Si$ skeleton to have higher stability than the $SiCH_2Si$ grouping.[17]

The pyrolysis of ethylsilicon hydrides in a static apparatus sometimes gives rise to alkylsilicon hydrides containing an even higher number of the Si—H bonds than the starting compound.[18,19] A similar situation arises in the pyrolysis of alkylsilicon hydrides in a flow apparatus.[20] The main products of the reaction, e.g., in the pyrolysis of tri-n-propylsilane, are polymers, propylene, and ethylene. Compounds with a higher content of the Si—H bonds such as propylsilane, dipropylsilane, and propylmethylsilane form only a small part of the reaction mixture, which further contains traces of dipropylmethylsilane.[20]

A marked decrease in thermal stability has been observed in the case of alkylsilanes containing alkyl groups substituted with an electronegative atom, e.g., halogens. This phenomenon is most pronounced when these substituents are attached to the α- and β-carbon atoms with respect to silicon. In this case, the reaction proceeds via the formation of complexes in the transition state, which are then heterolytically cleaved. Upon starting from γ-carbon the effect of substitution is less significant; decomposition temperatures (especially for fluoro-substituted alkylsilanes) are also much higher (see Table IV).

The silicon–aryl bond is comparatively heat-resistant;[21] however, it was found, that the silicon–phenyl bond is more readily split thermally than the silicon–methyl bond.[22,23] This is in harmony with the experimental bond energies for these compounds.[24] In the pyrolysis of phenyldimethylsilane at 500°, the Si—H bond is split most readily, the Si—C_6H_5 bond less readily, and the Si—CH_3 bond most slowly, the main products being diphenyl-dimethylsilane and 9,9-dimethyl-9-silafluorene:[23]

The formation of 9,9-dimethyl-9-silafluorene has been proved in the pyrolysis of diphenyldimethylsilane, triphenylmethylsilane and similar compounds at temperatures near 500°.[25]

The substitution of a benzene ring greatly lowers the thermal stability of organosilicon compounds.[26] The stability decreases in the sequence:

$$C_6H_5C_6H_4Si > C_6H_5Si > C_6H_5OC_6H_4Si > \text{cyclo-}C_6H_{11}C_6H_4Si$$
$$> C_6H_5C_6H_4C_6H_4Si > C_nH_{2n+1}C_6H_4Si$$

The introduction of a methyl group on a benzene ring also lowers the stability of its bond with silicon. The ortho position is more significantly affected than the para position.[22] It is of interest that phenyltrimethylsilane decomposes at temperatures above 700°, whereas its carbon analogue, *tert*-butylbenzene, at temperatures of about 600°. The increased stability of silicon compounds has been attributed[22] to the operation of a p_π-d_π conjugation between the aromatic ring and the silicon atom.[27]

Reactions of organosilicon compounds initiated by radiation (γ-rays, ultraviolet light) have some features similar to the thermally initiated radical fissions. However, since in most of the previous studies an application goal prevails (such as the resistance of silicone polymers toward irradiation[28–30] or the use of irradiation to vulcanize silicone elastomers[31,32]), it does not seem necessary to give them detailed attention here. However, a radical fission of the Si—CH_3 bonds[33] results in the formation of cross-linkages of type Si—Si and Si—CH_2—Si (in addition to Si—CH_2CH_2—Si) between molecules of dimethylsiloxanes. Gases formed in this case contain primarily methane, hydrogen, and ethane.[34–36]

A more detailed knowledge is available of reactions in a silent electric discharge. In particular, the decomposition of hexamethyldisiloxane,[37–41] trimethylethylsilane,[40,42] tetramethylsilane,[16] and methylchlorosilanes [40,43–46] has been thoroughly studied.

Compared to pyrolysis, a somewhat different situation arises in the thermal oxidation decomposition of organosilicon compounds. In these reactions the fission of the Si—C bonds also takes place; however, it is often very difficult to decide whether this fission proceeds by a homolytic or heterolytic mechanism.

Tetraarylsilanes are most stable toward thermal oxidation. Tetraphenylsilane can be distilled in air at 440° and tris-(p-biphenylyl)phenylsilane at 570°.[47] Tetrafurylsilanes show similar heat resistance in air.[48]

From the practical point of view it is of particular interest to know how the structure of organic substituents affects the thermal stability of polysiloxanes. It was found that this stability decreases with the increasing length of attached alkyl groups.[49] The oxidation of polydimethylsiloxanes starts around 200°: that of polyethylsiloxanes at 138° and of polydibutylsiloxanes at 120°.[50] Polysiloxanes, possessing vinyl groups in addition to methyl and phenyl groups, are distinctly less stable toward oxidation.[51] The replacement of even a small number of methyl groups by ethyl groups, or especially hydrogen atoms, markedly increases the rate of oxidation of the methyl groups in polydimethylsiloxanes.[52] On the other hand, if the methyl groups are replaced by phenyl groups, the thermal oxidation stability significantly increases.[50–54]

Polymers containing exclusively phenyl groups undergo oxidation only at temperatures above 400°. The stabilization effect of phenyl groups and other aryl groups has also been observed in the irradiating of polysiloxanes by γ-rays.[28,29,55,56] In these cases even a small number of aromatic groups exerts unexpectedly impressive stabilization on the oxidation of the methyl group. The same result can be achieved by introducing phenyl groups directly into the main chain of the polymer.[53,57] On the basis of thermal analysis and kinetic measurements of the methyl group fission, it is obvious[52] that polymers containing meta-phenylene links are more stable than those possessing para-phenylenes:

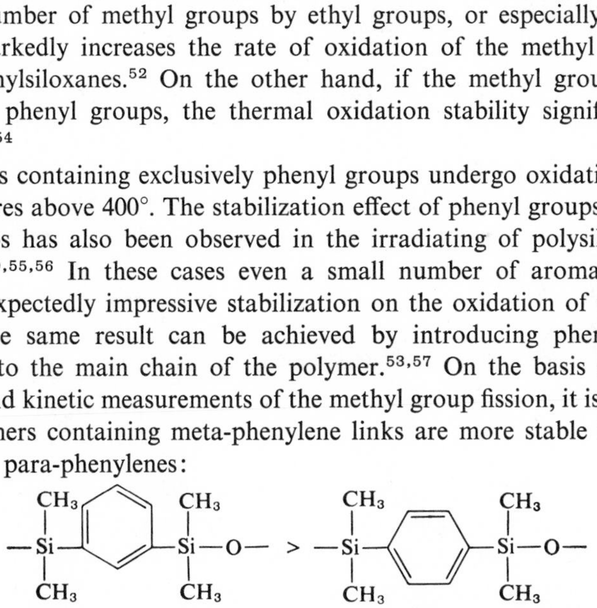

Either of these two types of polymers is markedly more stable than polydimethylsiloxanes. Since the investigation of pyrolysis of methylphenylsilanes in homogenous phase revealed that phenyl groups are thermally more readily split off from silicon than methyl groups,[22,23] it is obvious that thermally initiated fission of these groups is not decisive for the rate of oxidation at high temperatures.

Phenyl groups might also increase thermal oxidation stability of phenyl-methylsilicon compounds due to their steric effect;[49,58,59] however, a pronounced increase in oxidation stability of polydimethylsiloxanes, caused by introducing a relatively small number of phenyl groups into the polymer, cannot be explained by a steric hindrance of methyl groups. It seems that phenyl groups behave similarly to inhibitors and operate as free radical traps.[60] It has been found[61] that phenyl groups attached to a siloxane chain are approximately 16 times as active as benzene, as far as an addition of methyl radicals is concerned.

B. Splitting of the Silicon–Alkyl Bond

Alkyl groups are split off from the silicon atom most often by nucleophilic attack on silicon by strong bases.[62] This splitting proceeds more readily as the silicon becomes more electropositive because of substitution by electron-withdrawing groups. The same explanation is given for the substitution of alkyl groups.

Methylsiloxanes and ethylsiloxanes are cleaved by potassium hydroxide only at higher temperatures:[63–66]

$$(CH_3)_3SiOSi(CH_3)_3 + H_2O \xrightarrow{OH^-} (CH_3)_3SiO[Si(CH_3)_2O]_xSi(CH_3)_3 + CH_4$$
(Ref. 67)

The cleavage is facilitated by the increasing number of siloxane oxygen atoms on demethylated silicon. In some special cases, the splitting of the silicon–methyl bond by the action of organolithium agents has been observed:[68–70]

The splitting-off of alkyl groups substituted by electronegative atoms takes place at substantially milder conditions. Alkyl groups substituted in the β-position by halogen, oxygen, or nitrogen atoms are split off most readily. In this case the cleavage, giving rise to olefins, proceeds by a β-elimination mechanism:[67,71–77]

$$(C_2H_5)_3SiCH_2CH_2Cl + H_2O \longrightarrow (C_2H_5)_3SiOH + CH_2{=}CH_2 \quad \text{(Ref. 78)}$$

The elimination of β-bromo- and β-iodo-substituted derivatives proceeds analogously. This reaction takes place even at ambient temperatures so smoothly that β-halogeno-substituted alkyl groups can be quantitatively determined by titration. The β-elimination can be brought about by the action of Grignard reagents:[78]

$$(CH_3)_3SiCH_2CH_2Cl + CH_3MgBr \longrightarrow (CH_3)_4Si + CH_2{=}CH_2 \quad \text{(Ref. 72)}$$

Fluoro-derivatives substituted in the β-position undergo elimination less readily:[79,80]

$$F_3SiCH_2CHF_2 \xrightarrow{\;200°\;} SiF_4 + CHF{=}CH_2 \quad \text{(Refs. 81,82)}$$

Halogens in the α- and γ-positions[72,83,84] facilitate the splitting-off of alkyl groups less significantly. Nevertheless, the reaction proceeds smoothly at elevated temperatures by the action of both alkali metal hydroxides[85] or alkoxides[86] and alkali metal amides.[87] The reaction conditions are dependent on the structure of substituents attached to the dealkylated silicon. α-Chloroalkyltrialkyl derivatives[88] are cleaved distinctly less readily than α-chloroalkylsiloxanes.[64,89] The rate of the reaction is dependent on the solubility of the compounds cleaved in the studied medium and on the type of base used. Alkali metal hydroxides[90,91] are more efficient than the corresponding ethoxides.[86,92]

The splitting-off of chloromethyl groups usually proceeds simultaneously with the substitution on carbon. Depending on reaction conditions and the structure of starting compounds, the former or the latter reaction prevails; in most cases, however, the splitting-off of the whole group proceeds, giving rise to methyl chloride:[64,89,93–95]

$$(C_6H_5)_3SiCH_2Cl + H_2O \xrightarrow{\;K_2CO_3\;} (C_6H_5)_3SiOH + CH_3Cl \quad \text{(Ref. 96)}$$

The splitting-off of the bromomethyl group also proceeds in this way.[97]

The rate of the splitting-off of haloalkyl groups increases with the increasing number of halogen atoms in alkyl groups.[64] The dichloromethyl group in $(CH_3)(CHCl_2)SiCl_2$ can be split off by water, if the hydrogen chloride formed is neutralized.[98] The cleavage of dichloromethyl-substituted silanes, disilanes, and siloxanes by the action of potassium acetate[89] or alkali metal alkoxides in alcoholic medium proceeds quite smoothly:[64,85,98,99]

$$(CH_3)_3SiCHCl_2 + C_2H_5OH \xrightarrow{\;C_2H_5ONa\;} (CH_3)_3SiOC_2H_5 + CH_2Cl_2 \quad \text{(Ref. 100)}$$

The cleavage of dibromomethyltrimethylsilane[101] and dibromomethyl-substituted siloxanes[102] occurs at similar conditions, dibromomethylene being formed.

Trichloromethyltriphenylsilane[103] is cleaved quantitatively by means of alkali metal hydroxides; however, trichloromethyltrichlorosilane,[86,91,104] bis(trichloromethyl)dichlorosilane,[105] and similar compounds[98,106] undergo cleavage in the reaction with water:

$$CCl_3SiCl_3 + H_2O \longrightarrow HCCl_3 + SiO_2 + 3HCl$$

The splitting-off of the trichloromethyl group is also brought about by organolithium agents.[107] The tribromomethyl group is split off in a similar way:

$$Br_3CSi(CH_3)_3 + H_2O \xrightarrow{CH_3COCH_3} HCBr_3 + (CH_3)_3SiOSi(CH_3)_3 \quad \text{(Ref. 101)}$$

The splitting-off of the trifluoromethyl group proceeds less easily.[108] However, by the action of alkalies even polyfluoroalkyl groups can be quantitatively split off.[79,109–115] This can be utilized for their quantitative determination.

The effect of oxygen-containing substituents attached to alkyl groups in the ease of the splitting-off of the alkyl groups, is similar to that of halogens. Trialkylsilylcarbinols are relatively resistant toward alkalies; however, triphenylsilylmethanol is easily cleaved by the action of sodium ethoxide in ethanol:[116]

$$(C_6H_5)_3SiCH(OH)(CH_3)_2 + C_2H_5OH \xrightarrow[\text{reflux}]{KOH}$$
$$(C_6H_5)_3SiOC_2H_5 + CH_3CHOHCH_3 \quad \text{(Ref. 117)}$$

Compounds possessing the carbonyl group bound directly to silicon undergo cleavage most easily:[118–122]

$$(C_6H_5)_3SiCOC_6H_5 + H_2O \xrightarrow{10\% \text{ NaOH}} (C_6H_5)_3SiOH + C_6H_5CHO \quad \text{(Ref. 118)}$$

$$CH_3(C_6H_5)_2SiCOOH + C_2H_5OH + H_2O \xrightarrow{10\% \text{ NaOH}}$$
$$CH_3(C_6H_5)_2SiOH + CO \quad \text{(Ref. 118)}$$

This cleavage is further facilitated by electron-withdrawing substituents attached to silicon.[117,123,124] Silyl-substituted formaldehyde, which is formed as an intermediate in hydrolyzing trimethylvinylsilane ozonide, is also very easily cleaved:[125]

$$(CH_3)_3SiCH(O_3)CH_2 + H_2O \xrightarrow{ZnO} (CH_3)_3SiCHO + HCHO \longrightarrow$$
$$(CH_3)_3SiOH + HCHO \quad \text{(Ref. 125)}$$

Compounds containing β-oxo-substituted alkyl groups are cleaved by refluxing in ethanol:[126,127]

$$(CH_3)_3SiCH_2COCH_3 + C_2H_5OH \longrightarrow (CH_3)_3SiOC_2H_5 + CH_3COCH_3 \quad \text{(Ref. 126)}$$

Alkyl derivatives having oxygen-containing substituents bound to a γ-position are comparatively resistant toward splitting.[128]

Cyano-substituted derivatives are cleaved most easily, when the cyano group nitrogen is bound to the β-carbon:

$$(CH_3)_3SiCH(CH_3)CN \xrightarrow{KOH + H_2O} CH_3CH_2OH + (CH_3)_3SiOSi(CH_3)_3 \quad \text{(Ref. 128)}$$

The splitting-off of alkyl groups from silicon can also be brought about by the action of strong electrophilic agents. These reactions are sometimes undesirable; however, in some cases they can be employed to advantage for synthetic purposes.

Detailed attention has been paid to the cleavage by means of acids. The splitting-off of methyl groups[130]

$$C_6H_5CH_2Si(C_2H_5)(n\text{-}C_3H_7)CH_3 \xrightarrow[\text{(2) } H_2O]{\text{(1) } H_2SO_4}$$
$$CH_4 + [HSO_3C_6H_4CH_2Si(C_2H_5)\text{—}(n\text{-}C_3H_7)]_2O \quad \text{(Ref. 131)}$$

takes place in the sulfonation of benzylmethyl-substituted silanes, even under comparatively mild conditions. This apparently results from a good solubility of the sulfonic acid formed in concentrated sulfuric acid. The same principle can be used for the preparation of other disiloxanes substituted by organofunctional groups to increase the solubility of thè compounds in sulfuric acid:[93,132–141]

$$(CH_3)_3SiCH_2CH_2COCH_3 \xrightarrow[\text{(2) } H_2O]{\text{(1) } H_2SO_4} CH_4 + [CH_3COCH_2CH_2Si(CH_3)_2]_2O$$
$$\text{(Ref. 142)}$$

$$(CH_3)_3SiCH_2CH_2NH_2 \xrightarrow[\text{(2) } H_2O]{\text{(1) } H_2SO_4} CH_4 + [NH_2CH_2CH_2Si(CH_3)_2]_2O \quad \text{(Ref. 143)}$$

At relatively low temperatures the ethyl and propyl groups are split off more readily than the methyl group. On the other hand, the isoamyl, butyl, and amyl groups are split off less readily.[136,144,145] The reaction is facilitated by the addition of sodium sulfate.[134]

Tetraalkylsilanes, which are insoluble in sulfuric acid, are cleaved substantially less easily, and can be freed of siloxanes by shaking with the acid, in which siloxanes dissolve forming silyl-substituted sulfuric acids or disilyl sulfates. However, at elevated temperatures tetramethylsilane, as well as other alkyl-substituted derivatives, undergoes cleavage. The splitting-off of alkyl groups by hot sulfuric acid gives rise to the corresponding hydrocarbon in very good yields. Therefore, this procedure can be employed in semi-quantitative determination of alkyl groups.[146,147]

In the cleavage of hexamethyldisilalkylenes $(CH_3)_3Si(CH_2)_nSi(CH_3)_3$, under mild conditions predominantly, the methyl groups are split off, the Si—CSi bond being cleaved to a lesser extent.[148] In contrast, the splitting of the silicon–carbon bond of the four- and five-membered silacycloalkanes and spirosilacycloalkanes[149,150] (in particular those sterically strained) proceeds very easily, e.g.,

(Ref. 151)

In the case of six-membered methyl-substituted silacycloalkanes, the splitting-off of the methyl group occurs simultaneously with ring-opening.[151]

The splitting-off of the methyl groups of methyl-substituted disilanes can be brought about by hydrogen chloride or hydrogen fluoride in sulfuric acid, chloro-substituted derivatives being formed:

$$(CH_3)_3SiSi(CH_3)_3 + HCl \longrightarrow (CH_3)_3SiSi(CH_3)_2Cl + CH_4 \qquad \text{(Ref. 152)}$$

After the splitting-off of one methyl group, further reaction proceeds markedly less readily, apparently due to an electron withdrawal exerted by the electronegative substituent. The reaction can be carried out only to the first step with good yields of the corresponding products. The reaction proceeds via cleavage by the sulfuric acid, after which the Si—O—S bond is cleaved in the homogeneous phase by hydrogen halide:

$$(CH_3)_3SiSi(CH_3)_3 \xrightarrow[HCl]{H_2SO_4} [(CH_3)_3SiSi(CH_3)_2O]_2SO_2 \xrightarrow{HCl \text{ or } HF}$$

$$\xrightarrow{HCl} [(CH_3)_3SiSi(CH_3)]_2Cl \qquad \text{(Refs. 153,154)}$$

$$\xrightarrow{HF} [(CH_3)_3SiSi(CH_3)]_2F \qquad \text{(Ref. 155)}$$

In the cleavage of chloromethylpentamethylsilane, one of the methyl groups attached to the silicon unsubstituted by the chloromethyl group is split off, apparently because the electron-withdrawing effect of the chloromethyl group makes an electrophilic attack in its neighborhood more difficult.

In the presence of aluminum chloride the methyl groups are easily split off by the action of hydrogen chloride from both tetraalkylsilanes (the rate of the splitting-off is:

$$CH_3 \gg C_2H_5 > n\text{-}C_4H_9,\, n\text{-}C_3H_7 > i\text{-}C_3H_7 \qquad \text{(Ref. 156)}$$

the chloromethyl group being split off slowly[157]) and disilanes. By the use of this procedure, hexamethyldisilane can be demethylated to different degrees, depending on the reaction temperature used:

$$(CH_3)_3SiSi(CH_3)_3 \xrightarrow[20°]{HCl(AlCl_3)} (CH_3)_3SiSi(CH_3)_2Cl \xrightarrow[55°]{HCl(AlCl_3)}$$

$$Cl(CH_3)_2SiSi(CH_3)_2Cl \xrightarrow[90°]{HCl(AlCl_3)} Cl(CH_3)_2SiSiCH_3Cl_2$$

Disilmethylenes are cleaved less readily than disilanes; at high temperatures the reaction involves the splitting of the Si—CH$_2$Si bond:

$$(CH_3)_3SiCH_2Si(CH_3)_2Cl \xrightarrow{HCl}_{700°} (CH_3)_3SiCl + (CH_3)_2SiCl_2 \qquad \text{(Ref. 158)}$$

Alkyl groups substituted in the α- or β-positions by chlorine,[97,159-163] oxygen, or nitrogen[164-166] atoms are easily split off.

$$(CH_3)_3SiCH_2COOC_2H_5 \xrightarrow{HCl} CH_3COOC_2H_5 + (CH_3)_3SiCl \qquad \text{(Ref. 127)}$$

$$(CH_3)_3SiCH_2CHOHCH_3 \xrightarrow{H_2O(H^+)} CH_3CH{=}CH_2 + [(CH_3)_3Si]_2O \qquad \text{(Ref. 167)}$$

$$p\text{-}(CH_3)_3SiCH_2C_5H_4N \xrightarrow{H_2O(H^+)} CH_3C_5H_4N + [(CH_3)_3Si]_2O \qquad \text{(Ref. 168)}$$

Nitrogen dioxide cleaves even under mild reaction conditions in the liquid phase, tetraethylsilane giving rise to nitroethane and hexaethyldisiloxane;[169] nitrogen trioxide and nitrogen oxide react in a similar way.[170]

Halogens, in particular, iodine,[171] are of importance in the cleavage of the silicon-alkyl bonds. The reaction takes place smoothly upon refluxing the reaction mixture, especially if the corresponding aluminum halide is used as a catalyst. Reactions of this type can be employed to advantage, e.g., for the preparation of alkyliodosilanes derived from easily available tetraalkyl-silanes.[172] Since the presence of iodine in the molecule to be cleaved makes further splitting more difficult, the reaction can be stopped after the splitting-off of the first alkyl group. The second alkyl group can also be split off by the action of halogens. However, dialkyldiiodosilanes will resist further cleavage. The fact that alkyl groups are split off less readily than phenyl groups, and that there is appreciable difference in the reactivity of the individual alkyl groups ($CH_3 > C_2H_5 > n\text{-}C_3H_7 \approx i\text{-}C_3H_7$) can be exploited for the preparation of differently substituted alkyl iodides.

The perfluoropropyl group splits off very easily. Alkyl groups substituted by oxygen are extremely liable to splitting-off by the action of bromine, even in the absence of a catalyst:[127]

$$(CH_3)_3Si(CH_2)_3OCH_3 + Br_2 \longrightarrow (CH_3)_3SiBr + Br(CH_2)_3OCH_3 \qquad \text{(Ref. 138)}$$

A relatively ready splitting-off of alkyl groups takes place by means of aluminum halides[173] and other metal salts such as mercuric chloride,[174] magnesium chloride,[175] ferric chloride,[176] gallium trichloride,[177,178] and bismuth trichloride.[174,179] This reaction is in fact analogous to redistribution reactions of tetraalkylsilanes (see p. 212). Not only siliconalkyl, but even $Si-(CH_2)_nSi$ bonds are split:

$$(C_2H_5)_4Si + 4AlCl_3 \longrightarrow SiCl_4 + 4C_2H_5AlCl_2 \qquad \text{(Ref. 180)}$$
$$(CH_3)_3SiCH_2CH_2Si(CH_3)_3 + FeCl_3 \longrightarrow (CH_3)_3SiCl + \text{olefins} + \text{polymers} \qquad \text{(Ref. 176)}$$
$$(CH_3)_3SiCH_2Cl + GaCl_3 \longrightarrow ClCH_2Si(CH_3)_2Cl + CH_3GaCl_2$$
$$\text{(Refs. 177,178)}$$
$$(Cl_3Si)_4C + SbF_3 \longrightarrow SiF_4 \qquad \text{(Ref. 181)}$$
$$(C_2H_5)_4Si + HgCl_2 \longrightarrow (C_2H_5)_3SiCl + C_2H_5HgCl \qquad \text{(Ref. 174)}$$

This type of splitting is facilitated by electron-withdrawing groups and is sometimes undesired, e.g., if Friedel-Craft's alkylation is to be carried out using chloroalkylsilanes:[90]

$$(C_2H_5)Cl_2SiCHClCH_3 \xrightarrow{AlCl_3} CH_2{=}CH_2 + C_2H_5SiCl_3 \qquad \text{(Ref. 78)}$$

$$(CH_3)_3SiCH_2CH_2CH_2Cl \xrightarrow{AlCl_3} CH_2 \underset{\underset{\displaystyle CH_2}{\diagdown\diagup}}{\overline{\qquad}} CH_2 + (CH_3)_3SiCl \qquad \text{(Ref. 182)}$$

$$(CH_3)_3Si(CH_2)_4Cl \xrightarrow{AlCl_3} CH_3CH_2CH{=}CH_2 + (CH_3)_3SiCl \qquad \text{(Ref. 182)}$$

$$(CH_3)_3Si(CH_2)_5Cl \xrightarrow{AlCl_3} CH_3CH_2CH_2CH{=}CH_2 + (CH_3)_3SiCl \qquad \text{(Ref. 182)}$$

The cleavage brought about by the action of Grignard reagents is of a similar type.[72,183] That is why, e.g., in the alkylation

$$Cl_3SiCH_2CH_2Cl + 4C_2H_5MgBr \longrightarrow (C_2H_5)_4Si + CH_2{=}CH_2 + MgBrCl$$
(Ref. 83)

an excess of Grignard reagent has to be avoided, since the reagent also replaces the β-chloroethyl group.[83]

Alkoxyalkyl groups undergo ready splitting-off by means of metal salts such as aluminum chloride[138] or zinc chloride.[160] These two salts can be used, even in catalytic amount if acyl chlorides[160,184–186] or acid anhydrides are employed:

$$(CH_3)_3SiSi(CH_3)_3 + (CH_3CH_2CH_2CO)_2O \xrightarrow{\text{AlCl}_3} CH_3CH_2CH_2COCH_3$$
$$+ CH_3CH_2CH_2COO(CH_3)_2SiSi(CH_3)_3 \quad \text{(Ref. 187)}$$

$$(CH_3)_3SiCH_2Si(CH_3)_3 + CH_3COCl \xrightarrow{\text{AlCl}_3} (CH_3)_2CO$$
$$+ Cl(CH_3)_2SiCH_2Si(CH_3)_2Cl \quad \text{(Ref. 188)}$$

Aluminum halides used as catalysts, also alkyl halides,[180,188,189] even at ambient temperature, are effective as halogenation agents:

$$(n\text{-}C_4H_9)_4Si + i\text{-}C_5H_{11}Cl \xrightarrow{\text{AlCl}_3} (n\text{-}C_4H_9)_3SiCl + \text{hydrocarbons} \quad \text{(Ref. 190)}$$

$$(C_2H_5)_3SiSi(C_2H_5)_3 + i\text{-}C_3H_7Br \xrightarrow{\text{AlCl}_3} (C_2H_5)_3SiSi(C_2H_5)_2Br + \text{hydrocarbons}$$
(Ref. 191)

$$(CH_3)_3SiCH_2CH_2COCl \xrightarrow{\text{AlCl}_3} (CH_3)_3SiCl + CH_2{=}CH_2 + CO \text{ (Ref. 141)}$$

$$ClCH_2Si(CH_3)_2(CH_2)_3Si(CH_3)_3 \xrightarrow{\text{AlCl}_3} Si(CH_3)_2(CH_2)_4 + (CH_3)_3SiCl \quad \text{(Ref. 192)}$$

Alkyl groups substituted by electron-attracting atoms, in particular, halogens, are often split off from silicon at elevated temperatures. The mechanism of these reactions is in some cases homolytic; however, most often heterolytic fission occurs.

To a considerable extent such reactions occur with derivatives substituted only in the β-position of the silicon. The reactions follow the β-elimination mechanism and, as a rule, the β-elimination of halosilanes is accompanied with production of hydrogen halide:[193]

$$Cl_3SiCH_2CH_2Cl \xrightarrow{350°} SiCl_4 + CH_2{=}CH_2 + HSiCl_3 + CH_2{=}CHCl$$
$$+ CH_2{=}CHSiCl_3 + HCl \quad \text{(Refs. 194–196)}$$

$$\text{(Ref. 197)}$$

The reactions of this type often make the rectification of some β-chloro-substituted compounds quite impossible.[72,73,77,78,198] For instance, $(C_2H_5)_3SiCH_2CH_2Cl$ decomposes at 80°.[193]

Within the analogous range of temperatures, β-fluoro-substituted compounds are subject to decomposition:[79,80,82]

$$F_3SiCH_2CHF_2 \longrightarrow SiF_4 + CHF{=}CH_2 \qquad \text{(Ref. 81)}$$

The reaction proceeds in a similar way. On the other hand, the analogous decomposition

$$CHF_2CF_2SiF_3 \longrightarrow SiF_4 + CHF{=}CF_2 \qquad \text{(Ref. 82)}$$

cannot be reconciled with the β-elimination mechanism; e.g., in the presence of ethylene, trifluoroethylene is not formed. Instead, the reaction affords high yields of the cyclopropane derivative

$$\underset{\displaystyle CH_2}{CHF_2CF\diagdown\underline{}\diagup CH_2}$$

Apparently, the corresponding carbene $CHF_2\ddot{C}F$ is formed as a reaction intermediate in this case; in the absence of olefins it stabilizes by isomerization to trifluoroethylene, and in their presence it adds to them.

In general, if both the α- and β-carbons are substituted by halogens, the α- and β-elimination reactions proceed simultaneously.[79,199,200] Halo-substituted carbenes are formed by thermal decomposition of α-chloro-substituted derivatives. In this way, trichloromethyltrichlorosilane or other trichloromethyl-substituted silicon compounds[104,105,201,202] decompose at 200–250° to form dichlorocarbene,[199,203] which adds to the C=C double bond, giving rise to high yields of dichlorocyclopropane derivatives:[204]

$$CH_2{=}CHCH_2Si(CH_3)_3 + Cl_3CSiCl_3 \xrightarrow{250°} \underset{\displaystyle CCl_2}{CH_2\diagdown\underline{}\diagup CHCH_2Si(CH_3)_3} + SiCl_4$$

$$CH_2{=}CHSiCl_3 + Cl_3CSiCl_3 \xrightarrow{250°} \underset{\displaystyle CCl_2}{CH_2\diagdown\underline{}\diagup CHSiCl_3} + SiCl_4 \qquad \text{(Ref. 204)}$$

Alkylsilicon compounds having fluorine attached to the γ-position are appreciably more stable than the analogous α- and β- derivatives.[79,205] In their pyrolysis, the products of homolytic fission are formed. Therefore, 3,3,3-trifluoropropyl-substituted silanes undergo decomposition at high temperatures to yield $CF_3CH_2CH_3$, CF_3CH_3, and CF_3H; however, $CF_2{=}CHCH_3$ has been found among the gaseous products, and is apparently formed by the homolytic fission.[79] Upon pyrolysis of 3,3,3-trifluoropropyl-substituted silanes and siloxanes,[205,206] the 3,3,3-trifluoropropyl groups, because of their -I effect, are split off more readily than the methyl groups. At the same time, the presence of siloxane oxygen makes the splitting-off by both the homolytic and the heterolytic mechanism more difficult. With the increasing number of siloxane oxygens, the homolytic fission is slowed down more than the heterolytic.

C. Splitting-off of Alkenyl Groups

Vinyl groups are split off from silicon by means of nucleophilic agents with relative difficulty. It is necessary to use high concentrations of alkali metal hydroxides or alkoxides and elevated temperatures.[207] The vinyl groups substituted by halogens or oxygen undergo the reaction more easily:[208-213]

$$(C_2H_5)_3SiCF{=}CF_2 + NaOC_2H_5 \xrightarrow{C_2H_5OH} (C_2H_5)_3SiOC_2H_5 + CHF{=}CF_2$$
$$+ (C_2H_5)_3SiCF{=}CFOC_2H_5 \quad (Ref. 214)$$

$$Cl_3SiCH{=}CHCl + NaOH \xrightarrow{H_2O} CH_2{=}CHCl \quad (Refs. 215,216)$$

The splitting-off of allene groups, e.g., $-CH{=}C{=}CHCH_2N(C_2H_5)_2$,[217] $-CBr{=}C{=}CHCH_2Br$,[218] and $-CH{=}C{=}CHCH_2CH_2CH_3$,[219] proceeds relatively readily.

On the other hand, electrophilic agents, especially acids, easily split off the vinyl group:[220,221]

$$(CH_3)_3SiCH{=}CH_2 + H_2SO_4 \longrightarrow (CH_3)_3SiOSO_3H + CH_2{=}CH_2 \quad (Ref. 222)$$

Halogens and hydrogen halides do not bring about an appreciable cleavage, the only reaction usually being their addition to the double bond. In some cases desilylation has also been observed. This is the case, e.g., with $[(CH_3)_3Si]_2C{=}CH_2$, which reacts with both halogens and hydrogen halides at relatively low temperatures to give the corresponding trimethylhalogenosilane and mono-substituted derivative:

$$[CH_3)_3Si]_2C{=}CH_2 + Cl_2 \longrightarrow (CH_3)_3SiCl + (CH_3)_3SiCCl{=}CH_2 \quad (Ref. 223)$$

β-Styryltrimethylsilane undergoes a similar cleavage by the action of bromine.[215]

Allyl groups are split off from silicon very easily by means of a variety of agents. Of nucleophilic agents, aqueous alcoholic solutions of alkali metal hydroxides,[77] or even potassium carbonate,[73] can be used for this purpose. Aqueous solutions of the hydroxides seem to be less efficient, apparently because of the low solubility of organo-substituted silanes in water.

Sulfuric acid and hydrogen chloride bring about the ready splitting-off of the allyl group, resulting in the formation of propylene.[73,77,224,225] Cyclic derivatives with the double bond in the β-position to the silicon react in a similar way:

$$CH_3\diagdown CH—CH \diagup CH_3 \diagup \diagdown \begin{matrix} CH_2—CH_2 \\ \\ CH_2—CH \end{matrix} \diagdown \diagup C—CH_2Si(CH_3)_3 \; (+ \; H^+) \xrightarrow{H_2O}$$

$$CH_3 \diagdown CH—CH \diagup CH_3 \diagup \diagdown \begin{matrix} CH_2—CH_2 \\ \\ CH_2—CH_2 \end{matrix} \diagdown \diagup C{=}CH_2 \; + \; (CH_3)_3SiOSi(CH_3)_3 \quad (\text{Ref. 226})$$

However, hydrogen bromide and hydrogen iodide are ineffective. The reaction with bromine and iodine also proceeds smoothly:[208,225,227]

$$(CH_3)_3SiCH_2CH{=}CH_2 + I_2 \longrightarrow (CH_3)_3SiI + ICH_2CH{=}CH_2$$

In contrast, the allyl groups are not split off by the action of chlorine.

The readiness to split off alkenyl groups with the double bond in the γ- and more remote positions of the silicon is comparable to that of alkyl groups. Only the most efficient agents can be employed in the reaction.

D. Splitting-off of Alkynyl Groups

Alkynyl groups are split off from silicon by the action of nucleophilic agents more readily than are vinyl groups. It has been observed that the splitting of the Si—C≡CH bond occurs by means of water;[228] however, this observation seems to be disproved by further studies.[229,230] On the other hand, disilylacetylenes, silylphenylacetylenes and silylalkylacetylenes are cleaved by aqueous alkali metal hydroxides.[107,217,231–235]

The cleavage proceeds more easily, the more strongly the electrons of the C≡C bond are withdrawn by substituents attached to silicon or organic group bound to the acetylene. These structural effects have been studied in the splitting of silyl-substituted acetylenes by alkali metal fluorides or by potassium iodide.[236] Organolithium agents are also effective in the cleavage of the silicon-alkynyl bonds,[237,238] especially in the case of vinylethynyl derivatives:[219]

$$(C_6H_5)_3SiC{\equiv}CSi(C_6H_5)_3 + n\text{-}C_4H_9Li \longrightarrow (C_6H_5)_3SiC_4H_9\text{-}n$$
$$+ \; LiC{\equiv}CSi(C_6H_5)_3 \quad (\text{Ref. 239})$$

If the triple bond is located in the β-position of the silicon, the splitting-off of an alkynyl group by means of basic agents proceeds more readily than by means of acidic agents.[240] Propargyl derivatives, e.g., $(CH_3)_3SiCH_2C{\equiv}CH$, undergo the reaction under very mild conditions.

The ethynyl–silicon bond, similarly to the vinyl–silicon bond, is split by nucleophilic agents less easily than by acids.[241–245] The reaction proceeds smoothly even in the presence of silver nitrate:

$$C_6H_5C{\equiv}CSi(CH_3)_3 \xrightarrow{AgNO_3,H_2O} (CH_3)_3SiOSi(CH_3)_3 + C_6H_5C{\equiv}CH$$

In the case of halogens and hydrogen halides, instead of the splitting-off of the alkynyl group, the addition reaction occurs:

$$(C_2H_5)_3SiC\equiv CH + Br_2 \longrightarrow (C_2H_5)_3SiCBr=CHBr \qquad \text{(Ref. 245)}$$

The reactions of alkyl and acyl halides or organic acid anhydrides in the presence of aluminum chloride lead to ready replacement of silyl groups by organic substituents. These reactions may be of interest from the synthetic point of view:

$$(CH_3)_3SiC\equiv CSi(CH_3)_3 + (CH_3CO)_2O \xrightarrow{AlCl_3}$$
$$(CH_3)_3SiC\equiv CCOCH_3 + (CH_3)_3SiOOCCH_3 \quad \text{(Ref. 231)}$$

E. Cleavage of Aralkylsilicon Compounds

Aralkyl-substituted silanes with aryl groups bound to the α-carbon of the alkyl group exhibit extraordinarily high reactivity. These compounds are readily cleaved, particularly by means of nucleophilic agents, both by alkali metal hydroxides[246-248] and ethoxides[249] or alkali metal amides.[97,249] The stronger the electron-withdrawing effect of substituents bound to the silicon,[250] aryl,[95,251] or to the α-carbon groups, the more readily the reaction takes place.[97] A higher number of aryl groups attached to the α-carbon exerts great effect.[249] Thus diphenylmethyltrimethylsilane and the analogous 9-fluorenyltrimethylsilane is cleaved from two to five orders of magnitude more rapidly than benzyltrimethylsilane.[252]

The pyridyl group bound to the α-carbon exerts an effect similar to that of the phenyl group.[253] 4-Picolyltrimethylsilane undergoes ready cleavage by the action of both alkalies and acids.[168]

F. Splitting-off of Aryl Groups

This reaction proceeds most often by an electrophilic attack on the aryl group, probably by a mechanism similar to that of common electrophilic substitutions. A typical case is the cleavage of the silicon-aryl bonds by means of acids, halogens, or metal salts; the reaction is accelerated by electron-releasing groups attached to either the aryl group or silicon, whereas electron-withdrawing substituents exert a rate-retarding effect.

The cleavage by means of acids, e.g.,

$$(CH_3)_3SiC_6H_5 + H_2O \xrightarrow{H^+} (CH_3)_3SiOH + C_6H_6$$

is often from the synthetic point of view an undesired reaction. It may take place in the hydrolysis of a reaction mixture after Grignard synthesis of arylsilicon derivatives, while the magnesium salts are dissolved by acidified water, in acid-catalyzed reactions of functional groups, or in solvolysis of arylchlorosilanes. Therefore, detailed attention has been paid to the effect of the structure of arylsilicon compounds and to reaction conditions. Harmoniously, with their assumed mechanism, electron-releasing substituents facilitate the cleavage of the compounds of type $XC_6H_4Si(CH_3)_3$ in the following sequence: p-$N(CH_3)_2$ > p-OH > p-OCH_3 > o-OCH_3 > p-$CH_2Si(CH_3)_3$ > p-OC_6H_5 > p-SCH_3 > p-CH_3 > p-$C(CH_3)_3$ > p-SC_6H_5 > p-$CH_2C_6H_5$ > m-$CH_2Si(CH_3)_3$ > m-$C(CH_3)_3$ > p-C_6H_5 > m-CH_3 > p-$Si(CH_3)_3$.[254–257] Metallocene derivatives of type $RC_5H_5MC_5H_5SiR_3'$ are extraordinarily subject to the cleavage.[258–261] Electron-withdrawing substituents retard the cleavage of phenyltrialkylsilane derivatives, in the order: p-$N(CH_3)_3^+$ > p-NO_2 > m-NO_2 > p-SO_3H > m-CF_3 > p-$COOCH_3$ > p-COOH > m-COOH > m-Br > m-Cl > p-I > p-Br > p-Cl > m-SCH_3 > m-OC_6H_5 > m-OCH_3 > p-F.[262–272] The C_6F_5[273] group, with its very low basicity, is split off exceedingly slowly. The effect of substituents on the rate of cleavage can be roughly correlated with the values of their σ^+ constants.

The order of the rate of the splitting-off of different aryl groups corresponds as well to the order of reactivity of the respective positions in aromatic compounds in their electrophilic substitution.[263,274–276] The rate of the cleavage of the aryltrimethylsilanes decreases in the following way: 2-furyl > 2-thienyl > 3-pyrenyl > 1-thienyl > 2-fluorenyl > 2-benzothienyl > 2-dibenzofuryl > 9-phenanthryl > 2-naphthyl > phenyl.

Significant retardation of the silicon-aryl bond cleavage is brought about by electron-withdrawing substituents attached to dephenylated silicon atoms. Consequently, arylchlorosilanes,[275,276] arylethoxysilanes, and arylsiloxanes[277] are comparatively resistant to cleavage by acids. Since in these comparisons differences in solubility might play a certain role, the study has been performed on the effect of the number of oxygen-containing substituents in phenylmethylsilicon compounds at the same reaction conditions in dioxane or a dioxane–xylene mixture. The rate of the splitting-off of the phenyl groups by aqueous hydrogen chloride decreases in the sequence: $C_6H_5Si(CH_3)_3$ > $[(C_6H_5)(CH_3)_2Si]O$ > $[C_6H_5(CH_3)SiO]_3$ > $[(C_6H_5)SiO_{1.5}]_x$.[278,279]

Whereas in the acid-catalyzed cleavage of the aryl–silicon bond in aqueous or alcoholic medium siloxanes or alkoxysilanes, easily available by means of other synthetic methods, are formed from the silicon part of the molecule, the cleavage by the action of acids in the absence of a solvent can sometimes be utilized to advantage for preparing some organosilicon compounds. For instance, by cleaving phenylsilicon hydrides by means of anhydrous hydrogen halides, halogenosilanes can be prepared,[280–283] and by cleaving methylphenylsilanes some less available methylhalogenosilanes can be synthesized:

$$(C_6H_5)SiH_3 + HBr \longrightarrow C_6H_6 + SiH_3Br$$

$$(C_6H_5)(CH_3)_3Si + HBr \longrightarrow C_6H_6 + (CH_3)_3SiBr \qquad \text{(Ref. 284)}$$

The reaction with hydrogen bromide and hydrogen iodide proceeds most readily; hydrogen chloride cleaves phenylsilanes less readily; with hydrogen fluoride the reaction does not take place at all.[285]

The preparation of the pure isomers of nitrophenyltrialkylsilanes is important from the synthetic point of view. It has been found that in the action of concentrated nitric acid at low temperatures nitration to a mixture of o-, m-, and p-nitrophenyltrialkylsilanes (with less extensive cleavage of the phenyl–silicon bond under the formation of nitrobenzene) is the predominant reaction,[286–290] whereas at reflux temperatures the cleavage to give nitrobenzene proceeds quantitatively.[291] The nitro group in the product is attached exclusively to the carbon atom of the phenyl group, from which the trimethylsilyl group was split off.[291] This process can be utilized for synthetic purposes, e.g., in the cleavage of bis(p-trimethylsilyl)benzene:

$$p\text{-}(CH_3)_3SiC_6H_4Si(CH_3)_3 + HNO_3 \longrightarrow p\text{-}O_2NC_6H_4Si(CH_3)_3$$
$$+ (CH_3)_3SiOSi(CH_3)_3 \quad \text{(Ref. 292)}$$

The electronegative nitro group lowers the electron density on the benzene ring and further desilylation does not take place.

Similarly to other desilylation reactions of the aryl–silicon bonds occurring by the action of electrophilic agents, the rate of nitrodesilylation decreases with the increasing number of electron-withdrawing substituents on silicon. Thus, in the case of phenylhalogenosilanes and phenylmethylsiloxanes, the nitration of the phenyl groups proceeds without substantial cleavage of the silicon–carbon bonds.[293]

A principle similar to that used in the preparation of p-nitrophenyltrimethylsilane can be utilized for preparing p-trimethylsilylphenylsulfonic acids. Sulfuric acid at concentrations below 80% cleaves almost exclusively the phenyl–silicon bond with the formation of benzene, whereas concentrated sulfuric acid forms benzenesulfonic acid.[277] Similarly, the reaction of chlorosulfonic acid with tetraphenylsilane leads to benzensulfonyl chloride.[221,294] The sulfodesilylation is also brought about by the action of sulfur trioxide in carbon tetrachloride.[295] The esters of arylsulfonic acids so formed can be hydrolyzed to free sulfonic acids:

$$m\text{-}(CH_3)_3SiC_6H_4Si(CH_3)_3 + SO_3 \longrightarrow m\text{-}(CH_3)_3SiC_6H_4SO_3Si(CH_3)_3 \xrightarrow{H_2O}$$
$$m\text{-}(CH_3)_3SiC_6H_4SO_3H \quad \text{(Ref. 296)}$$

The rate of the sulfodesilylation reaction is controlled by usual rules of electrophilic substitution, and the effect of substituents X on the rate of cleavage of the compounds of type $XC_6H_4Si(CH_3)_3$ can be roughly correlated with their σ constants.

At higher temperatures, even weaker acids are effective in the cleavage of the phenyl–silicon bond. Formic acid splits the xylenyl–silicon bond; however, the phenyl–silicon bond is resistant toward cleavage.[276] At higher temperatures the splitting-off of phenyl groups occurs by the action of protons of silanols,[297]

$$Ar_2Si(OH)_2 \xrightarrow{200°} ArH + (ArSiO_{1.5})_x$$

the acidity of which is comparable to that of phenols. An interesting intramolecular reaction, which leads to silylpropionyloxysilanes, occurs at 200°. These compounds are obtainable by other methods only with difficulty:

$$CH_3(C_6H_5)_2SiCH_2CH_2COOH \xrightarrow{200°} CH_3(C_6H_5)Si(CH_2CH_2COOH)OCOCH_2CH_2$$
$$—Si(C_6H_5)_2CH_3 \quad \text{(Ref. 298)}$$

Splitting by means of halogens has been observed since the first attempts at halogenation of phenylsilicon compounds:

$$(C_6H_5)_4Si + Br_2 \longrightarrow C_6H_5Br + (C_6H_5)_3SiBr \qquad \text{(Ref. 299)}$$

$$(CH_3)_3SiC_6H_5 + I_2 \longrightarrow C_6H_5I + (CH_3)_3SiI \qquad \text{(Ref. 300)}$$

This type of splitting has sometimes been utilized for the determination of the mutual positions of substituents in substituted phenylsilanes.[286,301,302,304,305] For quantitative determination of phenyl groups, the cleavage by means of bromine in glacial acetic acid[303] can be employed to advantage; however, iodine monochloride proved to be the most efficient agent.[306]

The effect of the aryl group's structure on its ease of splitting-off from the silicon is similar to that observed in the cleavage by means of acids,[266,269] since the mechanism of the reaction is similar to that of aromatic electrophilic halogenation.[302,307–309] As a result, the danger of undesired splitting is less imminent when the phenyl group is substituted by an electron-withdrawing group.[302,310,311] In the chlorination and bromination of phenylchlorosilanes or phenylfluorosilanes, the participation of the halodesilylation reaction becomes increasingly pronounced with the decreasing number of halogen atoms bound to the silicon.[275,312–317] When aluminum chloride is used as the catalyst, the cleavage occurs to a greater extent, compared to using antimony trichloride, ferric chloride, or iodide.[312,313,318–320] This observation is also true for radical halogenation of methyl groups in tolylchlorosilanes:[288,321]

$$(CH_3C_6H_4)_2SiCl_2 + 2Cl_2 \xrightarrow{h\nu} CH_2ClC_6H_4SiCl_3 + CH_3C_6H_4Cl + HCl \quad \text{(Ref. 321)}$$

The rate of the cleavage of aryltrialkylsilanes markedly decreases with the increasing ability of alkyl substituents to withdraw electrons.[322]

The silicon-aryl bond is split less readily by iodine than by bromine.[283] The reaction can be facilitated by using aluminum iodide as a catalyst.[323]

The splitting reactions brought about by the action of metal salts, the cleavage of phenyl–silicon bonds by means of aluminum chloride, has practical value.[324] In the absence of hydrogen chloride the reaction leads to phenyldichloroaluminum[325–334] (but see Ref. 335), which can be utilized synthetically.[179,336] If stoichiometric amounts of hydrogen chloride are used, the reaction proceeds even in the presence of a catalytic amount of aluminum chloride:

$$(C_6H_5)_2SiCl_2 + HCl(+ AlCl_3) \longrightarrow C_6H_5SiCl_3 + C_6H_6 \qquad \text{(Ref. 337)}$$

The previous reaction is undesirable, e.g., in the rectification of a reaction mixture formed in the direct synthesis of phenylchlorosilanes, from aluminum contained in silicon of technical grade, aluminum chloride is formed. The aluminum chloride contaminates the condensate and, in its rectification, lowers the yield of diphenyldichlorosilane. This unwanted process can be avoided by the addition of sodium chloride which forms with aluminum chloride a less efficient complex compound, sodium tetrachloraluminate. A similar effect, though less pronounced than with aluminum chloride, is achieved with ferric chloride,[338] antimony pentachloride,[339] and phosphorus pentachloride.[275,294]

Under the catalysis of aluminum chloride, the silicon can be split off from aryl groups by the action of alkyl halides,[340] acyl halides,[335] and organic acid anhydrides:[341]

$$C_6H_5SiCl_3 + CH_3COCl \xrightarrow{\text{AlCl}_3} SiCl_4 + C_6H_5COCH_3 \qquad \text{(Ref. 335)}$$

Arylsilicon compounds are readily cleaved by mercuric oxide or salts of divalent mercury:[174,342,343]

$$[(C_6H_5)_2SiO]_3 + HgO \longrightarrow (C_6H_5)_2Hg + SiO_2 \qquad \text{(Ref. 344)}$$

$$[(C_6H_5)_3SiO]_2Hg \longrightarrow (C_6H_5)_3SiOHgC_6H_5$$
$$+ (C_6H_5)_3SiO[Si(C_6H_5)_2O]_nHgC_6H_5 \quad \text{(Ref. 345)}$$

The mercury again enters the position in the benzene ring from which the silyl group is split off. The effect of the structure on the reaction rate of this reaction—the so-called mercurydesilylation—is controlled by similar rules as protodesilylation. Its mechanism is apparently analogous to that of mercuration of aromatic compounds.[266,269,346]

Even though the splitting of the silicon-aryl bonds by means of nucleophilic agents is less common than the cleavage by acidic agents, it occurs in some cases.[116,347–351] In these reactions electron-withdrawing substituents facilitate nucleophilic attack on silicon.[107,322,352–355]. The reaction has been studied, in particular, using potassium hydroxide:

$$[(C_6H_5)SiO_{1.5}]_x \xrightarrow[500°]{\text{NaOH}} C_6H_6 + Si(ONa)_4 \qquad \text{(Ref. 350)}$$

The reaction rate rises with the acidity of the corresponding hydrocarbon: fluorenyl > m-$CF_3C_6H_4$ > 2-naphthyl > furyl.[107,167,253,351,356,357]

Still more efficient splitting agents than hydroxides of alkali metals are amides of these metals.[358-361] The splitting of the phenylsilicon bond has to be considered in the action of organolithium[70,362,363] or organosodium[364] agents, or even alkali metals.[365,366] In some cases this reaction can proceed by an intramolecular mechanism:

$$\underset{\displaystyle C_6Cl_5Si(C_6H_5)_2}{\overset{\displaystyle \overset{\textstyle H}{|}}{}} + C_6H_5Li \longrightarrow (C_6H_5)_3SiH + C_6Cl_5Li \qquad \text{(Ref. 367)}$$

$$(C_6H_5)_3SiOLi + n\text{-}C_4H_9Li \longrightarrow n\text{-}C_4H_9(C_6H_5)_2SiOLi + C_6H_5Li \qquad \text{(Ref. 368)}$$

$$(C_6H_5)_3Si(CH_2)_4Li \longrightarrow (C_6H_5)_2Si\underset{CH_2-CH_2}{\overset{CH_2-CH_2}{\big\langle}}\Big| + C_6H_5Li \qquad \text{(Ref. 69)}$$

$$\qquad \text{(Ref. 369)}$$

G. Disproportionation and Redistribution Reactions

In these types of reactions the same number of Si—C bonds is split and reformed, so that the over-all number of bonds in the system remains virtually unchanged. The reaction of tetraorgano-substituted silanes takes place slowly at elevated temperatures, even in the absence of a catalyst. It was observed in the case of phenylalkylsilanes at 400° and pressure in a hydrogen atmosphere:

$$C_6H_5Si(C_2H_5)_3 \xrightarrow{400°} (C_6H_5)_2Si(C_2H_5)_2 + (C_2H_5)_4Si \qquad \text{(Ref. 370)}$$

The usual method of redistribution of tetraalkylsilanes can be employed preparatively; as a rule, however, higher temperatures and Friedel-Crafts catalysts are used.[371,372] By refluxing a mixture of tetraethylsilane, tetrapropylsilane, and a small amount of aluminum chloride, a mixture of all the possible ethylpropylsilanes can be obtained in a statistical distribution without propyl groups being isomerized.[373] The redistribution of starting tetraorganosilanes with different substituents can be performed in a similar way.[327,328,374] The conditions and mechanism of these reactions have been studied in detail.[189,326-328] The effectiveness of the catalyst is proportional to its acidity,[327,328] and the reaction is accelerated by traces of polar compounds. While in the absence of the catalyst the reaction proceeds very slowly, with 2 mole % of aluminum chloride, a random distribution is achieved within 1 hr at 120°.[375] The redistribution of the Si—R and Si—H bonds proceeds more readily than the mutual exchange of organic groups:

$$4(C_6H_5)CH_3SiH_2 \xrightarrow{AlCl_3} (C_6H_5)_4Si + 2CH_3SiH_3 + (CH_3)_2SiH_2 \quad \text{(Ref. 376)}$$

$$4(C_2H_5)_2CH_3SiH \longrightarrow (C_2H_5)_2SiH_2 + 2C_2H_5(CH_3)_2SiH + (C_2H_5)_4Si$$
$$\text{(Ref. 377)}$$

Phenylsilicon compounds disproportionate, in general, more readily than alkylsilicon derivatives; organosilicon hydrides react most readily. Phenylsilicon hydrides disproportionate even in the presence of platinum or without any catalyst.[378] Disproportionation of phenylsilicon hydrides in a homogeneous gas phase was found to proceed not by a radical but by a bimolecular mechanism, via a four-center activated complex.[379] At temperatures above 300° the disproportionation of benzyl-, ethyl-, and propyl-substituted silicon hydrides takes place in the absence of catalyst.[381]

The disproportionation of alkyl groups and halogens bound to silicon proceeds less readily than the exchange of alkyl groups. In this case, not only the most active catalysts, such as aluminum chloride, boron chloride, zinc chloride, or cuprous chloride, but also larger quantities of these catalysts must be used,[375,380] and the reaction must be carried out at high temperatures (300–500°).

In the disproportionation of tetraalkylsilanes and silicon tetrachloride, the yields of the individual alkylchlorosilanes can be controlled by a suitable ratio of both components.[382] The method can also be applied to the preparation of arylchlorosilanes. In this case, in comparison with alkyl derivatives,[326,383] the reaction proceeds more readily, so that even cuprous chloride can be employed as a catalyst.[384] The reaction of tetraphenylsilane with silicon tetrachloride to give phenylchlorosilanes proceeds at 300° and 400° and increased pressure, even in the absence of a catalyst.[385,386] Diphenyldichlorosilane disproportionates at temperatures around 500° on a relatively less acidic aluminosilicate catalyst.[387,388]

The redistribution of alkylchlorosilanes is not random,[389–391] but the equilibrium is shifted to the left side:[392–393]

$$2(CH_3)_3SiCl \rightleftharpoons (CH_3)_2SiCl_2 + (CH_3)_4Si$$
$$2(CH_3)_2SiCl_2 \rightleftharpoons CH_3SiCl_3 + (CH_3)_3SiCl$$

The disproportionations of organo-substituted chlorosilanes can be utilized for the preparation of organochlorosilanes containing different organic groups and, eventually, the Si—H bonds:[394,395]

$(CH_3)_3SiCl + (C_6H_5)_2SiCl_2 \xrightarrow[500°]{NaAlCl_4} CH_3(C_6H_5)SiCl_2 + (CH_3)_2SiCl_2$
$+ CH_3SiCl_3 + C_6H_5SiCl_3 + (C_6H_5)_3SiCl + C_6H_6$ (48.6%)   (Ref. 396)

$C_2H_5SiHCl_2 + (C_6H_5)_2SiCl_2 \xrightarrow[500°]{NaAlCl_4} C_2H_5(C_6H_5)SiCl_2 + C_6H_5SiHCl_2$
$+ C_6H_5SiCl_3 + C_2H_5SiCl_3$ (52%)   (Ref. 396)

$C_2H_5SiHCl_2 \xrightarrow[reflux]{AlCl_3} C_2H_5SiH_3 + (C_2H_5)_2SiH_2 + 2(C_2H_5)_2SiCl_2$
$+ (C_2H_5)_3SiCl$ (Ref. 397)

$C_6H_5SiCl_3 + (C_2H_5)_2SiCl_2 \xrightarrow[325°]{AlCl_3} (C_2H_5)_3SiCl + C_2H_5(C_6H_5)SiCl_2$
$+ SiCl_4$ (Ref. 398)

$(CH_3)_3SiCl + C_6H_5SiCl_3 \xrightarrow[150°]{AlCl_3 + HSiCl_3} (CH_3)_2SiCl_2$
$+ CH_3(C_6H_5)SiCl_2$ (Ref. 399)

The presence of the Si–H bond in the reaction mixture facilitates the re-distribution of alkylchlorosilanes, so that the reaction of methylchlorosilanes

$$CH_3SiCl_3 + (CH_3)_3SiCl \xrightarrow[150°]{AlCl_3 + CH_3HSiCl_2} (CH_3)_2SiCl_2 \qquad (Ref. 399)$$

takes place in the presence of CH_3HSiCl_2 with a high yield of the product at 150°. These reactions can be performed with advantage in a flow reactor, using $NaAlCl_4$ on a suitable support as a nonvolatile heterogeneous catalyst.[396]

Redistribution reactions of methylchloro-substituted disilanes proceeds readily in the presence of aluminum chloride, even at ambient temperatures.[188,375]

Alkylbromosilanes are relatively more likely to disproportionate than alkylchlorosilanes.[395]

Redistribution cleavage of tetraorganosilanes catalyzed with aluminum halides can be utilized for the preparation of polymers with the Si—C_x—Si skeleton:[176,400,401]

p-$(CH_3)_3SiC_6H_4Si(CH_3)_3 \longrightarrow (CH_3)_4Si + [—Si(CH_3)_2C_6H_4—]_n$ (Ref. 400)

Similarly catalyzed reactions accompanied by the opening of the four- and five-membered silalkane and similar rings also lead to polymers:[402,403]

$$(CH_3)_2Si \overset{\displaystyle CH_2}{\underset{\displaystyle CH_2}{\diagup \diagdown}} CH_2 \longrightarrow [—(CH_3)_2Si(CH_2)_3—]_n \qquad (Ref. 402)$$

In the case of particularly sterically strained, four-membered silaalkane rings, the polymerization proceeds even in the absence of a catalyst;[404–406] however, with aluminum chloride it is substantially accelerated.[402,407,408]

$$(C_6H_5)_2Si \overset{\displaystyle CH_2}{\underset{\displaystyle CH_2}{\diagup \diagdown}} Si(C_6H_5)_2 \xrightarrow{180°} [—Si(C_6H_5)_2CH_2—]_n \qquad (Ref. 409)$$

Redistribution reactions can also be effected by means of basic catalysts. For the disproportionation of some alkenylethoxysilanes and arylethoxysilanes in the liquid phase, sodium ethoxide was employed as a catalyst:

$$C_6H_5(C_2H_5)Si(OC_2H_5)_2 \xrightarrow[\text{reflux}]{NaOC_2H_5} C_2H_5Si(OC_2H_5)_3 + (C_6H_5)_2C_2H_5SiOC_2H_5$$
$$+ (C_6H_5)_3SiC_2H_5 \quad \text{(Ref. 77)}$$

$$p\text{-}[C_2H_5O(CH_3)_2Si]_2C_6H_4 \xrightarrow[230°]{KOH} [\text{---}C_6H_4Si(CH_3)_2\text{---}]_n + (CH_3)_2Si(OC_2H_5)_2$$
$$\text{(Ref. 410)}$$

Phenylpolysiloxanes and methylphenylsiloxanes are disproportionated at high temperatures by the action of alkali metal hydroxides.[350]

H. The Cleavage of Silacycloalkanes

The ring-opening of silacycloalkanes proceeds easier the more they are sterically strained. The four-membered rings, whether saturated or unsaturated,[411] are cleaved most readily. The reaction is brought about by the action of alcohols or water at elevated temperatures,[412] and also by heating to temperatures about 150–200°:[404,406,407]

$$\longrightarrow [\text{---}Si(CH_3)C_2H_5(CH_2)_3\text{---}]_x$$

Disilacyclobutanes behave analogously:

$$\xrightarrow{180°} [\text{---}Si(C_6H_5)_2CH_2\text{---}]_x \quad \text{(Ref. 409)}$$

The polymerization of this type of compound proceeds still more easily if platinum metal is used as a catalyst.[413-416] Acidic[149] and basic[417,418] agents cleave silacyclobutanes under very mild conditions, similarly as do halogens, hydrogen halides,[412,415,419,420] and organolithium agents:[421,422]

$$C_6H_5CH\text{---}Si(C_6H_5)_2 + H_2O \xrightarrow{OH^-} C_6H_5(CH_2)_3Si(C_6H_5)_2OH \quad \text{(Ref. 422)}$$
$$\underset{CH_2\text{---}CH_2}{|\qquad\quad|}$$

Silacyclopentanes and silacyclohexanes are comparatively more resistant to the cleavage. Their polymerization does not proceed by the action of either high temperatures[423] or platinum metal.[424,425] The cleavage was only effected by using strong acidic agents, such as concentrated sulfuric acid[150,151,426] or aluminum chloride.[406] The rings containing the C=C bond or halogens are cleaved, of course, more easily. Such cases are analogous to reactions of either highly reactive alkenyl derivatives[427] or desilylation β-eliminations of

halogen derivatives. 1,1-Dichloro-1-silacyclopent-2-ene (9) and 1,1,3-
trichloro-1-silacyclohexane[428] (10)

$$
\begin{array}{cc}
\begin{array}{c}
CH_2\!\!-\!\!CH \\
| \qquad \| \\
CH_2 \quad CH \\
\diagdown \quad \diagup \\
Si \\
\diagup \quad \diagdown \\
Cl \qquad Cl
\end{array}
&
\begin{array}{c}
CH_2 \\
\diagup \quad \diagdown \\
CH_2 \quad CHCl \\
| \qquad | \\
CH_2 \quad CH_2 \\
\diagdown \quad \diagup \\
Si \\
\diagup \quad \diagdown \\
Cl \qquad Cl
\end{array} \\
(9) & (10)
\end{array}
$$

are examples of the former and the latter case, respectively.

I. Other Reactions Accompanied by Cleavage of the Si—C Bond

In the field of organosilicon chemistry, there is a great number of rearrangements occurring in such a way that an electronegative group or atom,
bound to the α-position of an organic substituent attached to the silicon, is
transferred to the silicon with simultaneous cleavage of the Si—C bond. As
a rule, these reactions proceed under the catalysis of strongly acidic or basic
agents:

$$(CH_3)_3SiCHClSi(CH_3)_3 \xrightarrow{\quad AlCl_3 \quad}$$
$$(CH_3)_3SiCH(CH_3)Si(CH_3)_2Cl \quad \text{(Ref. 94)}$$

$$(CH_3)_3SiSi(CH_3)_2CH_2Cl \xrightarrow{\quad AlCl_3 \quad}$$
$$(CH_3)_3SiCH_2Si(CH_3)_2Cl \quad \text{(Ref. 429)}$$

$$(C_6H_5)_3SiC(C_6H_5)_2OH \xrightarrow{\quad BF_3 \quad} (C_6H_5)_3CSi(C_6H_5)_2F \quad \text{(Ref. 430)}$$

$$(CH_3)_3SiSi(CH_3)_2CH_2Cl + C_2H_5OH \xrightarrow{\quad C_2H_5O^- \quad}$$
$$(CH_3)_3SiCH_2Si(CH_3)_2OC_2H_5 \quad \text{(Ref. 99)}$$

$$(CH_3)_3SiC(C_6H_5)_2OH \xrightarrow[(C_2H_5)_2O]{Na/K} (CH_3)_3SiOCH(C_6H_5)_2$$
$$\text{(Refs. 124,431)}$$

Interesting rearrangements occur in the reactions of diazomethane with
silylketones[432] of the type R_3SiCOR', which result in the formation of compounds of type $R_3SiOCR'\!\!=\!\!CH_2$, as well as other substances. The rearrangements of silylalkynylketones such as

$$(CH_3)_3SiC\!\!\equiv\!\!CCOCH_2COCH_2CH_3 \xrightarrow{120°} (CH_3)_3SiOC\!\!\equiv\!\!CH + CH_2\!\!=\!\!CH_2$$

are of interest.

However, the above-mentioned reactions are not intended to constitute
a definitive list. The reactions accompanied by the cleavage of the silicon–
carbon bond reported in the literature up to 1961 are compiled in the corresponding chapter of the monograph *Organosilicon Compounds*.[434] The

Register of Compounds[435] includes information as to whether each individual compound was prepared or whether it was just subjected to the reaction accompanying the bond cleavage. This problem is further treated in detail in the first volume of *Organometallic Compounds of the Group IV Elements,*[436] in which an excellent discussion of the mechanisms of individual types of the reactions mentioned above is presented.

III. EXPERIMENTAL PROCEDURES

1. Gasometric Determination of Alkyl Groups in Alkylsiloxanes[63]

$$\equiv Si-R + KOH \longrightarrow \equiv SiOK + RH \qquad (R = CH_3-, C_2H_5-)$$

A weighed sample (0.1–0.15 g) of alkylsiloxane placed in a decomposition test tube is combined with 2–3 g of powdered potassium hydroxide. The test tube is provided with an external electric heating jacket. The upper part of the jacket has a tubule leading gaseous products through a washing bottle of concentrated sulfuric acid and a three-way cock to a temperature-controlled gas burette. The burette is filled with mercury and connected by rubber tubing with a compensation flask. The decomposition takes place after heating the test tube to 250–270°; the evolution of gas ceases in about a 2-hr period. During the decomposition it is advisable to maintain the mercury level in the compensation flask somewhat higher than in the burette, so that the whole apparatus is under small overpressure. When the gas evolution is completed, the heating jacket is removed from the decomposition test tube and the whole apparatus is cooled to the temperature of the gas burette and the volume of gas is reduced to standard conditions. An average deviation of the determination from the theoretical volume of gas amounts to $\pm 0.7\%$.

The presence of aryl groups does not interfere with the determination. The method can also be used for the determination of alkyl groups in compounds possessing hydrolysable substituents bound to silicon (e.g., in methylphenyl-dichlorosilane).

2. Determination of Polyfluoroalkyl Groups by Hydrolysis[108]

$$\equiv SiCF_2CHF_2 + H_2O \xrightarrow{OH^-} \equiv SiOH + CHF_2CHF_2$$

A weighed amount of a volatile polyfluoroalkyl–silicon compound is transferred *in vacuo* to an evacuated 500-ml bulb fitted with a vacuum tap and taper joint. An excess of aqueous alkali is then added to the bulb by filling the taper joint above the tap with the solution and drawing it into the bulb by momentarily opening the tap. After being vigorously shaken, the volatile product is transferred to an apparatus for the vacuum manipulation of gases, where its volume and molecular weight are measured. Polyfluoroalkanes with boiling points up to 100° can be transferred quantitatively in this way. Less volatile polyfluoroalkylsilicon compounds (e.g., polysiloxanes) are weighed into a fragile tube which is sealed, and then inserted into a larger tube (50-ml) containing aqueous sodium hydroxide. The larger tube is sealed, then the inner tube broken by shaking. When the reaction is completed, the volatile products are transferred to the vacuum apparatus in the usual way.

3. 4,4,6,6-Tetramethyl-4,6-disila-5-oxanonanedioic Acid from β-Trimethyl-silylpropionic Acid[142]

$$2(CH_3)_3SiCH_2CH_2COOH \xrightarrow{H_2SO_4} \xrightarrow{H_2O}$$
$$[HO_2CCH_2CH_2Si(CH_3)_2]_2O + 2CH_4$$

β-Trimethylsilylpropionic acid (294 g) is added dropwise with stirring to 400 ml of cold (10°) concentrated sulfuric acid during 1.5 hr. A vigorous evolution of methane (*Caution!*) occurs during the addition. The reaction is completed by warming on a steam bath for 1 hr, until gas evolution ceases. Then the reaction mixture is cooled and poured onto cracked ice, giving immediate formation of a white solid. Recrystallization from *n*-hexane gives 265 g (95%) of 4,4,6,6-tetramethyl-4,6-disila-5-oxanoanedioic acid, mp53–54°.

4. Methylgallium Dichloride from Tetramethylsilane[178]

$$(CH_3)_4Si + GaCl_3 \longrightarrow CH_3GaCl_2 + (CH_3)_3SiCl$$

Into a tared three-necked flask fitted with a reflux condenser and drying tube under a nitrogen atmosphere is placed 9.4 g (0.0534 mole) of melted gallium trichloride prepared under nitrogen. Then 6.5 g (0.0737 mole) of tetramethylsilane is added with the exclusion of air, and the reaction mixture is refluxed at 70–90° for 10 min under the inert atmosphere. After the reaction mixture is cooled, the volatile products are distilled off *in vacuo* and collected in a trap. The distillation of the residue, the temperature of the flask being gradually increased, gives 7.6 g (91% yield) of methylgallium dichloride boiling at 70°/1 mm. The product can be repurified by sublimation (mp 75–76°).

5. Triethyliodosilane from Tetraethylsilane[172]

$$(C_2H_5)_4Si + I_2 \xrightarrow{AlI_3} (C_2H_5)_3SiI + C_2H_5I$$

In a three-neck flask fitted with a dropping funnel, nitrogen inlet, and a reflux condenser with a calcium chloride tube at its exit, 2 g of iodine and 0.4 g of aluminum iodide are added to 7.2 g of tetraethylsilane. The iodine is used up in a few minutes of boiling. The remaining iodine (10.7 g) is added in 2-g portions as it is used up, ethyl iodide being distilled off continuously from the top of the reflux air condenser. The reaction is completed in 3/4 hr. The reaction mixture is then distilled to give ethyl iodide (7.2 g, 90%) and 9.6 g (77%) of triethyliodosilane, bp 187–191°.

6. Pentaethylbromodisilane from Hexaethyldisilane[191]

$$(C_2H_5)_3SiSi(C_2H_5)_3 + (CH_3)_2CHBr \xrightarrow{AlCl_3} (C_2H_5)_3SiSi(C_2H_5)_2Br$$
$$+ C_3H_8 + CH_2{=}CH_2 + C_2H_6$$

Into a two-necked flask fitted with a dropping funnel and a reflux condenser topped with a calcium chloride drying tube are placed 25 g of hexaethyldisilane and 0.3 g of aluminum chloride. Then 12.3 g of isopropyl bromide is added dropwise, because the reaction is exothermic and involves the evolution of gaseous products. After the addition is completed, the reaction mixture is refluxed for 3 hr. A total of 2.2 liters of gas, containing 3.4% of ethane, 16.4% of ethylene, and 60.2% of propane, is evolved. The fractionation of the reaction mixture under reduced pressure yields 20.2 g (72. 2%) of pentaethylbromodisilane, bp 88°/2 mm (n_D^{20} 1.4680).

7. Cyclopropane from γ-Bromopropyltrimethylsilane[182]

$$(CH_3)_3Si(CH_2)_3Br \xrightarrow{AlCl_3} \underset{\underset{CH_2}{\diagdown\diagup}}{CH_2{-}CH_2} + (CH_3)_3SiBr$$

A solution of 19.1 g (0.098 mole) of γ-bromopropyltrimethylsilane is placed with a few crystals of sublimed aluminum chloride (ca. 0.2 g) in a 100-ml flask equipped with a reflux condenser and a dropping bottle for introduction of aluminum chloride. The exit end of the condenser leads to a 5-liter flask filled with a saturated salt solution, which is used to measure the volume of gas evolved. This reaction is spontaneous and the reaction mixture becomes somewhat cooler than room temperature. When most of the reaction has taken place, gentle heating is applied by means of a water bath held at 70°. Air is then passed into the reaction flask in order to sweep all of the gaseous product into the receiving flask. The gas mixture collected comprises 2290 ml of cyclopropane (92%) beside air. The gas mixture can be condensed in a trap cooled in a dry ice-acetone mixture.

8. Bis(3-trimethylsilylpropyn-2-yl)ether from 1,2-Bis(trimethylsilyl)-acetylene[231]

$$(CH_3)_3SiC{\equiv}CSi(CH_3)_3 + (ClCH_2)_2O \xrightarrow{AlCl_3} [(CH_3)_3SiC{\equiv}CCH_2]_2O + (CH_3)_3SiCl$$

To a mixture of 20 g of 1,2-bis(trimethylsilyl)acetylene and 15.6 g of aluminum chloride in 400 ml of carbon disulfide, 7.0 g of bis(chloromethyl)-ether dissolved in 20 ml of carbon disulfide is added dropwise with cooling to 2°. After 0.5 hr the reaction mixture is poured on ice-cooled dilute hydrochloric acid. After the decomposition of aluminum chloride is completed, the water layer is extracted several times by carbon disulfide. The organic layer is dried, and the solvent is stripped off. Fractionation of the residue under nitrogen yields 12.5 g (90% yield) of bis(3-trimethylsilylpropyn-2-yl)ether boiling at 121°/13 mm (n_D^{20} 1.4605).

9. 1-Trimethylsilyl-2-acetylacetylene from 1,2-Bis(trimethylsilyl)-acetylene [231]

$$(CH_3)_3SiC{\equiv}CSi(CH_3)_3 + (CH_3CO)_2O \xrightarrow{AlCl_3} (CH_3)_3SiC{\equiv}CCOCH_3$$
$$+ CH_3COOSi(CH_3)_3$$

To a mixture of 23.5 g of anhydrous aluminum chloride and carbon disulfide cooled to 2–8°, a solution of 15 g of 1,2-bis(trimethylsilyl)acetylene and 9 g of acetic anhydride in carbon disulfide is added dropwise. Stirring is continued for another half hour and then the reaction mixture is poured onto ice-cooled dilute hydrochloric acid. The water layer is extracted with carbon disulfide, the extract is dried, and the solvent is stripped off. Fractionation of the residue yields 8.5 g (68% yield) of 1-trimethylsilyl-2-acetylacetylene boiling at 156°/760 mm (n_D^{20} 1.4415).

10. Trimethylbromosilane from Phenyltrimethylsilane [300]

$$(CH_3)_3SiC_6H_5 + Br_2 \longrightarrow (CH_3)_3SiBr + C_6H_5Br$$

A 162-g (1 mole) portion of liquid bromine is added, while stirring, to 150 g (1 mole) of phenyltrimethylsilane in a flask cooled with cold tap water; the reaction mixture is heated on a steam bath for 1 hr. Fractional distillation gives 130 g (0.85 mole) of trimethylbromosilane, bp 79°/744 mm (85% yield) and 130 g (0.84 mole) of bromobenzene.

11. Trimethyl-p-nitrophenylsilane from p-Bis(trimethylsilyl)benzene [292]

$$p\text{-}(CH_3)_3SiC_6H_4Si(CH_3)_3 + HNO_3 \longrightarrow p\text{-}(CH_3)_3SiC_6H_4NO_2 + (CH_3)_3SiOSi(CH_3)_3$$

In a 100-ml flask are placed 5 g of p-bis(trimethylsilyl)benzene and 14 ml of acetic anhydride. A solution of fuming (95 wt %) nitric acid (6 ml) in 10 ml of acetic anhydride is added dropwise during 1.5 hr to the boiling solution. The cooled mixture is then added to water (100 ml) and extracted with ether. The extract is then washed with aqueous sodium hydroxide and water. After drying with anhydrous sodium sulfate, the ether is removed and the residue is taken up in light petroleum (bp 40–60°). The solution is passed through a column of alumina (which retains several colored bands) and is then concentrated and cooled in acetone-solid carbon dioxide, to give 3.6 g (82%) of trimethyl-p-nitrophenylsilane, mp 37°.

12. p-Trimethylsilylbenzenesulfonic Acid from p-Bis(trimethylsilyl)-benzene [296]

$$p\text{-}(CH_3)_3SiC_6H_4Si(CH_3)_3 \xrightarrow{SO_3} p\text{-}(CH_3)_3SiC_6H_4SO_2OSi(CH_3)_3 \xrightarrow{H_2O}$$
$$p\text{-}(CH_3)_3SiC_6H_4SO_2OH$$

A freshly prepared solution of sulfur trioxide (4.0 g, 0.05 mole), obtained by heating 65% oleum, in anhydrous carbon tetrachloride (40 ml) is added dropwise, excluding moisture, during a period of 10 min to a stirred solution of p-bis(trimethylsilyl)benzene (17 g, 0.077 mole) in carbon tetrachloride (70 ml) cooled with ice water. The mixture is refluxed gently for 15 min and then fractionally distilled to give bis(trimethylsilyl)benzene (5.1 g, 30%, bp 79°/2 mm) and 12.1 g (80% allowing for recovered starting material) of trimethylsilyl p-(trimethylsilyl)benzenesulfonate (bp 150–151°/2 mm, mp 83–86°). The sulfonate (3 g) is dissolved in water (15 ml); after 15 min the excess water and hexamethyldisiloxane are evaporated below 50° under reduced pressure, and the residue (2.4 g) recrystallized from benzene to give p-(trimethylsilyl)benzenesulfonic acid monohydrate (2.1 g, 85%, mp 89–90°, sealed tube).

13. Phenyldichlorophosphine from Phenyltrichlorosilane[334]

$$C_6H_5SiCl_3 + PCl_3 \xrightarrow{AlCl_3} C_6H_5PCl_2 + SiCl_4$$

In a flask fitted with a reflux condenser and a trap, cooled with acetone-solid carbon dioxide and topped with calcium chloride drying tube, is placed 100 g of phenyltrichlorosilane, 69.3 g of freshly resublimed anhydrous aluminum chloride and 65 g of phosphorus trichloride are added. The mixture is heated on a steam bath for 2 hr at 80°; then, after disconnecting the reflux condenser, it is freed of silicon tetrachloride (75.5 g, 94.4%) by distillation at reduced pressure, the chloride being collected in the trap. To the hot, oily distillation residue, 85.8 g of phosphorus oxychloride is added, producing a granular sediment. The sediment is washed several times with petroleum ether, the extracts collected and stripped of solvent. Distillation at reduced pressure affords 70.0 g (83.4%) of phenyldichlorophosphine (bp 140–141°/57 mm, d_{20}^{20} 1.3180).

14. (2,2-Dichlorocyclopropylmethyl)methyldichlorosilane from Allylmethyldichlorosilane and Dichlorocarbene Generated from Trichloromethyltrichlorosilane[204]

$$CH_2{=}CHCH_2(CH_3)SiCl_2 + Cl_3CSiCl_3 \longrightarrow \underset{\underset{CCl_2}{\diagdown\diagup}}{CH_2{-}}CHCH_2(CH_3)SiCl_2 + SiCl_4$$

In a 100-ml steel autoclave 15.5 g (0.1 mole) of allylmethyldichlorosilane and 25.3 g (0.1 mole) of trichloromethyltrichlorosilane are placed. The autoclave is dipped in a Wood's metal bath warmed at 270°. Within 1 min the temperature of the bath falls to the required reaction temperature 250° at which it is maintained for 30 min. Then the autoclave is removed from the bath and cooled to room temperature. The reaction mixture is distilled from glass wool under reduced pressure in a distillation apparatus connected to a trap cooled in an acetone-solid carbon dioxide mixture. After separation of the forerun (containing silicon tetrachloride and unreacted allylmethyldichlorosilane), the fraction of 15.9 g of (2,2-dichlorocyclopropylmethyldichlorosilane, bp 110–113°/18 mm (211°/742 mm, n_D^{20} 1.4865, d_4^{20} 1.3412, 62%) is isolated.

15. 1,1-Diphenylsilacyclopentane from Triphenylchlorosilane and Tetramethylenedilithium[69]

$$(C_6H_5)_3SiCl + Br(CH_2)_4Br + Li \longrightarrow (C_6H_5)_2Si\overset{\displaystyle CH_2CH_2}{\underset{\displaystyle CH_2CH_2}{\diagdown\diagup}} + C_6H_5Li$$

A solution of 21.6 g (0.1 mole) of 1,4-dibromobutane in 150 ml of anhydrous ether is added slowly with vigorous stirring to 5.0 g (0.72 g atom) of lithium sand, suspended in 50 ml of ether. The reaction is started by stirring for a few minutes at room temperature; the mixture thereafter is kept at −10 to −20°. After the addition is completed, the mixture is stirred for 1 hr at −10° and 0.5 hr at 10°. The solution is filtered through glass wool into an addition funnel. The tetramethylene dilithium solution is then slowly added, while stirring, to 55 g (0.187 mole) of triphenylchlorosilane in 50 ml of anhydrous ether. The reaction mixture is stirred for 1 hr at −10° and then allowed to warm to room temperature. The white precipitate is filtered and washed with ether and water, leaving 18 g of residue (A). The layers of the filtrate are separated, the organic layer is washed twice with water and the solvent removed by distillation.

In order to remove triphenylsilanol and hexaphenyldisiloxane, the hydrolysis products of unreacted triphenylchlorosilane, the residue from the distillation (B) is chromatographed on alumina. The products are eluted with petroleum ether (bp 60–70°) and benzene, combined with residue A and distilled at reduced pressure. At 159–160°/5 mm, 9.2 g (38.7%) of 1,1-diphenylsilacyclopentane (n_D^{20} 1.5855) are obtained. The second fraction, boiling at 210–230°/5 mm, an oil that partially solidifies, is recrystallized twice from methanol to give 1.3 g (5.4%) of n-butyltriphenylsilane, mp 85–86°. Further distillation gives 16 g of a fraction, boiling at 180–200°/0.05 mm, which is recrystallized from a mixture of benzene and ethanol to give 6.5 g of tetraphenylsilane, mp 232–234°. The yield of crude product is 48%, and of pure product 19.4%. The distillation residue can be dissolved in benzene, filtered, and precipitated with petroleum ether (bp 60–70°) to give 2.5 g (4.4%) of tetramethylene-bis-(triphenylsilane), mp 209–213° (after recrystallization from cyclohexane mp 215–216°).

16. Ethyl-n-propylsilanes from Tetramethylsilane and Tetra-n-propylsilane[374]

$$(C_2H_5)_4Si + (n\text{-}C_3H_7)_4Si \xrightarrow{\text{AlCl}_3} n\text{-}C_3H_7Si(C_2H_5)_3 + (n\text{-}C_3H_7)_2Si(C_2H_5)_2$$
$$+ (n\text{-}C_3H_5)_3SiC_2H_5$$

In a 100-ml, round-bottom flask is placed 20.2 g (0.14 mole) of tetraethylsilane and 30.1 g (0.15 mole) of tetra-n-propylsilane, together with 1.2 g of anhydrous aluminum chloride. The reaction mixture turns yellow, and then colorless during a 5-hr reflux period at 175–180°. The crude product is washed twice with water and dried over anhydrous potassium carbonate. Fractional distillation gives 2 g (5 mole %) of tetraethylsilane (bp 154.1°), 11.3 g (24 mole %) of n-propyltriethylsilane (bp 172.5°, n_D^{20} 1.4313), 18.6 g (39 mole %) of di-n-propyldiethylsilane (bp 187.4°, d^{20} 0.7764, n_D^{20} 1.4339), 4.4 g (26 mole %) of tri-n-propylethylsilane (bp 202.2°, d^{20} 0.7795, n_D^{20} 1.4362), and 3.9 g (7 mole %) of tetra-n-propylsilane (bp 213–215°).

17. Ethylphenyldichlorosilane from Diphenyldichlorosilane and Diethyldichlorosilane[396]

$$(C_2H_5)_2SiCl_2 + (C_6H_5)_2SiCl_2 \xrightarrow{\text{NaAlCl}_4} C_2H_5(C_6H_5)_2SiCl_2$$

The reaction is carried out in a glass flow reactor (25 mm i.d., 300 mm long) packed with brick shards as support for the catalyst, NaAlCl$_4$. The porous shards (65 g) are saturated with 17 ml of 10% sodium chloride solution and dried by heating at 150° for 3 hr. Then the shards are placed in a glass reaction tube through which 9 g of anhydrous aluminum chloride are sublimed in the stream of dry nitrogen. Over the catalyst prepared in this way a mixture of 126.7 g of diphenyldichlorosilane and 157.1 g of diethyldichlorosilane is charged from a container to the reactor (see Fig. 1), and heated by means of an electric heating jacket to 450°, for 9 hr. Gaseous reaction products are condensed and collected in a receiver. Before commencing the rectification, 5 g of sodium chloride are added to the reaction mixture to avoid the splitting-off of organic groups from silicon by the action of aluminum chloride. The rectification affords, beside a little benzene and silicon chloride, 13.1 g (0.08 mole %) of ethyltrichlorosilane, 110.0 g (0.70 mole %) of recovered diethyldichlorosilane, 19.0 g (10.09 mole %) of phenyltrichlorosilane, 43.1 g (0.21 mole %) of ethylphenyldichlorosilane (bp 226°, 43% yield based on diphenyldichlorosilane), and 68.4 g (0.17 mole %) of recovered diphenyldichlorosilane.

18. Dicrotyldiethoxysilane from Crotyltriethoxysilane[77]

$$CH_3CH{=}CHCH_2Si(OC_2H_5)_3 \xrightarrow{\text{NaOC}_2H_5} (CH_3CH{=}CHCH_2)_2Si(OC_2H_5)_2$$
$$+ Si(OC_2H_5)_4$$

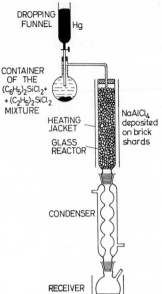

DROPPING FUNNEL Hg

CONTAINER OF THE $(C_6H_5)_2SiCl_2$ + $(C_2H_5)_2SiCl_2$ **MIXTURE**

HEATING JACKET

NaAlCl₄ deposited on brick shards

GLASS REACTOR

CONDENSER

RECEIVER

Fig. 1. Glass flow reactor for preparation of ethyl-phenyldichlorosilane.

In a 250-ml flask connected to a fractionating column are placed 134.5 g (0.62 mole) of crotyltriethoxysilane and 2.0 g of sodium ethoxide. The mixture is heated at the reflux temperature for 20 hr, during which time 46.0 g of material distilling below 175° is removed from the head of the column. At this point the residual material is stripped under reduced pressure. A total of 125 g of volatile material is obtained. Fractionation of this material gives 42 g (0.2 mole) of ethyl silicate (bp 162–165°, d^{20} 0.92), 45 g (0.21 mole) of recovered crotyltriethoxysilane and 21 g (0.092 mole) of dicrotyldiethoxy-silane (bp 217–221°, d^{20} 0.87).

19. 1,3-Dichlorohexamethyltrisilane from Octamethyltrisilane[188]

$$(CH_3)_3SiSi(CH_3)_2Si(CH_3)_3 + CH_3COCl \xrightarrow{AlCl_3}$$
$$Cl(CH_3)_2SiSi(CH_3)_2Si(CH_3)_2Cl + CH_3COCH_3$$

To a slurry of 40 g (0.20 mole) of octamethyltrisilane and 53 g (0.40 mole) of aluminum chloride is added dropwise, while stirring, 35 g (0.45 mole) of acetyl chloride. A moderate exothermic reaction takes place and the mixture becomes homogeneous. After the addition is completed, the mixture is stirred for 2 hr. The product is removed from the mixture by distillation at reduced pressure. Fractionation through a 25-cm column packed with glass helices gives 40 g (84%) of 1,3-dichlorohexamethyltrisilane as a colorless, pure liquid (bp 97–98°/20 mm, d_4^{20} 0.9769, n_D^{20} 1.4823).

20. Tetrakis(chlorodimethylsilyl)silane from Tetrakis(trimethylsilyl)-silane[186]

$$[(CH_3)_3Si]_4Si + 4CH_3COCl \xrightarrow{\text{AlCl}_3} [Cl(CH_3)_2Si]_4Si + (CH_3)_2CO$$

Thirty-nine milliliters (ca. 0.55 mole) of acetyl chloride in 50 ml of petroleum ether is added to a mixture of 10 g (0.031 mole) of tetrakis(trimethylsilyl)silane and 65 g (0.52 mole) of anhydrous aluminum chloride in 60 ml of petroleum ether over a period of 2.5 hr with vigorous stirring. A moderate exothermic reaction with the gentle reflux of petroleum ether takes place. The reaction proceeds stepwise. When the addition is complete, however, only the final product is to be found in the solution. The upper layer is then decanted and the residue is extracted twice with petroleum ether. Evaporation of the solvent from the combined solution gives white crystalline material. After recrystallization from carbon tetrachloride, followed by sublimation (about 150° at 6 mm), 10 g (0.025 mole, yield 80%) of pure tetrakis-(chlorodimethylsilyl)silane is obtained as white crystals. The melting point cannot be measured because of a high tendency of sublimation in this compound.

21. Ethyldimethylchlorosilane from Chloromethyltrimethylsilane[389]

$$(CH_3)_3SiCH_2Cl \xrightarrow{\text{AlCl}_3} CH_3CH_2(CH_3)_2SiCl$$

In a 500-ml, round-bottomed flask fitted with a reflux condenser, thermometer, and a sulfuric acid trap, are placed 184 g (1.5 mole) of chloromethyl trimethylsilane and 2 g of powdered, anhydrous aluminum chloride. Heating the reaction mixture to 85° with a small flame initiates a vigorous exothermic reaction, which continues spontaneously for 0.5 hr, after removal of the flame. It is necessary to cool the reaction flask intermittently in order to prevent the loss of material through the condenser. At the end of this reaction the liquid temperature is 90° with little reflux. The reaction product is then flash-distilled under reduced pressure. Fractionation of the distillate at 734 mm gives 98 g (53%) of ethyldimethylchlorosilane at 89–92.2°.

22. Pentamethylchlorodisilmethylene from Chloromethylpentamethyl-disilane[429]

$$(CH_3)_3SiSi(CH_3)_2CH_2Cl \xrightarrow{\text{AlCl}_3} (CH_3)_3SiCH_2Si(CH_3)_2Cl$$

To 40 g (0.22 mole) of chloromethylpentamethyldisilane, stirred and protected from moisture, is added a small amount of anhydrous aluminum chloride. A vigorous, exothermic reaction takes place and it is necessary to cool the flask. When the reaction subsides, gentle heat is applied to the flask for a short period of time and then an additional small amount of aluminum chloride is introduced with cooling. The addition of catalyst with cooling and the application of heat to the flask is continued repeatedly until no more noticeable change occurs. During the period (ca. 10 hr) required to complete the reaction, it is necessary to add the total of ca. 1 g of catalyst. The reaction mixture is heated on a steam bath for an additional 3 hr, and then is flash-distilled under vacuum to separate the product from the aluminum catalyst. Fractionation of this catalyst-free distillate (37 g) gives 32 g (82%) of pentamethylchlorodisilmethylene, bp 153° (n_D^{20} 1.4322, d_4^{20} 0.8846).

23. 2,3,3,4,4-Pentamethyl-2-fluoro-2,4-disilapentane from Isopropenyl-pentamethyldisilane [437]

$$CH_2=C(CH_3)(CH_3)_2SiSi(CH_3)_3 \xrightarrow{\ \ H_2SO_4\ +\ NH_4F\ \ } (CH_3)_2FSiC(CH_3)_2Si(CH_3)_3$$

To 1 30 g of concentrated sulfuric acid, stirred and cooled to $-15°$ is added dropwise 26 g (0.15 mole) of isopropenylpentamethyldisilane. After stirring for 4 hr, 18 g (0.32 mole) of dry pulverized ammonium hydrogen fluoride is added; stirring is continued for an additional 2 hr. The organic layer that forms upon standing, is separated and fractionated to give the following two fractions: 3 g (10% yield) of slightly impure 2,3,3,4-tetramethyl-2,4-difluoro-2,4-disilapentane $(CH_3)_2FSiC(CH_3)_2Si(CH_3)_2F$, bp 151 ($n_D^{20}$ 1.4080, d_4^{20} 0.9421) and 24 g (83% yield) of 2,3,3,4,4-pentamethyl-2-fluoro-2,4-disilapentane, bp 160° (n_D^{20} 1.4256, d_4^{20} 0.8690).

24. 1,1-Dimethylsilacyclopentane from 1-(Chloromethyldimethylsilyl)-3-trimethylsilylpropane [192]

$$ClCH_2Si(CH_3)_2CH_2CH_2CH_2Si(CH_3)_3 \xrightarrow{AlCl_3} (CH_3)_2Si \underset{\diagdown\ CH_2-CH_2}{\overset{CH_2-CH_2\ \diagup}{\underset{\ \ }{\big|\ \big|}}}$$
$$+ (CH_3)_3SiCl$$

Into a reaction flask, equipped with a mechanical stirrer and a reflux condenser topped with calcium chloride drying tube, are weighed 42 g (0.19 mole) of 1-(chloromethyldimethylsilyl)-3-trimethylsilylpropane and 1.33 g (0.01 mole) of aluminum chloride. The mixture is heated with stirring in an oil bath. At 180° (bath temperature) the contents of the flask begin to boil, and the boiling continues even at 140°. After 0.5 hr 3 g of anhydrous sodium chloride are added, and the stirring and heating of the reaction mixture is continued for an additional half hour. Then the mixture is cooled, and the liquid layer is separated from the precipitate. Fractionation on a column yields 8.5 g of trimethylchlorosilane, bp 58–58.2° (n_D^{20} 1.3878, d_4^{20} 0.8586); 8.2 g of 1,1-dimethylsilacyclopentane, bp 104–105.5°, (n_D^{20} 1.4338, d_4^{20} 0.8167), containing a small amount of chlorine; and 15 g of fraction, bp 82–91°/

17 mm, containing in the main starting 1-(chloromethyldimethylsilyl)-3-trimethylsilylpropane. The 1,1-dimethylcyclopentane fraction is purified by multiple washing of its ethereal solution by water, followed by redistillation.

25. Methoxypentamethyldisilylmethane from Chloromethylpentamethyldisilane[94]

$$(CH_3)_3SiSi(CH_3)_2CH_2Cl + CH_3ONa \xrightarrow{CH_3OCH_2CH_2OCH_3} (CH_3)_3SiCH_2Si(CH_3)_2\text{—}OCH_3 + NaCl$$

To a dispersion of methanol-free sodium methoxide (3.5 g, 0.06 mole) in ethylene glycol dimethyl ether (30 ml) is added 10 g (0.056 mole) of chloromethylpentamethyldisilane at room temperature with stirring. The reaction, which proceeds with considerable evolution of heat, requires cooling. It is complete after 30 min; the only product is methoxypentamethyldisilylmethane, which can be isolated after cautious neutralization by passing dry hydrogen chloride and filtration of the precipitate. Fractionation on a small column gives 6 g of the product (bp 58°/32 mm, n_D^{20} 1.4170, d_4^{20} 0.8154).

A. TABLE I
Thermal Fission of the Silicon-Alkyl Bond

Compound split	Temperature, deg	Products (% yield)	Refs.
$(CH_3)_4Si$	660–720[a]	Alkynes, alkenes, H_2, CH_4, Si, C (gaseous products contain about 60% of CH_4 and 40% of H_2)	1,10
$(CH_3)_4Si$	700[b]	H_2, CH_4, C_2H_4, C_2H_6, alkylsilicon hydrides (e.g., $(CH_3)_3SiH$), $(CH_3)_3SiCH_2SiH(CH_3)C_2H_5$ 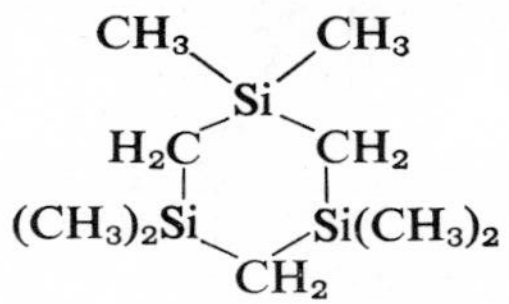 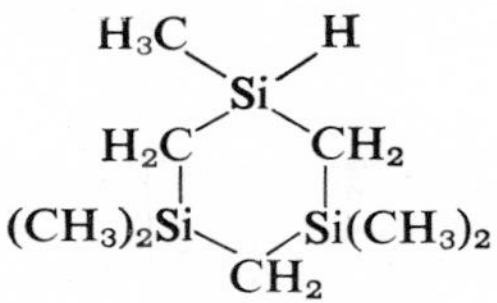 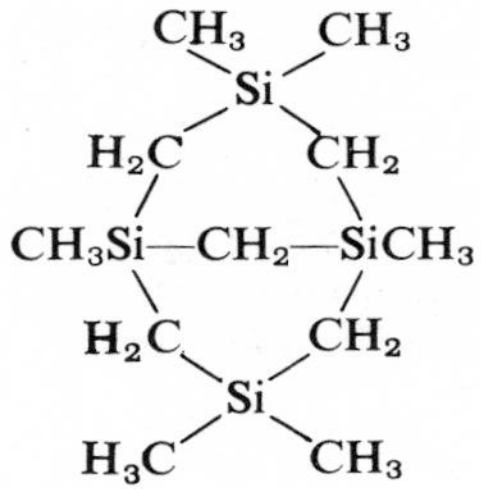 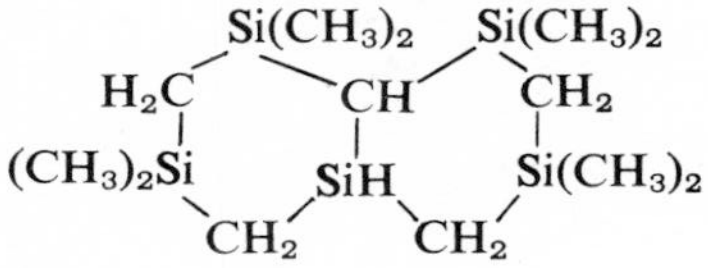 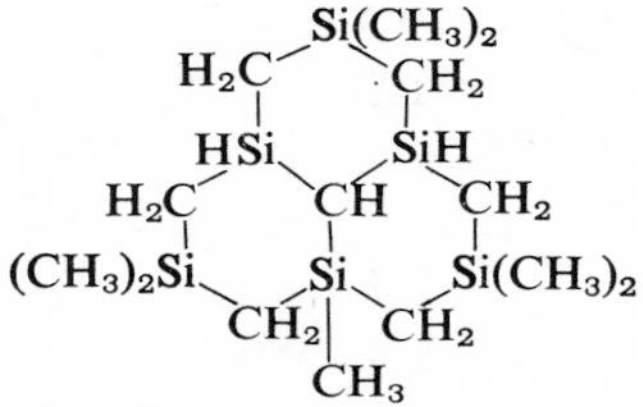	11,14, 438,439– 442

The products also include the cyclic organosilicon structures shown below:

(continued)

229

A. TABLE I (continued)

Compound split	Temperature, deg	Products (% yield)	Refs.
$(C_2H_5)_4Si$	360/H_2	[cyclosilmethylene structures]	21
$(C_2H_5)_4Si$	360/H_2	C_2H_6, $(C_2H_5)_3SiSi(C_2H_5)_3$ and other higher cyclosilmethylenes and traces of CH_4, SiH_4, $(C_2H_5)_3SiH$	21
$(C_2H_5)_4Si$	560–600	CH_4, H_2, C_2H_4, Si, C	2
$(C_2H_5)_4Si$	550/H_2 Aluminosilicate	$(C_2H_5)_3SiH$, C_2H_6, Si	443
$(C_2H_5)_4Si$	530–600/H_2 Cr catalyst	$(C_2H_5)_3SiH$, C_2H_6	444
$(C_2H_5)_3SiC_6H_5$	350–450/H_2	C_6H_6, $(C_2H_5)_3SiSi(C_2H_5)_3$, $[(C_2H_5)_3Si]_2O$, $(C_2H_5)_4Si$, $(C_2H_5)_2Si(C_6H_5)_2$	21
$C_4H_9Si(CH_3)_3$	550–575 Cr catalyst	$CH_3CH_2CH{=}CHSi(CH_3)_3$ (6–9%), $(CH_3)_4Si$, C_3H_6, $(CH_3)_3SiH$, CH_4	445
$(C_3H_7)_4Si$	550	CH_4, C_3H_6, C_2H_4, H_2, Si, C	2
$(CH_3)_3SiCl$	800[b]	$R_3SiCH_2SiR_2CH_2SiR_3$ ($R = CH_3$ or Cl) and cyclosil-methylenes of the type	446,447

8

448

(continued)

(CH₃)₃SiCl   680/200 mm

(CH₃)₃SiCH₂SiCl₃   or   (CH₃)₂ClSiCH₂SiCl₂(CH₃)

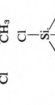

(CH₃)₃SiCl   Over 500/AlCl₃

231

A. TABLE 1 (*continued*)

Compound split	Temperature, deg	Products (% yield)	Refs.
$(CH_3)_2SiCl_2$	720/300 mm	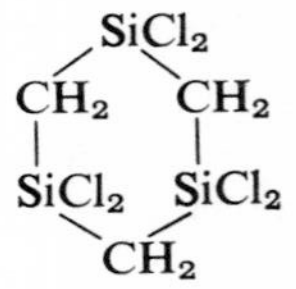 **(11)**	8
CH_3SiCl_3	710/230 mm	**(11)**, $Cl_3SiCH_2SiCl_3$ 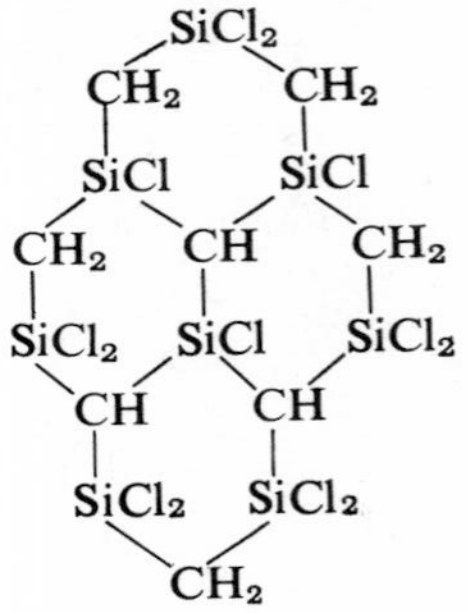 **(12)**	8,449
CH_3SiCl_3	800	**(11)**	450
CH_3SiCl_3	710	**(11)**, **(12)**	451

[a] Static apparatus.
[b] Flow reactor.

B. TABLE II
Fission Reactions in Silent Electric Discharge

Compound split	Products (% yield)	Refs.
$(CH_3)_4Si$	$(CH_3)_3SiC_2H_5$ (7.6%), $(CH_3)_3SiSi(CH_3)_2H$ (2.7%), $(CH_3)_3SiSi(CH_3)_3$ (4.7%), $(CH_3)_3SiCH_2Si(CH_3)H$ (2.0%), $(CH_3)_3SiCH_2Si(CH_3)_3$ (0.7%), $(CH_3)_3SiCH_2CH_2Si(CH_3)_2H$ (0.1%), $(CH_3)_3SiCH_2CH_2Si(CH_3)_3$ (0.3%)	16
$(CH_3)_3SiC_2H_5$	$CH{\equiv}CH$, C_2H_4, $[(CH_3)_3SiCH_2]_2$, $C_2H_5(CH_3)_2SiCH_2Si(CH_3)_3$, $C_2H_5(CH_3)_2SiCH(CH_3)Si(CH_3)_3$, mixture of isomers $C_9H_{24}Si_2$, $C_{12}H_{32}Si_3$, polymers $(C_{3.6}H_{8.8}Si)_x$	40
$(CH_3)_2Si(C_2H_5)_2$	$CH{\equiv}CH$, $C_{10}H_{26}Si_2$, $C_{11}H_{28}Si_2$, $C_{14}H_{34}Si_3$, $C_{19}H_{48}Si_4$, $(C_{4.5}H_{11}Si)_x$	40
$(CH_3)_3SiOSi(CH_3)_3$	$CH{\equiv}CH$, $[(CH_3)_3SiO]_2Si(CH_3)_2$, $[(CH_3)_3SiOSi(CH_3)_2]_2CH_2$, $[(CH_3)_3SiOSi(CH_3)_2CH_2]_2$, $[(CH_3)_3SiOSi(CH_3)_2CH_2Si(CH_3)_2]_2O$, higher polymers	40
$(CH_3)_3SiOSi(CH_3)_3$	$(CH_3)_3SiSi(CH_3)_3$, $(CH_3)_3SiOSi(CH_3)_2C_2H_5$, $(CH_3)_3SiOSi(CH_3)_2C_3H_7$, $(CH_3)_3SiOSi(CH_3)_2OSi(CH_3)_3$, $(CH_3)_3SiOSi(CH_3)_2CH_2Si(CH_3)_3$, $(CH_3)_3SiOSi(CH_3)_2OSi(CH_3)_2C_2H_5$, $(CH_3)_3SiOSi(CH_3)_2OSi(CH_3)_2Si(CH_3)_3$, $(CH_3)_3SiOSi(CH_3)_2CH_2Si(CH_3)_3$, $(CH_3)_3SiOSi(CH_3)_2OSi(CH_3)_2CH_2Si(CH_3)_3$, $(CH_3)_3SiOSi(CH_3)_2CH_2CH_2Si(CH_3)_2OSi(CH_3)_3$, $(CH_3)_3SiOSi(CH_3)_2OSi(CH_3)_2OSi(CH_3)_3$	16
CH_3SiCl_3	$CH{\equiv}CH$, HCl, $Cl_3SiSiCl_3$, $CH_3Cl_2SiCH_2SiCl_3$, $CH_3Cl_2SiCH_2CH_2SiCl_3$, mixture of isomers $C_3H_7Cl_7Si_3$, $C_4H_9Cl_7Si_3$	40,43,44, 452,453
$(CH_3)_2SiCl_2$	$CH{\equiv}CH$, HCl, $(CH_3)_2ClSiCH_2SiCl_2CH_3$, $(CH_3)_2ClSiCH_2CH_2SiCl_2CH_3$, $CH_3Cl_2SiCH_2CH_2SiCl_2CH_3$, $(CH_3Cl_2Si)_2CHSiCl(CH_3)_2$, $C_6H_{15}Cl_5Si_3$	45,453

233

C. TABLE III
Fission Reactions Initiated by Irradiation

Compound split	Products (% yield)	Refs.
$(CH_3)_4Si$ (active N_2)	HCN (3%), NH_3 (1%)	454
$(CH_3)_3SiOSi(CH_3)_3$	H_2, CH_4, C_2H_6, $C_2H_5(CH_3)_2SiOSi(CH_3)_3$, $(CH_3)_3SiOSi(CH_3)_2OSi(CH_3)_3$, $(CH_3)_3SiOCH_2Si(CH_3)_2OSi(CH_3)_3$, $(CH_3)_3SiOSi(CH_3)_2CH_2Si(CH_3)_2OSi(CH_3)_3$, $(CH_3)_3SiOSi(CH_3)_2Si(CH_3)_2OSi(CH_3)_3$,	455
$(CH_3)_3SiOSi(CH_3)_3$[a]	$(CH_3)_3SiOSi(CH_3)_2CH_2CH_2Si(CH_3)_2OSi(CH_3)_3$, also $(CH_3)_3SiOSi(CH_3)_2COOH$, $(CH_3)_3SiOSi(CH_3)_2CH_2OOSi(CH_3)_3$, $(CH_3)_3SiOSi(CH_3)_2OOCH_3$	456
$[(CH_3)_2SiO]_4$	H_2, CH_4, C_2H_6	457
$[(CH_3)_2SiO]_7$ (active N_2)	HCN, NH_3	458
$[(CH_3)_2SiO]_n$	H_2, CH_4, C_2H_6, cross-linking	34,35, 458–463
$[(CH_3)_2SiO]_n$ (acrylo-nitrile)	Grafted polymer	464

[a] In the presence of O_2.

234

D. TABLE IV
Thermal Fission of the Silicon-Haloalkyl Bond

Compound split	Temperature, deg	Products (% yield)	Refs.
$CH_3CHClSiCl_3$	610	$CH_2{=}CH_2$, $SiCl_4$	208
$CH_3CHClSiCl_3$	600	$SiCl_4$ (16%), $CH_2{=}CHSiCl_3$ (61%)	197
$CH_3CHClSiCl_2CH_3$	600	CH_3SiCl_3 (16%), $CH_2{=}CHSi(CH_3)Cl_2$ (75%)	197
$\overset{\displaystyle CH_2CHCl}{\underset{\textstyle}{\big\lfloor}}\!Si(CH_3)Cl$	580	$\overset{\displaystyle CH{=}CH}{\underset{\displaystyle CH_2-CHCl}{\big\lfloor}}\!Si(CH_3)Cl$ (25%), $CH_2{=}CHCH{=}CHSi(CH_3)Cl_2$ (75%)	197
CCl_3SiCl_3 (+ $FeCl_3$)	Reflux	$Cl_2C{=}CCl_2$ (13%), $SiCl_4$ (90%)	203
CCl_3SiF_3	140	$CF_2{=}CF_2$ (59%), $CF_2\!\!\overset{CCl_2}{\underset{CCl_2}{-\!\!-}}\!\!CF_2$, $SiClF_3$	201
		$CF_2{=}CFCl$, $CF_2\!\!\overset{CCl_2}{\underset{CCl_2}{-\!\!-}}\!\!CFCl$, $CF_2{=}CCl_2$, $CF_2\!\!\overset{CCl_2}{\underset{CCl_2}{-\!\!-}}\!\!CCl_2$	
$ClCH_2CH_2SiCl_3$	392	$CH_2{=}CH_2$, $SiCl_4$ (85%)	194,196
$ClCH_2CH_2SiCl_3$	417	$CH_2{=}CH_2$ (33%), $SiCl_4$ (33%), $CH_2{=}CHSiCl_3$ (13%), $CH_2{=}CHCl$ (1.5%), $CH_3CH_2SiCl_3$ (0.5%)	195
$ClCH_2CH_2SiCl_3$	600	$CH_2{=}CH_2$, $SiCl_4$ (65%), $CH_2{=}CHSiCl_3$ (29%)	197
$ClCH_2CH_2Si(CH_3)Cl_2$	600	$CH_2{=}CH_2$, CH_3SiCl_3 (74%), $CH_2{=}CHSi(CH_3)Cl_2$ (20%)	197
$ClCH_2CH_2Si(C_2H_5)Cl_2$	350	$CH_2{=}CH_2$ (90%), $C_2H_5SiCl_3$	196
$ClCH_2CH_2Si(C_2H_5)_2Cl$	298–352	$CH_2{=}CH_2$ (ca. 99%), $(C_2H_5)_2SiCl_2$	196
$ClCH_2CH_2Si(CH_3)_3$	300–385	$CH_2{=}CH_2$, $(CH_3)_3SiCl$ (96%), $CH_2{=}CHCl$, $(CH_3)_3SiH$ (2%)	193

(continued)

D. TABLE IV (*continued*)

Compound split	Temperature, deg	Products (% yield)	Refs.
ClCH₂CH₂Si(C₂H₅)₃	300–386	$CH_2{=}CH_2$, $(C_2H_5)_3SiCl$ (99%)	193
CHF₂CH₂SiF₃	151–221	$CHF{=}CH_2$, SiF_4	81
(CHF₂CH₂SiO₁.₅)ₙ	158–320	$CHF{=}CH_2$ (95%), SiF_4 (58%)	79

CHCl—CH₂
  ＼SiCl₂
CHCl—CH₂
	540	CH—CH₂
		  ＼SiCl₂ (ca. 85%), $CH_2{=}CHCH{=}CHSiCl_3$ (15%)
		CH—CH₂
			197

(CF₃CH₂CH₂)₄Si	500	SiF_4, $CF_3CH_2CH_3$, $CF_3CH_2CH_2SiF_3$, CF_3CH_3, CHF_3, CH_4	79
[(CF₃CH₂CH₂)₂SiO]ₙ	500	SiF_4, $CF_3CH_2CH_3$ (41%), CF_3CH_3 (16%), CHF_3	79
(CF₃CH₂CH₂SiO₁.₅)ₙ	450	$CF_2{=}CHCH_3$ (5–10%), $CF_3CH_2CH_3$, CF_3CH_3, CHF_3, SiF_4	79
	500	$CF_3CH_2CH_3$ (26%), CF_3CH_3 (3.1%), CHF_3 (11%), SiF_4 (12.2%)	79
[(CF₃CH₂CH₂)₂SiO]₃[a]	400	$CF_2{=}CHCH_3$, $CF_3CH{=}CH_2$, $CF_2CH_2CH_3$, CF_3H, CF_3CH_3	206
CF₃CH₂CH₂Si(CH₃)₃[b]	400	$(CH_3)_3SiF$, $(CH_3)_2SiF_2$, $CF_3CH_2CH_2Si(CH_3)_2F$, $CF_2{=}CHCH_3$, $CF_3CH{=}CH_2$, $CF_3CH_2CH_3$, CF_3H, CF_3CH_3, CH_4	206
ClCH₂CHClSi(CH₃)₃	250	$CH_2{=}CHCl$ (80%), $(CH_3)_3SiCl$	193

CH₂—CH₂
  ＼SiCl₂
CHClCHCl
	540	CH=CCl
		  ＼SiCl₂ (50%), $CH_2{=}CClCH_2CH_2SiCl_3$ (35%),
		CH₂CH₂
		$CH_2{=}CHCH{=}CHSiCl_3$ (15%)
			197

CHFClCF₂SiCl₃	250	$CHF{=}CFCl$	200
CFCl₂CF₂SiCl₃	250	$CFCl{=}CFCl + SiFCl_3$	200
CHF₂CF₂SiCl₃	220	$CF_2{=}CHF$ (34%) + $CHCl{=}CF_2$ (49%)	108
CF₂ClCF₂SiCl₃	220	$CF_2{=}CFCl$ (90%)	108
(CHF₂CF₂SiO₁.₅)ₙ	150–220	$CHF{=}CF_2$, SiF_4	79

[a] Analogous products were obtained during pyrolysis of other 3,3,3-trifluoropropyl-substituted siloxanes at 400°.[206]

[b] Analogous products were obtained during pyrolysis of 3,3,3-trifluoropropylmethyl-substituted silanes and siloxanes at 400°.[206]

236

E. TABLE V
Splitting of the Silicon-Alkyl Bond

Compound split	Temperature, deg	Agent	Products (% yield)	Refs.
$(CH_3)_4Si$	25	$t\text{-}C_4H_9OK/(CH_3)_2SO$	CH_4, $t\text{-}C_4H_9OSi(CH_3)_3$	62
$[(CH_3)_3Si]_2O$	200[a]	KOH	CH_4 (76%)	64
$[(CH_3)_2SiO]_n$	200[a]	KOH	CH_4 (77%)	64
$[CH_3SiO_{1.5}]_n$	200[a]	KOH	CH_4 (89%)	64
$[(CH_3)_3Si]_2O$	170–200[a]	KOH/H_2O	CH_4	65
$[(CH_3)_3SiO]_3$	250–270	KOH	CH_4 (100%)[b]	63
$[(C_2H_5)_2SiO]_3$	250–270	KOH	C_2H_6 (100%)[b]	63
$[(C_2H_5)_2SiO]_4$	250–270	KOH	C_2H_6 (100%)[b]	63
$[CH_3(C_6H_5)SiO]_n$[c]	250–270	KOH	CH_4 (100%)[b], C_6H_6	63
$[CH_3SiO_{1.5}]_n$	250–270	KOH	CH_4 (100%)[b]	63
$[(CH_3)_{1.6}SiO_{1.2}]_n$	250	KOH[d]	CH_4	465
$Si(CH_3)_2OSi(CH_3)_2$				
$Si(CH_3)_2OSi(CH_3)CH_2Cl$	110	KOH/C_4H_9OH	CH_3Cl (42%)	64
$[ClCH_2(CH_3)_2Si]_2O$	45	KOH/C_2H_5OH	CH_3Cl (78%)	64
$[(CH_3)C_2H_5SiNH]_3$	200–250	KOH	CH_4, $(CH_3)_5(C_2H_5)_6Si_6N_3(NH_2)_2$, NH_3	66
$[(CH_3)(C_4H_9)SiNH]_3$	250	KOH	CH_4, $(CH_3)_5(C_4H_9)_6Si_6N_3(NH_2)_2$, NH_3	66
$[(CH_3)(C_6H_{13})SiNH]_3$	250	KOH	CH_4, $(CH_3)_5(C_6H_{13})_6Si_6N_3(NH_2)_2$, NH_3	66
$[(C_2H_5)_2SiNH]_3$	250–300	KOH	C_2H_6, $(C_2H_5)_{11}Si_6N_3(NH_2)_2$, NH_3	66
$[(CH_3)(C_2H_5)SiNH]_3$	230–320	C_2H_5ONa/C_2H_5OH	CH_4, $(CH_3)_5(C_2H_5)_6Si_6N_3(NH_2)_2$, NH_3	66
$[(CH_3)(C_2H_5)SiNH]_4$	250–300	KOH	CH_4, $(CH_3)_5(C_2H_5)_6Si_6N_3(NH_2)_2$, NH_3	66
$CH_2{-}Si(CH_3)_2$ $CH_2{-}CH_2$	20	KOH/C_2H_5OH	$CH_3CH_2CH_2Si(CH_3)_2OH$	149
$(n\text{-}C_3H_7)(C_2H_5)C_6H_5C_6H_5CH_2SiCH_3$	20	H_2SO_4	CH_4, $[HSO_3C_6H_4CH_2(C_2H_5)(n\text{-}C_3H_7)Si]_2O$	131
$(C_6H_5)_2(CH_3)_2Si$	175	$H_2SO_4 + V_2O_5$	CH_4, C_2H_6, CO_2	147
$(CH_3)_3SiOSi(C_6H_5)_3$[c]	175	$H_2SO_4 + V_2O_5$	CH_4 (100%)[b], C_6H_6	147

(continued)

237

Compound split	Temperature, deg	Agent	Products (% yield)	Refs.
$(CH_3)_3SiC_6H_4Cl$	175	$H_2SO_4 + V_2O_5$	CH_4,[b] C_6H_5Cl	147
$C_3H_7SiCl_3$	175	$H_2SO_4 + V_2O_5$	C_3H_8,[b] CO_2	147
$(CH_3)_2SiCl_2$	175	$H_2SO_4 + V_2O_5$	CH_4, CO_2	147
$(C_2H_5)_2SiCl_2$	175	$H_2SO_4 + V_2O_5$	C_2H_6, CO_2	147
$(C_3H_7)CH_3SiCl_2$[e]	175	$H_2SO_4 + V_2O_5$	CH_4, C_3H_8, CO_2	147
$[(CH_3)HSiO]_4$	175	$H_2SO_4 + V_2O_5$	CH_4, H_2	147
$[(CH_3)_3Si]_2$	175	$H_2SO_4 + V_2O_5$	CH_4, H_2, CO_2	147
$(CH_3)_2ClSiCH_2SiCl_2CH_3$	175	$H_2SO_4 + V_2O_5$	CH_4, CO_2	147
$CH_3Cl_2SiCH_2SiCl_2CH_3$	175	$H_2SO_4 + V_2O_5$	CH_4, CO_2	147
$[(CH_3)_2(C_2H_5)Si]_2O$	175	$H_2SO_4 + V_2O_5$	CH_4, C_2H_6	147
$ClCH_2SiCl(CH_3)_2$	175	$H_2SO_4 + V_2O_5$	CH_4, CH_3Cl, CO_2	147
$(C_2H_5)_4Si$	20	$H_2SO_4 (+ H_2O)$	$[(C_2H_5)_3Si]_2O$ (4%), C_2H_6	150
$(C_2H_5)_4Si$	20	NO_2	$[(C_2H_5)_3Si]_2O$, CH_3COOH	170
$[(C_2H_5)_3Si]_2O$	20	NO_2	$[(C_2H_5)_2SiO]_{13}$, $[(C_2H_5)_2SiO]_4$ $(C_2H_5)_3SiOSi(C_2H_5)_2OSi(C_2H_5)_3$	170
$(CH_3)_2(C_2H_5)_2Si$	Reflux	$H_2SO_4/(C_2H_5)_2O$	$[(CH_3)_2C_2H_5Si]_2O$, C_2H_6	172
$(CH_3)_3SiSi(CH_3)_3$	30	$H_2SO_4 + NH_4Cl$	CH_4, $(CH_3)_3SiSi(CH_3)_2Cl$ (66%)	152
$(CH_3)_3SiSi(CH_3)_2Si(CH_3)_3$	30	$H_2SO_4 + NH_4Cl$	CH_4 (100%), $(CH_3)_3SiSi(CH_3)_2Cl$ (18%), $(CH_3)_6Si_3Cl_2$ (26%)	152
$(CH_3)_3SiCH_2Si(CH_3)_3$	350–700	HCl	$(CH_3)_4Si$, $(CH_3)_3SiCH_2Cl$	158
$(CH_3)_3SiCH_2SiCl_3$	350–700	HCl	$(CH_3)_3SiCl$, CH_3SiCl_3	158
$(CH_3)_3SiCH_2Si(CH_3)_2Cl$	350–700	HCl	$(CH_3)_3SiCl$, $(CH_3)_2SiCl_2$	158
$(CH_3)_3Si(CH_2)_4Si(CH_3)_3$	20	H_2SO_4	CH_4 (92%), $[—Si(CH_3)_2(CH_2)_4Si(CH_3)_2O—]_n$ $(CH_3)_3Si(CH_2)_3CH_3$ (8%)	137
$\begin{array}{c}CH_2{-}CH_2 \\ \quad \diagdown \\ \quad Si \\ \quad \diagup \\ CH_2{-}CH_2\end{array}\Big\rangle Si \Big\langle \begin{array}{c} CH_2{-}CH_2 \\ \quad \\ CH_2{-}CH_2 \end{array}$	20	$H_2SO_4 (+ H_2O)$	$\begin{array}{c}CH_2{-}CH_2 \\ \quad \diagdown \\ Si(C_4H_9)O(C_4H_9)Si \\ \quad \diagup \\ CH_2{-}CH_2\end{array}$ (90%)	151
$\begin{array}{c}CH_2{-}CH_2 \\ \quad \diagdown \\ Si(C_2H_5)O(C_2H_5)Si \\ \quad \diagup \\ CH_2{-}CH_2\end{array}$	20	$H_2SO_4 (+ H_2O)$	$[(C_4H_9)C_2H_5SiO]_4$ (60%)	151

238

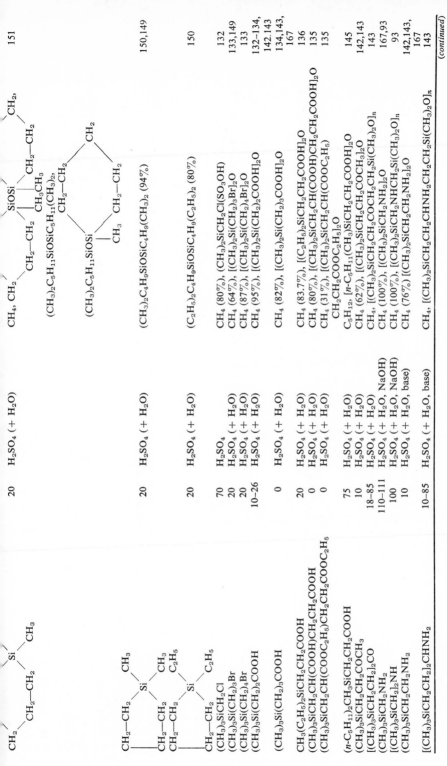

Substrate	Temp	Acid	Products	Refs
[cyclic/bicyclic silicon structure]	20	H_2SO_4 (+ H_2O)	CH_4, CH_2 [structure]	151
$(CH_3)_2C_5H_{11}SiOSiC_5H_{11}(CH_3)_2$, [structure]	20	H_2SO_4 (+ H_2O)	$(CH_3)_2C_4H_9SiOSiC_4H_9(CH_3)_2$ (94%)	150,149
$(CH_3)_2C_5H_{11}SiOSi$ [structure]	20	H_2SO_4 (+ H_2O)	$(C_2H_5)_2C_4H_9SiOSiC_4H_9(C_2H_5)_2$ (80%)	150
$(CH_3)_3SiCH_2CH_2Cl$	70	H_2SO_4	CH_4 (80%), $(CH_3)_2SiCH_2Cl(SO_3OH)$	132
$(CH_3)_3Si(CH_2)_3Br$	20	H_2SO_4 (+ H_2O)	CH_4 (64%), $[(CH_3)_2Si(CH_2)_3Br]_2O$	133,149
$(CH_3)_3Si(CH_2)_4Br$	20	H_2SO_4 (+ H_2O)	CH_4 (87%), $[(CH_3)_2Si(CH_2)_4Br]_2O$	133
$(CH_3)_3Si(CH_2)_2COOH$	10–26	H_2SO_4 (+ H_2O)	CH_4 (95%), $[(CH_3)_2Si(CH_2)_2COOH]_2O$	132–134, 142.143
$(CH_3)_3Si(CH_2)_3COOH$	0	H_2SO_4 (+ H_2O)	CH_4 (82%), $[(CH_3)_2Si(CH_2)_3COOH]_2O$	134,143, 167
$CH_3(C_2H_5)_2SiCH_2CH_2COOH$	20	H_2SO_4 (+ H_2O)	CH_4 (83.7%), $[(C_2H_5)_2SiCH_2CH_2COOH]_2O$	136
$(CH_3)_3SiCH_2CH(COOH)CH_2CH_2COOH$	0	H_2SO_4 (+ H_2O)	CH_4 (80%), $[(CH_3)_2SiCH_2CH(COOH)CH_2CH_2COOH]_2O$	135
$(CH_3)_3SiCH_2CH(COOC_2H_5)CH_2CH_2COOC_2H_5$	0	H_2SO_4 (+ H_2O)	CH_4 (31%), $[(CH_3)_2SiCH_2CH(COOC_2H_5)CH_2CH_2COOC_2H_5]_2O$	135
$(n\text{-}C_5H_{11})_2CH_3SiCH_2CH_2CH_2COOH$	75	H_2SO_4 (+ H_2O)	C_5H_{12}, $[n\text{-}C_5H_{11}(CH_3)SiCH_2CH_2COOH]_2O$	145
$(CH_3)_3SiCH_2CH_2COCH_3$	10	H_2SO_4 (+ H_2O)	CH_4 (62%), $[(CH_3)_2SiCH_2CH_2COCH_3]_2O$	142,143
$[(CH_3)_3SiCH_2CH_2]_2CO$	18–85	H_2SO_4 (+ H_2O)	CH_4, $[(CH_3)_2SiCH_2CH_2COCH_2CH_2Si(CH_3)_2O]_n$	143
$(CH_3)_3SiCH_2NH_2$	110–111	H_2SO_4 (+ H_2O, NaOH)	CH_4 (100%), $[(CH_3)_2SiCH_2NH_2]_2O$	167,93
$[(CH_3)_3SiCH_2]_2NH$	100	H_2SO_4 (+ H_2O, NaOH)	CH_4 (100%), $[(CH_3)_2SiCH_2NHCH_2Si(CH_3)_2O]_n$	93
$(CH_3)_3SiCH_2CH_2NH_2$	10	H_2SO_4 (+ H_2O, base)	CH_4 (76%) $[(CH_3)_2SiCH_2CH_2NH_2]_2O$	142,143, 167
$[(CH_3)_3SiCH_2CH_2CH_2CHNH_2$	10–85	H_2SO_4 (+ H_2O, base)	CH_4, $[(CH_3)_2SiCH_2CH_2CHNH_2CH_2CH_2Si(CH_3)_2O]_n$	143

(continued)

239

E. TABLE V (continued)

Compound split	Temperature, deg	Agent	Products (% yield)	Refs.
(CH₃)₃SiCH₂NHC₆H₁₁-cyclo	100	H₂SO₄ (+ H₂O, NaOH)	CH₄, [(CH₃)₂SiCH₂NHC₆H₁₁-cyclo]₂O (80%)	93
[(CH₃)₃SiCH₂]₃N	110–111	H₂SO₄ (+ H₂O, base)	CH₄ (100%), siloxane	93
(CH₃)₃Si(CH₂)₃NH₂		H₂SO₄ (+ H₂O, base)	CH₄, [(CH₃)₂Si(CH₂)₃NH₂]₂O	167
(CH₃)₃Si(CH₂)₄NH₂		H₂SO₄ (+ H₂O, CH₃COOH)	CH₄, [(CH₃)₂Si(CH₂)₄NH₂]₂O	167
(CH₃)₃Si(CH₂)₃OCH₃		H₂SO₄ (+ H₂O)	CH₄, [(CH₃)₂Si(CH₂)₃OCH₃]₂O	138
(CH₃)₂C₂H₅Si(CH₂)₃OCH₃		H₂SO₄ (+ H₂O)	CH₄, [(CH₃)₂C₂H₅Si(CH₂)₃OCH₃]₂O	138
C₂H₅]₄Si	140–150	HgCl₂	C₂H₅HgCl (15%)	174
(CH₃)₄Si	20	GaCl₃	CH₃GaCl₂ (90%), (CH₃)₃SiCl	177,178
(C₂H₅)₄Si	20	GaCl₃	C₂H₅GaCl₂, (C₂H₅)₃SiCl	177,178
(CH₃)₃CH₂ClSi	20	GaCl₃	CH₃GaCl₂ (93%), (CH₃)₂CH₂ClSiCl	177,178
(CH₃)₃SiC₂H₅	70–90	GaCl₃	CH₃GaCl₂ (72%), C₂H₅GaCl₂, (CH₃)₂C₂H₅SiCl, (CH₃)₃SiCl	178
C₆H₅Si(CH₃)₃	70–90	GaCl₃	C₆H₅GaCl₂ (64%), CH₃GaCl₂, (CH₃)₃SiCl, C₆H₅(CH₃)₂SiCl	178
[(CH₃)₃Si]₂O	100	GaCl₃	CH₃GaCl₂ (74%), (CH₃)₃SiCl, [(CH₃)₂SiO]ₙ	178
[(CH₃)₃SiO]₄	100	GaCl₃	CH₃GaCl₂ (85%), [(CH₃)ClSiO]ₙ	178
(CH₃)₄Si	70–90	GaBr₃	CH₃GaBr₂ (87%), (CH₃)₃SiBr	178
(C₂H₅)₄Si	70–90	GaBr₃	C₂H₅GaBr₂ (84%), (C₂H₅)₃SiBr	178
(CH₃)₃SiC₂H₅	70	GaBr₃	CH₃GaBr₂, C₂H₅GaBr₂, (CH₃)₂C₂H₅SiBr, (CH₃)₃SiBr	178
(C₂H₅)₄Si	Reflux	BiCl₃	(C₂H₅)₃SiCl	466
(CH₃)₃Si(CH₂)₃Si(CH₃)₃	90–100	AlCl₃	(CH₃)₄ (93%), (CH₃)₃Si(CH₂)₃Si(CH₃)₂(CH₂)₃—Si(CH₃)₃	401
(CH₃)₃Si(CH₂)₂Si(CH₃)₃	120–125	AlCl₃	(CH₃)₃Si, [Si(CH₃)₂(CH₂)₂]ₙ	176
(CH₃)₃Si(CH₂)₂SiCl₂CH₃	105–115	AlCl₃	(CH₃)₄Si (7.5%), (CH₃)₃SiCl (65%)	176
(CH₃)₃Si(CH₂)₂SiCl₃	130–150	AlCl₃	(CH₃)₄Si (10%), (CH₃)₃SiCl (40%)	176
[(CH₃)₂Si(CH₂)₃]ₙ	120–200	AlCl₃	(CH₃)₄Si, polymer	401
(CH₃)₃Si(CH₂)₃Si(CH₃)₃	80–90	AlBr₃	(CH₃)₄Si (91%), (CH₃)₃Si(CH₂)₃Si(CH₃)₂—(CH₂)₃Si(CH₃)₃	401
(CH₃)₃Si(CH₂)₂Si(CH₃)₃	120–125	AlBr₃	(CH₃)₃Si, [Si(CH₃)₂(CH₂)₂]ₙ	176
(CH₃)₃Si(CH₂)₂SiCl₂CH₃	75–110	AlBr₃	(CH₃)₄Si (5%), (CH₃)₃SiCl (92.5%)	176
(CH₃)₃Si(CH₂)₂SiCl₃	110–130	AlBr₃	(CH₃)₄Si (22%), (CH₃)₃SiCl (29%)	176
(CH₃)₃Si(CH₂)₃SiCl₂CH₃	80–180	AlBr₃	(CH₃)₄Si (7.5%), (CH₃)₃SiCl (72%), (CH₃)₃Si(CH₂)₃ClSi(CH₃)₂Si(CH₂)₃SiCl₂CH₃	401
(CH₃)₃Si(CH₂)₃SiCl₃	120–220	AlBr₃	(CH₃)₄Si (22%), CH₃Cl₂Si(CH₂)₃Si(CH₃)₂(CH₂)₃SiCl₂CH₃	401

Compound	Reagent	Temp.	Methylchlorosilanes and polymer (low yield of splitting)	Ref.
Cl₃Si(CH₂)₃SiCl₃	AlBr₃	200	CH₂=CH₂, (CH₃)₃SiCl	401
(CH₃)₃Si(CH₂)₂Si(CH₃)₃	FeCl₃	20	(CH₃)₃SiSi(CH₃)₂Cl (73%)	176
(CH₃)₃SiSi(CH₃)₃	HCl/AlCl₃	20	(CH₃)₂ClSiSi(CH₃)₂Cl (81%)	188
(CH₃)₃SiSi(CH₃)₃	HCl/AlCl₃	50–60	(CH₃)₂ClSiSiCl₂CH₃ (70%)	188
(CH₃)₃SiSi(CH₃)₃	HCl/AlCl₃	90	(C₂H₅)₃SiCl (71.3%)	180
C₂H₅)₄Si	i-C₃H₇Cl/AlCl₃	Reflux	(CH₃)₃SiCl (97%)	188
(CH₃)₄Si	CH₃COCl/AlCl₃	20	(C₂H₅)₂SiCl₂ (92%)	188
(C₂H₅)₄Si	CH₃COCl/AlCl₃	20	(CH₃)₃SiSi(CH₃)₂Cl (85%)	188
[(CH₃)₃Si]₂	CH₃COCl/AlCl₃	20	Cl(CH₃)₂SiSi(CH₃)₂Cl (87%)	188
[(CH₃)₃Si]₂	CH₃COCl/AlCl₃	125	Cl(CH₃)₂SiSi(CH₃)Cl₂	188
[(CH₃)₃Si]₂	CH₃COCl/AlCl₃	20	(CH₃)₃SiSi(CH₃)₂Si(CH₃)₂Cl (66%)	188
[(CH₃)₃Si]₂Si(CH₃)₂	CH₃COCl/AlCl₃	20	[(CH₃)₂ClSi]₂Si(CH₃)₂ (84%)	188
[(CH₃)₃Si]₂Si(CH₃)₂	CH₃COCl/AlCl₃	20	[Cl(CH₃)₂Si]₂CH₂ (70%)	188
[(CH₃)₃Si]₂CH₂	CH₃COCl/AlCl₃	20	[Cl(CH₃)₂Si]₃CH (87%)	188
[(CH₃)₃Si]₃CH	CH₃COCl/AlCl₃	20	Cl(CH₃)₂SiCH₂CH₂Si(CH₃)₂Cl (95%)	188
(CH₃)₃SiCH₂CH₂CH₂Si(CH₃)₃	CH₃COCl/AlCl₃	20	(C₂H₅)₂CO, (C₂H₅)₅Si₂Cl	187
[(C₂H₅)₃Si]₂	C₂H₅COCl/AlCl₃	20	C₃H₇COC₂H₅, (C₂H₅)₅Si₂Cl	187
[(C₂H₅)₃Si]₂	C₃H₇COCl/AlCl₃	20	C₂H₅COCH₃, (CH₃)₅Si₂Cl	187
[(CH₃)₃Si]₂	C₂H₅COCl/AlCl₃	20	C₃H₇COCH₃, (CH₃)₅Si₂Cl	187
[(CH₃)₃Si]₂	C₃H₇COCl/AlCl₃	20	C₆H₅COCH₃, (CH₃)₅Si₂Cl	187
[(C₂H₅)₃Si]₂	C₆H₅COCl/AlCl₃	20	C₆H₅COC₂H₅, (C₂H₅)₅Si₂Cl	187
(C₂H₅)₄Si	AlI₃/AlI₃ (+ H₂O)	Reflux	C₂H₅AlI₂, [(C₂H₅)₅Si₂]₂O (90%)	172
(C₂H₅)₄Si	I₂/AlI₃	Reflux	C₂H₅I (95%), (C₂H₅)₃SiI (65%)	172
(CH₃)(C₂H₅)₃Si	I₂/AlI₃	Reflux	CH₃I, C₂H₅I, CH₃(C₂H₅)₂SiI, (C₂H₅)₃SiI	172
(CH₃)₂(C₂H₅)₂Si	I₂/AlI₃	Reflux	CH₃I, C₂H₅I, (CH₃)₂C₂H₅SiI, CH₃(C₂H₅)₂SiI	172
CH₃(n-C₃H₇)₃Si	I₂/AlI₃	Reflux	n-C₃H₇I, C₂H₆, (n-C₃H₇)₃SiI, CH₃(n-C₃H₇)₂SiI	172
(CH₃)₂(i-C₃H₇)₂Si	I₂/AlI₃	Reflux	CH₃I, CH₃(i-C₃H₇)₂SiI	172
(C₂H₅)₃SiI	I₂/AlI₃	Reflux	C₂H₅ (70%), (C₂H₅)₂SiI₂	172

a Autoclave.
b Analytical method for determination of alkyl groups.
c A number of other methylsiloxanes and methylphenylsiloxanes was split.
d 0.4% weight dispersed in the polymer.
e A number of other alkylhalosilanes was split.
f A number of other alkyl-substituted disilanes and disilmethylenes was split.

241

F. TABLE VI
Splitting of the Silicon-Haloalkyl Bond by Means of Nucleophilic Agents

Compound split	Temperature, deg	Agent	Products (% yield)	Refs.
$(CH_3)_3SiCH_2Cl$	20–103	C_2H_5ONa/C_2H_5OH or KOH/C_4H_9OH	CH_3Cl, $(CH_3)_3$ $SiOC_2H_5$, CH_3Cl, siloxanes	89,92
$(CH_3)_3SiCH_2Cl$	Reflux	$n\text{-}C_4H_9ONa/n\text{-}C_4H_9OH$	$CH_3OC_4H_9$, $(CH_3)_3SiOC_4H_9$ (31%)	92
$(CH_3)_3SiCH_2Cl$	–103	$NaNH_2/NH_3$	$CH_3NHSi(CH_3)_3$ (28%)	93
$CH_3(CH_2Cl)_2SiCl$	20	KOH/C_2H_5OH, H_2O	CH_3Cl, siloxanes	85
$CH_3(CH_2Cl)SiCl_2$	20	KOH/H_2O	CH_3Cl, siloxanes	85
$CH_3CH_2CHClSiCl_3$	80	KOH/C_2H_5OH	$CH_2CH_2CH_2Cl$ (99%)	467
$CH_3CHClSiCl_3$	80	KOH/C_2H_5OH	CH_3CH_2Cl (99%)	467
$p\text{-}CH_3C_6H_4(CH_3)_2SiCH_2Cl$	79	C_2H_5ONa/C_2H_5OH	CH_3Cl, $p\text{-}CH_3C_6H_4(CH_3)_2SiOC_2H_5$	86,95
$C_6H_5(CH_3)_2SiCH_2Cl$	79	C_2H_5ONa/C_2H_5OH	CH_3Cl, $C_6H_5(CH_3)_2SiOC_2H_5$	86,95
$p\text{-}CH_3OC_6H_4(CH_3)_2SiCH_2Cl$	79	C_2H_5ONa/C_2H_5OH	CH_3Cl, $p\text{-}CH_3OC_6H_4(CH_3)_2SiOC_2H_5$	86,95
$p\text{-}ClC_6H_4(CH_3)_2SiCH_2Cl$	79	C_2H_5ONa/C_2H_5OH	CH_3Cl, $p\text{-}ClC_6H_4(CH_3)_2SiOC_2H_5$	86,95
$(C_6H_5)_3SiCH_2Br$	Reflux	KCN/CH_3OH	CH_3CN (77%), $(CH_3)_3SiOCH_3$	97
$C_6H_5(CCl_3)SiCl_2$	80–90	KOH/H_2O	$CHCl_3$ (82.4%), $(C_6H_5SiO_{1.5})_n$ (85.7%)	121
$(CCl_3)_3SiCl$	60–70	$NaOH/H_2O$	$CHCl_3$	202
$(CH_2Cl)_2Si(CH_3)_2$	Reflux	KOH/C_2H_5OH	$CH_2{=}CH_2$, $[(CH_3)_2SiO]_n$	167
$CH_3(C_2H_5O)_2SiCH_2SiCH_3(CH_2Cl)_2$	Reflux	$NaOH/H_2O$	CH_3Cl (100%)	98
$(CH_3)_3SiOSi(CH_3)_2CH_2Cl$	80	KOH/C_2H_5OH, H_2O or KOH/C_4H_9OH	CH_3Cl, $[(CH_3)_3Si]_2O$ and higher methylsiloxanes	64,89, 145
$(CH_3)_3SiOSi(CH_3)_2CH_2Cl$	20	NH_3/C_2H_5OH	CH_3Cl, $[(CH_3)_3Si]_2O$, $[(CH_3)_3SiO]_2Si(CH_3)_2$	64

Compound	Temp	Reagent	Products	Ref.
[(CH$_3$)$_2$CH$_2$ClSi]$_2$O	90	KOH/n-C$_4$H$_9$OH, H$_2$O	CH$_3$Cl, methylsiloxanes	85
[(CH$_3$)$_2$CHCl$_2$Si]$_2$O	45	KOH/n-C$_4$H$_9$OH, H$_2$O	CH$_2$Cl$_2$ (78%)	64
Si(CH$_3$)$_2$OSi(CH$_3$)$_2$O	110	KOH/n-C$_4$H$_9$OH, H$_2$O	CH$_3$Cl (42%), polymer	64
OSi(CH$_3$)$_2$—O—Si(CH$_3$)CH$_2$Cl				
(CH$_3$)$_3$SiCHCl$_2$	20	C$_2$H$_5$ONa/C$_2$H$_5$OH	CH$_2$Cl$_2$ (71%), (CH$_3$)$_3$SiOC$_2$H$_5$	100
(CH$_3$)$_3$SiCHCl$_2$	200	CH$_3$COOK/CH$_3$COOH	CH$_2$Cl$_2$	100
(CH$_3$)$_2$CHCl$_2$SiCl	Reflux	NaOH/H$_2$O	CH$_2$Cl$_2$	85
(CH$_3$)CHCl$_2$SiCl$_2$	Reflux	KOH/H$_2$O	CH$_2$Cl$_2$	85,98
H$_3$SiCCl$_2$SiH$_3$	Reflux	NaOH/H$_2$O	CH$_2$Cl$_2$	468
Cl$_3$SiCCl$_2$SiCl$_3$	Reflux	NaOH/H$_2$O	CH$_2$Cl$_2$	468,98
Cl$_3$SiCCl$_2$SiCl$_3$	Reflux	H$_2$O	CH$_2$Cl$_2$	98
CH$_3$(C$_2$H$_5$O)$_2$SiCH$_2$SiCHCl$_2$(CH$_3$)$_2$	Reflux	NaOH/H$_2$O	CH$_2$Cl$_2$	98
[CHCl$_2$(CH$_3$)$_2$Si]$_2$O	45	KOH/n-C$_4$H$_9$OH, H$_2$O	CH$_2$Cl$_2$ (78%)	64
Cl$_3$CSi(OCH$_3$)$_3$		H$_2$O (base)	CHCl$_3$, Si(OH)$_4$	104
Cl$_3$CSi(OC$_2$H$_5$)$_3$	0	C$_2$H$_5$ONa/C$_2$H$_5$OH	HC(OC$_2$H$_5$)$_3$, Si (OC$_2$H$_5$)$_4$	469
Cl$_3$CSiCl$_3$	20	NH$_4$OH/H$_2$O, (C$_4$H$_9$)$_2$O	CHCl$_3$	91,104
Cl$_3$CSiCl$_3$	0	H$_2$O	CHCl$_3$	91
(CH$_3$)Cl$_3$CSiCl$_2$	Reflux	NaOH/H$_2$O	CHCl$_3$	85,98
(C$_6$H$_5$)$_3$SiCCl$_3$	Reflux	KOH/H$_2$O	CHCl$_3$, [(C$_6$H$_5$)$_3$Si]$_2$O	103
(p-ClC$_6$H$_4$)$_3$SiCCl$_3$	Reflux	NaOH/H$_2$O	CHCl$_3$, [(p-ClC$_6$H$_4$)$_3$Si]$_2$O	103
Si(CH$_3$)$_2$OSi(CH$_3$)$_2$	100	KOH/H$_2$O	CH$_2$Br$_2$ (72%)	102
O—Si(CH$_3$)$_2$OSiO(CH$_3$)CHBr$_2$				
Si(CH$_3$)$_2$OSi(CH$_3$)$_2$	100	KOH/H$_2$O	CHBr$_3$ (65%)	102
OSi(CH$_3$)$_2$OSiO(CH$_3$)CBr$_3$				
(C$_6$H$_5$)$_3$SiCCl$_3$	25	n-C$_4$H$_9$Li/(C$_2$H$_5$)$_2$O	(C$_6$H$_5$)$_3$SiC$_4$H$_9$-n	107

(continued)

243

F. TABLE VI (continued)

Compound split	Temperature, deg	Agent	Products (% yield)	Refs.
$(C_6H_5)_3SiCCl_3$	0	$C_6H_5Li/(C_2H_5)_2O$	$(C_6H_5)_4Si$	107
$ClCH_2CH_2Si(CH_3)_3$		Quinoline	$CH_2{=}CH_2$, $(CH_3)_3SiCl$	470
$ClCH_2CH_2Si(CH_3)_3$	30	C_2H_5OH, H_2O	$CH_2{=}CH_2$, $(CH_3)_3SiOH$, $(CH_3)_3SiOC_2H_5$	76
$BrCH_2CH_2Si(CH_3)_3$	20	$NaOH/H_2O$	$CH_2{=}CH_2$ (100%), $(CH_3)_3SiOH$	215
$ICH_2CH_2Si(CH_3)_3$	20	$NaOH/H_2O$	$CH_2{=}CH_2$ (100%), $(CH_3)_3SiOH$	215
$C_6H_5(CH_3)_2SiCH_2CH_2Cl$	30	C_2H_5OH, H_2O	$CH_2{=}CH_2$, $C_6H_5(CH_3)_2SiOH$	76
$m\text{-}CF_3C_6H_4(CH_3)_2SiCH_2CH_2Cl$	30	C_2H_5OH, H_2O	$CH_2{=}CH_2$, $m\text{-}CF_3C_6H_4(CH_3)_2SiOH$	76
$(C_2H_5)_3SiCH_2CH_2Cl$	Reflux	—	$CH_2{=}CH_2$ (87%), $(C_2H_5)_3SiCl$	78
$(C_2H_5)_3SiCH_2CH_2Cl$	20	H_2O	$CH_2{=}CH_2$ (traces), ethylsiloxanes	78
$(C_2H_5)_3SiCH_2CH_2Cl$	70	CH_3OH, H_2O	$CH_2{=}CH_2$ (5%), ethylsiloxanes	78
$(C_2H_5)_3SiCH_2CH_2Cl$	20	CH_3ONa/CH_3OH	$CH_2{=}CH_2$ (10%), ethylsiloxanes	78
$(C_2H_5)_3SiCH_2CH_2Cl$	70	$NaOH/H_2O$, CH_3OH	$CH_2{=}CH_2$ (40–50%), ethylsiloxanes	78
$(C_2H_5)_2SiCl(CH_2CH_2Cl)$	20	H_2O	$CH_2{=}CH_2$ (30–40%), ethylsiloxanes	78
$(C_2H_5)_2SiCl(CH_2CH_2Cl)$	70	CH_3OH	$CH_2{=}CH_2$ (5%), ethylsiloxanes	78
$(C_2H_5)_2SiCl(CH_2CH_2Cl)$	20	$NaOH/H_2O$	$CH_2{=}CH_2$ (85–90%), ethylsiloxanes	78
$(C_2H_5)_2SiCl(CH_2CH_2Cl)$	20	$NaOH/H_2O$, CH_3OH	$CH_2{=}CH_2$ (98%), ethylsiloxanes	90
$(C_2H_5)_2SiF(CH_2CH_2Cl)$	20	$NaOH/H_2O$, CH_3OH	$CH_2{=}CH_2$ (98%), ethylsiloxanes	90
$(C_2H_5)_2SiCl(CH_2CH_2Cl)$	Reflux	CH_3COOH	$CH_2{=}CH_2$ (5%), ethylsiloxanes	78
$(C_2H_5)_2SiCl(CH_2CH_2Cl)$	Reflux	CH_3COOK/CH_3COOH	$CH_2{=}CH_2$ (30–40%), ethylsiloxanes	78
$(C_2H_5)_2SiF(CH_2CH_2Cl)$	20	H_2O	$CH_2{=}CH_2$ (1%), ethylsiloxanes	78
$(C_2H_5)_2SiF(CH_2CH_2Cl)$	100	H_2O	$CH_2{=}CH_2$ (35–45%), ethylsiloxanes	78

Compound	Temp (°C)	Reagent	Products	Ref.
$(C_2H_5)_2SiF(CH_2CH_2Cl)$	70	CH_3OH	$CH_2=CH_2$ (5%), ethylsiloxanes	78
$(C_2H_5)_2SiF(CH_2CH_2Cl)$	Reflux	CH_3COOH	$CH_2=CH_2$ (5%), ethylsiloxanes	78
$(C_2H_5)_2SiF(CH_2CH_2Cl)$	Reflux	CH_3COOK/CH_3COOH	$CH_2=CH_2$ (30–40%), ethylsiloxanes	78
$Cl_3SiCH_2CH_2Cl$	20	$NaOH$ or KOH/H_2O	$CH_2=CH_2$ (100%)	67,72
$Cl_3SiCH_2CHClCH_3$	20	$NaOH$ or KOH/H_2O	$CH_2=CHCH_3$ (100%)	72,467
$(CH_3)_3SiCH_2CH_2Cl$	35	$CH_3MgBr/(C_2H_5)_2O$	$(CH_3)_4Si$ (55%), $CH_2=CH_2$	72
$Cl_3SiCH_2CH_2Cl$	0	$CH_3MgBr/(C_2H_5)_2O$	$(CH_3)_4Si$ (55%), $CH_2=CH_2$	72
$(C_2H_5)_2ClSiCH_2CH_2Cl$	35	$CH_3MgBr/(C_2H_5)_2O$	$(CH_3)_2(C_2H_5)_2Si$, $CH_2=CH_2$ (25%)	78
$(C_2H_5)_2FSiCH_2CH_2Cl$	35	$CH_3MgBr/(C_2H_5)_2O$	$(CH_3)_2(C_2H_5)_2Si$, $CH_2=CH_2$ (36%)	78
$H_3SiCH_2CH(CH_3)Cl$	35	$C_2H_5MgBr/(C_2H_5)_2O$	$H_3SiC_2H_5$, $CH_2=CHCH_3$	471
$Cl_3SiCH_2CH_2CH_2Cl$	20	KOH/C_2H_5OH	$CH_2\!-\!CH_2\!-\!CH_2$ (100%)	467
$Cl_3SiCH_2CH_2CH_2Cl$		$NaOH/H_2O$	$\triangle$ (cyclopropane)	470
$(CH_3)_3SiCHClCH_2Cl$	20	$NaOH/H_2O$	$CH_2=CHCl$, $(CH_3)_3SiOH$	125
$(CH_3)_3SiCHBrCH_2Br$	20	$NaOH/H_2O$	$CH_2=CHBr$, $(CH_3)_3SiOH$	125
$CH_3Cl_2SiCF_2CHF_2$	20	$NaOH/H_2O$	CF_2HCF_2H (98%)	114
$Cl_3SiCCl_2CH_2Cl$	20	$NaOH/H_2O$	$CH_2=CCl_2$	208
$Cl_3SiCCl_2CH_2Cl$	20	Quinoline	$CH_2=CCl_2$, $SiCl_4$	208
$Cl_3SiCClBrCH_2Br$	20	$NaOH/H_2O$	$CH_2=CClBr$	208
$Cl_3SiCHBrCHClBr$	20	$NaOH/H_2O$	$CHCl=CHBr$	208
$Cl_3SiCCl_2CHCl_2$	20	$NaOH/H_2O$	$CHCl=CCl_2$	74
$Cl_3SiCClBrCHClBr$	20	$NaOH/H_2O$	$CHCl=CClBr$	74
$Cl_3SiCHBrCHBr_2$	20	$NaOH/H_2O$	$CHBr=CHBr$	472
$Cl_3SiCHBrCH_2Br$	20	$NaOH/H_2O$	$CH_2=CHBr$	472
$Cl_3SiCBr_2CH_2Br$	20	$NaOH/H_2O$	$CH_2=CBr_2$	472

(continued)

245

F. TABLE VI (*continued*)

Compound split	Temperature, deg	Agent	Products (% yield)	Refs.
$Cl_3SiCBr_2CH_2Br$	20	Quinoline	$CH_2{=}CBr_2$, $SiCl_3Br$	472
$Cl_3SiCHClCHClCH_3$	Reflux	$NaOH/H_2O$	$CH_3CH{=}CHCl$ (100%)	77
$Cl_3SiCH_2CCl(CH_3)_2$		$NaOH/H_2O$, CH_3OH	$(CH_3)_2C{=}CH_2$	216
$Cl_3SiCF_2CF_2Cl$	20	$NaOH/H_2O$	CHF_2CF_2Cl (99%)	108
$Cl_3SiCF_2CHF_2$	20	$NaOH/H_2O$	CHF_2CHF_2 (100%)	108
$(CH_3O)_3SiCF_2CHF_2$	20	$NaOH/H_2O$	CHF_2CHF_2 (100%)	108
$Cl_3SiCH_2CHClCHClCH_3$	Reflux	$NaOH/H_2O$	$CH_3CHClCH{=}CH_2$	77
$Cl_3SiCF_2CF_2CF_2CHF_2$	100	$NaOH/H_2O$	$CHF_2CF_2CF_2CHF_2$ (100%)	108
$Cl_3SiCHClCH_2CFClCF_2Cl$	100	$NaOH/H_2O$	$CF_2ClCFClCH{=}CH_2$ (58%)	113
$Cl_3Si(CF_2)_5CHF_2$	100	$NaOH/H_2O$	$CHF_2(CF_2)_4CHF_2$ (100%)	108
$Cl_3SiCHClCHClSiCl_3$	20	$NaOH/H_2O$	$CHCl{=}CHSi(OH)_3$ (100%)	74
$Cl_3SiCH_2CCl(CH_3)CH_2Cl$	Reflux	Quinoline	$CH_2{=}C(CH_3)CH_2Cl$, $SiCl_4$	473
$(CHF_2CH_2SiO_{1.5})_n$	20	$NaOH/H_2O$	$CHF{=}CH_2$ (90%)	79,99
$[Si(CH_3)CF_2CHF_2O]_n$	20	$NaOH/H_2O$	CF_2HCF_2H (96%), $(CH_3SiO_{1.5})_n$	114
$(CHF_2CF_2SiO_{1.5})_n$	20	$NaOH/H_2O$	CF_2HCF_2H (100%)	99,108

246

Splitting of the Silicon-Haloalkyl Bond by Means of Electrophilic Agents

Compound split	Temperature, deg	Agent	Products (% yield)	Refs.
$(CH_3)_3SiCH_2Cl$		$AlCl_3$	$(CH_3)_2SiClCH_2CH_3$	474
$(CH_3)_3SiCHCl_2$		$AlCl_3$	$CH_2{=}CH_2$, $(CH_3)_2SiCl_2$	474
$(C_2H_5)_2ClSiCHClCH_3$		$AlCl_3$	$CH_2{=}CH_2$, $(C_2H_5)_2SiCl_2$	474
$(C_2H_5)_3SiCH_2CH_2Cl$	20	$AlCl_3/C_5H_{12}$	$CH_2{=}CH_2$, $(C_2H_5)_3SiCl$ (79%)	78
$(C_2H_5)_3SiCH_2CH_2Cl$	20	$AgNO_3/CH_3OH$	$CH_2{=}CH_2$, $(C_2H_5)_3SiOCH_3$ (95%)	78
$(C_2H_5)_2SiCl(CH_2CH_2Cl)$	20	$AgNO_3/CH_3OH$	$CH_2{=}CH_2$ (97%), ethylsiloxanes	78
$(C_2H_5)_2SiF(CH_2CH_2Cl)$	20	$AgNO_3/CH_3OH$	$CH_2{=}CH_2$ (45%), ethylsiloxanes	78
$(C_2H_5)_2SiCl(CH_2CH_2Cl)$	20	$AlCl_3/C_5H_{12}$	$CH_2{=}CH_2$ (70%), $(C_2H_5)_2SiCl_2$ (77%)	78
$(C_2H_5)_2SiF(CH_2CH_2Cl)$	20	$AlCl_3/C_5H_{12}$	$CH_2{=}CH_2$ (71%), $(C_2H_5)_2SiCl_2$	78
$(CH_3)_3SiCH_2CH_2CH_2Cl$	20	$AlCl_3$	$CH_2{-}CH_2$ with CH_2 (cyclopropane), $(CH_3)_3Cl$	470
$(CH_3)_3SiCH_2CH_2CH_2Br$	20–70	$AlCl_3$	$CH_2{-}CH_2$ with CH_2 (cyclopropane) (92%), $(CH_3)_3SiBr$ (82%)	182
$(CH_3)_3Si(CH_2)_5Br$		$AlCl_3$	$CH_2{=}CHCH_2CH_2CH_3$, $(CH_3)_3SiBr$, $(C_5H_{10})_n$	182
$ClCH_2Cl_2SiOSi(CH_3)_2CH_2Cl$	175	H_2SO_4, V_2O_5	CH_3Cl, CH_4, CO_2	147
$(C_2H_5O)_3SiCHClCH_3$	175	H_2SO_4, V_2O_5	CH_3Cl, H_2CO_2	147
$(C_2H_5O)_3SiCH_2CH_2Cl$	175	H_2SO_4, V_2O_5	CH_3Cl, C_2H_5Cl (?), H_2CO_2	147
$(C_2H_5O)_3SiCH_2CH_2Cl$	175	H_2SO_4, V_2O_5	CH_3Cl, CO_2	147
Cl_3SiCH_2Cl	175	H_2SO_4, V_2O_5	CH_3Cl, CO_2	147
Cl_3SiCCl_3	0	HCl/H_2O, $(C_2H_5)_2O$	$CHCl_3$	91
$Cl_3Si(CH_2)_3Cl$	165	$AlCl_3$	$CH_2{=}CHCH_3$, $SiCl_4$	77
$Cl_3Si(CH_2)_2Cl$		$AlCl_3$	$CH_2{=}CH_2$, $SiCl_4$	470
$Cl_3SiCF_2CHF_2$	205	HCl	CHF_2CHF_2, $SiCl_4$	108
$(Cl_3Si)_3CH$	0–20	$SbF_3/xylene$	SiF_4 (6.4%)	181
$(Cl_3Si)_3CH$	−70	$SbF_3/n{-}(C_4H_9)_2O$[a]	SiF_4	181

[a] This reaction was studied even in benzene, toluene, and xylene.

247

H. TABLE VIII

Splitting-off of the Alkyl Groups Containing Oxygen, Sulfur, or Nitrogen

Compound split	Temperature, deg	Agent	Products (% yield)	Refs.
$(CH_3)_2C_6H_5SiCOOH$		$NaOH/C_2H_5OH, H_2O$	$CO, [(CH_3)_2C_6H_5SiOH]$	123
$CH_3(C_6H_5)_2SiCOOH$		$NaOH/C_2H_5OH, H_2O$	$CO, [(C_6H_5)_2CH_3SiOH]$	123
$(C_6H_5)_3SiCOOH$	20	$NaOH/C_2H_5OH, H_2O$	$CO, (C_6H_5)_3SiOH$ (90%) $[(C_6H_5)_3Si]_2O$ (8%)	475
$(C_6H_5)_3SiCOOH$	20	CH_3ONa/CH_3OH	$CO, (C_6H_5)_3SiOH$ (55%)	475
$(C_6H_5)_3SiCOOH$	20	$C_5H_5N/C_2H_5OH, H_2O$	$CO, (C_6H_5)_3SiOH$	475
$(C_6H_5)_3SiCOOH$	20	C_2H_5ONa/C_2H_5OH	$CO, (C_6H_5)_3SiOH$ (98%)	475
$(C_6H_5)_3SiCOOH$	Reflux	HCl/H_2O	No reaction	475
$(C_6H_5)_3SiCOOH$	Reflux	H_2SO_4 6N	70% $(C_6H_5)_3SiCOOH$ regenerated	475
$(CH_3)_3SiCOOCH_3$	150–230	—	$(CH_3)_3SiOCH_3$ (98%), CO	120
$(CH_3)_3SiCOOCH_3$		$NaOH/H_2O$	$(CH_3)_3SiOH$ (98%)	475
$(CH_3)_3SiCOOCH_3$	20	CH_3ONa	$(CH_3)_3SiOCH_3$ (82%)	475
$(CH_3)_3SiCOOCH_3$		$C_2H_5ONa(C_2H_5OH)$	$(CH_3)_3SiOC_2H_5$ (73%)	475
$(C_6H_5)_3SiCOOC_2H_5$	122–185	—	$(C_6H_5)_3SiOSi((C_6H_5)_3$ (98%)	120
$p\text{-}CH_3C_6H_4)_3SiCOOCH_3$	140–220	—	$(p\text{-}CH_3C_6H_4)_3SiOCH_3$ (98%)	120
$p\text{-}CH_3C_6H_4)_3SiCOOC_2H_5$	135–230	—	$(p\text{-}CH_3C_6H_4)_3SiOC_2H_5$ (92%)	120
$(C_6H_5)_3SiCOCH_3$	Reflux	$NaOH/C_2H_5OH$	$(C_6H_5)_3SiOH$ (65%)	119
$(C_6H_5)_3SiCOC_6H_5$	250	—	C_6H_5CHO	118
$(C_6H_5)_3SiCOC_6H_5$	20	$NaOH/H_2O, C_2H_5OH$	$(C_6H_5)_3SiOH$ (89%), C_6H_5CHO	118
$(C_6H_5)_3SiCOC_6H_5$		$C_6H_5MgBr/(C_2H_5)_2O$	$(C_6H_5)_4Si$ (5%), $(C_6H_5)_3SiOH$ (15%)	118
$(C_6H_5)_3SiCOC_6H_5$		$C_6H_5Li//(C_2H_5)_2O$	$(C_6H_5)_4Si$ (15%), $(C_6H_5)_3SiOH$ (42%)	118
$(CH_3)_3SiCH_2COOC_2H_5$		H_2O	$CH_3COOC_2H_5, [(CH_3)_3Si]_2O$	210

Compound	Temp.	Reagent	Products	Ref.
$(CH_3)_3SiCH_2COOC_4H_9$		H_2O	$CH_3COOC_4H_9$, $[(CH_3)_3Si]_2O$	210
$(CH_3)_3SiCH_2COOC_2H_5$	Reflux	HCl/H_2O	CH_3COOH, $[(CH_3)_3Si]_2O$ (88%)	127
$(CH_3)_3SiCH_2COOC_2H_5$	Reflux	$NaOH/H_2O$	$CH_3COOC_2H_5$, $[(CH_3)_3Si]_2O$ (84%)	127
$(CH_3)_3SiCH_2COOC_2H_5$	Reflux	HCl (gas)	$CH_3COOC_2H_5$ (66%), $(CH_3)_3SiCl$ (71%)	127
$(CH_3)_3SiCH_2COOC_2H_5$	Reflux	C_2H_5OH (abs.)	$CH_3COOC_2H_5$, $(CH_3)_3SiOC_2H_5$	127
$(CH_3)_3SiCH_2COOC_2H_5$	Reflux	Br_2	$BrCH_2COOC_2H_5$ (73%), $(CH_3)_3SiBr$ (73%)	127
$(CH_3)_3SiCH_2CBr(COOC_2H_5)_2$	200	—	$(CH_3)_3SiBr$, $CH_2{=}C(COOC_2H_5)_2$ (73%)	128
$(CH_3)_3SiCH_2CBr(COOC_2H_5)_2$	Reflux	KOH/C_2H_5OH, H_2O	$[(CH_3)_3Si]_2O$ (12%)	128
$(CH_3)_3SiCH_2CBr(COOC_2H_5)_2$	Reflux	Br_2	$(CH_3)_3SiBr$, $BrCH_2CBr(COOC_2H_5)_2$ (79%)	128
$(CH_3)_3SiCH_2COCH_3$	Reflux	H_2O	CH_3COCH_3, $[(CH_3)_3Si]_2O$ (81%)	476
$(CH_3)_3SiCH_2COCH_3$	Reflux	C_2H_5OH	CH_3COCH_3, $(CH_3)_3SiOC_2H_5$	97
$(CH_3)_3SiCH_2COCH_3$	20	HCl/C_2H_5OH	CH_3COCH_3, $(CH_3)_3SiCl$	163
$(CH_3)_3SiCOH(CH_3)_2$	Reflux	KOH/C_2H_5OH	$(C_6H_5)_3SiOC_2H_5$ (10%)	117
$(CH_3)_3SiCOH(CH_3)_2$	Reflux	KOH/C_2H_5OH	$(C_6H_5)_3SiOH$ (48%)	117
$(CH_3)_3Si(CH_2)_2OH$		H_2SO_4, H_2O	$CH_2{=}CH_2$, $[(CH_3)_3Si]_2O$	167
$(CH_3)_3Si(CH_2)_2OH$		$HClO_4$, H_2O	$CH_2{=}CH_2$, $[(CH_3)_3Si]_2O$	167
$(CH_3)_3Si(CH_2)_2OH$		HNO_3, H_2O	$CH_2{=}CH_2$, $[(CH_3)_3Si]_2O$	167
$(CH_3)_3Si(CH_2)_2OH$		HCl, H_2O	$CH_2{=}CH_2$, $[(CH_3)_3Si]_2O$	167
$(CH_3)_3SiCH_2CHOHCH_3$	Reflux	H_2SO_4, H_2O	$CH_3CH{=}CH_2$, $[(CH_3)_3Si]_2O$	167,476
$(CH_3)_3SiCH_2CHOHCCl_3$	Reflux		$(CH_3)_3SiOH$	162
$(CH_3)_3SiCH_2COH(CH_3)C_2H_5$	40–50		$(CH_3)_3SiOH$, $(CH_3)_3SiCH_2C(CH_3){=}CHCH_3$	162
$[(CH_3)_3SiCH_2]_2CHOH$	Reflux		$(CH_3)_3SiCH_2CH{=}CH_2$	162

(continued)

H. TABLE VIII (continued)

Compound split	Temperature, deg	Agent	Products (% yield)	
$[(CH_3)_3SiCH_2]_2COHC_3H_7$	20	HCl, H_2O	$[(CH_3)_3Si]_2O$, $[(CH_3)_3SiCH_2]_2\text{-}C(C_3H_7)\!=\!CH_2$ (17%)	161
$(CH_3)_3SiCH_2COH(CH_3)CH_2Si(CH_3)_3$	20	HCl, H_2O	$[(CH_3)_3Si]_2O$ (15%), $(CH_3)_3SiCH_2C(CH_3)\!=\!CH_2$	161
$C_6H_5)_3SiCOH(CH_3)_2$	Reflux	PBr_3/C_6H_6	$(C_6H_5)_3SiC(CH_3)\!=\!CH_2$ (70%)	117
$CH_3(C_6H_5)_2SiCOH(C_6H_5)_2$	Reflux	C_5H_5N	$CH_3(C_6H_5)_2SiOCH(C_6H_5)_2$ (68%)	124
$CH_3(C_6H_5)_2SiCOH(C_6H_5)_2$	Reflux	$NaOH/H_2O$	$(C_6H_5)_2CHOH$ (20%)	124
$(C_6H_5)_3SiCOH(C_6H_5)_2$	Reflux	C_5H_5N	$(C_6H_5)_3SiOCH(C_6H_5)_2$ (80%)	124
$(C_6H_5)_3SiCOH(C_6H_5)_2$		$NaOH/C_2H_5OH$	$(C_6H_5)_3SiOCH(C_6H_5)_2$ (84–85%)	124
$(C_6H_5)_3SiCOH(C_6H_5)_2$	Reflux	$NaOH/H_2O$	$(C_6H_5)_3SiOH$ (89%), $(C_6H_5)_2CHOH$ (72%)	124
$(C_6H_5)_3SiCOH(C_6H_5)_2$		Na/K	$(C_6H_5)_3SiOCH(C_6H_5)_2$ (96%)	124
$(C_6H_5)_3SiCOH(C_6H_5)_2$		$NaH/(C_2H_5)_2O$	$(C_6H_5)_3SiOCH(C_6H_5)_2$ (90%)	124
$(C_6H_5)_3SiCOH(C_6H_5)_2$		$C_6H_5Li/(C_2H_5)_2O$	$(C_6H_5)_4Si$ (15%), $(C_6H_5)_2CHOH$ (42%)	124
$(C_6H_5)_3SiCOH(C_6H_5)_2$		$Ag_2O/C_6H_6, (CH_3)_2CO, H_2O$	$(C_6H_5)_3SiOH$ (15%), $(C_6H_5)_3SiOCH(C_6H_5)_2$ (56%)	124
$(CH_3)_3SiCH_2CH_2OCH_3$	200		$(CH_3)_3SiOCH_3$ (25%), $CH_2\!=\!CH_2$	150
$(CH_3)_3Si(CH_2)_3OCH_3$		$C_6H_5COCl/ZnCl_2$	$(CH_3)_3SiCl$, $C_6H_5COOCH_3$, $\underset{\underset{CH_2}{\diagup\diagdown}}{CH_2\text{—}CH_2}$	185
$(CH_3)_3Si(CH_2)_3OCH_3$		$(CH_3CO)_2O/ZnCl_2$	$(CH_3)_3SiOOCCH_3$, CH_3COOCH_3, $\underset{\underset{CH_2}{\diagup\diagdown}}{CH_2\text{—}CH_2}$, $CH_3CH\!=\!CH_2$	184

250

Compound	Temp	Reagent	Product	Ref
(CH₃)₃Si(CH₂)₃OCH₃	50–60	AlCl₃	(CH₃)₃SiCl	138
(CH₃)₃Si(CH₂)₃OCH₃		Br₂	(CH₃)₃SiBr, CH₃O(CH₂)₃Br	138
$O[Si(CH_3)_2O]_3Si(CH_3)CH_2COOH$		H_2SO_4, H_2O	CH_3COOH	160
$(CH_3)_3SiCH\!\!-\!\!CH_2$ (O₃)		Zn, H_2O	$(CH_3)_3SiOH$, H_2CO	125
$Cl_3SiCH_2CH\!\!-\!\!CH_2$ (O₃)		H_2O	SiO_2	77
$(CH_3)_3SiCH_2SO_2Cl$		H_2O	$[(CH_3)_3Si]_2O$ (82%)	477
$(CH_3)_3SiCH_2SO_2Cl$		$NaOH/H_2O$	$[(CH_3)_3Si]_2O$ (80%)	477
$(CH_3)_3SiCH_2SO_2Cl$		$CaCO_3/H_2O$	$(CH_3SO_3)_2Ca$ (45%)	477
$(CH_3)_3SiCH_2SO_2NH_2$		$NaOH/H_2O$	$[(CH_3)_3Si]_2O$	477
$(CH_3)_3SiCH_2SO_2CH_3$	20	$NaOH/H_2O$	$[(CH_3)_3Si]_2O$ (100%)	478
$[(CH_3)_3SiCH_2]_2SO_2$	20	NH_3/C_2H_5OH, H_2O	$[(CH_3)_3Si]_2O$	478
$O[Si(CH_3)_2O]_3Si(CH_3)CH_2SO_2NH_2$		$NaOH/H_2O$	$\overline{O[Si(CH_3)_2O]_3Si(CH_3)OH}$	477
$(CH_3)_3SiCH_2SCN$	Reflux	$NaOH/H_2O$	$[(CH_3)_3Si]_2O$ (93%)	479
$[OSi(CH_3)CH_2SC(NH_2)\!=\!NH]_n$		H_2O	$(CH_3SiO_{1.5})_n$, CH_3SH, $NCNH_2$	222
$[O_{1.5}SiCH_2SC(NH_2)\!=\!NH \cdot HCl]_n$		NH_3/H_2O	SiO_2, CH_3SH, $NCNH_2$	222
$(CH_3)_3SiCH_2NH_2 \cdot HCl$		$NaNO_2$, HCl/H_2O	CH_2N_2, $[(CH_3)_3Si]_2O$	164
$(CH_3)_3SiCH_2CN$	Reflux	H_2O	CH_3CN (100%)	165
$(CH_3)_3SiCH_2CN$	Reflux	HCl/H_2O	CH_3CN (100%)	165
$(CH_3)_3SiCH_2CN$	Reflux	$NaOH/H_2O$	CH_3CN (100%)	165
$(CH_3)_3SiCH(CH_3)CN$		KOH/C_2H_5OH, H_2O	CH_3CH_2COOH	129
$(CH_3)_3SiCH(CH_3)CN$		$HCl/HSCH_2COOH$	$(CH_3)_3SiCl$, CH_3CH_2CN	129
$Cl_3SiCH(CH_3)CN$		$NaOH/H_2O$	SiO_2, CH_3CH_2CN	129
$(CH_3)_3SiCH(C_6H_5)CN$	65	CH_3OH	$(CH_3)_3SiOCH_3$, $C_6H_5CH_2CN$	97

(continued)

251

H. TABLE VIII (continued)

Compound split	Temperature, deg	Agent	Products (% yield)	Refs.
$(CH_3)_3SiSi(CH_3)_2CH_2CN$	Reflux	CN^-/C_2H_5OH	$(CH_3)_3SiSi(CH_3)_2OC_2H_5$, CH_3CN	94
$(CH_3)_3SiOSi(CH_3)_2CH_2CN$	Reflux	H_2O	58% conversion	165
$(CH_3)_3SiOSi(CH_3)_2CH_2CN$	Reflux	HCl/H_2O	86% conversion	165
$(CH_3)_3SiOSi(CH_3)_2CH_2CN$	Reflux	$NaOH/H_2O$	100% conversion	165
$O[(CH_3)_2SiO]_3Si(CH_3)CH_2CN$	Reflux	H_2O	No conversion	165
$O[(CH_3)_2SiO]_3Si(CH_3)CH_2CN$	Reflux	HCl/H_2O	38% conversion	165
$O[(CH_3)_2SiO]_3Si(CH_3)CH_2CN$	Reflux	$NaOH/H_2O$	100% conversion	165

I. TABLE IX
Splitting of the Silicon-Alkenyl Bond by Means of Nucleophilic Agents

Compound split	Temperature, deg	Agent	Products (% yield)	Refs.
$(CH_3)_3SiCH=CH_2$	Reflux	KOH/CH_3OH	$(CH_3)_3SiOCH_3$, $(CH_3)_3SiOH$	222
$H_3SiCH=CH_2$	170	$NaOH/H_2O$	$CH_2=CH_2$ (90–95%)	207
$Cl_3SiCH=CHCH_3$	Reflux	$NaOH/H_2O$	$CH_3CH=CH_2$ (5%)	77
$Cl_3SiCBr=CHBr$	20	$NaOH/H_2O$	$CHBr=CHBr$	472
$Cl_3SiCCl=CH_2$	0	$NaOH/H_2O$	$CH_2=CHCl$	208
$Cl_3SiCCl=CH_2$	610	$NaOH/H_2O$	$CH≡CH$, $SiCl_4$	208
$Cl_3SiCH=CCl_2$	20–100	KOH/H_2O	$CH_2=CCl_2$	208,209
$Cl_3SiCCl=CHCl$	100	KOH/H_2O	$CHCl=CHCl$	209
$(C_2H_5)_3SiCF=CF_2$	0–10	C_2H_5ONa/C_2H_5OH	$(C_2H_5)_3SiOC_2H_5$ (69%)	212
$Si(CF=CF_2)_4$	20	KOH/H_2O	$CF_2=CHF$ (100%)	211,213
$trans$-$(C_2H_5)_3SiCF=CFC_6H_5$	Reflux	$C_6H_5Li/(C_2H_5)_2O$, THF	$C_6H_5C≡CC_6H_5$ (45%), $(C_2H_5)_3SiC_6H_5$ (50%)	212
$(CH_3)_3SiCH_2CH=CH_2$	Reflux	KF/C_2H_5OH	$CH_3CH=CH_2$ (35%)	236
$(C_2H_5O)_3SiCH_2CH=CH_2$	Reflux	C_2H_5ONa	$(CH_2=CHCH_2)_2Si(OC_2H_5)_2$, $Si(OC_2H_5)_4$	77
$Cl_3SiCH_2CH=CH_2$	Reflux	H_2O	$CH_3CH=CH_2$ (traces)	77
$Cl_3SiCH_2CH=CH_2$	Reflux	$NaHCO_3/H_2O$	$CH_3CH=CH_2$ (traces)	77
$Cl_3SiCH_2CH=CH_2$	Reflux	C_5H_5N/H_2O	$CH_3CH=CH_2$ (ca. 3%)	77
$Cl_3SiCH_2CH=CH_2$	Reflux	$NaOH/H_2O$	$CH_3CH=CH_2$ (ca. 100%)	77
$Cl_3SiCH_2CH=CHCH_3$	Reflux	$NaOH/H_2O$	$CH_3CH_2CH=CH_2$ (75%)	77
$(C_2H_5O)_3SiCH_2CH=CHCH_2$	Reflux	C_2H_5ONa	$(CH_3CH=CHCH_2)_2Si(OC_2H_5)_2$, $Si(OC_2H_5)_4$	77

(continued)

253

I. TABLE IX (continued)

Compound split	Temperature, deg	Agent	Products (% yield)	Refs.
$(CH_3)_3SiCH_2C(CH_3)=CH_2$	70–85	(1) $CH_3MgI/(C_2H_5)_2O$ (2) H_2O	$[(CH_3)_3Si]_2O$ (42%)	473
$(C_2H_5)_3SiCH_2C(CH_3)=CH_2$	70–85	(1) $CH_3MgI/(C_2H_5)_2O$ (2) H_2O	$[(C_2H_5)_3Si]_2O$, $(CH_3)_2C=CH_2$ (70%)	473
$Cl(CH_3)_2SiCH_2C(CH_3)=CH_2$	35	(1) $CH_3MgCl/(C_2H_5)_2O$ (2) H_2O	$[(CH_3)_3Si]_2O$ (5%)	473
$Cl(CH_3)_2SiCH_2C(CH_3)=CH_2$	35	(1) $C_2H_5MgI/(C_2H_5)_2O$ (2) H_2O	$[C_2H_5(CH_3)_2Si]_2O$	473
$Cl_3SiCH_2C(CH_3)=CH_2$	35	(1) $CH_3MgI/(C_2H_5)_2O$ (2) H_2O	$[(CH_3)_3Si]_2O$ (97%)	473
	100	$(CH_3)_3SiCH=CHCH=CHOC_4H_9$ O, C_6H_6	O,$[(CH_3)_3Si]_2O$,C_4H_9OH	244

J. TABLE X

Splitting of the Silicon-Alkenyl Bond by Means of Electrophilic Agents

Compound split	Temperature, deg	Agent	Products (% yield)	Refs.
$(CH_3)_3SiCH=CH_2$	−20	H_2SO_4	$CH_2=CH_2$, $[(CH_3)_3Si]_2SO_4$	222
$(CH_3)_3SiCH=CH_2$	70–90	$GaCl_3$	CH_3GaCl_2, $CH_2=CHGaCl_2$, $CH_2=CH(CH_3)_2SiCl$, $(CH_3)_3SiCl$	178
$C_6H_5CH_2Si(CH_3)_2CH=CH_2$	100	(1) H_2SO_4, (2) H_2O	$[C_6H_5CH_2(CH_3)_2Si]_2O$	220
$C_6H_5CH_2Si(CH_3)_2CH=CH_2$	110–115	H_2SO_4, BF_3	$C_6H_5CH_2(CH_3)_2SiF$	220
$(CH_3)_3SiCH=CHC_6H_5$	0	(1) H_2SO_4, (2) H_2O	Polystyrene (90%), $[(CH_3)_3Si]_2O$ (69%)	125,215
$(CH_3)_3SiCH=CHC_6H_5$	0–20	Br_2	$C_6H_5CH=CHBr$ (35%), $(CH_3)_3SiBr$ (58.5%)	125,215
$(C_6H_5)_3SiCH=CHC_6H_5$	Reflux	HCl/CH_3COOH	$[(C_6H_5)_3Si]_2O$ (21%)	243
$(n\text{-}C_4H_9O)_3SiCH=CCl_2$	Reflux	H_2SO_4, H_2O	$CH_2=CCl_2$	208
$[(CH_3)_3Si]_2C=CH_2$	−60	Br_2	$(CH_3)_3SiBr$, $(CH_3)_3SiCBr=CH_2$	223
$[(CH_3)_3Si]_2C=CH_2$	−20	Cl_2	$(CH_3)_3SiCl$, $(CH_3)_3SiCCl=CH_2$	223
$[(CH_3)_3Si]_2C=CH_2$	−70	HBr	$(CH_3)_3SiBr$, $(CH_3)_3SiCH=CH_2$	223
$[(CH_3)_3Si]_2C=CH_2$	−70	HI	$(CH_3)_3SiI$, $(CH_3)_3SiCH=CH_2$	223
$(CH_3)_3SiCH_2CH=CH_2$	−20	H_2SO_4	$CH_3CH=CH_2$ (48%), $[(CH_3)_3Si]_2SO_4$	73
$(CH_3)_3SiCH_2CH=CH_2$	Reflux	HCl	$CH_3CH=CH_2$ (20%), $(CH_3)_3SiCl$	73,77
$(CH_3)_3SiCH_2CH=CH_2$	0	$Br_2/(C_2H_5)_2O$	$CH_2BrCH=CH_2$ (18%), $(CH_3)_3SiBr$	73
$(C_2H_5)_3SiCH_2CH=CH_2$	20	HBr	$CH_3CH=CH_2$	183
$(CH_3)_3SiCH_2CH=CH_2$		$CF_2BrCFClBr$	$(CH_3)_3SiBr$, $CF_2BrCFClCH_2CH=CH_2$	480
$(CH_3)_3SiCH_2CH=CH_2$	0–5	I_2	$ICH_2CH=CH_2$ (100%), $[(CH_3)_3Si]_2O$	225
$(CH_3)_3SiCH_2CH=CH_2$	20	Perphthalic acid	$[(CH_3)_3Si]_2O$	481
$(CH_3)_2C_2H_5OSiCH_2CH=CH_2$	0–5	I_2	C_2H_5I (81%), $ICH_2CH=CH_2$ (76%), $[Si(CH_3)_2O]_n$	225

(continued)

J. TABLE X (continued)

Compound split	Temperature, deg	Agent	Products (% yield)	Refs.
$CH_3(C_2H_5O)_2SiCH_2CH{=}CH_2$	0–5	I_2	C_2H_5I (77%), $ICH_2CH{=}CH_2$ (67%)	225
$C_6H_5(C_2H_5O)_2SiCH_2CH{=}CH_2$	0–5	I_2	C_2H_5I (89%), $ICH_2CH{=}CH_2$ (66%)	225
$(C_6H_5)_3SiCH_2CH{=}CH_2$		Br_2	$BrCH_2CHBrCH_2Br$, $(C_6H_5)_3SiBr$	241
$(C_2H_5O)_3SiCH_2CH{=}CH_2$	10	(1) H_2SO_4, (2) H_2O	$CH_3CH{=}CH_2$	227,482
$(C_2H_5O)_3SiCH_2CH{=}CH_2$		HCl/CH_3COOH, H_2O	$CH_3CH{=}CH_2$, $[C_3H_5SiO_{1.5}]_n$	77,227
$H_3SiCH_2CH{=}CH_2$	80	HCl	$CH_3CH{=}CH_2$, H_3SiCl	471
$Cl_3SiCH_2CH{=}CH_2$	Reflux	HCl	$CH_3CH{=}CH_2$	77
$Cl_3SiCH_2CH{=}CH_2$		Br_2/CH_3OH	$BrCH_2CH{=}CH_2$, $Cl_3SiCH_2CHBrCH_2Br$	77
$(C_2H_5O)_2Si(CH_2CH{=}CH_2)_2$	20	H_2SO_4	$CH_3CH{=}CH_2$	227,482
$(C_2H_5O)_2Si(CH_2CH{=}CH_2)_2$	20	HCl, KBr, $KBrO_3/CH_3COOH$	$CH_2BrCHBrCH_2Br$	227,482
$C_2H_5OSi(CH_2CH{=}CH_2)_3$	20	H_2SO_4	$CH_3CH{=}CH_2$	227, 482
$C_2H_5OSi(CH_2CH{=}CH_2)_3$	20	HCl, KBr, $KBrO_3/CH_3COOH$	$CH_2BrCHBrCH_2Br$	227,482
$C_6H_{11}Si(CH_2CH{=}CH_2)_3$		Br_2/CCl_4	$BrCH_2CHBrCH_2Br$, $C_6H_{11}(BrCH_2CHBrCH_2)SiBr_2$	241
$n{-}C_4H_9Si(CH_2CH{=}CH_2)_3$		Br_2/CCl_4	$BrCH_2CHBrCH_2Br$, $n{-}C_4H_9(BrCH_2CHBrCH_2)SiBr_2$	241
$1{-}C_{10}H_7Si(CH_2CH{=}CH_2)_3$		Br_2/CCl_4	$BrCH_2CHBrCH_2Br$, $1{-}C_{10}H_7(BrCH_2CHBrCH_2)SiBr_2$	241
$Si(CH_2CH{=}CH_2)_4$		Br_2/CCl_4	$BrCH_2CHBrCH_2Br$, $(BrCH_2CHBrCH_2)_2SiBr_2$	241
$(C_2H_5O)_3SiCH(CH_3)CH{=}CH_2$	0–5	I_2	C_2H_5I (49%), $ICH_2CH{=}CH_2$	225
$Cl_3SiCH_2CH{=}CHCH_3$		Br_2/CH_3OH	$CH_3CH{=}CHCH_2Br$	77

256

Reactant	Conditions	Product	Ref.
CH₃–CH–CH₂CH₂ / CH–CH=C–CH₂Si(CH₃)₃ / CH₃–CH–CH₂CH ... (C=CH₂)	Acid medium	CH₃–CH–CH₂CH₂–C=CH₂, / CH₃–CH–CH₂CH₂	226
CH₃–CH–CH₂–C(–CH₃)=... / CH–CH ... CH₂–CH–Si(CH₃)₃ / CH₃	Acid medium	CH₃–CH–CH₂–C–CH₃ / CH–CH₂–CH / CH₃ [(CH₃)₃Si]₂O	226
C₆H₅–C=C–Si(CH₃)₃ / C₆H₅–N–N=N (triazole)	Reflux HCl/H₂O, CH₃OH	C₆H₅C=CH / C₆H₅–N–N=N (triazole)	231
C₆H₅–C=C–Si(CH₃)₃ / N–C₆H₅ / N=N (triazole)	Reflux HCl/H₂O, CH₃OH	CH / C₆H₅–C–C / N–N–C₆H₅ / N=N (triazole)	231

K. TABLE XI

Splitting of the Silicon-Alkynyl Bond

Compound split	Temperature, deg	Agent	Products (% yield)	Refs.
$(CH_3)_3SiC\equiv CC_6H_5$	170	CH_3ONa	$C_6H_5C\equiv CNa$, $(CH_3)_3SiOCH_3$	231
$(CH_3)_3SiC\equiv CC_6H_5$	170	$(CH_3)_3SiONa$	$C_6H_5C\equiv CNa$, $(CH_3)_3SiOSi(CH_3)_3$	231
$(CH_3)_3SiC\equiv CH$	50	KF/C_2H_5OH	$HC\equiv CH$, $(CH_3)_3SiOC_2H_5$ (100%)	236
$(CH_3)_3SiC\equiv CC_4H_9$-$n$	Reflux	KF/C_2H_5OH	n-$C_4H_9C\equiv CH$ (60%), $(CH_3)_3SiOC_2H_5$	236
$(CH_3)_3SiC\equiv CC_4H_9$-$t$	Reflux	KF/C_2H_5OH	t-$C_4H_9C\equiv CH$ (60%), $(CH_3)_3SiOC_2H_5$	236
$(CH_3)_3SiC\equiv CC_6H_5$	44	KF/CH_3OH	$C_6H_5C\equiv CH$ (50%), $(CH_3)_3SiOCH_3$	236
$(C_2H_5)_3SiC\equiv CC_6H_5$	29.4	$NaOH/H_2O$, CH_3OH	$C_6H_5C\equiv CH$, $(C_2H_5)_3SiOH$	235
$CH_3(C_2H_5)_2SiC\equiv CC_6H_5$	29.4	$NaOH/H_2O$, CH_3OH	$C_6H_5C\equiv CH$, $CH_3(C_2H_5)_2SiOH$	235
$C_2H_5(CH_3)_2SiC\equiv CC_6H_5$	29.4	$NaOH/H_2O$, CH_3OH	$C_6H_5C\equiv CH$, $C_2H_5(CH_3)_2SiOH$	235
$(C_6H_5)_3SiC\equiv CC_6H_5$	25	KOH/H_2O, C_2H_5OH, dioxane	$C_6H_5C\equiv CH$	107
$(C_6H_5)_3SiC\equiv CC_6H_5$	Reflux	(1) n-$C_4H_9Li/(C_2H_5)_2O$ (2) CO_2	$C_6H_5C\equiv CCOOH$ (19%), $(C_6H_5)_3$ SiC_4H_9-n (58%)	238
$(C_6H_5)_3SiC\equiv CC_6H_5$	29.4	$NaOH/H_2O$, CH_3OH	$C_6H_5C\equiv CH$, $(C_6H_5)_3SiOH$	235
$(CH_3)_3SiC\equiv CC_6H_5$	29.4	$NaOH/H_2O$, CH_3OH	$C_6H_5C\equiv CH$, $(CH_3)_3SiOH$	235
$(i\text{-}C_3H_7)_3SiC\equiv CC_6H_5$	50	$NaOH/H_2O$, CH_3OH	$C_6H_5C\equiv CH$, $(i\text{-}C_3H_7)_3SiOH$	235
$(p\text{-}CH_3OC_6H_4)_3SiC\equiv CC_6H_5$[a]	30	$NaOH/H_2O$, CH_3OH	$C_6H_5C\equiv CH$, $(p\text{-}CH_3OC_6H_4)_3SiOH$	235
$(C_2H_5)_3SiC\equiv CC_6H_4Cl\text{-}p$[b]	30	$NaOH/H_2O$, CH_3OH	p-$ClC_6H_4C\equiv CH$, $(C_2H_5)_3SiOH$	235
$p\text{-}CH_3C_6H_4C\equiv CSi(CH_3)_3$[c]	29.4	$NaOH/H_2O$, CH_3OH	p-$CH_3C_6H_4C\equiv CH$, $(CH_3)_3SiOH$	235
$(CH_3)_3SiC\equiv CSi(CH_3)_3$	Reflux	KF/C_2H_5OH	$(CH_3)_3SiC\equiv CH$, $(CH_3)_3SiOC_2H_5$	236
$(CH_3)_3SiC\equiv CC_6H_5$	Reflux	NaF/C_2H_5OH	$C_6H_5C\equiv CH(50\%)$, $(CH_3)_3SiOC_2H_5$	236
$(CH_3)_3SiC\equiv CC_4H_9$-$n$	Reflux	NaF/C_2H_5OH	n-$C_4H_9C\equiv CH$ (13%), $(CH_3)_3SiOC_2H_5$	236
$(CH_3)_3SiC\equiv CC_6H_5$	Reflux	KI/C_2H_5OH	$C_6H_5C\equiv CH$ (50%), $(CH_3)_3SiOC_2H_5$	236
$(C_6H_5)_3SiC\equiv CSi(C_6H_5)_3$	20	n-$C_4H_9Li/(C_2H_5)_2O$, C_6H_{14}	n-$C_4H_9Si(C_6H_5)_3$, $(C_6H_5)_3SiC\equiv CLi$	239
$(CH_3)_3SiC\equiv CC_6H_5$	60	$HgSO_4$, H_2SO_4/CH_3OH, H_2O	$C_6H_5COCH_3$	241

Compound	Reagent	Conditions	Product	Ref.
$(CH_3)_3SiC≡CC_6H_5$	$ClCH_2COCl(AlCl_3)$	2–8	$C_6H_5C≡CCOCH_2Cl$ (54%), $C_6H_5CCl=C(COCH_2Cl)Si(CH_3)_3$	231
$(CH_3)_3SiC≡CC_6H_5$	$CH_3COCl(AlCl_3)/CS_2$ or $C_6H_5NO_2$	15	$C_6H_5C≡CCOCH_3$ (50%), $(CH_3)_3SiCl$	231
$(CH_3)_3SiC≡CC_4H_9$	$CH_3COCl(AlCl_3)/CS_2$ or $C_6H_5NO_2$	2–8	$C_4H_9C≡CCOCH_3$ (75%), $(CH_3)_3SiCl$	231
$(CH_3)_3SiC≡CC_4H_9$	$(C_2H_5CO)_2O(AlCl_3)$	2	$C_4H_9C≡CCOC_2H_5$ (57%), $C_2H_5COOSi(CH_3)_3$	231
$(CH_3)_3SiC≡CSi(CH_3)_3$	$CH_3COCl(AlCl_3)/CS_2$ or $C_6H_5NO_2$	2–8	$(CH_3)_3SiC≡CCOCH_3$ (90%), $(CH_3)_3SiCl$	231
$(CH_3)_3SiC≡CSi(CH_3)_3$	$C_2H_5COCl(AlCl_3)/CS_2$ or $C_6H_5NO_2$	2–8	$(CH_3)_3SiC≡CCOC_2H_5$ (85%), $(CH_3)_3SiCl$	231
$(CH_3)_3SiC≡CSi(CH_3)_3$	$p-NO_2C_6H_4COCl(AlCl_3)/CS_2$ or $C_6H_5NO_2$	2–8	$(CH_3)_3SiC≡CCOC_6H_4NO_2-p$ (43%), $(CH_3)_3SiCl$	231
$(CH_3)_3SiC≡CSi(CH_3)_3$	$ClCH_2COCl(AlCl_3)/CS_2$ or $C_6H_5NO_2$	2–8	$(CH_3)_3SiC≡CCOCH_2Cl$ (81%), $(CH_3)_3SiCl$	231
$(CH_3)_3SiC≡CSi(CH_3)_3$	$(CH_3CO)_2O(AlCl_3)/CS_2$	2–8	$(CH_3)_3SiC≡CCOCH_3$ (68%), $(CH_3)_3SiCl$	231
$(CH_3)_3SiC≡CSi(CH_3)_3$	$(ClCH_2)_2O(AlCl_3)/CS_2$	2	$(CH_3)_3SiC≡CCH_2OCH_2C≡CSi(CH_3)_3$ (90%), $(CH_3)_3SiCl$	231
$(C_2H_5)_3SiC≡CC_6H_5$	$HgSO_4, H_2SO_4/CH_3OH, H_2O$	60	$C_6H_5COCH_3$	241
$(C_6H_5)_3SiC≡CC_6H_5$	HCl/CH_3COOH	Reflux	$CH_3COC_6H_5$ (67%), $[(C_6H_5)_3Si]_2O$ (32%)	243
$(CH_3)_3SiC≡CSi(CH_3)_3$	$HgSO_4/H_2O$		$[(CH_3)_3Si]_2O$	483
$(C_2H_5)_3SiC≡CSi(C_2H_5)_3$	$HgSO_4/H_2O$		$[(C_2H_5)_3Si]_2O$	483
$(C_2H_5)_3SiC≡CCH=CHOC_4H_9$	$HgSO_4, H_2SO_4/H_2O$		$[(C_2H_5)_3Si]_2O$	484
$(CH_3)_3SiC≡CCH=CHOC_4H_9$	H_2SO_4/H_2O	20	$CH≡CCH_2CHO$ (74%), $[(CH_3)_3Si]_2O$	244
$(C_2H_5)_3SiC≡CCH=CHOC_4H_9$	H_2SO_4/H_2O	20	$CH≡CCH_2CHO$ (79.5%), $[(C_2H_5)_3Si]_2O$	244
$(C_2H_5)_3SiC≡CSi(C_2H_5)_3$	$H_2(Raney\ Ni)$		$(C_2H_5)_4Si$ (90%), $(C_2H_5)_3SiCH_2CH_2Si(C_2H_5)_3$	483

a Analogous p- and m-substituted compounds of the type $(XC_6H_4)_3SiC≡CC_6H_5$ (X = H, CH_3, F, Cl) were split under these conditions.[235]

b Analogous o-, m-, and p-substituted compounds of the type $(C_2H_5)_3SiC≡CC_6H_4X$ (X = H, CH_3, Cl, Br) were split under these conditions.[235]

c Analogous o-, m-, and p-substituted compounds of the type $XC_6H_4C≡CSi(CH_3)_3$ (X = H, CH_3, CH_3O, Br) were split under these conditions.[235]

L. TABLE XII
Splitting of the Silicon-Aralkyl Bond

Compound split	Temperature, deg	Agent	Products (% yield)	Refs.
$(CH_3)_3SiCH_2C_6H_5$	49.7	$NaOH/CH_3OH, H_2O$	$C_6H_5CH_3, (CH_3)_3SiOH, (CH_3)_3SiOCH_3$	250
$(CH_3)_3SiCH_2C_6H_4CH_3\text{-}p$	49.7	$NaOH/CH_3OH, H_2O$	$p\text{-}CH_3C_6H_4CH_3, (CH_3)_3SiOH, (CH_3)_3SiOCH_3$	250
$(CH_3)_3SiCH_2C_6H_4Si(CH_3)_3\text{-}p^a$	49.7	$NaOH/CH_3OH, H_2O$	$p\text{-}(CH_3)_3SiC_6H_4CH_3, (CH_3)_3SiOH, (CH_3)_3SiOCH_3$	250
$(CH_3)_3SiCH_2C_6H_4C_6H_5NHCO\text{-}m$	49.7	$NaOH/CH_3OH, H_2O$	$m\text{-}CONHC_6H_5C_6H_4CH_3, (CH_3)_3SiOH, (CH_3)_3SiOCH_3$	250
$(CH_3)_3SiCH_2C_6H_5$	Reflux	KOH/C_2H_5OH	$C_6H_5CH_3$ (60%)	249
$(CH_3)_3SiCH_2C_6H_5$	Reflux	C_2H_5ONa/C_2H_5OH	$C_6H_5CH_3$ (24%)	249
$(CH_3)_3SiCH_2C_6H_5$	25	$t\text{-}C_4H_9OK/(CH_3)_2SO$	$C_6H_5CH_3$	62
$(CH_3)_3SiCH_2C_6H_5$	25	$CH_3ONa/HCON(CH_3)_2$	$(CH_3)_3SiOCH_3$	62
$(CH_3)_3SiCH_2C_6H_5$	Reflux	KF/C_2H_5OH	$C_6H_5CH_3$	236
$(CH_3)_3SiCH_2C_6H_5$	Reflux	$KOH/H_2O, C_2H_5OH$	$C_6H_5CH_3$ (65%)	250
$(C_6H_5)_3SiCH_2C_6H_5$	Reflux	$KOH/H_2O, C_2H_5OH$	$C_6H_5CH_3, (C_6H_5)_3SiOH$ (86%)	250
$(p\text{-}CH_3C_6H_4)_3SiCH_2C_6H_5$	Reflux	$KOH/H_2O, C_2H_5OH$	$C_6H_5CH_3, (p\text{-}CH_3C_6H_4)_3SiOH$ (47%)	250
$(C_2H_5)_3SiCH_2C_6H_4Cl\text{-}p$	Reflux	$NaOH/H_2O, C_2H_5OH$	$p\text{-}ClC_6H_4CH_3$ (47%)	252
$(CH_3)_3SiCH(C_6H_5)_2$	50	$NaOH/H_2O, CH_3OH$	$CH_2(C_6H_5)_2$	252
$(C_2H_5)_3SiCH(C_6H_5)_2$	50	$NaOH/H_2O, CH_3OH$	$CH_2(C_6H_5)_2$	252
$(CH_3)_3SiC(C_6H_5)_3$	50	$NaOH/H_2O, CH_3OH$	$HC(C_6H_5)_3$	252
$(C_2H_5)_3SiC(C_6H_5)_3$	50	$NaOH/H_2O, CH_3OH$	$HC(C_6H_5)_3$	252

Substrate	Temp (°C)	Reagent	Product (yield)	Ref.
9-fluorenyl, H, Si(CH$_3$)$_3$	50	NaOH/H$_2$O, CH$_3$OH	9-methylenefluorene	252
9-fluorenyl, H, Si(C$_2$H$_5$)$_3$	50	NaOH/H$_2$O, CH$_3$OH	9-methylenefluorene (100%)	252
(C$_2$H$_5$)$_3$SiCH$_2$SiCH(C$_6$H$_5$)$_2$	Reflux	NaOH/H$_2$O, CH$_3$OH	CH$_2$(C$_6$H$_5$)$_2$ (81%)	252
(CH$_3$)$_3$SiCH$_2$C$_6$H$_4$Cl-p	Reflux	NaOH/H$_2$O, CH$_3$OH	p-ClC$_6$H$_4$CH$_3$ (98%)	252
(CH$_3$)$_3$SiCH$_2$C$_6$H$_4$Cl-m	Reflux	NaOH/H$_2$O, CH$_3$OH	m-ClC$_6$H$_4$CH$_3$ (62%)	252
(CH$_3$)$_3$SiCH$_2$C$_6$H$_5$[b]	50	NaOH/H$_2$O, CH$_3$OH	CH$_3$C$_6$H$_5$	252
(C$_6$H$_5$)$_3$SiCH$_2$C$_6$H$_5$	Reflux	KNH$_2$/NH$_3$ liq.	CH$_3$C$_6$H$_5$, C$_6$H$_5$	360
(CH$_3$)$_3$SiC(C$_6$H$_5$)$_3$	Reflux	KOH/H$_2$O, (CH$_3$)$_2$CO	HC(C$_6$H$_5$)$_3$ (95%)	107
(C$_6$H$_5$)$_3$SiCH$_2$C$_6$H$_5$	Reflux	(1) n-C$_4$H$_9$Li/(C$_2$H$_5$)$_2$O (2) CO$_2$	(C$_6$H$_5$)$_3$SiOH (52%), C$_6$H$_5$CH$_2$COOH (43%)	238
(CH$_3$)$_3$SiCH$_2$C$_6$H$_5$	Reflux	KNH$_2$/NH$_3$ liq.	CH$_3$C$_6$H$_5$ (77%), [(CH$_3$)$_3$Si]$_2$NH	249
(CH$_3$)$_3$SiCH(C$_6$H$_5$)$_2$	Reflux	KNH$_2$/NH$_3$ liq.	CH$_2$(C$_6$H$_5$)$_2$ (90%)	249
(CH$_3$)$_3$SiC(C$_6$H$_5$)$_3$	Reflux	KNH$_2$/NH$_3$ liq.	HC(C$_6$H$_5$)$_3$ (91%)	249
(CH$_3$)$_3$SiCH(C$_6$H$_5$)$_2$	Reflux	C$_2$H$_5$ONa/C$_2$H$_5$OH	CH$_2$(C$_6$H$_5$)$_2$ (87%)	249
(CH$_3$)$_3$SiC(C$_6$H$_5$)$_3$	Reflux	C$_2$H$_5$ONa/C$_2$H$_5$OH	HC(C$_6$H$_5$)$_3$ (97%)	249
(CH$_3$)$_3$SiC(C$_6$H$_5$)$_3$	Reflux	KOH/C$_2$H$_5$OH	HC(C$_6$H$_5$)$_3$ (97%)	249
(CH$_3$)$_3$SiC(C$_6$H$_5$)$_3$	Reflux	NaNH$_2$/NH$_3$ liq.	HC(C$_6$H$_5$)$_3$ (92%)	249
(CH$_3$)$_3$SiC(C$_6$H$_5$)$_3$	Reflux	LiNH$_2$/NH$_3$ liq.	HC(C$_6$H$_5$)$_3$ (1-5%)	249
(CH$_3$)$_3$SiC(C$_6$H$_5$)$_3$	Reflux	C$_2$H$_5$OLi/C$_2$H$_5$OH	HC(C$_6$H$_5$)$_3$ (97%)	249

(continued)

261

L. TABLE XII (*continued*)

Compound split	Temperature, deg	Agent	Products (% yield)	Refs.
$(CH_3)_3SiCH(C_6H_5)CH(C_6H_5)Si(CH_3)_3$		$\begin{array}{c} CH_2C=O \\ \big\backslash \quad NBr \\ CH_2C=O \end{array}$	$C_6H_5CHBrCHBrC_6H_5$, $(CH_3)_3SiBr$	97
$p\text{-}(CH_3)_3SiCH_2C_6H_4COOH$	49.7	NaOH or KOH or LiOH/H_2O	$(CH_3)_3SiOH$	251
$p\text{-}(CH_3)_3SiCH_2C_6H_4COOH$	49.7	NaOH/CH_3OH, H_2O	$(CH_3)_3SiOH$	251
$o\text{-}(CH_3)_3SiCH_2C_6H_4COOH$	49.7	NaOH/CH_3OH, H_2O	$(CH_3)_3SiOH$	251
$m\text{-}(CH_3)_3SiCH_2C_6H_4COOH$	49.7	NaOH/CH_3OH, H_2O	$(CH_3)_3SiOH$	251
$CH_3(C_6H_5CH_2)_2SiCH(COOC_2H_5)_2$		$H_2O(OH^-)$	$CH_3C_6H_5$ (100%)	145
$(C_6H_5)_3SiC_6H_4C(CH_3)_2Si(C_6H_5)_3$	Reflux	(1) K/Na/$(C_2H_5)_2O$ (2) H_2O	$(C_6H_5)_3SiC_6H_4CH(CH_3)_2$, $(C_6H_5)_3SiOH$	485
$(C_2H_5)(C_3H_7)Si((CH_2C_6H_4SO_3H\text{-}p)_2$	100	KOH/H_2O	$p\text{-}CH_3C_6H_4SO_3H$	246
benzene ring with $CH_2Si(CH_3)_3$ and NH_2	0	NOCl	benzene ring with CH_2 (16%) and N=N azo group, $(CH_3)_3SiOH$	166
$(CH_3)_3SiCBr(C_6H_5)_2$	Reflux	CH_3COOK/CH_3COOH	$(C_6H_5)_2COCOCH_3$ (79%)	97
$(CH_3)_3SiCHBrC_6H_5$	Reflux	KCN/CH_3OH	$C_6H_5CH_2CN$ (64%), $(CH_3)_3SiOCH_3$	97
$(CH_3)_3SiCHClC_6H_5$	−33	$NaNH_2/NH_3$ liq.	$C_6H_5CH=CHC_6H_5$ (31%), $[(CH_3)_3Si]_2NH$	97
$(C_6H_5)_3SiCH(C_6H_5)CH(C_6H_5)\text{-}Si(C_6H_5)_3$	Reflux	KOH/dioxane, H_2O, $CH_3OCH_2CH_2OH$	$C_6H_5CH_2CH_2C_6H_5$ (80%), $(C_6H_5)_3SiOH$	248

Reactant	Temp.	Conditions	Product (yield)	Ref.
$(C_6H_5)_3SiCH(C_6H_5)CH(C_6H_5)CH(C_6H_5)CH_2C_6H_5$ 4-pyridyl–$CH_2Si(CH_3)_3$	Reflux	KOH/dioxane, H$_2$O, CH$_3$OCH$_2$CH$_2$OH	$C_6H_5CH_2CH(C_6H_5)CH(C_6H_5)CH(C_6H_5)$, 4-CH$_3$-pyridine (39%), $(C_6H_5)_3SiOH$	248
4-pyridyl–$CH_2Si(CH_3)_3$	80	C$_2$H$_5$OH, H$_2$O	4-CH$_3$-pyridine (82%), $[(CH_3)_3Si]_2O$	168
4-pyridyl–$CH_2Si(CH_3)_3$	20	KOH/C$_2$H$_5$OH, H$_2$O	4-CH$_3$-pyridine (96%), $[(CH_3)_3Si]_2O$	168
4-pyridyl–$CH_2Si(CH_3)_3$	20	HCl, H$_2$O	4-CH$_3$-pyridine (94%), $[(CH_3)_3Si]_2O$	168
2-pyridyl–$CH_2Si(CH_3)_3$	20	KOH/C$_2$H$_5$OH, H$_2$O	2-CH$_3$-pyridine (81%), $[(CH_3)_3Si]_2O$	168
2-pyridyl–$CH_2Si(CH_3)_3$	20	HCl, H$_2$O	2-CH$_3$-pyridine (86%), $[(CH_3)_3Si]_2O$	168

(continued)

L. TABLE XII (continued)

Compound split	Temperature, deg	Agent	Products (% yield)	Refs.
pyridine–CH[Si(CH$_3$)$_3$]$_2$	80	KOH/C$_2$H$_5$OH	pyridine–CH$_3$ (91%), [(CH$_3$)$_3$Si]$_2$O	168
pyridine–CH[Si(CH$_3$)$_3$]$_2$	20	HCl, H$_2$O	pyridine–CH$_3$ (92%), [(CH$_3$)$_3$Si]$_2$O	168
indene–C(H)–Si(CH$_3$)$_3$	100	NaOH/H$_2$O	Indene (40%), [(CH$_3$)$_3$Si]$_2$O	486
indene–C(H)–Si(C$_2$H$_5$)$_3$	100	NaOH/H$_2$O	Indene, [(C$_2$H$_5$)$_3$Si]$_2$O	486
indene=C[Si(CH$_3$)$_3$]$_2$	100	NaOH/H$_2$O	Indene (35.8%), [(CH$_3$)$_3$Si]$_2$O	486

264

(continued)

[Si(CH$_3$)$_3$]$_2$ (indene)	25	C$_2$H$_5$OH	Indene (19.8%) H–Si(CH$_3$)$_3$	486
[Si(C$_2$H$_5$)$_3$]$_2$ (indene)	25	C$_2$H$_5$OH	Indene (7%) H–Si(C$_2$H$_5$)$_3$	486
SiCl(CH$_3$)$_2$	0	NaOH/H$_2$O, (C$_2$H$_5$)$_2$O	Indene (44.5%), polymer	486
H–SiCl(CH$_3$)$_2$	25	NH$_3$/C$_5$H$_{12}$	Indene (26%), polymer	486
H–SiCl$_2$(CH$_3$)	0	NaOH/H$_2$O	Indene (42%), polymer	486
H–SiCl$_2$(CH$_3$)	0	H$_2$O	Indene (23%), polymer	486

L. TABLE XII (continued)

Compound split	Temperature, deg	Agent	Products (% yield)	Refs.
(structure) $Si(CH_3)_3$	0	H_2SO_4	Indene, $[(CH_3)_3Si]_2O$ (67%)	486
(structure) $Si(C_2H_5)_3$	0	H_2SO_4	Indene, $[(C_2H_5)_3Si]_2O$ (87.6%)	486
(structure) $Si(CH_3)_3$	100	H_2SO_4, H_2O	Indene, $[(CH_3)_3Si]_2O$	486
(structure) $Si(CH_3)_3$		Br_2	$(CH_3)_3SiBr$ (72.1%)	486
(structure) $Si(C_2H_5)_3$		Br_2	$(C_2H_5)_3SiBr$ (83.1%)	486

Structure	Temp	Reagent	Product	Ref
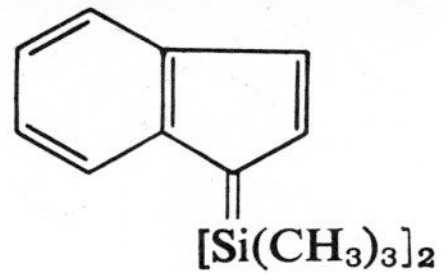		Br$_2$	(CH$_3$)$_3$SiBr (62.1%)	486
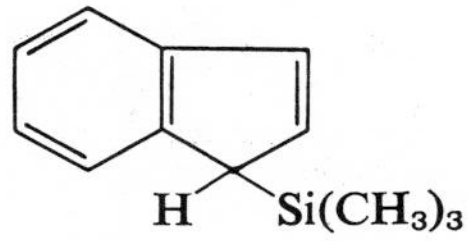	100	SnCl$_4$	(CH$_3$)$_3$SiCl (29.8%)	486
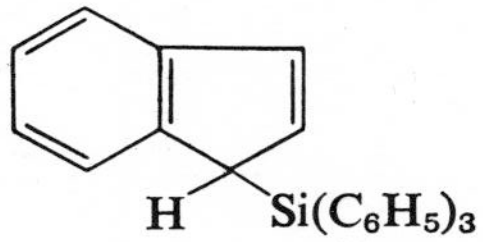	25	KOH/H$_2$O, C$_2$H$_5$OH, dioxane	(C$_6$H$_5$)$_3$SiOH (83%)	107
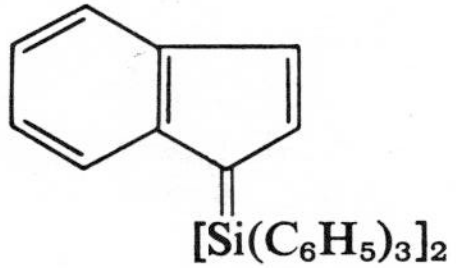	25	KOH/H$_2$O, C$_2$H$_5$OH, dioxane	(C$_6$H$_5$)$_3$SiOH (85%)	107
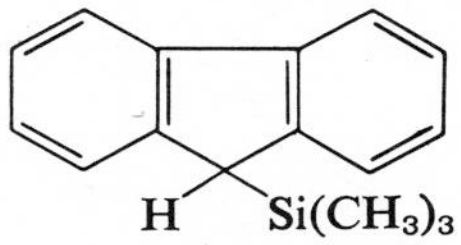	80	HNO$_3$/CH$_3$COOH	2,9-Dinitrofluorene (41%)	253
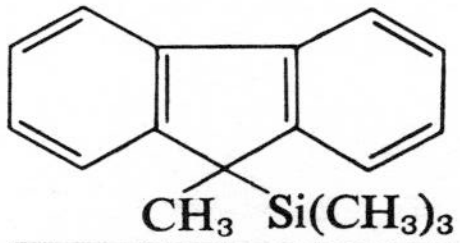	80	HNO$_3$/CH$_3$COOH	9-Nitromethylenefluorene	253

(continued)

267

L. TABLE XII (*continued*)

Compound split	Temperature, deg	Agent	Products (% yield)	Refs.
	20	NaI/CH$_3$COCH$_3$	Fluorenone (80%)	253
	Reflux	KMnO$_4$/CH$_3$COCH$_3$	9,9′-Dibromo-9,9′-difluorenyl	253
	55	C$_6$H$_5$OH/cyclohexane	9-*p*-Hydroxyphenylfluorene (85%)	253
	Reflux	H$_2$O/CH$_3$COCH$_3$	9-Bromofluorene (5%)	253
	Reflux	AgNO$_3$/C$_2$H$_5$OH	Fluorenone (8%)	253

Structure	Time/Temp	Reagents	Product (yield)	Ref.
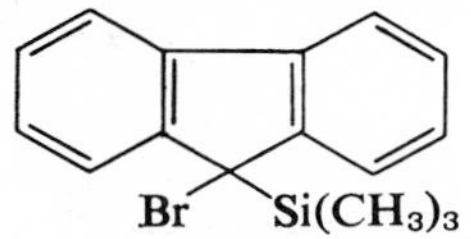 Fluorenyl, 9-Br, 9-Si(CH₃)₃	20	$AgNO_3/(CH_3)_2CO$, H_2O	Fluorenone (85%)	253
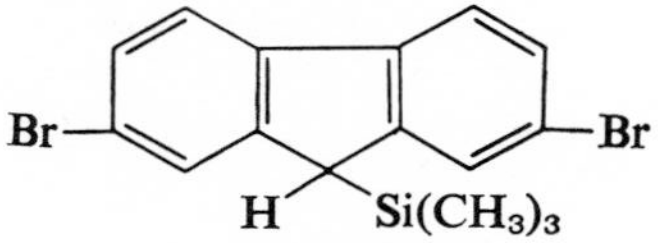 2,7-dibromo-9-H-9-Si(CH₃)₃ fluorene	Reflux	H_2O/C_2H_5OH	2,7-Dibromofluorene (90%)	253
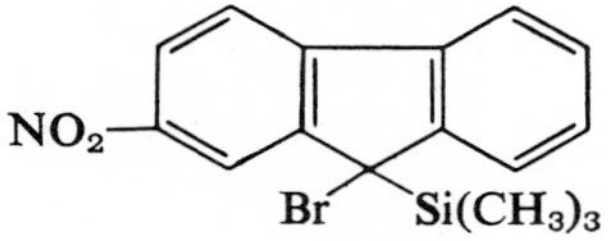 2-nitro-9-Br-9-Si(CH₃)₃ fluorene	18	$H_2O/(CH_3)_2CO$	9-Bromo-2-nitrofluorene (90%)	253
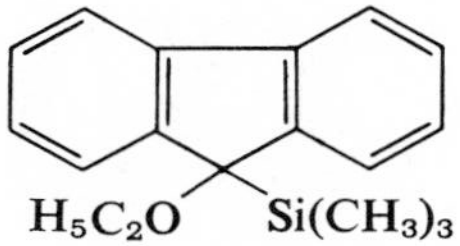 H_5C_2O, 9-Si(CH₃)₃ fluorene	Reflux	HCl/H_2O, C_2H_5OH	Ethyl 9-fluorenyl ether (80%)	253
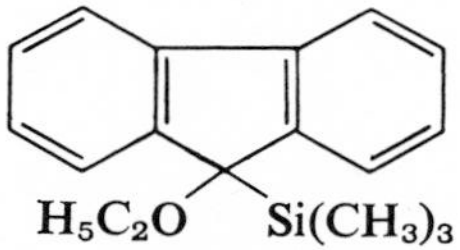 H_5C_2O, 9-Si(CH₃)₃ fluorene		KOH/C_2H_5OH, H_2O	Ethyl 9-fluorenyl ether (82%)	253
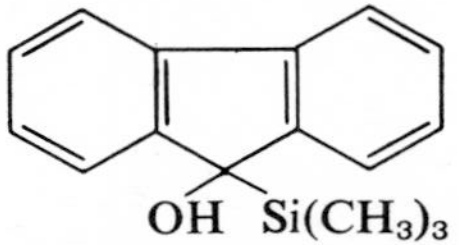 9-OH, 9-Si(CH₃)₃ fluorene	20	Slow decomposition on light	9-Fluorenol, fluorenone	253

(continued)

269

L. TABLE XII (*continued*)

Compound split	Temperature, deg	Agent	Products (% yield)	Refs.
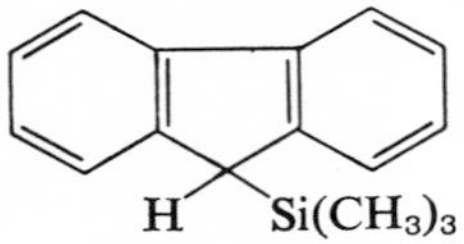	Reflux	KOH/H_2O, C_2H_5OH	Fluorene (94%)	107,253
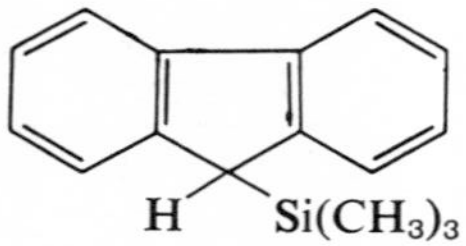	Reflux	NaN_3/H_2O, C_2H_5OH	Fluorene (97%)	253
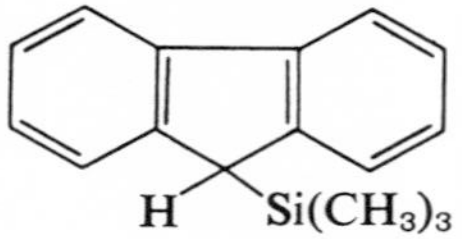	25	KOH/H_2O, C_2H_5OH, dioxane	Fluorene (88%)	107
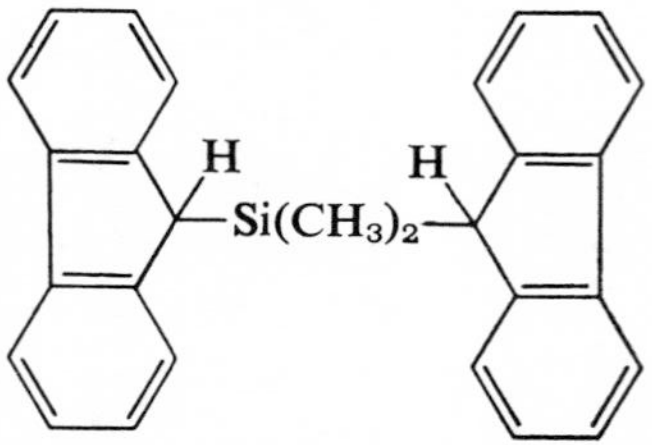	Reflux	KOH/H_2O, C_2H_5OH	Fluorene (90%)	253

270

Structure		Conditions	Product	Ref.
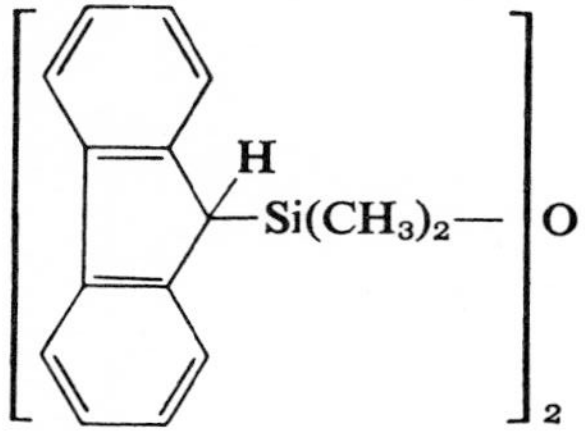	Reflux	KOH/H_2O, $(CH_3)_2CO$	Fluorene (90%)	253
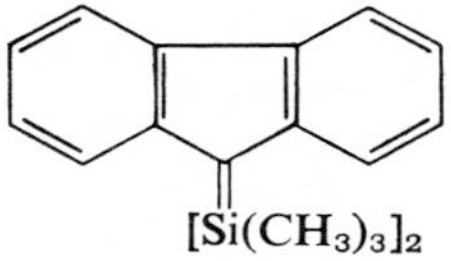	Reflux	KOH/H_2O, $(CH_3)_2CO$	Fluorene (90%)	253
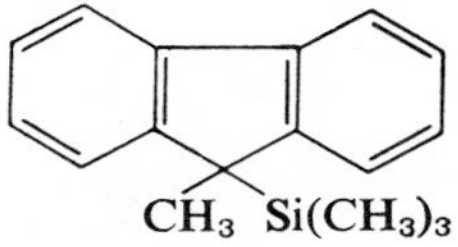	Reflux	KOH/H_2O, $(CH_3)_2CO$	9-Methylfluorene (91%)	253
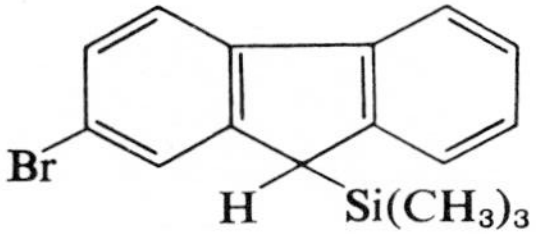	Reflux	H_2O, C_2H_5OH	2-Bromofluorene (90%)	253
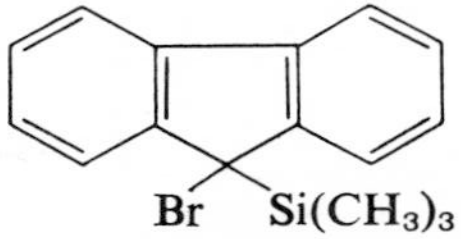	Reflux	NaN_3/CH_3OH	9-Azidofluorene (85%)	253

271

(continued)

L. TABLE XII (*continued*)

Compound split	Temperature, deg	Agent	Products (% yield)	Refs.
	Reflux	KOH/H_2O, $(CH_3)_2CO$	Fluorene (100%), $[(C_6H_5)_3Si]_2O$	107

^{a} Analogous o-, m-, and p-substituted compounds of the type $(CH_3)_3SiCH_2C_6H_4X$ ($X = Cl$, Br, CH_3O, COO^-, NO_2, $CONH_2$) were split under these conditions.

^{b} Under the same conditions p- and m-Cl-substituted compounds were split.

272

M. TABLE XIII

Splitting of the Silicon-Aryl Bond by Means of Nucleophilic Agents

Compound split	Temperature, deg	Agent	Products (% yield)	Refs.
$(C_6H_5)_3SiC_6H_4Cl$-p	60	KOH/H_2O, C_2H_5OH, dioxane	C_6H_5Cl (traces)	107
$(C_6H_5)_3SiC_6H_4CF_3$-m	85	KOH/H_2O, C_2H_5OH, dioxane	$C_6H_5CF_3$ (51%), $(C_6H_5)_3SiOH$ (48%)	107
$(C_6H_5)_3SiC_{10}H_7$-1	85	KOH/H_2O, C_2H_5OH, dioxane	Naphthalene (traces)	107
$Si(C_6F_5)_4$		$H_2O(OH^-)$	C_6HF_5	352
$Cl_2Si(C_6Cl_5)_2$		$H_2O(OH^-)$	C_6HCl_5 (70–80%)	352
$FSi(C_6Cl_5)_3$		$H_2O(OH^-)$	C_6HCl_5 (70–80%)	352
$[(CH_3)C_6H_5SiO]_n$	300	$LiOH$ (0.1%)	C_6H_6, siloxanes, $[(C_6H_5)_2CH_3Si]_2O$	350
$(C_6H_5SiO_{1.5})_n$	500	$NaOH$	C_6H_6, $(C_6H_5)_4Si$ (75–80%), $[(C_6H_5)_3Si]_2O$ (20–25%)	350
$Si(C_6H_5)_4$		KNH_2/NH_3 liq.	C_6H_6 (62%)	360
5-Ethyl-4-carbazolyl-triphenylsilane	85	KOH/H_2O, C_2H_5OH, dioxane	5-Ethylcarbazole (64%), $(C_6H_5)_3SiOH$ (45%)	356
4-Dibenzothienyltriphenylsilane	85	KOH/H_2O, C_2H_5OH, dioxane	Dibenzothiophene (44%), $(C_6H_5)_3SiOH$ (44%)	356
4-Dibenzofuryltriphenylsilane	85	KOH/H_2O, C_2H_5OH, dioxane	Dibenzofuran (48%), $(C_6H_5)_3SiOH$ (73%)	356
2-Thienyltriphenylsilane	85	KOH/H_2O, C_2H_5OH, dioxane	$(C_6H_5)_3SiOH$ (69%)	356

(continued)

M. TABLE XIII (*continued*)

Compound split	Temperature, deg	Agent	Products (% yield)	Refs.
2-Benzothienyltriphenylsilane	85	KOH/H_2O, C_2H_5OH, dioxane	Benzothiophene (33%), $(C_6H_5)_3SiOH$ (83%)	356
2-Benzothiazolyltriphenylsilane	85	KOH/H_2O, C_2H_5OH, dioxane	$(C_6H_5)_3SiOH$ (73%)	356
2-Difuryldimethylsilane	50	$NaOH/H_2O$, C_2H_5OH	Furan, 2-furyldimethylsilanol, 2-furyldimethylethoxysilane	357
$C_6H_5ClSi(C_6Cl_5)_2$	100	$NaOH/H_2O$, THF	C_6HCl_5 (74%)	363
$(C_6H_5)_2Si(OH)_2$	100	KOH/H_2O	C_6H_6	348
$(C_6H_5)_3SiC_6H_4CHO$-m	100	KOH/H_2O	$[(C_6H_5)_3Si]_2O$, $(C_6H_5)_3SiC_6H_4COOH$-m	355
$(C_6H_5)_3SiC_6H_4CHO$-p	100	KOH/H_2O	$[(C_6H_5)_3Si]_2O$, $(C_6H_5)_3SiC_6H_4COOH$-p	355
$Si(C_6H_5)_4$		Li/THF	C_6H_5Li, $(C_6H_5)_3SiLi$	322
$(C_6H_5)_2Si(OCH_3)_2$		$C_6H_4(OH)_2$, $(C_2H_5)_3N/CH_3OH$	$[C_6H_5Si(C_6H_4O_2)_2]^-[(C_2H_5)_3NH]^+$, C_6H_6, CH_3OH	347
$(C_6H_5)_3SiNHC_2H_5$		$Li/C_2H_5NH_2$	C_6H_6, $(C_6H_5)_2Si(NHC_2H_5)_2$	359
$(C_6H_5)_3SiCH_2OH$		$Na/K/(C_2H_5)_2O$	C_6H_6, CH_3OH, $(C_6H_5)_3SiCH_2OSi(C_6H_5)_2OCH_2Si(C_6H_5)_3$	116
$(C_6H_5)_3SiOH$	Reflux	n-$C_4H_9Li/(C_2H_5)_2O$	C_6H_5Li, $(C_6H_5)_2(n$-$C_4H_9)SiOLi$	368
$(p$-$CH_3C_6H_4)(C_6H_5)_2SiOH$	Reflux	n-$C_4H_9Li/(C_2H_5)_2O$	p-$CH_3C_6H_4Li$, $(C_6H_5)_2(n$-$C_4H_9)SiOLi$; C_6H_5Li, p-$CH_3C_6H_4(C_6H_5)(n$-$C_4H_9)SiOLi$	368
$(p$-$CH_3C_6H_4)_3SiOH$	Reflux	n-$C_4H_9Li/(C_2H_5)_2O$	p-$CH_3C_6H_4Li$, $(p$-$CH_3C_6H_4)_2(n$-$C_4H_9)SiOLi$	368
$(p$-$C_6H_5C_6H_4)_3SiOH$	Reflux	$C_6H_5Li/(C_2H_5)_2O$	p-$C_6H_5C_6H_4Li$	362
$C_6Cl_5(C_6H_5)_2SiH$	-65	CH_3Li/THF	C_6Cl_5Li, $CH_3(C_6H_5)_2SiH$ (37%)	367

274

Compound	Conditions	Temp.	Products	Ref.
$C_6F_5(C_6H_5)_2SiH$	$n\text{-}C_4H_9Li/THF$	-65	C_6F_5Li, $n\text{-}C_4H_9(C_6H_5)_2SiH$ (55.7%)	367
$C_6F_5(C_6H_5)_2SiH$	CH_3Li/THF	-65	C_6F_5Li, $CH_3(C_6H_5)_2SiH$ (60.5%)	367
$C_6Cl_5(C_6H_5)_2SiH$	$CH_3Li/(C_2H_5)_2O$	-65	C_6Cl_5Li, $CH_3(C_6H_5)_2SiH$ (37%)	363
$C_6Cl_5(C_6H_5)_2SiH$	$C_6H_5Li/(C_2H_5)_2O$	-65	C_6Cl_5Li, $(C_6H_5)_3SiH$	363
$[(C_6H_5)_2Si]_2O$	$n\text{-}C_4H_9Li/(C_2H_5)_2O$	Reflux	C_6H_5Li, $n\text{-}C_4H_9(C_6H_5)_2SiOLi$, $n\text{-}C_4H_9(C_6H_5)_3Si$	368
$(CH_3)_3SiSi(C_6H_5)_2Si(CH_3)_3$	Li/THF		$[(CH_3)_3Si]_2Si(C_6H_5)Li$	366
$[(C_6H_5)_2Si]_5$	(1) Li (2) $(CH_3)_3SiCl$	20	$[(CH_3)_3Si]_2Si(C_6H_5)_2$, $[(CH_3)_3Si]_2Si(C_6H_5)Si(CH_3)_3$	366
5,5′-Spirobis-(dibenzosilol)	$C_6H_5Li/(C_2H_5)_2O$		5-(2-Biphenylyl)-5-phenyldibenzosilol (87%)	70
$(C_6H_5)_3Si(CH_2)_4Li$	$(C_2H_5)_2O$		(cyclic $(C_6H_5)_2Si(CH_2CH_2)(CH_2CH_2CH_2)$), C_6H_5Li	96
$(C_6H_5)_3Si(CH_2)_5Li$	$(C_2H_5)_2O$		(cyclic $(C_6H_5)_2Si(CH_2CH_2)(CH_2CH_2CH_2CH_2)$), C_6H_5Li	69
$(C_6H_5)_3Si(CH_2)_4Br$	(1) $Li/(C_2H_5)_2O$ (2) Cl_2		(cyclic $(C_6H_5)_2Si(CH_2CH_2)(CH_2CH_2)$) (50.4%),	69
(2-chloro-substituted aryl structure with CH_2CH_2, CH_2, $Si(C_6H_5)_3$)	$Na/C_6H_5CH_3$	Reflux	C_6H_5COOH (56.6%), $(C_6H_5)_2CO$; (silol structure with CH_2, CH_2, CH_2, $Si(C_6H_5)_2$) (32.4%), C_6H_5Na	369

Splitting of the Silicon-Aryl Bond by Means of Acids

Compound split	Temperature, deg	Agent	Products (% yield)	Refs.
$(CH_3)_3SiC_6H_5$	Reflux	HCl (g)/CH_3COOH	$(CH_3)_3SiCl$ (70%), C_6H_6 (60%)	487,488
$(CH_3)_3SiC_6H_4CH_3$-p	Reflux	HCl (g)/CH_3COOH	$(CH_3)_3SiCl$ (53.5%), $CH_3C_6H_5$ (62%)	487,488
$(CH_3)_3SiC_6H_4Cl$-p	Reflux	HCl (g)/CH_3COOH	$(CH_3)_3SiCl$ (43%), C_6H_5Cl (48%)	487,488
$(CH_3)_3Si$⟨thiophene⟩	Reflux	HCl (g)/CH_3COOH	$(CH_3)_3SiCl$ (87%), thiophene (37%)	[487
$(CH_3)_3SiC_6H_4OCH_3$-p	Reflux	HCl (g)/CH_3COOH	$(CH_3)_3SiCl$ (69.5%), $C_6H_5OCH_3$ (76%)	487,488
$(CH_3)_3SiC_6H_4N(CH_3)_2$-$p$	Reflux	HCl (g)/CH_3COOH	$(CH_3)_3SiCl$ (67%), $C_6H_5N(CH_3)_2$ (73.5%)	487,488
$(n$-$C_4H_9)_3SiC_6H_5$	Reflux	(1) HCl (g)/CH_3COOH (2) H_2O	$(n$-$C_4H_9)_3SiOH$ + $[(n$-$C_4H_9)_3Si]_2O$ (72%), C_6H_6 (68%)	487
$(C_2H_5)_2Si(C_6H_5)_2$	Reflux	HCl (g)/CH_3COOH	C_6H_6 (68%)	487
$(C_6H_5CH_2)_3SiC_6H_4OCH_3$-$p$	Reflux	HCl (g)/CH_3COOH	$(C_6H_5CH_2)_3SiCl$ (79%), $C_6H_5OCH_3$ (84%)	487
$HOSi(C_6H_5)_3$	Reflux	HCl (g)/CH_3COOH	C_6H_6 (82%)	487
$C_2H_5Si(C_6H_5)_3$	Reflux	HCl (g)/CH_3COOH	C_6H_6 (44%)	487
p-$CH_3OC_6H_4Si(C_6H_5)_3$	Reflux	HCl (g)/CH_3COOH	$(C_6H_5)_3SiOSi(C_6H_5)_3$ (1.7%), $C_6H_5OCH_3$ (41%)	487
⟨thiophene⟩-$Si(C_6H_5)_3$	Reflux	HCl (g)/CH_3COOH	$C_6H_5)_3SiOH$ (12.7%), thiophene	487
p-$(CH_3)_2NC_6H_4Si(C_6H_5)_3$	Reflux	HCl (g)/CH_3COOH	$(C_6H_5)_3SiOH$ (2.3%), $C_6H_5N(CH_3)_2$ (76%)	487
$(CH_3)_3SiC_6H_4CH_3$-m	Reflux	HCl (g)/CH_3COOH	$(CH_3)_3SiCl$ (81%), $CH_3C_6H_5$	488

Compound	Temp (°C)	Reagent	Products	Ref.
$(CH_3)_3SiC_6H_4N(CH_3)_2$-$m$	Reflux	HCl (g)/CH_3COOH	$(CH_3)_3SiCl$ (8%), $C_6H_5N(CH_3)_2$	488
$(CH_3)_3SiC_6H_4Cl$-m	Reflux	HCl (g)/CH_3COOH	$(CH_3)_3SiCl$ (11%), C_6H_5Cl	488
$(CH_3)_3SiC_6H_4OCH_3$-m	Reflux	HCl (g)/CH_3COOH	$(CH_3)_3SiCl$ (82%), $C_6H_5OCH_3$	488
[dibenzothiophene substituted with $Si(CH_3)_3$]	Reflux	HCl (g)/CH_3COOH	Dibenzothiophene (97%), $(CH_3)_3SiCl$	489
[dibenzothiophene substituted with $Si(CH_3)_3$]	Reflux	HCl (g)/CH_3COOH	Dibenzothiophene (99%), $(CH_3)_3SiCl$	489
(3,5-Dimethylphenyl)trimethylsilane	25	$CH_3C_6H_4SO_3H$, H_2O, CH_3COOH	$[(CH_3)_3Si]_2O$, m-$(CH_3)_2C_6H_4$	490
(3,4-Dimethylphenyl)trimethylsilane	25	$CH_3C_6H_4SO_3H$, H_2O, CH_3COOH	$[(CH_3)_3Si]_2O$, o-$(CH_3)_2C_6H_4$	490
(2,5-Dimethylphenyl)trimethylsilane	25	$CH_3C_6H_4SO_3H$, H_2O, CH_3COOH	$[(CH_3)_3Si]_2O$ (68%), p-$(CH_3)_2C_6H_4$	490
(2,3-Dimethylphenyl)trimethylsilane	25	$CH_3C_6H_4SO_3H$, H_2O, CH_3COOH	$[(CH_3)_3Si]_2O$, o-$(CH_3)_2C_6H_4$	490
(2,4-Dimethylphenyl)trimethylsilane	25	$CH_3C_6H_4SO_3H$, H_2O, CH_3COOH	$[(CH_3)_3Si]_2O$, m-$(CH_3)_2C_6H_4$	490
(2,6-Dimethylphenyl)trimethylsilane	25	$CH_3C_6H_4SO_3H$, H_2O, CH_3COOH	$[(CH_3)_3Si]_2O$, m-$(CH_3)_2C_6H_4$	490
$(CH_3)_3SiC_6H_4CH_3$-o	25	$CH_3C_6H_4SO_3H$, H_2O, CH_3COOH	$(CH_3)_3SiOH$, $CH_3C_6H_5$	491
$(CH_3)_2C_2H_5SiC_6H_5$[a]	25	$CH_3C_6H_4SO_3H$, H_2O, CH_3COOH	C_6H_6	265

(continued)

Compound split	Temperature, deg	Agent	Products (% yield)	Refs.
$(C_2H_5)_3SiC_6H_5{}^a$	25	$CH_3C_6H_4SO_3H, H_2O$, CH_3COOH	C_6H_6	265
$(i-C_3H_7)_3SiC_6H_5$	25	$CH_3C_6H_4SO_3H, H_2O$, CH_3COOH	C_6H_5	265
$(CH_3)_3SiC_6H_4Br-m^{b,c}$	25	$HCl/H_2O, CH_3COOH$	$(CH_3)_3SiOH, C_6H_5Br$	491
$(CH_3)_3SiC_6H_3(OCH_3)_2-3,5$	25	$HCl/H_2O, CH_3COOH$	$(CH_3)_3SiOH, m-(CH_3O)_2C_6H_4$	491
$(CH_3)_3SiC_6H_4C_2H_5-m$	25	$HCl/H_2O, CH_3COOH$	$(CH_3)_3SiOH, C_2H_5C_6H_5$	272,491
$(CH_3)_3SiC_6H_4(i-C_3H_7)-m$	25	$HCl/H_2O, CH_3COOH$	$(CH_3)_3SiOH, i-C_3H_7C_6H_5$	272,491
$(CH_3)_3SiC_6H_4(t-C_4H_9)-m$	25	$HCl/H_2O, CH_3COOH$	$(CH_3)_3SiOH, t-C_4H_9C_6H_5$	272,491
$(C_2H_5)_3SiC_6H_5$	25	$HCl/H_2O, CH_3COOH$	C_6H_6	272
$(C_2H_5)_3SiC_6H_4CH_3-m$	25	$HCl/H_2O, CH_3COOH$	$CH_3C_6H_5$	272
$(C_2H_5)_3SiC_6H_4C_2H_5-m$	25	$HCl/H_2O, CH_3COOH$	$C_2H_5C_6H_5$	272
$(C_2H_5)_3SiC_6H_4 (i-C_3H_7)-m$	25	$HCl/H_2O, CH_3COOH$	$i-C_3H_7C_6H_5$	272
$(C_2H_5)_3SiC_6H_4(t-C_4H_9)-m$	25	$HCl/H_2O, CH_3COOH$	$t-C_4H_9C_6H_5$	272
$(i-C_3H_7)_3SiC_6H_5$	25	$H_2SO_4/H_2O, CH_3COOH$	C_6H_6	272
$(i-C_3H_7)_3SiC_6H_4CH_3-m$	25	$H_2SO_4/H_2O, CH_3COOH$	$CH_3C_6H_5$	272
$(i-C_3H_7)_3SiC_6H_4C_2H_5-m$	25	$H_2SO_4/H_2O, CH_3COOH$	$C_2H_5C_6H_5$	272
$(i-C_3H_7)_3SiC_6H_4(C_3H_7-i)-m$	25	$H_2SO_4/H_2O, CH_3COOH$	$i-C_3H_7C_6H_5$	272
$(i-C_3H_7)_3SiC_6H_4(C_4H_9-t)-m$	25	$H_2SO_4/H_2O, CH_3COOH$	$t-C_4H_9C_6H_5$	272
$(CH_3)_3SiC_6H_4OH-p$	51.2	$HClO_4/H_2O, CH_3OH$	C_6H_5OH	495
$(CH_3)_3SiC_6H_2(CH_3)_3-2,4,6$	51.2	$HClO_4/H_2O, CH_3OH$	$1,3,5-(CH_3)_3C_6H_3$	495
$(CH_3)_3SiCH_2C_6H_4Si(CH_3)_3-p$	51.2	$HClO_4/H_2O, CH_3OH$	$(CH_3)_3SiCH_2C_6H_5$	495

$(CH_3)_3SiCH_2C_6H_4Si(CH_3)_3$-$m$	51.2	$HClO_4/H_2O, CH_3OH$	$(CH_3)_3SiCH_2C_6H_5$	495
$(CH_3)_3SiC_6H_4Si(CH_3)_3$-$p$	51.2	$HClO_4/H_2O, CH_3OH$	$(CH_3)_3SiC_6H_5$	495
$(CH_3)_3SiC_6H_4C_6H_5$-p^d	51.2	$HClO_4/H_2O, CH_3OH$	$C_6H_5C_6H_5$	495
$(CH_3)_3SiC_6H_4F$-p	51.2	$HClO_4/H_2O, CH_3OH$	C_6H_5F	495
$(CH_3)_3SiC_6H_4NO_2$-p	50.18	$H_2SO_4/H_2O, CH_3COOH$	$C_6H_5NO_2$	254
$(CH_3)_3SiC_6H_4N(CH_3)_3$-$p$	50.18	$H_2SO_4/H_2O, CH_3COOH$	$C_6H_5N(CH_3)_2$	254
$(CH_3)_3SiC_6H_4COOH$-p	50.18	$H_2SO_4/H_2O, CH_3COOH$	C_6H_5COOH	254
$(CH_3)_3SiC_6H_4I$-p	50.18	$H_2SO_4/H_2O, CH_3COOH$	C_6H_5I	254
$(CH_3)_3SiC_6H_4C_6H_5$-m	50.18	$H_2SO_4/H_2O, CH_3COOH$	$C_6H_5C_6H_5$	254,269
$(CH_3)_3SiC_6H_4C_6H_5$-p	50.18	$H_2SO_4/H_2O, CH_3COOH$	$C_6H_5C_6H_5$	254,269
$(CH_3)_3SiC_6H_4C_6H_5$-o^e	50.18	$H_2SO_4/H_2O, CH_3COOH$	$C_6H_5C_6H_5$	254,269
	50.18	$H_2SO_4/H_2O, CH_3COOH$	Thiophene	255
	50.18	$H_2SO_4/H_2O, CH_3COOH$	C_6HF_5	273
	50.18	$H_2SO_4/H_2O, CH_3COOH$	Thiophene	255
	50.18	$H_2SO_4/H_2O, CH_3COOH$	$(2\text{-}C_4H_4S)C_6H_5$	254
	50	$HClO_4/CH_3OH$	Naphthalene	266

(continued)

N. TABLE XIV (continued)

Compound split	Temperature, deg	Agent	Products (% yield)	Refs.
(naphthalene)—Si(CH$_3$)$_3$	50	HClO$_4$/CH$_3$OH	Naphthalene	266
m-C$_6$H$_5$OC$_6$H$_4$Si(CH$_3$)$_3$	50	HClO$_4$/CH$_3$OH, H$_2$O	C$_6$H$_5$OC$_6$H$_5$	274
o-C$_6$H$_5$OC$_6$H$_4$Si(CH$_3$)$_3$	50	HClO$_4$/CH$_3$OH, H$_2$O	C$_6$H$_5$OC$_6$H$_5$	274
m-C$_6$H$_5$SC$_6$H$_4$Si(CH$_3$)$_3$	50	HClO$_4$/CH$_3$OH, H$_2$O	C$_6$H$_5$SC$_6$H$_5$	274
o-C$_6$H$_5$SC$_6$H$_4$Si(CH$_3$)$_3$	50	HClO$_4$/CH$_3$OH, H$_2$O	C$_6$H$_5$SC$_6$H$_5$	274
(furan)—Si(CH$_3$)$_3$	50	HClO$_4$/CH$_3$OH, H$_2$O	Furan	274
(thiophene)—Si(CH$_3$)$_3$	50	HClO$_4$/CH$_3$OH, H$_2$O	Thiophene	274
(N-ethylcarbazole)—Si(CH$_3$)$_3$	50	HClO$_4$/CH$_3$OH, H$_2$O		274
(dibenzofuran)—Si(CH$_3$)$_3$	50	HClO$_4$/CH$_3$OH, H$_2$O	Dibenzofuran	274

Structure		Reagent	Product	Ref.
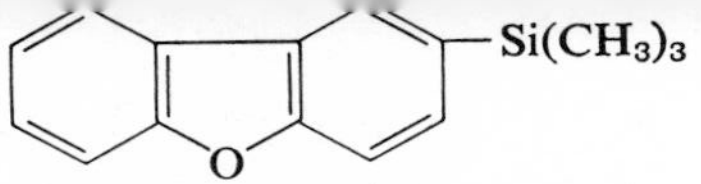 Si(CH₃)₃ on dibenzofuran	50	$HClO_4/CH_3OH$, H_2O	Dibenzofuran	274
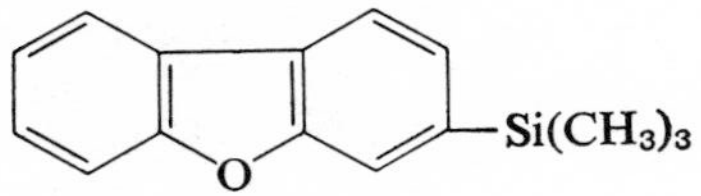 Si(CH₃)₃ on dibenzofuran	50	$HClO_4/CH_3OH$, H_2O	Dibenzofuran	274
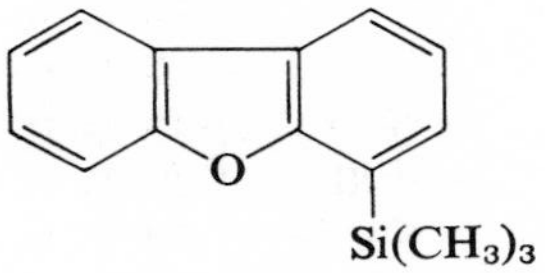 Si(CH₃)₃ on dibenzofuran	50	$HClO_4/CH_3OH$, H_2O	Dibenzofuran	274
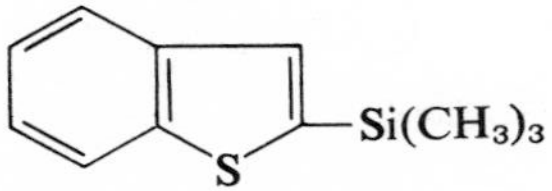 Si(CH₃)₃ on benzothiophene	50	$HClO_4/CH_3OH$, H_2O	Benzothiophene	274
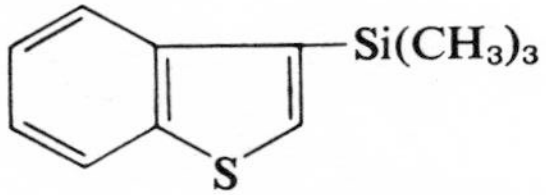 Si(CH₃)₃ on benzothiophene	50	$HClO_4/CH_3OH$, H_2O	Benzothiophene	274
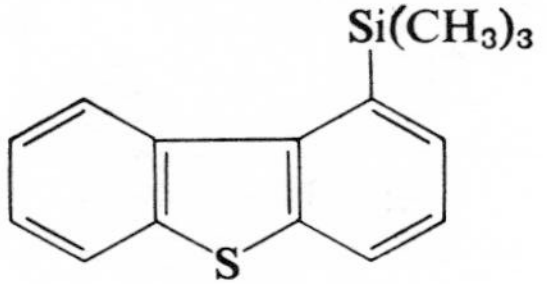 Si(CH₃)₃ on dibenzothiophene	50	$HClO_4/CH_3OH$, H_2O	Dibenzothiophene	274
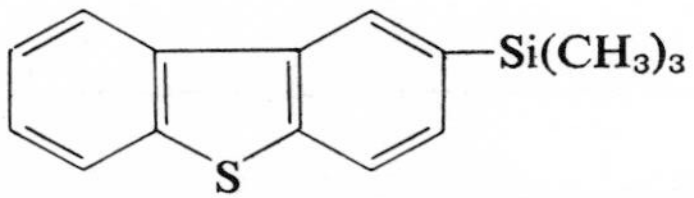 Si(CH₃)₃ on dibenzothiophene	50	$HClO_4/CH_3OH$, H_2O	Dibenzothiophene	274

(continued)

281

N. TABLE XIV (continued)

Compound split	Temperature, deg	Agent	Products (% yield)	Refs.
(dibenzothiophene with Si(CH$_3$)$_3$ substituent)	50	HClO$_4$/CH$_3$OH, H$_2$O	Dibenzothiophene	274
(dibenzothiophene with Si(CH$_3$)$_3$ substituent)	50	HClO$_4$/CH$_3$OH, H$_2$O	Dibenzothiophene	274
(CH$_3$)$_3$SiC$_6$H$_5$	Reflux	HNO$_3$/(CH$_3$CO)$_2$O	C$_6$H$_5$NO$_2$ (71%), [(CH$_3$)$_3$Si]$_2$O (85.5%)	291
(CH$_3$)$_3$SiC$_6$H$_4$F-p	Reflux	HNO$_3$/(CH$_3$CO)$_2$O	p-FC$_6$H$_4$NO$_2$ (67.5%), [(CH$_3$)$_3$Si]$_2$O (94.5%)	291
(CH$_3$)$_3$SiC$_6$H$_4$Cl-p	Reflux	HNO$_3$/(CH$_3$CO)$_2$O	p-ClC$_6$H$_4$NO$_2$ (93%), [(CH$_3$)$_3$Si]$_2$O (80%)	291
(CH$_3$)$_3$SiC$_6$H$_4$Br-p	Reflux	HNO$_3$/(CH$_3$CO)$_2$O	p-BrC$_6$H$_4$NO$_2$ (91%), [(CH$_3$)$_3$Si]$_2$O (89%)	291
(CH$_3$)$_3$SiC$_6$H$_4$CH$_3$-m	Reflux	HNO$_3$/(CH$_3$CO)$_2$O	m-CH$_3$C$_6$H$_4$NO$_2$ (77%), [(CH$_3$)$_3$Si]$_2$O (71.2%)	291
(CH$_3$)$_2$Si(C$_6$H$_5$)$_2$	Reflux	HNO$_3$/(CH$_3$CO)$_2$O	C$_6$H$_5$NO$_2$ (72.5%), [(CH$_3$)$_2$SiO]$_n$ (46%)	291
(CH$_3$)$_2$Si(C$_6$H$_4$F-p)$_2$	Reflux	HNO$_3$/(CH$_3$CO)$_2$O	p-FC$_6$H$_4$NO$_2$ (61%), [(CH$_3$)$_2$SiO]$_n$ (61.7%)	291
(CH$_3$)$_2$Si(C$_6$H$_4$Cl-p)$_2$	Reflux	HNO$_3$/(CH$_3$CO)$_2$O	p-ClC$_6$H$_4$NO$_2$ (96.5%), [(CH$_3$)$_2$SiO]$_n$ (65.6%)	291
(CH$_3$)$_2$Si(C$_6$H$_4$Br-p)$_2$	Reflux	HNO$_3$/(CH$_3$CO)$_2$O	p-BrC$_6$H$_4$NO$_2$ (89%), [(CH$_3$)$_2$SiO]$_n$ (69%)	291
[(C$_6$H$_5$)$_{0.7}$(CH$_3$)$_{1.3}$SiO]$_n$	Reflux	HNO$_3$/(CH$_3$CO)$_2$O	C$_6$H$_5$NO$_2$ (72%), [(C$_6$H$_5$)$_{0.3}$(CH$_3$)$_{1.3}$SiO$_{1.2}$]$_n$	291
[(p-FC$_6$H$_4$)$_{0.5}$(CH$_3$)$_{1.6}$SiO$_{0.95}$]$_n$	Reflux	HNO$_3$/(CH$_3$CO)$_2$O	p-FC$_6$H$_4$NO$_2$ (81%), [(p-FC$_6$H$_4$)$_{0.3}$(CH$_3$)$_{1.6}$SiO$_{1.05}$]$_n$	291
(CH$_3$)$_3$SiC$_6$H$_4$OCOCH$_3$-p	Reflux	HNO$_3$/CH$_3$COOH	p-NO$_2$C$_6$H$_4$OCOCH$_3$	499
p-(CH$_3$)$_3$SiC$_6$H$_4$Si(CH$_3$)$_3$	Reflux	HNO$_3$/(CH$_3$CO)$_2$O	p-NO$_2$C$_6$H$_4$Si(CH$_3$)$_3$ (82%)	292

282

Dibenzothiophene with Si(CH₃)₃ group	Reflux	HCl (g)/CH₃COOH	Dibenzothiophene, (CH₃)₃SiCl	243
Dibenzothiophene sulfone with Si(CH₃)₃ group	Reflux	HCl (g)/CH₃COOH	No reaction	243
Dibenzothiophene with Si(C₆H₅)₃ group	Reflux	HCl (g)/CH₃COOH	No reaction	243
Naphthalenediol with Si(C₆H₅)₃ group	Reflux	HCl (g)/CH₃COOH	2-Naphthol (56%), polymers	497
Naphthol with Si(CH₃)₃ and OH		HCl/H₂O	2-Naphthol (100%)	497
5-Ethyl-2-carbazolyltriphenylsilane	Reflux	HCl (g)/CH₃COOH	5-Ethylcarbazol (51%), (C₆H₅)₃SiOH (25%)	356
Diphenylbis(5-ethyl-2-carbazolyl)-silane	Reflux	HCl (g)/CH₃COOH	5-Ethylcarbazol (75%)	356
Phenyltris(5-ethyl-2-carbazolyl)-silane	Reflux	HCl (g)/CH₃COOH	5-Ethylcarbazol (66%)	356
Tetrakis(5-ethyl-2-carbazolyl)-silane	Reflux	HCl (g)/CH₃COOH	5-Ethylcarbazol (73%)	356

(continued)

Compound split	Temperature, deg	Agent	Products (% yield)	Refs.
5-Ethyl-4-carbazolyltriphenylsilane	Reflux	HCl (g)/CH₃COOH	5-Ethylcarbazol (84%), $(C_6H_5)_3SiOH$ (33%), traces of C_6H_6	356
2-Dibenzothienyltriphenylsilane	Reflux	HCl (g)/CH₃COOH	No reaction	356
4-Dibenzothienyltriphenylsilane	Reflux	HCl (g)/CH₃COOH	No reaction	356
2-Dibenzofuryltriphenylsilane	Reflux	HCl (g)/CH₃COOH	Dibenzofuran (31%), $(C_6H_5)_3SiOH$ (19%), C_6H_6 (8%)	356
4-Dibenzofuryltriphenylsilane	Reflux	HCl (g)/CH₃COOH	No reaction	356
2-Benzothienyltriphenylsilane	Reflux	HCl (g)/CH₃COOH	$(C_6H_5)_3SiOH$ (7%)	356
2-Thienyltriphenylsilane	Reflux	HCl (g)/CH₃COOH	$(C_6H_5)_3SiOH$ (21%)	356
2-Benzothiazolyltriphenylsilane	Reflux	HCl (g)/CH₃COOH	$(C_6H_5)_3SiOH$ (20%), C_6H_6 (7%)	356
$Si(C_4H_9)_3$	Reflux	HCl (g)/CH₃COOH	No reaction	332
$Si(C_2H_5)_3$	Reflux	HCl (g)/CH₃COOH	Naphthalene	332
$Si(C_2H_5)_3$	Reflux	HCl (g)/CH₃COOH		332

284

Compound	Reagent	Temp.	Products	Ref.
(CH$_3$)$_3$SiC$_6$H$_4$CH$_3$-o	(CH$_3$COO)$_2$Hg/CH$_3$COOH	25	CH$_3$C$_6$H$_5$, (CH$_3$)$_3$SiOOCH$_3$	269,340
(CH$_3$)$_3$SiC$_6$H$_4$CH$_3$-m	(CH$_3$COO)$_2$Hg/CH$_3$COOH	25	CH$_3$C$_6$H$_5$, (CH$_3$)$_3$SiOOCH$_3$	269,346
(CH$_3$)$_3$SiC$_6$H$_4$CH$_3$-p	(CH$_3$COO)$_2$Hg/CH$_3$COOH	25	CH$_3$C$_6$H$_5$, (CH$_3$)$_3$SiOOCH$_3$	269,346
(CH$_3$)$_3$SiC$_6$H$_3$(CH$_3$)$_2$-2,3	(CH$_3$COO)$_2$Hg/CH$_3$COOH, H$_2$O	25	o-C$_6$H$_4$(CH$_3$)$_2$, (CH$_3$)$_3$SiOH	346
(CH$_3$)$_3$SiC$_6$H$_3$(CH$_3$)$_2$-3,4	(CH$_3$COO)$_2$Hg/CH$_3$COOH, H$_2$O	25	o-C$_6$H$_4$(CH$_3$)$_2$, (CH$_3$)$_3$SiOH	346
(CH$_3$)$_3$SiC$_6$H$_3$(CH$_3$)$_2$-2,4	(CH$_3$COO)$_2$Hg/CH$_3$COOH, H$_2$O	25	m-C$_6$H$_4$(CH$_3$)$_2$, (CH$_3$)$_3$SiOH	346
(CH$_3$)$_3$SiC$_6$H$_3$(CH$_3$)$_2$-2,6	(CH$_3$COO)$_2$Hg/CH$_3$COOH, H$_2$O	25	m-C$_6$H$_4$(CH$_3$)$_2$, (CH$_3$)$_3$SiOH	346
(CH$_3$)$_3$SiC$_6$H$_3$(CH$_3$)$_2$-3,5	(CH$_3$COO)$_2$Hg/CH$_3$COOH, H$_2$O	25	m-C$_6$H$_4$(CH$_3$)$_2$, (CH$_3$)$_3$SiOH	346
(CH$_3$)$_3$SiC$_6$H$_3$(CH$_3$)$_2$-2,5	(CH$_3$COO)$_2$Hg/CH$_3$COOH, H$_2$O	25	p-C$_6$H$_4$(CH$_3$)$_2$, (CH$_3$)$_3$SiOH	346
(CH$_3$)$_3$SiC$_6$H$_4$C$_6$H$_5$-o	(CH$_3$COO)$_2$Hg/CH$_3$COOH, H$_2$O	25	C$_6$H$_5$C$_6$H$_5$	269
(CH$_3$)$_3$SiC$_6$H$_4$C$_6$H$_5$-m	(CH$_3$COO)$_2$Hg/CH$_3$COOH, H$_2$O	25	C$_6$H$_5$C$_6$H$_5$	269
(CH$_3$)$_3$SiC$_6$H$_4$C$_6$H$_5$-p	(CH$_3$COO)$_2$Hg/CH$_3$COOH, H$_2$O	25	C$_6$H$_5$C$_6$H$_5$	269
(CH$_3$)$_3$SiC$_{10}$H$_7$-1	(CH$_3$COO)$_2$Hg/CH$_3$COOH, H$_2$O	25	Naphthalene	266
(CH$_3$)$_3$SiC$_{10}$H$_7$-2	(CH$_3$COO)$_2$Hg/CH$_3$COOH, H$_2$O	25	Naphthalene	266
(CH$_3$)$_3$SiC$_5$H$_4$FeC$_5$H$_5$[f]	HCl/CH$_3$OH	50	C$_5$H$_5$FeC$_5$H$_5$ (90%)	258,259
(C$_2$H$_5$)$_3$SiC$_5$H$_4$FeC$_5$H$_4$CH$_3$	HCl/CH$_3$COOH, H$_2$O	25	C$_5$H$_5$FeC$_5$H$_4$CH$_3$, (C$_2$H$_5$)$_3$SiOH, [(C$_2$H$_5$)$_3$Si]$_2$O	260
(C$_2$H$_5$)$_3$SiC$_5$H$_4$FeC$_5$H$_4$C$_2$H$_5$	HCl/CH$_3$COOH, H$_2$O	25	C$_5$H$_5$FeC$_5$H$_4$C$_2$H$_5$, (C$_2$H$_5$)$_3$SiOH, [(C$_2$H$_5$)$_3$Si]$_2$O	260
(C$_2$H$_5$)$_3$SiC$_5$H$_4$FeC$_5$H$_4$C$_3$H$_7$-i	HCl/CH$_3$COOH, H$_2$O	25	C$_5$H$_5$FeC$_5$H$_4$C$_3$H$_7$-i, (C$_2$H$_5$)$_3$SiOH, [(C$_2$H$_5$)$_3$Si]$_2$O	260
(C$_2$H$_5$)$_3$SiC$_5$H$_4$FeC$_5$H$_4$C$_4$H$_9$-t	HCl/CH$_3$COOH, H$_2$O	25	C$_5$H$_5$FeC$_5$H$_4$C$_4$H$_9$-t, (C$_2$H$_5$)$_3$SiOH, [(C$_2$H$_5$)$_3$Si]$_2$O	260
(CH$_3$)$_3$Si(CH$_3$)$_2$SiC$_5$H$_4$FeC$_5$H$_5$	HCl/C$_2$H$_5$OH	Reflux	C$_5$H$_5$FeC$_5$H$_4$Si(CH$_3$)$_2$OC$_2$H$_5$, (CH$_3$)$_3$SiOC$_2$H$_5$, [(CH$_3$)$_3$Si]$_2$O	261

(continued)

N. TABLE XIV (continued)

Compound split	Temperature, deg	Agent	Products (% yield)	Refs.
$(CH_3)_3Si(CH_3)_2SiC_5H_4FeC_5H_4Si$-$(CH_3)_2Si(CH_3)_3$	Reflux	HCl/CH_3OH or C_2H_5OH	$C_5H_5FeC_5H_5$ 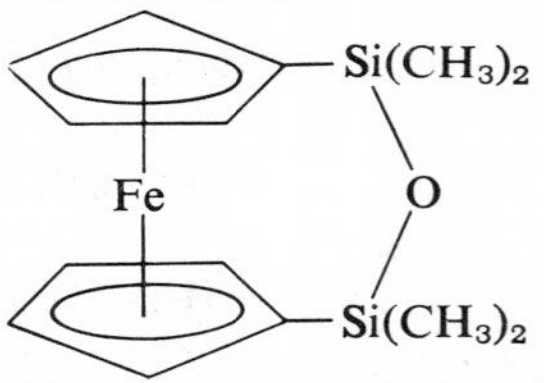	261
$(CH_3)_3SiCH_2CH_2C_5H_4FeC_5H_5$	20–30	H_2SO_4	CH_4, $[C_5H_5FeC_5H_4OC(CH_2)_2Si(CH_3)_2]_2O$ (76%)	141
$(CH_3)_3Si(CH_2)_3C_5H_4FeC_5H_5$	20–30	H_2SO_4	CH_4, $[C_5H_5FeC_5H_4OC(CH_2)_3Si(CH_3)_2]_2O$ (77%)	141
$(CH_3)_3Si(CH_2)_3COC_5H_4FeC_5H_4CO$-$(CH_2)_2Si(CH_3)_3$	20–30	H_2SO_4	CH_4, $[(CH_3)_2Si(CH_2)_2COC_5H_4FeC_5H_4CO(CH_2)_2$-$Si(CH_3)_2O]_n$ (73%)	141
$(CH_3)_3Si(CH_2)_3COC_5H_4FeC_5H_4CO$-$(CH_2)_3Si(CH_3)_3$	20–30	H_2SO_4	CH_4, polymer	141
$(CH_3)_3Si(CH_2)_4C_5H_4FeC_5H_5$	20–30	H_2SO_4	CH_4, $[C_5H_5FeC_5H_4(CH_2)_4Si(CH_3)_2]_2O$ (67%)	141
$(CH_3)_3Si(CH_2)_3C_5H_4FeC_5H_4$-$(CH_2)_3Si(CH_3)_3$	20–30	H_2SO_4	CH_4 (90%), polymer (89%)	141
$(CH_3)_3Si(CH_2)_4C_5H_4FeC_5H_4$-$(CH_2)_4Si(CH_3)_3$	20–30	H_2SO_4	CH_4, polymer (91%)	141
$(C_6H_5)_3SiH$		HCOOH	C_6H_6 (8.8%)	276
$(p\text{-}CH_3C_6H_4)_3SiOH$		HCOOH	No splitting	276
$(2\text{-}C_6H_5C_6H_4)_3SiOH$		HCOOH	$C_6H_5C_6H_5$ (76.5%)	276

286

(1-C$_{10}$H$_7$)$_3$SiOH		HCOOH	Naphthalene (41.4%)	276
(C$_6$H$_5$)$_3$SiC$_6$H$_4$C$_6$H$_5$-2		HCOOH	C$_6$H$_5$C$_6$H$_5$ (45.5%)	276
(CH$_3$)$_3$SiC$_{10}$H$_7$-1	25	HCl/H$_2$O, CH$_3$COOH	Naphthalene	265
(CH$_3$)$_3$SiC$_{10}$H$_7$-2	25	HCl/H$_2$O, CH$_3$COOH	Naphthalene	265
(C$_6$H$_5$)$_3$SiC$_6$H$_4$C$_6$H$_4$CH$_3$-4'^{g}	25	HCl/H$_2$O	(C$_6$H$_5$)$_3$SiOH	265
(C$_2$H$_5$)$_3$SiC$_6$H$_3$CH$_3$-2-NH$_2$-5	100	HCl/C$_2$H$_5$OH	After acetylation p-CH$_3$C$_6$H$_4$NHCOCH$_3$ (30%)	287
(C$_6$H$_5$)$_4$Si	130–140	HCl/CH$_3$COOH	(C$_6$H$_5$)$_3$SiOH, C$_6$H$_6$	294
C$_6$H$_5$SiCl$_3$	200	HCl/H$_2$O	C$_6$H$_6$, SiO$_2$	498
(CH$_3$)$_3$SiC$_6$H$_5$	100	HCl/H$_2$O, dioxane (xylene)	[(CH$_3$)$_3$Si]$_2$O, C$_6$H$_6$	278
[(CH$_3$)$_2$C$_6$H$_5$Si]$_2$O	100	HCl/H$_2$O, dioxane (xylene)	[(CH$_3$)$_2$SiO]$_n$, C$_6$H$_6$	278
[CH$_3$(C$_6$H$_5$)SiO]$_3$	100	HCl/H$_2$O, dioxane (xylene)	(CH$_3$SiO$_{1.5}$)$_n$, C$_6$H$_5$	278
C$_6$H$_5$SiO$_{1.5}$)$_n$	100	HCl/H$_2$O, dioxane (xylene)	SiO$_2$, C$_6$H$_6$	278
(C$_2$H$_5$)$_3$SiC$_{10}$H$_7$ (isomer not given)	Reflux	HCl/H$_2$O	Naphthalene (89%)	332
(C$_2$H$_5$)$_3$SiC$_6$H$_4$C$_6$H$_5$-p		HCl (g)/CH$_3$COOH	C$_6$H$_5$C$_6$H$_5$ (43%)	332
(CH$_3$)$_3$SiCl	Reflux	HCl/CH$_3$COOH	C$_6$H$_6$ (2%)	356
p-CH$_3$OC$_6$H$_4$(CH$_3$)(C$_6$H$_5$)SiC$_{10}$H$_7$-1		HBr/C$_6$H$_6$	p-CH$_3$OC$_6$H$_4$(CH$_3$)(C$_6$H$_5$)SiBr	309
(dibenzosilole structure with Si bearing two C$_6$H$_5$ groups: C$_6$H$_5$–Si–C$_6$H$_5$, C$_6$H$_5$)	Reflux	HCOOH	C$_6$H$_5$C$_6$H$_5$ (35%)	70
CH$_3$(C$_2$H$_5$)(C$_6$H$_5$)SiCH$_2$CH$_2$COOH	90	HCl/H$_2$O	[CH$_3$(C$_2$H$_5$)SiCH$_2$CH$_2$COOH]$_2$O (58.4%), C$_6$H$_6$	298
C$_6$H$_5$SiH$_3$	−78	HBr	C$_6$H$_6$ (100%), SiH$_3$Br (100%)	280,284
C$_6$H$_5$SiH$_3$		HCl/diphenyl ether	C$_6$H$_6$, SiH$_3$Cl (75.5%)	280
C$_6$H$_5$SiH$_2$Br	−78	HBr	C$_6$H$_6$, SiH$_2$Br$_2$	284
(C$_6$H$_5$)$_2$SiH$_2$	−78	HCl	C$_6$H$_6$ (78%), C$_6$H$_5$SiH$_2$Cl (62%)	284
(C$_6$H$_5$)$_2$SiH$_2$	−78	HBr	C$_6$H$_6$ (94%), C$_6$H$_5$SiH$_2$Br (85%)	284

(continued)

287

N. TABLE XIV (continued)

Compound split	Temperature, deg	Agent	Products (% yield)	Refs.
$(C_6H_5)_2SiH_2$	-40	HI	C_6H_6 (92%), SiH_2I_2 (88%)	284
$(C_6H_5)_2SiH_2$		HI	C_6H_6, SiH_2I_2 (55%)	281
$ClC_6H_4SiH_3$		HI	C_6H_5Cl, SiH_3I (60%)	281
$(CH_3)_3SiC_6H_4OH-p$[h]	Reflux	HCl/H_2O	C_6H_5OH	499
$(CH_3)_3SiC_6H_4N(CH_3)_2-p$	Reflux	HCl/H_2O	$C_6H_5N(CH_3)_2$ (90%)	500
$(CH_3)_2NC_6H_3[Si(CH_3)_3-3]N=NC_6H_4NO_2-4$	100	(1) HCl/H_2O, Sn (2) $(CH_3CO)_2O$	p-$NO_2C_6H_4NHCOCH_3$, p-$(CH_3)_2NC_6H_4NHCOCH_3$	501
$(CH_3)_3SiC_6H_4N(CH_3)_2-m$		HCl (g)/CH_3COOH	$C_6H_5N(CH_3)_2$ (80%)	501
1-$(NO_2C_6H_4N=N-p)$-2-(OH)-6-$[(CH_3)_3Si]C_{10}H_5$		HCl (g)/CH_3COOH	1-$(NO_2C_6H_4N=N-p)$-2-(OH)-$C_{10}H_6$	501
$(CH_3)_3SiC_6H_5$	20, 40, 60	H_2SO_4 (62.8%, 80.3%, 86.8%)	C_6H_6, $C_6H_5SO_3H$	277
$[C_6H_5(CH_3)_2Si]_2O$	20, 40	H_2SO_4 (62.8%, 86.8%)	C_6H_6, $C_6H_5SO_3H$	277
$(C_6H_5)_4Si$		H_2SO_4	$C_6H_5SO_3H$	505
$(C_6H_5)_3SiF$		H_2SO_4	$C_6H_5SO_3H$	505
$(C_2H_5)_3SiC_6H_5$		H_2SO_4	$C_6H_5SO_3H$	506,507, 508
$C_6H_5CH_2)(C_6H_5)(n$-$C_3H_7)(C_2H_5)Si$	100	H_2SO_4	C_6H_6, $(C_6H_5CH_2)(n$-$C_3H_7)(C_2H_5)SiOH$	131
$(C_6H_5)_2SiCl_2$	175	H_2SO_4, V_2O_5	C_6H_6, CO_2	147
$[(C_6H_5)_2CH_3Si]_2O$	175	H_2SO_4, V_2O_5	C_6H_6, CH_4, CO_2	147
$C_6H_5SiCl_3$	175	H_2SO_4, V_2O_5	C_6H_6	147
$(C_6H_5)_2Si(OH)_2$	175	H_2SO_4, V_2O_5	C_6H_6	147

Compound	Temp.	Reagent	Product	Ref.
$ArSi(CH_3)_3$		SO_3/CCl_4	$ArSO_2OSi(CH_3)_3$	295,296
$p\text{-}(CH_3)_3SiC_6H_4Si(CH_3)_3$		SO_3/CCl_4	$p\text{-}(CH_3)_3SiC_6H_4SO_2OSi(CH_3)_3$	295
$C_6H_5SiCl_3$	Reflux	SO_2Cl_2 (uv light)[i]	$ClC_6H_4SiCl_3$ (14%), C_6Cl_6 (50–60%)	316
$(CH_3)_3SiC_6H_5$	0–70	$HNO_3/(CH_3CO)_2O$	$NO_2C_6H_4Si(CH_3)_3$ ($o\text{-}$, $m\text{-}$, and p-isomers), $C_6H_5NO_2$	290
$(CH_3)_3SiC_6H_5$	20	NO_2	$C_6H_5NO_2$, $[(CH_3)_3Si]_2O$	170

[a] Under similar conditions $(CH_3)_3SiC_6H_5$,[265,491] $(CH_3)_3SiC_6H_4CH_3\text{-}m$[491] and $(CH_3)_3SiC_6H_4CH_3\text{-}p$[491] were split.

[b] Under similar conditions $(CH_3)_3SiC_6H_5$,[272,491] $(CH_3)_3SiC_6H_3(CH_3)_2\text{-}2,5$[491] and analogous 2,4-, 2,6-, 3,4-, 2,3-isomers[491] were split.

[c] In different acid medium a number of other aryltrimethylsilanes was split.[492-494]

[d] Under these conditions $o\text{-}$, $m\text{-}$, and p-substituted compounds of the type $(CH_3)_3SiC_6H_4X$ (X = H, CH_3, C_2H_5, $i\text{-}C_3H_7$, $t\text{-}C_4H_9$, Cl, Br, CH_3O, $(CH_3)_2N$) and of the types $(CH_3)_3SiC_6H_3X_2$ and $(CH_3)_3SiC_6H_2X_3$ (X = CH_3) were split.[274,495,496]

[e] Under these conditions $o\text{-}$, $m\text{-}$, and p-substituted compounds of the type $(CH_3)_3SiC_6H_4X$ (X = H, F, Cl, Br, OCH_3, CH_3, $CH_2Si(CH_3)_3$, and $(CH_3)_3N^+$) were split.[254,255,269,273]

[f] Under these conditions analogous ruthenium and osmium compounds were split.[258]

[g] Under these conditions 4' and 2' Cl- and CH_3-substituted compounds were split.

[h] Other substituted phenyltrimethylsilanes were split under similar conditions.[259,502-504]

[i] Ultraviolet light.

O. TABLE XV

Splitting of the Silicon-Aryl Bond by Means of Metal Salts

Compound split	Temperature, deg	Agent	Products (% yield)	Refs.
$C_6H_5SiCl_3$	70	$AlCl_3$	$SiCl_4$, $C_6H_5AlCl_2$ (50%)	330,333, 335,336
$(C_6H_5)_2SiCl_2$	30–35	$AlCl_3$	$SiCl_4$ (60%), C_6H_6 (61.2%), $C_6H_5SiCl_3$	330,333, 336
p-$ClC_6H_4SiCl_3$	25	$AlCl_3$	C_6H_5Cl (56.5%), $SiCl_4$	330,333
p-$ClC_6H_4(C_6H_5)SiCl_2$	30–35	$AlCl_3$	C_6H_5Cl (50%), $C_6H_5SiCl_3$ (57%)	330,333
$Br_2C_6H_3SiCl_3$	70	(1) $AlCl_3$, (2) H_2O	$C_6H_4Br_2$, SiO_2	329
$C_6H_{5-n}Cl_nSiCl_3$	70–85	(1) $AlCl_3$, (2) H_2O	$C_6H_{6-n}Cl_n$, SiO_2	319,509
$C_6H_{5-n}Cl_n(C_6H_{5-m}Cl_m)SiCl_2$	50–85	(1) $AlCl_3$, (2) H_2O	$C_6H_{6-n}Cl_n$, $C_6H_{6-m}Cl_m$, SiO_2	319,509
$(C_2H_5)_3SiC_6H_5$	75	$AlCl_3$	$(C_2H_5)_3SiCl$, $C_6H_5AlCl_2$	335
$(CH_3)_3SiC_6H_5$	40	(1) $AlCl_3$, (2) H_2O	$[(CH_3)_3Si]_2O$	327
$(C_6H_5)_4Si$	50	$AlCl_3/CHCl_3$	$SiCl_4$ (68%), C_6H_6 (67%)	179,333, 336
$(C_2H_5)_3SiC_{10}H_7$ (isomer not given)	20–25	(1) $AlCl_3$, (2) H_2O	Naphthalene (93%)	332
$(C_2H_5)_3SiC_6H_4C_6H_5$-p	20–25	(1) $AlCl_3$, (2) H_2O	$C_6H_5C_6H_5$ (90%)	332
[cyclohexadiene ring bearing $Si(C_4H_9$-$n)_2$ and $Si(C_4H_9$-$n)_3$ substituents with phenyl]	20–25	(1) $AlCl_3$, (2) H_2O	$C_6H_5C_6H_5$	332
$[(C_6H_5)_2Si]_4$	50	$AlCl_3/CHCl_3$	$(SiCl_2)_4$	336

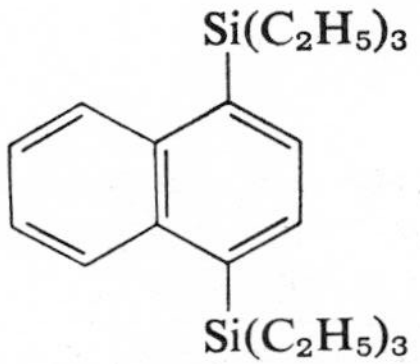 Si(C₂H₅)₃ ... Si(C₂H₅)₃ ... Si(C₂H₅)₃	20–25	(1) AlCl₃, (2) H₂O	Naphthalene (85%)	332
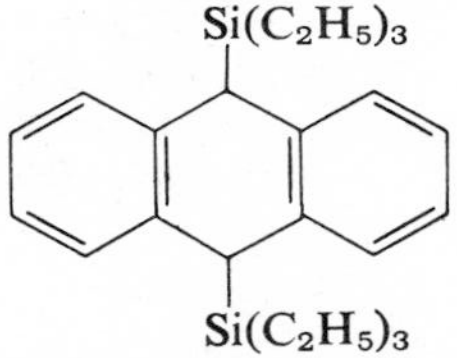 Si(C₂H₅)₃	20–25	(1) AlCl₃, (2) H₂O	Anthracene (86%)	332
$(CH_3)_3SiC_6H_5$	40	(1) AlBr₃, (2) H₂O	C_6H_6, $[(CH_3)_3Si]_2O$	327
$(CH_3)_3SiC_6H_5$	70	GaBr₃	$C_6H_5GaBr_2$, $(CH_3)_3SiBr$	178,327
$(CH_3)_3SiC_6H_5$	60	(1) GaCl₃, (2) H₂O	C_6H_6, $[(CH_3)_3Si]_2O$	327
$(CH_3)_3SiC_6H_5$	60	(1) BCl₃, (2) H₂O	C_6H_6, $[(CH_3)_3Si]_2O$	327
$(CH_3)_3SiC_6H_5$	60	(1) BBr₃, (2) H₂O	C_6H_6, $[(CH_3)_3Si]_2O$	327
$(CH_3)_3SiC_6H_5$	60	(1) ZrCl₄, (2) H₂O	C_6H_6, $[(CH_3)_3Si]_2O$	327
$(C_6H_5)_2SiCl_2$	25–30	FeCl₃	C_6H_6 (35%)	338
$(C_6H_5)_2SiCl_2$	60–70	FeCl₃·2.5H₂O	C_6H_6 (37%)	338
$(C_6H_5)_2SiCl_2$	150–200	SbCl₃	No reaction	339
$(C_6H_5)_2SiCl_2$	80–90	SbCl₅	C_6H_5Cl (81.4%)	339
$(p\text{-}ClC_6H_4)_2SiCl_2$	80–90	SbCl₅	$p\text{-}ClC_6H_4Cl$ (78.2%), SbCl₃	339
$C_6H_5SiCl_3$	75	AlCl₃, PCl₃	$SiCl_4$ (81%), $C_6H_5PCl_2$ (82%)	335
$C_6H_5SiCl_3$	80–85	AlCl₃, PCl₅	$SiCl_4$ (89.6%), C_6H_6	334

(continued)

291

Compound split	Temperature, deg	Agent	Products (% yield)	Refs.
$C_6H_5(CH_3)_2SiOCOCH_3$	140	$FeCl_3$	C_6H_6 (4.2%)	324
$C_6H_5Si(OC_2H_5)_3$ + $C_6H_5(CH_3)_2SiCl$	100	$FeCl_3$	C_6H_6	324
$C_6H_5Si(CH_3)_2OC_2H_5$	160	$FeCl_3$	C_6H_6 (8%)	324
$C_6H_5(CH_3)_2SiOCOCH_3$	160	—	C_6H_6 (7%)	324
$(CH_3)_3SiC_6H_5$	16	$Cu(NO_3)_2 \cdot 3H_2O/(CH_3CO)_2O$	$C_6H_5NO_2$ (24.7%), $NO_2C_6H_4Si(CH_3)_3$ (mixture of isomers)	286,290
$[(C_6H_5)_2SiO]_n$[a]		HgO	$(C_6H_5)_2Hg$, SiO_2	344
$C_6H_5SiCl_3$[b]	500	$HCl/AlCl_3$[b]	$SiHCl_3$ (9.4%), $SiCl_4$ (55.8%), C_6H_5Cl (1.5%), C_6H_6 (1%)	337
$(C_6H_5)_2SiCl_2$	500	$HCl/AlCl_3$[b]	$SiHCl_3$ (1.35%), $SiCl_4$ (9.6%), C_6H_6 (1.6%), $C_6H_5SiCl_3$ (10.6%)	337
$(C_6H_5)_2SiCl_2$		$C_2H_5Br/AlCl_3$	Halosilanes, $C_6H_5SiCl_3$, $C_2H_5C_6H_5$	336
$C_6H_5SiCl_3$	50–80	$CH_3COCl/AlCl_3$	$SiCl_4$ (84%), $C_6H_5COCH_3$ (90%)	330,335
p-$ClC_6H_4SiCl_3$	70–80	$CH_3COCl/AlCl_3$	p-$ClC_6H_4COCH_3$ (53%)	330
p-$BrC_6H_4SiCl_3$	80	$PCl_3/AlCl_3$	$SiCl_4$ (89.6%), p-$BrC_6H_4PCl_2$ (72%)	330
p-$(CH_3)_3SiC_6H_4OCOCH_3$	Reflux	$CH_3COCl/AlCl_3$, CS_2	p-$CH_3COC_6H_4OCOCH_3$	499

[a] For splitting of aryl silanes by means of $Hg(OCOCH_3)_2$, see Table XIV and Ref. 503 (splitting of trimethyltolylsilanes and xylylsilanes) and Ref. 510 (splitting of trimethyl(alkylphenyl)silanes).
[b] Reaction on the surface of the $AlCl_3$, containing Si/Cu contact mass from the direct synthesis of phenylchlorosilanes.

Splitting of the Silicon-Aryl Bond by Means of Halogens

Compound split	Temperature, deg	Agent	Products (% yield)	Refs.
$(CH_3)_3SiC_6H_5$	60	$Cl_2/3\%$ Fe[a]	C_6H_5Cl (47.2%)[b]	312,315
$(CH_3)_3SiC_6H_5$	60	$Cl_2/0.1\%$ I_2	C_6H_5Cl (27.3%), C_6H_5I (1%)	312
$(CH_3)_3SiC_6H_5$	60	$Cl_2/10\%$ I_2	C_6H_5Cl (19.7%), C_6H_5I (71.8%)	312
$(CH_3)_2ClSiC_6H_5$	60	$Cl_2/3\%$ Fe	C_6H_5Cl (30.8%)	312
$(CH_3)_2ClSiC_6H_5$	60	$Cl_2/0.1\%$ I_2	C_6H_5Cl (38.9%), C_6H_5I (2.5%)	312
$(CH_3)_2ClSiC_6H_5$	60	$Cl_2/10\%I_2$	C_6H_5Cl (3.8%), C_6H_5I (42.8%)	312
$CH_3Cl_2SiC_6H_5$	60	$Cl_2/3\%$ Fe	C_6H_5Cl (23.9%)	312
$CH_3Cl_2SiC_6H_5$	60	$Cl_2/1\%$ I_2	C_6H_5Cl (9.8%), C_6H_5I (3.9%)	312
$CH_3Cl_2SiC_6H_5$	60	$Cl_2/10\%$ I_2	C_6H_5Cl (13.7%), C_6H_5I (18.6%)	312
$Cl_3SiC_6H_5$	60	$Cl_2/1\%$ Fe	C_6H_5Cl (16.2%)	312
$Cl_3SiC_6H_5$	60	$Cl_2/10\%$ Fe	C_6H_5Cl (33.5%)	312,325
$Cl_3SiC_6H_5$	60	$Cl_2/3\%$ Sb	C_6H_5Cl (13.2%)	312
$Cl_3SiC_6H_5$	60	$Cl_2/3\%$ Al	C_6H_5Cl (21.8%)	312
$Cl_3SiC_6H_5$	30	$Cl_2/3\%$ Fe	C_6H_5Cl (8.1%)	312
$Cl_3SiC_6H_5$	30	$Cl_2/3\%$ I_2	C_6H_5Cl (9.8%)	312
$(CH_3)_2FSiC_6H_5$	60	$Cl_2/3\%$ Fe	C_6H_5Cl (47%)	313
$(CH_3)_2FSiC_6H_5$	60	$Cl_2/3\%$ I_2	C_6H_5Cl (30.1%), C_6H_5I (23.9%)	313
$CH_3F_2SiC_6H_5$	60	$Cl_2/3\%$ Fe	C_6H_5Cl (49.8%)	313
$CH_3F_2SiC_6H_5$	60	$Cl_2/3\%$ I_2	C_6H_5Cl (37.9%), C_6H_5I (11.3%)	313
$F_3SiC_6H_5$	60	$Cl_2/3\%$ Fe	C_6H_5Cl (3.5%)	313
$F_3SiC_6H_5$	60	$Cl_2/3\%$ I_2	C_6H_5Cl (3.5%), C_6H_5I (4.5%)	313

(continued)

Compound split	Temperature, deg	Agent	Products (% yield)	Refs.
$(C_6H_5)_2SiCl_2$	35–40	$Cl_2/SbCl_3$	p-ClC_6H_4Cl, trichlorobenzene	319
$CH_3Cl_2SiC_6H_5$	50–115	Cl_2	$C_6H_{5-n}Cl_n(CH_3)SiCl_2$, $C_6H_{5-n}Cl_{n+1}$	122
$CH_3Cl_2SiC_6H_5$	145–150	Cl_2	CCl_4, $C_6H_{5-n}Cl_nSiCl_3$	122
$(CH_3)_2Si(C_6H_4Cl-p)_2$		Cl_2	p-ClC_6H_4Cl, $CH_3(CHCl_2)Si(C_6H_4Cl-p)_2$	103
$CH_3(C_6H_5)SiCl_2$	24–27	$Cl_2/SbCl_3$	C_6H_5Cl, p-ClC_6H_4Cl, CH_3SiCl_3	318
$CH_3(C_6H_5)SiCl_2$	24–27	Cl_2/I_2	C_6H_5Cl, p-ClC_6H_4Cl, CH_3SiCl_3	318
$(C_2H_5)_3SiC_6H_5$		Cl_2, Br_2	Splitting off of the phenyl group	507
$(CH_3)_3SiC_6H_5$	25	$Cl_2/H_2O, CH_3COOH$	C_6H_5Cl (60%), $[(CH_3)_3Si]_2O$	310
p-$Cl_3SiC_6H_4CH_3$	70–100	$Cl_2/SbCl_3$	$SiCl_4$, pentachlorotoluene	511
$Cl_3SiC_6H_4CCl_3$-p	115–130	$Cl_2/FeCl_3$	$SiCl_4$	512
$C_6H_5Cl_2SiC_6H_4CH_3$-p	80	Cl_2/uv light	2.3% splitting reaction	321
$C_6H_5Cl_2SiC_6H_4CH_3$-m	80	Cl_2/uv light	4.3% splitting reaction	321
$(C_6H_5)_2ClSiC_6H_4CH_3$-p	80	Cl_2/uv light	ca. 30% splitting reaction	321
$(C_6H_5)_2ClSiC_6H_4CH_3$-m	80	Cl_2/uv light	ca. 30% splitting reaction	321
$(CH_3)_3SiC_6H_5$	25	Br_2	C_6H_5Br, $(CH_3)_3SiBr$	302,307, 300
$(CH_3)_3SiC_6H_4CH_3$-m	25	Br_2	$CH_3C_6H_4Br$-m, $(CH_3)_3SiBr$	307
$(CH_3)_3SiC_6H_4CH_3$-p	25	Br_2	$CH_3C_6H_4Br$-p, $(CH_3)_3SiBr$	307
$(CH_3)_3SiC_6H_4C_2H_5$-p	25	Br_2	$C_2H_5C_6H_4Br$-p, $(CH_3)_3SiBr$	307
$(CH_3)_3Si((C_6H_4C_3H_7-i)$-$p$	25	Br_2	i-C_3H_7-C_6H_4Br-p, $(CH_3)_3SiBr$	307
$(CH_3)_3Si((C_6H_4C_4H_9-t)$-$p$	25	Br_2	t-$C_4H_9C_6H_4Br$-p, $(CH_3)_3SiBr$	307
$(CH_3)_3SiC_6H_4Si(CH_3)_3$-$p$	25	Br_2	p-$(CH_3)_3SiC_6H_4Br$, $(CH_3)_3SiBr$	307
$(CH_3)_3SiC_6H_4Si(CH_3)_3$-$m$	25	Br_2	m-$(CH_3)_3SiC_6H_4Br$, $(CH_3)_3SiBr$	307

(CH$_3$)$_3$SiC$_6$H$_4$F-p	Br$_2$	25	p-FC$_6$H$_4$Br, (CH$_3$)$_3$SiBr	307
(CH$_3$)$_3$SiC$_6$H$_4$Cl-p	Br$_2$	25	p-ClC$_6$H$_4$Br, (CH$_3$)$_3$SiBr	307,318
(CH$_3$)$_3$SiC$_6$H$_4$Br-p	Br$_2$	25	p-BrC$_6$H$_4$Br, (CH$_3$)$_3$SiBr	307
(CH$_3$)$_3$SiC$_6$H$_4$I-p	Br$_2$	25	p-IC$_6$H$_4$Br, (CH$_3$)$_3$SiBr	307
(CH$_3$)$_3$SiC$_6$H$_4$Cl-m	Br$_2$	25	m-ClC$_6$H$_4$Br, (CH$_3$)$_3$SiBr	307
2-(CH$_3$)$_3$Si-5-BrC$_4$H$_2$S	Br$_2$/CCl$_4$	35	2,5-Dibromothiophene, (CH$_3$)$_3$SiBr	302
(CH$_3$)$_3$SiC$_6$H$_4$NO$_2$-o	Br$_2$/C$_6$H$_5$NO$_2$	40	o-BrC$_6$H$_4$NO$_2$, (CH$_3$)$_3$SiBr	302
(CH$_3$)$_3$SiC$_6$H$_4$NO$_2$-m	Br$_2$/C$_6$H$_5$NO$_2$	40	m-BrC$_6$H$_4$NO$_2$, (CH$_3$)$_3$SiBr	302
(CH$_3$)$_3$SiC$_6$H$_4$NO$_2$-p	Br$_2$/C$_6$H$_5$NO$_2$	40	p-BrC$_6$H$_4$NO$_2$, (CH$_3$)$_3$SiBr	302
(CH$_3$)$_3$SiC$_6$H$_4$NO$_2$	Br$_2$/Fe	100	BrC$_6$H$_4$NO$_2$, (CH$_3$)$_3$SiBr	286
(C$_2$H$_5$)$_3$SiC$_6$H$_4$COOH-p	Br$_2$	100	p-BrC$_6$H$_4$COOH, (C$_2$H$_5$)$_3$SiBr	305
(CH$_3$)$_3$SiC$_6$H$_4$C$_6$H$_5$-o	Br$_2$/H$_2$O, CH$_3$COOH	25	o-BrC$_6$H$_4$C$_6$H$_5$	269
(CH$_3$)$_3$SiC$_6$H$_4$C$_6$H$_5$-m	Br$_2$/H$_2$O, CH$_3$COOH	25	m-BrC$_6$H$_4$C$_6$H$_5$	269
(CH$_3$)$_3$SiC$_6$H$_4$C$_6$H$_5$-p^c	Br$_2$/H$_2$O, CH$_3$COOH	25	p-BrC$_6$H$_4$C$_6$H$_5$	269
(CH$_3$)$_3$SiC$_{10}$H$_7$-1	Br$_2$/H$_2$O, CH$_3$COOH	25	1-Bromonaphthalene	266
(CH$_3$)$_3$SiC$_{10}$H$_7$-2	Br$_2$/H$_2$O, CH$_3$COOH	25	2-Bromonaphthalene	266,310
(CH$_3$)$_3$SiC$_6$H$_4$NHCOCH$_3$-p	Br$_2$/CH$_3$COOH	25	p-BrC$_6$H$_4$NHCOCH$_3$	499
(CH$_3$)$_3$SiC$_6$H$_4$OCOCH$_3$	Br$_2$/CH$_3$COOH	0	p-BrC$_6$H$_4$OCOCH$_3$	499
(CH$_3$)$_3$SiC$_6$H$_4$N(CH$_3$)$_2$	Br$_2$/CH$_3$COOH	25	p-BrC$_6$H$_4$N(CH$_3$)$_2$	500
1-(CH$_3$)$_3$SiC$_6$H$_3$(NHCOCH$_3$)$_2$-3,4	Br$_2$/CH$_3$COOH	25	1-BrC$_6$H$_3$(NHCOCH$_3$)$_2$-3,4	513
(CH$_3$)$_3$SiC$_6$H$_4$NHCOCH$_3$-m	Br$_2$/CHCl$_3$	25	1,2-Br$_2$-(4-CH$_3$CONH)C$_6$H$_3$	513
(CH$_3$)$_3$SiC$_6$H$_4$OH-p	Br$_2$/CS$_2$	0	p-BrC$_6$H$_4$OH (85%)	499
[structure: C$_2$H$_5$–N heterocycle with Si(C$_6$H$_5$)(C$_6$H$_5$)]	Br$_2$/CH$_3$COOH	0	Silanol	514
	Br$_2$/CH$_3$COOH	25	(2,4-Br$_2$C$_6$H$_3$)$_2$NC$_2$H$_5$ (71%)	514

295

(continued)

P. TABLE XVI (*continued*)

Compound split	Temperature, deg	Agent	Products (% yield)	Refs.
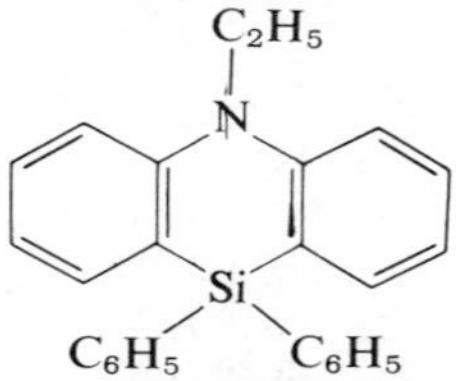 (structure: phenothiazine ring with N–C$_2$H$_5$ and Si bearing two C$_6$H$_5$ groups)	150	Br$_2$	(C$_6$H$_5$)$_3$SiBr, C$_6$H$_5$Br	299,515
1-C$_{10}$H$_7$(C$_6$H$_5$)(CH$_3$)SiCH$_2$C(CH$_3$)$_3$		Br$_2$	C$_6$H$_5$(CH$_3$)BrSiCH$_2$C(CH$_3$)$_3$	308
1-C$_{10}$H$_7$(C$_6$H$_5$)(CH$_3$)SiC$_2$H$_5$		Br$_2$	C$_6$H$_5$(CH$_3$)BrSiCH$_2$CH$_3$	308
1-C$_{10}$H$_7$(C$_6$H$_5$)(CH$_3$)SiC$_6$H$_4$OCH$_3$-p		Br$_2$	1-C$_{10}$H$_7$(C$_6$H$_5$)(CH$_3$)SiBr, BrC$_6$H$_4$OCH$_3$-p	308,309
(C$_6$H$_5$)$_3$SiBr	150	Br$_2$	(C$_6$H$_5$)$_2$SiBr$_2$, C$_6$H$_5$Br	299
(CH$_3$)$_2$Si(C$_6$H$_4$Cl)$_2$		Br$_2$	o-ClC$_6$H$_4$Br, m-ClC$_6$H$_4$Br	320
(CH$_3$)$_2$Si(C$_6$H$_4$Br)$_2$		Br$_2$	Br$_2$C$_6$H$_4$ (mixture of isomers)	320
Cl$_3$SiC$_6$H$_4$Br	150–160	Br$_2$	SiCl$_3$Br, C$_6$H$_4$Br$_2$ (83%)	329
Cl$_3$SiC$_6$H$_3$Br$_2$	180–190	Br$_2$/H$_2$O	C$_6$H$_3$Br$_3$ (60%)	329
Cl$_3$SiC$_6$H$_5$[d]	80–90	Br$_2$/Fe	C$_6$H$_3$Br$_3$, C$_6$H$_2$Br$_4$	275,314, 329
F$_3$SiC$_6$H$_5$	31–33	Br$_2$/Fe	F$_3$SiBr, C$_6$H$_4$Br$_2$, F$_3$SiC$_6$H$_4$Br	315
(CH$_3$)$_3$SiC$_6$H$_5$	45–50	Br$_2$/Fe	(CH$_3$)$_3$SiBr (92%), C$_6$H$_5$Br (87%)	315
(C$_6$H$_{5-n}$Cl$_n$)$_2$SiCl$_2$	140–150	Br$_2$/H$_2$O	C$_6$H$_{5-n}$Cl$_n$Br, SiO$_2$	319,509
(C$_6$F$_5$)$_4$Si	25	Br$_2$	C$_6$F$_5$Br, (C$_6$F$_5$)$_3$SiBr	322
C$_6$H$_{5-n}$Cl$_n$SiCl$_3$	150	Br$_2$/H$_2$O	C$_6$H$_{5-n}$Cl$_n$Br, SiO$_2$	509

296

Cl$_3$SiC$_6$H$_4$CH$_3$-p	180–220	Br$_2$/H$_2$O	p-CH$_3$C$_6$H$_4$Br (73%)	511
1-Cl$_3$Si-3-Br-4-CH$_3$C$_6$H$_3$	180–240	Br$_2$/H$_2$O	1,3-Br$_2$-4-CH$_3$—C$_6$H$_3$	511
(CH$_3$)$_3$SiC$_6$H$_4$CCl=CClC$_6$H$_4$Si(CH$_3$)$_3$	90	Br$_2$	(CH$_3$)$_3$SiBr (90%), BrC$_6$H$_4$CCl=CClC$_6$H$_4$Br (80.2%)	512
m-(NO$_2$C$_6$H$_4$)$_4$Si	180–200	Br$_2$/H$_2$O	m-BrC$_6$H$_4$NO$_2$ (27%)	304,516
(C$_2$H$_5$)$_3$SiC$_6$H$_4$NO$_2$-m	110	Br$_2$/H$_2$O	m-BrC$_6$H$_4$NO$_2$ (95%), [(C$_2$H$_5$)$_3$Si]$_2$O	354
(C$_2$H$_5$)$_2$Si(C$_6$H$_4$NO$_2$-m)$_2$	110	Br$_2$/H$_2$O	m-BrC$_6$H$_4$NO$_2$ (98%)	354
(C$_2$H$_5$)$_3$SiC$_6$H$_4$Si(C$_2$H$_5$)$_3$-p		Br$_2$/Fe	p-BrC$_6$H$_4$Br, (C$_2$H$_5$)$_3$SiBr	301
(CH$_3$)$_3$SiC$_6$H$_5$	Reflux	I$_2$	(CH$_3$)$_3$SiI (56%)	300
(CH$_3$)$_3$SiC$_6$H$_5$	Reflux	I$_2$/AlI$_3$	(CH$_3$)$_3$SiI (92%), C$_6$H$_5$I (90%)	172,323
(CH$_3$)$_2$Si(C$_6$H$_5$)$_2$	Reflux	I$_2$/AlI$_3$	(CH$_3$)$_2$SiI$_2$ (74%), C$_6$H$_5$I	323
1-(C$_2$H$_5$)$_3$Si-3-CH$_3$-4-NH$_2$C$_6$H$_3$	100	I$_2$/CH$_3$COOH	1-Iodo-3-methyl-4-acetoxyaminobenzene	387
(CH$_3$)$_3$SiC$_6$H$_5$	25	ICl/CH$_3$COOH	C$_6$H$_5$Cl, C$_6$H$_5$I	306

[a] In this and other measurements,[312,313] the amount of catalyst is given in wt % related to the phenylsilane used.

[b] Percent yield related to the whole conversion, including chlorophenyl-substituted products.[312,313]

[c] Under similar conditions bromodesilylation of o-, m-, and p-substituted derivatives of the type (CH$_3$)$_3$SiC$_6$H$_4$X (X = H, CH$_3$, Cl) was studied.[269,310,311,492]

[d] For bromodesilylation of (trichloromethylphenyl)trichlorosilanes, followed by oxidation to substituted benzene carboxylic acids see Ref. 512.

Q. TABLE XVII
Redistributions and Disproportionations Involving the Silicon-Carbon Bond

Compound split	Temperature deg	Agent	Products (% yield)	Refs.
$C_2H_5Si(CH_3)_3$	280	H_2/100 atm	$(CH_3)_2Si(C_2H_5)_2$, $(CH_3)_4Si$, $[(CH_3)_3Si]_2$, C_2H_6	370
$C_3H_7Si(C_2H_5)_3$	300	H_2/100 atm	$(C_2H_5)_2Si(C_3H_7)_2$, $(C_2H_5)_4Si$, $[(C_2H_5)_3Si]_2$, C_3H_8, C_6H_{14}	370
$i\text{-}C_4H_9Si(C_2H_5)_3$	300	H_2/100 atm	$(C_2H_5)_2Si(C_4H_9)_2$, C_4H_{10}	370
$i\text{-}C_5H_{11}Si(C_2H_5)_3$	300	H_2/100 atm	$(C_2H_5)_4Si$, $[(i\text{-}C_5H_{11})_2(C_2H_5)_2Si]_2$, $[(C_2H_5)_3Si]_2$, $i\text{-}C_5H_{11}$	370
$C_6H_5Si(CH_3)_3$	300	H_2/100 atm	$(CH_3)_2Si(C_6H_5)_2$, $(CH_3)_4Si$, $[(CH_3)_3Si]_2$, CH_4, C_6H_6	370
$C_2H_5Si(C_6H_5)_3$	300–320	H_2/100 atm	$(C_6H_5)_2C_6H_5SiH$, $(C_6H_5)_4Si$, C_6H_6	370
$(C_6H_5)_3SiH$	300–310		$(C_6H_5)_2SiH_2$ (4.5%), $C_6H_5SiH_3$ (0.5%), $(C_6H_5)_4Si$ (16%), SiH_4 (?)	381
$(C_6H_5)_3SiH$	425–525		$(C_6H_5)_2SiH_2$, $(C_6H_5)_4Si$	379
$(C_6H_5CH_2CH_2)_3SiH$	300–310		$(C_6H_5CH_2CH_2)_4Si$ (8.5%), $(C_6H_5CH_2CH_2)_2SiH_2$ (5.8%), $C_6H_5CH_2CH_2SiH_3$ (traces)	381
$(C_6H_5CH_2CH_2CH_2)_3SiH$	300–310		$(C_6H_5CH_2CH_2CH_2)_4Si$ (4.7%), $(C_6H_5CH_2CH_2CH_2)_2SiH_2$ (2.5%), $C_6H_5CH_2CH_2CH_2SiH_3$ (traces)	381
$(C_6H_5)_2SiH_2$	230		$(C_6H_5)_4Si$ (8.1%), $(C_6H_5)_3SiH$ (15.7%), $C_6H_5SiH_3$ (28.2%)	517
$(C_6H_5CH_2)_2SiH_2$	310–320		$C_6H_5CH_2SiH_3$ (1%), $(C_6H_5CH_2)_3SiH$ (0.4%)	381

$(C_6H_5CH_2CH_2)_2SiH_2$		310–320	$C_6H_5CH_2CH_2SiH_3$ (3%), $(C_6H_5CH_2CH_2)_3SiH$ (10.5%)	381
$C_6H_5CH_2CH_2)_2SiH_2$		310–320	$(C_6H_5CH_2CH_2)_3SiH$ (2.8%), $(C_6H_5CH_2CH_2)_4Si$ (3.5% impure)	381
$(CH_3)_3SiH$	$AlCl_3$	30	CH_3SiH_3, $(CH_3)_2SiH_2$, $(CH_3)_4Si$	518
$(CH_3)_3SiH$	BF_3[a]	40–60	SiH_4, CH_3SiH_3, $(CH_3)_2SiH_2$, $(CH_3)_4Si$	326
$(CH_3)_3SiC_2H_5$	$AlCl_3$[b]	80–100	$(CH_3)_4Si$, $(CH_3)_2Si(C_2H_5)_2$, $CH_3Si(C_2H_5)_3$, $(C_2H_5)_4Si$	327
$(C_2H_5)_4Si + (n\text{-}C_3H_7)_4Si$	$AlCl_3$	180	$(C_2H_5)_3SiC_3H_7\text{-}n$ (24 mole-%), $(C_2H_5)_2Si(C_3H_7\text{-}n)_2$ (39 mole-%), $C_2H_5Si(C_3H_7\text{-}n)_3$ (26 mole-%)	372–374
$(CH_3)_2C_6H_5SiF$	$AlBr_3$		$(CH_3)_3SiBr$, C_6H_6	395
$(i\text{-}C_4H_9)_3SiF$	$AlCl_3$		$i\text{-}C_4H_9SiCl_3$, $(i\text{-}C_4H_9)_2SiCl_2$, $(i\text{-}C_4H_9)_3SiCl$	395
$(CH_3)_2SiCl_2 + (CH_3)_3SiCl$ (1:1)	$AlCl_3$	375/77 atm	$(CH_3)_2SiCl_2$, $(CH_3)_3SiCl$	390
$(CH_3)_3SiCl + SiCl_4$ (1:1)	$AlCl_3$	375	$(CH_3)_2SiCl_2$ (46%), CH_3SiCl_3 (30%)	390
$(CH_3)_4Si + SiCl_4$ (1:1)	$AlCl_3$	290–325	$(CH_3)_3SiCl$ (58 mole-%), $(CH_3)_2SiCl_2$ (3 mole-%), CH_3SiCl_3 (0%)	390,393
$CH_3SiCl_3 + (CH_3)_3SiH$	$AlCl_3$	100	CH_3SiHCl_2 (83%), $(CH_3)_2SiH_2$	518
$CH_3SiCl_3 + (CH_3)_2SiH_2$	$AlCl_3$	100	CH_3SiHCl_2 (78%)	518
$CH_3SiCl_3 + CH_3SiH_3$	$AlCl_3$	100	CH_3SiHCl_2 (82%)	518
$CH_3SiCl_3 + SiH_4$	$AlCl_3$	100	CH_3SiHCl_2 (18%)	518
$C_2H_5SiHCl_2$	$AlCl_3$	235/50 atm	$C_2H_5SiH_2Cl$, $C_2H_5SiCl_3$, $(C_2H_5)_2SiCl_2$	394
$(CH_3)_2C_2H_5SiBr$	$AlBr_3$		$(CH_3)_3SiBr$, $(C_2H_5)_3SiBr$	395
$(CH_3)_3SiBr$	$AlBr_3$ or $GaBr_3$		$(CH_3)_4Si$	326
CH_3SiHCl_2	$AlCl_3$	325/70 atm	SiH_4, H_3SiCl, H_2SiCl_2, $HSiCl_3$ (7.2%), CH_3SiCl_3, $(CH_3)_2SiCl_2$ (17.5%)	390
$C_2H_5SiCl_3 + (CH_3)_2SiCl_2$	$AlCl_3$	375	$CH_3(C_2H_5)SiCl_2$	390

(continued)

Compound split	Temperature, deg	Agent	Products (% yield)	Refs.
$C_6H_5SiH_3$	50	$AlCl_3$	$(C_6H_5)_4Si$, SiH_4	376
$C_6H_5(CH_3)SiH_2$	50	$AlCl_3$	$(C_6H_5)_4Si$, CH_3SiH_3, $(CH_3)_2SiH_2$	376
$C_6H_5Si(CH_3)_3$	40–60	(1) $AlCl_3^c$ (2) H_2O	$(CH_3)_4Si$, $[(CH_3)_3Si]_2O$, C_6H_6	326
$C_6H_5Si(CH_3)_3$ + $Cl(CH_3)_2SiSi(CH_3)_3$	25	$AlCl_3$	$(CH_3)_3SiCl$, $C_6H_5(CH_3)_2SiSi(CH_3)_3$	340
$(CH_3)_3SiSi(CH_3)_3$ + $Cl(CH_3)_2SiSi(CH_3)_2Cl$	25	$AlCl_3$	$(CH_3)_3SiSi(CH_3)_2Cl$ (68.5%)	340
$C_6H_5SiCl_3$	230	$Zn(C_2H_5)_2$	$C_6H_5Si(C_2H_5)_3$, $(C_6H_5)_2Si(C_2H_5)_2$, $(C_2H_5)_4Si$	507
$C_6H_5SiH_2Cl$	50	$AlCl_3$	$(C_6H_5)_2SiCl_2$, $(C_6H_5)_3SiCl$, SiH_4, SiH_3Cl	376
$(C_6H_5)_2SiCl_2$	480–540	SiO_2 (50–65%), Al_2O_3 (45–30%)	C_6H_6 (16.1%), $C_6H_5C_6H_5$, $C_6H_5SiCl_3$ (38.9%), $(C_6H_5)_3SiCl$, $(C_6H_5)_2ClSiC_6H_4SiCl_2C_6H_5$	387,388
$(CH_3)_3SiCH_2CH_2Si(CH_3)_3$	90–97	$AlBr_3$	$(CH_3)_4Si$, $(CH_3)_2Si\!\!\begin{array}{c}CH_2CH_2\\[-2pt]\diagdown\!\!\!\diagup\end{array}\!\!Si(CH_3)_2$ (ring with CH_2CH_2 bridges)	400
$C_6H_5SiCl_3$ + $(CH_3)_3SiCl$	325 pressure	$AlCl_3$	$(CH_3)_2SiCl_2$, CH_3SiCl_3, $C_6H_5(CH_3)SiCl_2$, C_6H_6	390
$C_6H_5SiCl_3$ + $(CH_3)_2SiCl_2$	350 pressure	$AlCl_3$	$C_6H_5(CH_3)_2SiCl_2$, CH_3SiCl_3	390
$(CH_3)_2SiCl_2$ + $(C_6H_5)_2SiCl_2$	500	$NaAlCl_4^d$	$C_6H_5(CH_3)SiCl_2$ (26%)	396
$(CH_3)_3SiCl$ + $(C_6H_5)_2SiCl_2$	500	$NaAlCl_4^d$	$C_6H_5(CH_3)_2SiCl$ (49%)	396
$(C_2H_5)_2SiCl_2$ + $C_6H_5SiCl_3$	500	$NaAlCl_4^d$	$C_6H_5(C_2H_5)SiCl_2$ (3%)	396
CH_3SiHCl_2 + $(C_6H_5)_2SiCl_2$	500	$NaAlCl_4^d$	$C_6H_5(CH_3)SiCl_2$ (51%)	396
$C_6H_5SiHCl_2$ + $(C_2H_5)_2SiCl_2$	500	$NaAlCl_4$	$C_6H_5(C_2H_5)SiCl$ (52%)	396

Compound	Temp.	Catalyst	Products	Ref.
(C₆H₅)₂SiH₂	100	H₂PtCl₆·6H₂O/furan	$C_6H_5SiH_3$ (35.5%), $(C_6H_5)_3SiH$ (19%), $(C_6H_5)_4Si$ (0.1%)	517
(C₆H₅)₂SiH₂	160	H₂PtCl₆·6H₂O	$C_6H_5SiH_3$ (73%), $(C_6H_5)_4Si$ (16%)	517
(C₆H₅)₂SiH₂	230	PtO₂	SiH_4, $C_6H_5SiH_3$ (23%), $(C_6H_5)_3SiH$ (10%), $(C_6H_5)_4Si$ (7.3%)	517
CH₃Si(OCH₃)₃	230	Na[e]	$(CH_3)_2Si(OCH_3)_2$, $(CH_3)_3SiOCH_3$	519
CH₃(n-C₃H₇)Si(OCH₃)₂	270	Na	$(CH_3)_2(n\text{-}C_3H_7)SiOCH_3$, $(n\text{-}C_3H_7)_2Si(OCH_3)_2$	519
C₆H₅CH₂Si(OC₂H₅)₃	240	Na	$(C_6H_5CH_2)_2Si(OC_2H_5)_2$, $Si(OC_2H_5)_4$	519
CH₂=CHCH₂Si(OC₂H₅)₃	175	C₂H₅ONa	$(CH_2=CHCH_2)_3SiOC_2H_5$, $(CH_2=CHCH_2)_2Si(OC_2H_5)_2$, $Si(OC_2H_5)_4$	77
CH₃CH=CHCH₂Si(OC₂H₅)₃	178	C₂H₅ONa	$(CH_3CH=CHCH_2)_3SiOC_2H_5$, $(CH_3CH=CHCH_2)_2Si(OC_2H_5)_2$, $Si(OC_2H_5)_4$	77
C₂H₅(C₆H₅)Si(OC₂H₅)₂	175	C₂H₅ONa	$(C_6H_5)_3SiC_2H_5$, $C_2H_5Si(OC_2H_5)_3$, $C_2H_5(C_6H_5)_2SiOC_2H_5$	77
p-C₂H₅O(CH₃)₂-SiC₆H₄Si(CH₃)₂OC₂H₅	230	KOH	$(CH_3)_2Si(OC_2H_5)_2$, $[(CH_3)_2SiC_6H_4]_n$	520
(C₆H₅)₃SiH	Reflux	Na/K/toluene	$(C_6H_5)_4Si$	365
(C₆H₅)₂SiH₂	Reflux	Na/K/decalin	$(C_6H_5)_3SiH$, $(C_6H_5)_4Si$	365
C₆H₅SiH₃	Reflux	Na/K/decalin	$(C_6H_5)_2SiH_2$, $(C_6H_5)_3SiH$, $(C_6H_5)_4Si$	365
C₆H₅SiCl₃		Na/K/decalin	$(C_6H_5)_4Si$	365
(C₆H₅)₂SiCl₂		Na/K/decalin	$(C_6H_5)_4Si$	365
[C₆H₅SiO₁.₅]ₙ	500/2 mm	NaOH	$(C_6H_5)_4Si$ (75%), $[(C_6H_5)_3Si]_2O$ (25%)	350
[(C₆H₅)CH₃SiO]ₙ	300/1 mm	LiOH	$[(C_6H_5)_2CH_3Si]_2O$	350
[(C₆H₅)CH₃SiO]ₙ	300/1 mm	NaO[(CH₃)₂SiO]₂Na[f]	$(C_6H_5)_3SiCH_3$, $[(C_6H_5)_2CH_3Si]_2O$	350

[a] Under these conditions, BCl₃, BBr₃, AlBr₃, GaCl₃, and GaBr₃ were also used as catalysts.[326]

[b] For this reaction, AlF₃, AlBr₃, AlI₃, GaCl₃, GaBr₃, FeCl₃, TiCl₃, and BCl₃ were also used as catalysts.[327]

[c] Under these conditions, AlBr₃, GaCl₃, GaBr₃, BCl₃, and ZrCl₄ were also used as catalysts.[326]

[d] Flow reactor.

[e] For this reaction, Li, K, Na₂O, CH₃ONa, and [KOSi(CH₃)₂]₂O were also used as catalysts.[519]

[f] For this reaction, KO[(CH₃)₂SiO]₂K and CsO[(CH₃)₂SiO]₂Cs were also used as catalysts.[350]

REFERENCES

1. D. F. Helm and E. Mack, Jr., *J. Amer. Chem. Soc.*, **59**, 60 (1937).
2. C. E. Waring, *Trans. Faraday Soc.*, **36**, 1142 (1940).
3. S. Tannenbaum, *J. Amer. Chem. Soc.*, **76**, 1027 (1954).
4. W. C. Steele, L. D. Nichols, and F. G. A. Stone, *J. Amer. Chem. Soc.*, **84**, 4441 (1962).
5. G. G. Hess, F. W. Lampe, and L. H. Sommer, *J. Amer. Chem. Soc.*, **86**, 3174 (1964).
6. T. Tanaka, *Technol. Repts., Osaka Univ.*, **10**, 825 (1960); *Chem. Abstr.*, **55**, 13,959 (1961).
7. A. E. Beezer and C. T. Mortimer, *J. Chem. Soc.*, **A1966**, 514.
8. G. Fritz, D. Habel, D. Kummer, and G. Teichmann, *Z. Anorg. Allg. Chem.*, **302**, 60 (1959); *Chem. Abstr.*, **54**, 5686 (1960).
9. G. Fritz and D. Ksinsik, *Z. Anorg. Allg. Chem.*, **322**, 46 (1963); *Chem. Abstr.*, **59**, 6428 (1963).
10. T. V. Sathyamurthy, S. Swaminathan, and L. M. Yeddanapalli, *J. Indian Chem. Soc.*, **27**, 509 (1950); *Chem. Abstr.*, **45**, 6469 (1951).
11. G. Fritz and B. Raabe, *Z. Anorg. Allg. Chem.*, **286**, 149 (1956); *Chem. Abstr.*, **54**, 4267 (1957).
12. G. Fritz and J. Grobe, *Z. Anorg. Allg. Chem.*, **315**, 157 (1962); *Chem. Abstr.*, **57**, 8173 (1962).
13. A. D. Petrov, V. M. Vdovin, G. Golubyeva, and K. S. Pushchevaya, *Zh. Obshch. Khim.*, **31**, 3230 (1961); *Chem. Abstr.*, **57**, 851 (1962).
14. G. Fritz and B. Raabe, *Z. Anorg. Allg. Chem.*, **299**, 232 (1959); *Chem. Abstr.*, **53**, 18055 (1959).
15. G. Fritz, *Fortschritte Chem. Forsch.*, **4**, 459 (1963); *Chem. Abstr.*, **60**, 6462 (1964).
16. R. C. Golesworthy and R. A. Shaw, *Proc. Roy. Soc., Ser. A.*, **292**, 489 (1966).
17. N. Ya. Chernyak, R. A. Khmelnitskii, T. V. Dyakova, K. S. Pushchevaya, and V. M. Vdovin, *Zh. Obshch. Khim.*, **37**, 917 (1967); *Chem. Abstr.*, **68**, 12,275 (1968).
18. G. Fritz, *Z. Anorg. Allg. Chem.*, **273**, 275 (1953); *Chem. Abstr.*, **47**, 12,223 (1953).
19. G. Fritz and H. Kautsky, British Patent 760,036 (1950); *Chem. Abstr.*, **51**, 11,757 (1957).
20. F. Mareš and V. Chvalovský, *J. Organometal. Chem.*, **6**, 327 (1966); *Chem. Abstr.*, **65**, 18,461 (1966).
21. V. Ipatiev and B. N. Dolgov, *Ber.*, **62**, 1220 (1929); *Chem. Abstr.*, **23**, 3661 (1929).
22. F. H. Pollard, G. Nickless and D. B. Thomas, *J. Chromatog.*, **22**, 286 (1966); *Chem. Abstr.*, **65**, 10,609 (1966).
23. F. Mareš and V. Chvalovský, *Coll. Czech. Chem. Commun.*, **32**, 382 (1967); *Chem. Abstr.*, **66**, 76,074 (1967).
24. K. H. Birr, *Z. Anorg. Allg. Chem.*, **315**, 175 (1962); *Chem. Abstr.*, **57**, 4108 (1962).
25. R. W. Coutant and A. Levy, *J. Organometal. Chem.*, **10**, 175 (1967).
26. H. C. Kaufman, *J. Chem. Eng. Data*, **7**, Part 2, 556 (1962); *Chem. Abstr.*, **58**, 10,229 (1963).
27. V. Chvalovský, *Pure Appl. Chem.*, **13**, 231 (1966).
28. I. Ya. Poddubnii and S. V. Averyanov, *Radiotsionnaya Khimiya Polimerov*, publ. by Nauka Moscow, 1966, p. 306; *Chem. Abstr.*, **66**, 116,446 (1967).
29. T. I. Ponomareva, T. A. Krasovskaya, M. V. Sobolevskii, and A. N. Ponomarov *Kinet. Katal.*, **7**, 983 (1966); *Chem. Abstr.*, **66**, 95,576 (1967).
30. D. J. Fisher, R. G. Chaffee, and E. L. Warrick, *Rubber Age*, **88**, 77 (1960); *Chem. Abstr.*, **55**, 8910 (1961).

31. I. Ya., Poddubnii and S. V. Averyanov, *Trudy 2-go Vsessoyuz, Soveshch. po Rad. Khim.*, AN SSSR, Otd. Khim. Nauk, Moscow, 1960, p. 563; *Chem. Abstr.*, **58**, 2555 (1963).
32. D. J. Fisher and V. Flegel, *Rubber Age*, **88**, 816 (1961); *Chem. Abstr.*, **55**, 13,890 (1961).
33. S. Okamura, H. Inagaki, and K. Ohdan, *Doitai to Hoshasen*, 1, 214 (1968); *Chem. Abstr.*, **53**, 6788 (1959).
34. A. Charlesby, *Proc. Roy. Soc., Ser. A*, **230**, 120 (1955); *Chem. Abstr.*, **49**, 15,277 (1955).
35. A. A. Miller, *J. Amer. Chem. Soc.*, **82**, 3519 (1960).
36. J. F. Zack, E. L. Warrick, and G. Knoll, *J. Chem. Eng. Data*, **6**, 279 (1961); *Chem. Abstr.*, **55**, 18,263 (1961).
37. D. Andreev, *Zh. Prikl. Khim.*, **32**, 2808 (1959); *Chem. Abstr.*, **54**, 9733 (1960).
38. D. N. Andreev and E. V. Kukharskaya, *Dokl. Akad. Nauk SSSR*, **134**, 817 (1960); *Chem. Abstr.*, **55**, 6363 (1961).
39. D. N. Andreev and E. V. Kukharskaya, *Dokl. Akad. Nauk SSSR*, **134**, 1069 (1960).
40. D. N. Andreev, *J. Prakt. Chem.*, **285**, 288 (1964); *Chem. Abstr.*, **61**, 4388 (1964).
41. R. A. Shaw, *Pure Appl. Chem.*, **13**, 297 (1966); *Chem. Abstr.*, **67**, 11,750 (1967).
42. D. N. Andreev and E. V. Kukharskaya, *Dokl. Akad. Nauk SSSR*, **134**, 89 (1960); *Chem. Abstr.*, **55**, 359 (1961).
43. D. N. Andreev, *Dokl. Akad. Nauk SSSR*, **100**, 697 (1955); *Chem. Abstr.*, **50**, 1575 (1956).
44. D. N. Andreev, *Izv. Akad. Nauk SSSR*, **1957**, 818; *Chem. Abstr.*, **52**, 2741 (1958).
45. D. N. Andreev, *Izv. Akad. Nauk SSSR*, **1960**, 237; *Chem. Abstr.*, **54**, 20,842 (1960).
46. D. N. Andreev and E. V. Kukharskaya, *Zh. Prikl. Khim.*, **36**, 2309 (1963); *Chem. Abstr.*, **60**, 5063 (1964).
47. L. Spialter, D. C. Priest, and C. W. Harris, *J. Amer. Chem. Soc.*, **77**, 6227 (1955).
48. D. Shopov and S. S. Dyankov, Intern. Symp. Organosilicon Chem., Sci. Commun., Prague, Czechoslovakia, 1965, p. 276; *Chem. Abstr.*, **65**, 8732 (1966).
49. K. A. Andrianov and N. N. Sokolov, *Khim. Prom.*, **6**, 329 (1955); *Chem. Abstr.*, **50**, 7499 (1956).
50. C. M. Murphy, C. E. Sauders, and D. C. Smith, *Ind. Eng. Chem.*, **42**, 2462 (1960).
51. L. C. Scala and W. M. Hickam, *Ind. Eng. Chem.*, **50**, 1583 (1958); *Chem. Abstr.*, **53**, 13,649 (1959).
52. E. A. Goldovskii and A. S. Kuzminskii, *Rev. Gen. Caoutchouc Plastiques*, **45**, 457 (1968); *Chem. Abstr.*, **69**, 78,278 (1968).
53. G. P. Brown, J. A. Hill, and C. B. Murphy, *J. Polymer Sci.*, **55**, 419 (1961).
54. E. M. Oparina, G. S. Tubyanskaya, and A. S. Ermilov, *Khim. Prakt. Prim. Kremneorg. Soyedinenii*, Trudy Konf., Leningrad, 1958, No. 2, p. 50; *Chem. Abstr.*, **53**, 11,281 (1959).
55. M. Koike and A. Danno, *J. Phys. Soc. Jap.*, **15**, 1501 (1960); *Chem. Abstr.*, **55**, 6905 (1961).
56. A. A. Miller, *Ind. Eng. Chem., Prod. Res. Develop.*, **3**, 252 (1964). *Chem. Abstr.*, **61**, 9630 (1964).
57. T. I. Ponomareva, T. A. Krasovskaya, and M. V. Sobolevskii, *Plast. Massy*, **1964**, No. 6, 21; *Chem. Abstr.*, **61**, 8420 (1964).
58. J. Beneš, V. Chvalovský, and V. Bažant, *Collect. Czech. Chem. Commun.*, **26**, 1617 (1961).
59. J. Beneš, V. Chvalovský, and V. Bažant, *Collect. Czech. Chem. Commun.*, **26**, 1627 (1961).

60. D. H. Eargle Jr. and W. B. Moniz, *J. Polymer Sci.*, *Part A-1*, **6**, 1153 (1968); *Chem. Abstr.*, **69**, 3302 (1968).
61. S. I. Beilin, N. A. Pokatilo, and B. A. Dolgoplosk, *Vysokomol. Soyed.*, **7**, 1085 (1965); *Chem. Abstr.*, **63**, 11,721 (1965).
62. C. C. Price and J. R. Sowa, *J. Org. Chem.*, **32**, 4126 (1967).
63. M. G. Voronkov and V. T. Shemyatenkova, *Izv. Adad. Nauk SSSR*, **1961**, 178; *Chem. Abstr.*, **55**, 16,285 (1961).
64. R. H. Krieble and J. R. Elliott, *J. Amer. Chem. Soc.*, **68**, 2291 (1946).
65. W. S. Tatlock and E. G. Rochow, *J. Amer. Chem. Soc.*, **72**, 528 (1950).
66. K. A. Andrianov, G. V. Kotrelev and L. O. Kogan, *Khim. Geterotsikl. Soedin.*, *Akad. Nauk Latv. SSR*, **1967**, 364; *Chem. Abstr.*, **67**, 9431 (1967).
67. L. H. Sommer and F. C. Whitmore, *J. Amer. Chem. Soc.*, **68**, 485 (1946).
68. H. Gilman and R. D. Gorsich, *J. Amer. Chem. Soc.*, **80**, 1883 (1958).
69. D. Wittenberg and H. Gilman, *J. Amer. Chem. Soc.*, **80**, 2677 (1958).
70. H. Gilman and R. D. Gorsich, *J. Amer. Chem. Soc.*, **80**, 3243 (1958).
71. L. H. Sommer, E. Dorfman, G. M. Goldberg, and F. C. Whitmore, *J. Amer. Chem. Soc.*, **68**, 488 (1946).
72. L. H. Sommer, G. M. Goldberg, E. Dorfman, and F. C. Whitmore, *J. Amer. Chem. Soc.*, **68**, 1083 (1946).
73. L. H. Sommer, L. J. Tyler, and F. C. Whitmore, *J. Amer. Chem. Soc.*, **70**, 2872 (1948).
74. C. L. Agre, *J. Amer. Chem. Soc.*, **71**, 300 (1949).
75. A. D. Petrov and V. F. Mironov, *Dokl. Akad. Nauk SSSR*, **80**, 761 (1951); *Chem. Abstr.*, **46**, 11,102 (1952).
76. L. H. Sommer and G. A. Baughman, *J. Amer. Chem. Soc.*, **83**, 3346 (1961).
77. D. L. Bailey and A. N. Pines, *Ind. Eng. Chem.*, **46**, 2363 (1954).
78. L. H. Sommer, D. L. Bailey, and F. C. Whitmore, *J. Amer. Chem. Soc.*, **70**, 2869 (1948).
79. T. N. Bell, R. N. Haszeldine, M. J. Newlands, and J. B. Plumb, *J. Chem. Soc.*, **1965**, 2107.
80. V. A. Ponomarenko, V. H. Cherkaev, and N. A. Zadorozhnyi, *Izv. Akad. Nauk SSSR*, **1960**, 1610; *Chem. Abstr.*, **55**, 9261 (1961).
81. R. N. Haszeldine, P. J. Robinson, and R. F. Simmons, *J. Chem. Soc.*, **1964**, 1890.
82. G. Fishwick. R. N. Haszeldine, C. Parkinson, P. J. Robinson, and R. F. Simmons, *Chem. Commun.*, **1965**, 382.
83. A. D. Petrov and V. F. Mironov, *Izv. Akad. Nauk SSSR*, **1952**, 635; *Chem. Abstr.*, **47**, 10,471 (1953).
84. V. F. Mironov, *Izv. Akad. Nauk SSSR*, **1959**, 1862; *Chem. Abstr.*, **54**, 8607 (1960).
85. R. H. Krieble and J. R. Elliott, *J. Amer. Chem. Soc.*, **67**, 1810 (1945).
86. C. Eaborn and J. C. Jeffrey, *Chem. Ind. (London)*, **1955**, 1041.
87. N. S. Marans, L. H. Sommer, and F. C. Whitmore, *J. Amer. Chem. Soc.*, **73**, 5127 (1951).
88. S. N. Ushakov and A. M. Itenberg, *Zh. Obshch. Khim.*, **7**, 2495 (1937); *Chem. Abstr.*, **32**, 2083 (1938).
89. G. F. Roedel, *J. Amer. Chem. Soc.*, **71**, 269 (1949).
90. L. H. Sommer, D. L. Bailey, W. A. Strong, and F. C. Whitmore, *J. Amer. Chem. Soc.*, **68**, 1881 (1946).
91. P. A. Di Giorgio, L. H. Sommer, and F. C. Whitmore, *J. Amer. Chem. Soc.*, **70**, 3512 (1948).
92. J. L. Speier, *J. Amer. Chem, Soc.*, **70**, 4142 (1948).

93. J. E. Noll, J. L. Speier, and B. F. Daubert, *J. Amer. Chem. Soc.*, **73**, 3867 (1951).
94. M. Kumada, M. Ishikawa, and K. Tamao, *J. Organometal. Chem.*, **5**, 226 (1966).
95. C. Eaborn and J. C. Jeffrey, *J. Chem. Soc.*, **1957**, 137.
96. Chih-Tang Huang and Pao-Jen Wang, *Hua Hsueh Hsueh Pao*, **25**, 341 (1959); *Chem. Abstr.*, **54**, 16,413 (1960).
97. C. R. Hauser and C. R. Hance, *J. Amer. Chem. Soc.*, **74**, 5091 (1952).
98. G. Fritz, J. Grobe, and D. Ksinsik, *Z. Anorg. Allg. Chem.*, **302**, 175 (1959).
99. M. Kumada and M. Ishikawa, *J. Organometal. Chem.*, **1**, 411 (1964).
100. J. L. Speier and B. F. Daubert, *J. Amer. Chem. Soc.*, **70**, 1400 (1948).
101. S. Brynolf, *Kgl. Fysiograf. Sallskap. Lund. Forh.*, **29**, 121 (1959); *Chem. Abstr.*, **54**, 11,976 (1960).
102. A. I. Ponomarev and A. L. Klebanskii, *Zh. Obshch. Khim.*, **32**, 4022 (1962); *Chem. Abstr.*, **58**, 13,980 (1963).
103. H. Gilman and L. S. Miller, *J. Amer. Chem. Soc.*, **73**, 968 (1951).
104. W. Zimmermann, *Ber.*, **87**, 887 (1954); *Chem. Abstr.*, **49**, 9496 (1955).
105. G. V. Motsarev, V. R. Rozenberg, and T. Ya. Chashnikova, *Zh. Prikl. Khim.*, **34**, 430 (1961); *Chem. Abstr.*, **55**, 19,767 (1961).
106. G. V. Motsarev and V. R. Rozenberg, *Zh. Obshch. Khim.*, **30**, 3011 (1960); *Chem Abstr.*, **55**, 16,456 (1961).
107. H. Gilman, A. G. Brook, and L. S. Miller, *J. Amer. Chem. Soc.*, **75**, 4531 (1953).
108. R. N. Haszeldine and R. J. Marklow, *J. Chem. Soc.*, **1956**, 962.
109. R. N. Haszeldine and J. C. Young, *J. Chem. Soc.*, **1960**, 4503.
110. O. R. Pierce, E. T. McBee, and R. E. Cline, *J. Amer. Chem. Soc.*, **75**, 5618 (1953).
111. H. C. Clark, J. T. Kwan, and D. Whyman, *Can. J. Chem.*, **41**, 2628 (1963).
112. A. M. Geyer and R. N. Haszeldine, *J. Chem. Soc.*, **1957**, 1038.
113. A. M. Geyer, R. N. Haszeldine, K. Leedham, and R. J. Marklow, *J. Chem. Soc.*, **1957**, 4472.
114. A. M. Geyer and R. N. Haszeldine, *J. Chem. Soc.*, **1957**, 3925.
115. R. N. Haszeldine, M. J. Newlands, and J. B. Plumb, *Proc. Chem. Soc.*, **1960**, 147.
116. A. G. Brook and B. Iachia, *J. Amer. Chem. Soc.*, **83**, 827 (1961).
117. H. Gilman and G. D. Lichtenwalter, *J. Amer. Chem. Soc.*, **80**, 2680 (1958).
118. A. G. Brook, *J. Amer. Chem. Soc.*, **79**, 4373 (1957).
119. D. Wittenberg and H. Gilman, *J. Amer. Chem. Soc.*, **80**, 4529 (1958).
120. A. G. Brook and R. J. Mauris, *J. Amer. Chem. Soc.*, **79**, 971 (1957).
121. G. V. Motsarev and V. R. Rozenberg, *Zh. Obshch. Khim.*, **32**, 909 (1962); *Chem. Abstr.*, **58**, 1485 (1963).
122. G. V. Motsarev and V. R. Rozenberg, *Zh. Obshch. Khim.*, **33**, 255 (1963); *Chem. Abstr.*, **59**, 2843 (1963).
123. H. Gilman and W. J. Trepka, *J. Org. Chem.*, **25**, 2201 (1960).
124. A. G. Brook, *J. Amer. Chem. Soc.*, **80**, 1886 (1958).
125. L. H. Sommer, D. L. Bailey, G. M. Goldberg, C. E. Buck, T. R. Pye, F. J. Evans, and F. C. Whitmore, *J. Amer. Chem. Soc.*, **76**, 1613 (1954).
126. W. C. Schumb and E. L. Gamble, *J. Amer. Chem. Soc.*, **54**, 3943 (1932).
127. J. R. Gold, L. H. Sommer, and F. C. Whitmore, *J. Amer. Chem. Soc.*, **70**, 2874 (1948).
128. L. Eberson, *Acta Chem. Scand.*, **10**, 633 (1956); *Chem. Abstr.*, **51**, 8002 (1957).
129. S. Nozakura and S. Konotsune, *Bull. Chem. Soc. Jap.*, **29**, 326 (1956); *Chem. Abstr.*, **51**, 3599 (1957).
130. F. S. Kipping, *Proc. Chem. Soc.*, **23**, 9 (1907).
131. F. S. Kipping, *J. Chem. Soc.*, **91**, 717 (1907).

132. L. H. Sommer, W. P. Barie, and J. R. Gould, *J. Amer. Chem. Soc.*, **75**, 3765 (1953).
133. L. H. Sommer, W. D. English, G. R. Ansul, and D. N. Vivona, *J. Amer. Chem. Soc.*, **77**, 2485 (1955).
134. L. M. Shorr, H. Freiser, and J. L. Speier, *J. Amer. Chem. Soc.*, **77**, 547 (1955).
135. L. H. Sommer, G. M. Goldberg, G. H. Barnes, and L. S. Stone, *J. Amer. Chem. Soc.*, **76**, 1609 (1954).
136. B. N. Dolgov, E. V. Kukharskaya, and D. N. Andreev, *Izv. Akad. Nauk SSSR*, **1957**, 968; *Chem. Abstr.*, **52**, 4473 (1958).
137. L. H. Sommer and G. R. Ansul, *J. Amer. Chem. Soc.*, **77**, 2482 (1955).
138. S. I. Sadykh-Zade, I. I. Tsetlin, and A. D. Petrov, *Zh. Obshch. Khim.*, **26**, 1239 (1956); *Chem. Abstr.*, **50**, 14,514 (1956).
139. S. Kohama and S. Fukukawa, *Nippon Kagaku Zasshi*, **80**, 1492 (1959); *Chem. Abstr.*, **55**, 7272 (1961).
140. S. Nozakura, *Nippon Kagaku Zasshi*, **75**, 958 (1954); *Chem. Abstr.*, **51**, 14,543 (1957).
141. E. V. Wilkus and W. H. Rauscher, *J. Org. Chem.*, **30**, 2889 (1965).
142. L. H. Sommer, N. S. Marans, G. M. Goldberg, J. Rockett, and R. P. Pioch, *J. Amer. Chem. Soc.*, **73**, 882 (1951).
143. L. H. Sommer, R. P. Pioch, N. S. Marans, G. M. Goldberg, J. Rockett, and J. Kerlin, *J. Amer. Chem. Soc.*, **75**, 2932 (1953).
144. B. N. Dolgov, D. N. Andreev, and V. P. Lyutyi, *Dokl. Akad. Nauk SSSR*, **118** 501 (1958); *Chem. Abstr.*, **52**, 10,870 (1958).
145. D. N. Andreev, B. N. Dolgov, and S. V. Butts, *Zh. Obshch. Khim.*, **32**, 1275 (1962); *Chem. Abstr.*, **58**, 2467 (1963).
146. C. A. Burkhard and F. J. Norton, *Anal. Chem.*, **21**, 304 (1949).
147. J. Franc and J. Dvořáček, *J. Chromatogr.*, **14**, 340 (1964); *Chem. Abstr.*, **61**, 5684 (1964).
148. M. Kumada, K. Naka, and Y. Yamamoto, *Bull. Chem. Soc. Jap.*, **37**, 871 (1964).
149. L. H. Sommer and G. A. Baum, *J. Amer. Chem. Soc.*, **76**, 5002 (1954).
150. A. F. Plate, N. A. Belikova, and Yu. P. Egorov, *Dokl. Akad. Nauk SSSR*, **102**, 1131 (1955); *Chem. Abstr.*, **50**, 4911 (1956).
151. A. F. Plate, N. A. Belikova, and Yu. P. Egorov, *Izv. Akad. Nauk SSSR*, **1956**, 1085; *Chem. Abstr.*, **51**, 5085 (1957).
152. G. R. Wilson and A. G. Smith, *J. Org. Chem.*, **26**, 557 (1961).
153. U. G. Stolberg, *Ber.*, **96**, 2798 (1963); *Chem. Abstr.*, **59**, 15,303 (1963).
154. M. Kumada and M. Ishikawa, *J. Organometal. Chem.*, **1**, 153 (1963).
155. M. Kumada, M. Yamaguchi, Y. Yamamoto, J. Nakajima, and K. Shiina, *J. Org. Chem.*, **21**, 1264 (1956).
156. G. A. Russel and K. L. Nagpal, *Tetrahedron Lett.*, **1961**, 421.
157. P. D. George, U.S. Patent 2,802,852 (1957); *Chem. Abstr.*, **51**, 17,982 (1957).
158. K. Shiina and M. Kumada, *J. Chem. Soc. Jap., Ind. Chem. Sect.*, **60**, 1395 (1957); *Chem. Abstr.*, **53**, 17,889 (1959).
159. A. L. Klebanskii, A. I. Ponomarev, and V. I. Kudina, *Khim. Nauka Prom.*, **3**, 285 (1958).
160. R. Calas, J. Valade, and M. L. Josien, *Compt. Rend.*, **249**, 826 (1959).
161. E. V. Kukharskaya, D. N. Andreev, and V. A. Kolesova, *Izv. Akad. Nauk SSSR*, **1958**, 1372; *Chem. Abstr.*, **53**, 6993 (1959).
162. A. D. Petrov, V. A. Ponomarenko, and A. D. Snegova, *Dokl. Akad. Nauk SSSR*, **112**, 79 (1957); *Chem. Abstr.*, **51**, 11,239 (1957).
163. W. K. Musker and G. L. Larson, *J. Organometal. Chem.*, **6**, 627 (1966).

164. R. Fessenden and F. J. Freenor, *J. Org. Chem.*, **26**, 1681 (1961).
165. M. Prober, *J. Amer. Chem. Soc.*, **77**, 3224 (1955).
166. R. A. Benkeser and P. E. Brumfield, *J. Amer. Chem. Soc.*, **74**, 253 (1952).
167. R. A. Miller, *Univ. Microfilms Publ.* No. 24813. *Diss. Abstr.*, **17**, 2847 (1957).
168. C. Eaborn and R. A. Shaw, *J. Chem. Soc.*, **1955**, 3306.
169. Z. Nowak and T. Urbanski, *Biul. Wojskowej Akad. Tech.*, **11**, 149 (1962); **60**, 5535 (1964).
170. L. Spialter and J. D. Austin, *J. Amer. Chem. Soc.*, **88**, 1828 (1966).
171. M. J. Hunter, E. L. Warrick. J. F. Hyde, and C. C. Currie, *J. Amer. Chem. Soc.*, **68**, 2284 (1946).
172. C. Eaborn, *J. Chem. Soc.*, **1949**, 2755.
173. J. R. Elliott and E. M. Boldebuch, *J. Amer. Chem. Soc.*, **74**, 1853 (1952).
174. Z. M. Manulkin, *Zh. Obshch. Khim.*, **16**, 235 (1946); *Chem. Abstr.*, **41**, 80 (1947).
175. M. F. Shostakovskii and D. A. Kochkin., *Izv. Akad. Nauk SSSR*, **1954**, 174; *Chem. Abstr.*, **49**, 6090 (1955).
176. V. M. Vdovin, K. S. Pushchevaya, and A. D. Petrov, *Izv. Akad. Nauk SSSR*, **1961**, 281; *Chem. Abstr.*, **55**, 19,763 (1961).
177. H. Schmidbaur and W. Findeiss, *Angew. Chem. (Intern. ed.)*, **3**, 696 (1964).
178. H. Schmidbaur and W. Findeiss, *Ber.*, **99**, 2187 (1966).
179. Z. M. Manulkin, *Zh. Obshch. Khim.*, **18**, 299 (1948); *Chem. Abstr.*, **42**, 6742 (1948).
180. G. A. Razuvaev, N. S. Vyazankin, Yu. I. Dergunov, and O. S. Dyachkovskaya, *Dokl. Akad. Nauk SSSR*, **132**, 364 (1960); *Chem. Abstr.*, **54**, 20,937 (1960).
181. R. Müller, S. Reichel, and C. Dathe, *Ber.*, **97**, 1673 (1964).
182. L. H. Sommer, R. E. van Strien, and F. C. Whitmore, *J. Amer. Chem. Soc.*, **71**, 3056 (1949).
183. A. D. Petrov and V. F. Mironov, *Dokl. Akad. Nauk SSSR*, **75**, 707 (1950); *Chem. Abstr.*, **45**, 7003 (1951).
184. R. Calas and J. Valade, *Bull. Soc. Chim. Fr.*, **1957**, 282.
185. R. Calas and J. Valade, *Bull. Soc. Chim. Fr.*, **1958**, 919.
186. A. Sakurai, T. Watanabe, and M. Kumada, *J. Organometal. Chem.*, **9**, 11 (1967).
187. E. Frainnet, R. Calas, P. Gerval, Y. Dentone, and J. Bonastre, *Bull. Soc. Chim. Fr.*, **1965**, 1259.
188. H. Sakurai, K. Tominaga, T. Watanabe, and M. Kumada, *Tetrahedron Lett.*, **1966**, 5493.
189. G. A. Russell, *J. Amer. Chem. Soc.*, **81**, 4831 (1959).
190. Dao-Huy-Giao, *Compt. Rend.*, **260**, 6937 (1965).
191. N. A. Vyazankin, G. A. Razuvaev, and O. S. Dyachkovskaya, *Zh. Obshch. Khim.*, **33**, 613 (1963). *Chem. Abstr.*, **59**, 1670 (1963).
192. N. S. Nametkin, V. M. Vdovin, and K. S. Pushchevaya, *Dokl. Akad. Nauk SSSR*, **150**, 562 (1963); *Chem. Abstr.*, **59**, 8779 (1963).
193. I. M. T. Davidson, M. R. Jones, and C. Pett, *J. Chem. Soc., Ser. B*, **1967**, 937.
194. I. M. T. Davidson, *Chem. Ind. (London)*, **1960**, q107.
195. I. M. T. Davidson, C. Eaborn, and M. N. Lilly, *J. Chem. Soc.*, **1964**, 2624.
196. I. M. T. Davidson and M. R. Jones, *J. Chem. Soc.*, **1965**, 5481.
197. Y. Nagai, H. Kono, H. Matsumoto, and K. Yamazaki, *J. Org. Chem.*, **33**, 1966 (1968).
198. V. V. Ponomarev, A. S. Shapatin, and S. A. Golubtsov, *Zh. Obshch. Khim.*, **36**, 364 (1966); *Chem. Abstr.*, **64**, 15,915 (1966).
199. W. I. Bevan, R. N. Haszeldine, and J. C. Young, *Chem. Ind. (London)*, **1961**, 789.
200. R. N. Haszeldine and J. C. Young, *Proc. Chem. Soc.*, **1959**, 394.

201. J. M. Birchall, R. N. Haszeldine, and D. W. Roberts, *Chem. Commun.*, **1967**, 287.
202. G. V. Motsarev and V. R. Rozenberg, *Zh. Prikl. Khim.*, **38**, 211 (1965); *Chem. Abstr.*, **62**, 13,171 (1965).
203. G. V. Motsarev and V. R. Rozenberg, *Zh. Prikl. Khim.*, **37**, 747 (1964); *Chem. Abstr.*, **61**, 4389 (1964).
204. J. Koutková and V. Chvalovský, *Collect. Czech. Chem. Commun.* (in press).
205. S. N. Novikov, E. G. Kogan, and A. N. Pravednikov, *Vysokomol. Soyed.*, **8**, 1015 (1966); *Chem. Abstr.*, **65**, 9033 (1966).
206. S. N. Novikov, E. G. Kogan, and A. N. Pravednikov, *Zh. Obshch. Khim.*, **38**, 402 (1968); *Chem. Abstr.*, **69**, 96,806 (1968).
207. S. Tannenbaum, S. Kaye, and G. F. Lewenz, *J. Amer. Chem. Soc.*, **75**, 3753 (1953).
208. C. L. Agre and W. Hilling, *J. Amer. Chem. Soc.*, **74**, 3895 (1952).
209. G. H. Wagner and A. N. Pines, *J. Amer. Chem. Soc.*, **71**, 3567 (1949).
210. L. L. Shchukovskaya and R. I. Palchik, *Izv. Akad. Nauk SSSR*, **1964**, 2228; *Chem. Abstr.*, **62**, 9167 (1965).
211. R. N. Sterlin, I. L. Knunyants, L. N. Pinkina, and R. D. Yatsenko, *Izv. Akad. Nauk SSSR*, **1959**, 1492; *Chem. Abstr.*, **54**, 1270 (1960).
212. D. Seyferth and T. Wada, *Inorg. Chem.*, **1**, 78 (1962).
213. R. N. Sterlin, S. S. Dubov, Wei-Kang Li, L. P. Vakhomchik, and I. L. Knunyants, *Zh. Vses. Khim. Obshchest.* 6, 110 (1961); *Chem. Abstr.*, **55**, 15,336 (1961).
214. D. Seyferth, T. Wada, and G. Raab, *Tetrahedron Lett.*, **1960**, 20.
215. L. H. Sommer, D. L. Bailey, G. M. Goldberg, C. E. Buck, T. S. Bye, F. J. Evans, and F. C. Whitmore, *J. Amer. Chem. Soc.*, **76**, 1613 (1954).
216. L. H. Sommer and F. J. Evans, *J. Amer. Chem. Soc.*, **76**, 1186 (1954).
217. A. A. Petrov, V. A. Kormer, and M. D. Stadnichuk, *Zh. Obshch. Khim.*, **31**, 1135 (1961); *Chem. Abstr.*, **55**, 23,330 (1961).
218. M. D. Stadnichuk and A. A. Petrov, *Zh. Obshch. Khim.*, **31**, 411 (1961); *Chem. Abstr.*, **55**, 23,329 (1961).
219. A. A. Petrov, V. A. Kormer, and M. D. Stadnichuk, *Zh. Obshch. Khim.*, **30**, 2243 (1960); *Chem. Abstr.*, **55**, 13,301 (1961).
220. V. M. Vdovin, N. S. Nametkin, E. Sh. Finkelshtein, and V. D. Oppengeim, *Izv. Akad. Nauk SSSR*, **1964**, 458; *Chem. Abstr.*, **60**, 15,902 (1964).
221. R. Calas, P. Bourgeois, and N. Duffaut, *Compt. Rend.*, **C263**, 243 (1966); *Chem. Abstr.*, **65**, 18,605 (1966).
222. M. Kanazashi, *Bull. Chem. Soc. Jap.*, **28**, 44 (1955); *Chem. Abstr.*, **52**, 4556 (1958).
223. G. Fritz and J. Grobe, *Z. Anorg. Allg. Chem.*, **309**, 98 (1961); *Chem. Abstr.*, **55**, 233,320 (1961).
224. G. M. Guzman and J. L. Orbiso, *An. Real. Soc. Espan. Fis. Quim.*, *Ser. B*, **52**, 745 (1956); *Chem. Abstr.*, **54**, 11,976 (1960).
225. D. Grafstein, *J. Amer. Chem. Soc.*, **77**, 6650 (1955).
226. E. Frainnet, *Bull. Soc. Chim. Fr.*, **1959**, 1441.
227. E. Larsson, *Kgl. Fysiograf. Sellskap. Lund Forh.*, **25**, 60 (1955); *Chem. Abstr.*, **50**, 16,662 (1956).
228. Yu. N. Volnov and A. Reutt, *Zh. Obshch. Khim.*, **10**, 1600 (1940); *Chem. Abstr.*, **35**, 2853 (1941).
229. S. D. Ibekwe and M. J. Newlands, *J. Chem. Soc.*, **1965**, 4608.
230. K. C. Frisch and R. B. Young, *J. Amer. Chem. Soc.*, **74**, 4853 (1952).
231. L. Birkofer, A. Ritter, and H. Uhlenbrauck, *Ber.*, **96**, 3280 (1963); *Chem. Abstr.*, **60**, 5537 (1964).
232. C. Beermann and H. Hartmann, *Z. Anorg. Allg. Chem.*, **276**, 20 (1954); *Chem. Abstr.*, **49**, 6087 (1955).

233. H. Hartmann, *Angew. Chem.*, **65**, 323 (1953).
234. H. Hartmann and H. Honig, *Angew. Chem.*, **69**, 614 (1957).
235. C. Eaborn and D. R. M. Walton, *J. Organometal. Chem.*, **4**, 217 (1965).
236. C. S. Kraihanzel and J. E. Poist, *J. Organometal. Chem.*, **8**, 239 (1967).
237. H. Gilman and D. Aoki, *Chem. Ind. (London)*, **1961**, 1619.
238. H. Gilman and H. Hartzfeld, *J. Amer. Chem. Soc.*, **73**, 5878 (1951).
239. W. Findeiss, W. Davidsohn, and M. C. Henry, *J. Organometal. Chem.*, **9**, 435 (1967).
240. Le Quan Minh, J. C. Billiotte, and P. Cadiot, *Compt. Rend.*, **251**, 730 (1960).
241. A. D. Petrov and L. L. Shchukovskaya, *Zh. Obshch. Khim.*, **25**, 1128 (1955); *Chem. Abstr.*, **50**, 3275 (1956).
242. R. W. Bott, C. Eaborn, and D. R. M. Walton, *J. Organometal. Chem.*, **1**, 420 (1964).
243. H. Gilman and J. F. Nobis, *J. Amer. Chem. Soc.*, **72**, 2629 (1950).
244. M. F. Shostakovskii, E. P. Gracheva, and L. A. Kayutenko, *Dokl. Akad. Nauk SSSR*, **132**, 153 (1960); *Chem. Abstr.*, **54**, 20,848 (1960).
245. L. L. Shchukovskaya and A. D. Petrov, *Izv. Akad. Nauk SSSR*, **1958**, 1011; *Chem. Abstr.*, **53**, 1119 (1959).
246. F. Challenger and F. S. Kipping, *J. Chem. Soc.*, **97**, 755 (1910).
247. D. C. Bradley, R. C. Mehrotra, and W. Wardlaw, *J. Chem. Soc.*, **1952**, 4204.
248. A. G. Brook, K. N. Tai, and H. Gilman, *J. Amer. Chem. Soc.*, **77**, 6219 (1955).
249. C. R. Hauser and C. R. Hance, *J, Amer. Chem. Soc.*, **73**, 5846 (1951).
250. C. Eaborn and S. H. Parker, *J. Chem. Soc.*, **1955**, 126.
251. C. Eaborn and S. H. Parker, *J. Chem. Soc.*, **1957**, 955.
252. R. W. Bott, C. Eaborn, and T. W. Swaddle, *J. Chem. Soc.*, **1963**, 2342.
253. C. Eaborn and R. A. Shaw, *J. Chem. Soc.*, **1955**, 1420.
254. F. B. Deans and C. Eaborn, *J. Chem. Soc.*, **1959**, 2299.
255. F. B. Deans and C. Eaborn, *J. Chem. Soc.*, **1959**, 2303.
256. R. W. Bott, B. F. Dowden, and C. Eaborn, *J. Chem. Soc.*, **1965**, 6306.
257. E. B. Baker, R. W. Bott, C. Eaborn, and P. M. Greasley, *J. Chem. Soc.*, **1964**, 627.
258. G. Marr and D. E. Webster, *J. Organometal. Chem.*, **2**, 99 (1964).
259. G. Marr and D. E. Webster, *J. Chem. Soc., B*, **1968** (202).
260. R. A. Benkeser, Y. Nagai, and J. Hooz, *J. Amer. Chem. Soc.*, **86**, 3742 (1964).
261. M. Kumada, K. Mimura, M. Ishikawa, and K. Shiina, *Tetrahedron Lett.*, **1965**, 83.
262. C. Eaborn and D. R. M. Walton, *J. Organometal. Chem.*, **3**, 169 (1965).
263. R. Baker, C. Eaborn, and J. A. Sperry, *J. Chem. Soc.*, **1962**, 2382.
264. R. W. Bott, C. Eaborn, and P. M. Greasley, *J. Chem. Soc.*, **1964**, 4804.
265. R. A. Benkeser, W. Schroeder, and O. H. Thomas, *J. Amer. Chem. Soc.*, **80**, 2283 (1958).
266. C. Eaborn, Z. Lasocki, and D. E. Webster, *J. Chem. Soc.*, **1959**, 3034.
267. C. Eaborn and K. C. Pande, *J. Chem. Soc.*, **1960**, 1566.
268. R. A. Benkeser, R. A. Hickner, and D. I. Hoke, *J. Amer. Chem. Soc.*, **80**, 2279 (1958).
269. F. B. Deans, C. Eaborn, and D. E. Webster, *J. Chem. Soc.*, **1959**, 3031.
270. J. Nasielski and M. Planchon, *Bull. Soc. Chim. Belges*, **69**, 123 (1960); *Chem. Abstr.*, **54**, 1489 (1960).
271. R. W. Bott, C. Eaborn, and K. Leyshon, *J. Chem. Soc.*, **1964**, 1971.
272. R. A. Benkeser and F. S. Clark, *J. Amer. Chem. Soc.*, **82**, 4881 (1960).
273. C. Eaborn, J. A. Treverton, and D. R. M. Walton, *J. Organometal. Chem.*, **9**, 259 (1967).
274. C. Eaborn and J. A. Sperry, *J. Chem. Soc.*, **1961**, 4921.

275. A. Ya. Yakubovich and G. V. Motsarev, *Zh. Obshch. Khim.*, **25**, 1748 (1955); *Chem. Abstr.*, **50**, 5550 (1956).
276. H. Gilman and K. Oita, *J. Amer. Chem. Soc.*, **77**, 3386 (1955).
277. V. Chvalovský and V. Bažant, *Collect. Czech. Chem. Commun.*, **26**, 282 (1961); *Chem. Abstr.*, **55**, 15,388 (1961).
278. V. Chvaloský and V. Bažant, *Collect. Czech. Chem. Commun.*, **21**, 93 (1956); *Chem. Abstr.*, **50**, 10,030 (1956).
279. V. Chvalovský and V. Bažant, *Trudy Konferencii*, Leningrad, 1958, **1**, 223 (1958).
280. R. D. Verma and C. Leitch, *Can. J. Chem.*, **41**, 1652 (1963).
281. B. J. L. Aylett and I. A. Ellis, *J. Chem. Soc.*, **1960**, 3415.
282. G. Fritz and D. Kummer, *Z. Anorg. Allg. Chem.*, **310**, 327 (1961); *Chem. Abstr.*, **56**, 6876 (1962).
283. G. Fritz and D. Kummer, *Z. Anorg. Allg. Chem.*, **304**, 322 (1960).
284. G. Fritz and D. Kummer, *Ber.*, **94**, 1143 (1961); *Chem. Abstr.*, **55**, 22,196 (1961).
285. G. Fritz and D. Kummer, *Z. Anorg. Allg. Chem.*, **308**, 105 (1961); *Chem. Abstr.*, **55**, 18,612 (1961).
286. R. A. Benkeser and P. E. Brumfield, *J. Amer. Chem. Soc.*, **73**, 4770 (1951).
287. R. A. Benkeser and H. Landesman, *J. Amer. Chem. Soc.*, **76**, 904 (1954).
288. Shih-Huei Wu and Tung-Yin Yu, *Hua Hsueh Hsueh Pao*, **25**, 289 (1959); *Chem. Abstr.*, **54**, 16,412 (1960).
289. B. N. Dolgov and O. K. Panina, *Zh. Obshch. Khim.*, **18**, 1129 (1948); *Chem. Abstr.*, **43**, 1737 (1949).
290. J. L. Speier, *J. Amer. Chem. Soc.*, **75**, 2930 (1953).
291. V. Chvalovský and V. Bažant, *Collect. Czech. Chem. Commun.*, **16**, 580 (1951); *Chem. Abstr.*, **48**, 10,642 (1954).
292. F. B. Deans and C. Eaborn, *J. Chem. Soc.*, **1957**, 498.
293. D. L. Bailey and R. M. Pike, U.S. Patent 3,020,302 (1962); *Chem. Abstr.*, **56**, 15,548 (1962).
294. F. S. Kipping and L. L. Lloyd, *J. Chem. Soc.*, **79**, 449 (1901).
295. C. Eaborn and T. Hashimoto, *Chem. Ind.* (London), **1961**, 1081.
296. R. W. Bott, C. Eaborn and T. Hashimoto, *J. Organometal. Chem.*, **3**, 442 (1965).
297. G. Schott and M. M. Sprung, *Z. Anorg. Allg. Chem.*, **333**, 76 (1964).
298. D. N. Andreev and E. V. Kukharskaya, *Izv. Akad. Nauk SSSR*, **1958**, 702; *Chem. Abstr.*, **52**, 20,001 (1958).
299. A. Ladenburg, *Ber.*, **40**, 2274 (1907).
300. B. O. Pray, L. H. Sommer, G. M. Goldberg, G. T. Kerr, P. A. Di Giorgio, and F. C. Whitmore, *J. Amer. Chem. Soc.*, **70**, 433 (1948).
301. G. Grüttner and M. Caner, *Ber.*, **51**, 1283 (1918).
302. R. A. Benkeser and A. Torkelson, *J. Amer. Chem. Soc.*, **76**, 1252 (1954).
303. G. Fritz and H. Burdt, *Z. Anorg. Allg. Chem.*, **317**, 35 (1962); *Chem. Abstr.*, **57**, 5945 (1962).
304. F. S. Kipping and J. C. Blackburn, *J. Chem. Soc.*, **1932**, 2200.
305. J. Chatt and A. A. Williams, *J. Chem. Soc.*, **1954**, 4403.
306. L. M. Stock and A. R. Spector, *J. Org. Chem.*, **28**, 3272 (1963).
307. C. Eaborn and D. E. Webster, *J. Chem. Soc.*, **1957**, 4449.
308. L. H. Sommer, K. W. Michael, and W. D. Korte, *J. Amer. Chem. Soc.*, **89**, 868 (1967).
309. C. Eaborn and O. W. Steward, *J. Chem. Soc.*, **1965**, 521.
310. C. Eaborn and D. E. Webster, *J. Chem. Soc.*, **1960**, 179.
311. A. Taketa, M. Kumada, and K. Tarama, *J. Chem. Soc. Jap., Pure Chem. Sect.*, **78**, 1003 (1957); *Chem. Abstr.*, **52**, 5943 (1958).

312. B. Lepeška and V. Chvalovský, *Collect. Czech. Chem. Commun.* **34**, 3553 (1969); *Chem. Abstr.*, **72**, 3528 (1970).
313. B. Lepeška, V. Bažant, and V. Chvalovský, *J. Organometal. Chem.* **23**, 41 (1970).
314. A. D. Petrov, M. I. Batuev, V. A. Ponomarenko, A. D. Snegova, A. D. Matveeva, and B. A. Sokolov, *Zh. Obshch. Khim.*, **27**, 2057 (1957); *Chem. Abstr.*, **52**, 6237 (1958).
315. V. A. Ponomarenko, A. D. Snegova, and Yu. P. Egorov, *Izv. Akad. Nauk SSSR*, **1960**, 244; *Chem. Abstr.*, **54**, 20,932 (1960).
316. M. G. Voronkov and V. P. Davydova, *Dokl. Akad. Nauk SSSR*, **125**, 553 (1959); *Chem. Abstr.*, **53**, 19,850 (1959).
317. G. V. Motsarev, A. Ya. Yakubovich, V. A. Ponomarenko, A. D. Snegova, and T. M. Ivanova, *Zh. Obshch. Khim.*, **35**, 2167 (1965); *Chem. Abstr.*, **64**, 11,237 (1966).
318. G. V. Motsarev and V. R. Rozenberg, *Zh. Obshch. Khim.*, **31**, 2004 (1961). *Chem. Abstr.*, **55**, 27,168 (1961).
319. A. Ya. Yakubovich and G. V. Motsarev, *Zh. Obshch. Khim.*, **26**, 1413 (1956); *Chem. Abstr.*, **50**, 14,605 (1956).
320. G. V. Motsarev, G. N. Mashkova, and V. R. Rozenberg, *Zh. Obshch. Khim.*, **36**, 2179 (1966); *Chem. Abstr.*, **66**, 8916 (1967).
321. J. Hradil and V. Chvalovský, *Collect Czech. Chem. Commun.*, **32**, 171 (1967); *Chem. Abstr.*, **66**, 76,073 (1967).
322. C. Tamborski, E. J. Soloski, and S. M. Dec, *J. Organometal. Chem.*, **4**, 446 (1965).
323. C. Eaborn, *J. Chem. Soc.*, **1950**, 3077.
324. W. J. Haggerty, Jr. and L. W. Breed, *J. Org. Chem.*, **26**, 2464 (1961).
325. A. Ya. Yakubovich and G. V. Motsarev, *Zh. Obshch. Khim.*, **26**, 568 (1956); *Chem. Abstr.*, **50**, 13,784 (1956).
326. G. A. Russell, *J. Amer. Chem. Soc.*, **81**, 4825 (1959).
327. G. A. Russell, *J. Amer. Chem. Soc.*, **81**, 4815 (1959).
328. G. A. Russell, *J. Amer. Chem. Soc.*, **81**, 4834 (1959).
329. A. Ya. Yakubovich and G. V. Motsarev, *Zh. Obshch. Khim.*, **23**, 412 (1953); *Chem. Abstr.*, **48**, 3286 (1954).
330. A. Ya. Yakubovich and G. V. Motsarev, *Zh. Obshch. Khim.*, **23**, 771 (1953); *Chem. Abstr.*, **48**, 4462 (1954).
331. B. N. Dolgov and O. K. Panina, *Zh. Obshch. Khim.*, **18**, 1293 (1948); *Chem. Abstr.*, **43**, 2177 (1949).
332. A. D. Petrov, T. I. Chernysheva, and E. A. Chernyshev, *Zh. Obshch. Khim.*, **26**, 138 (1956); *Chem. Abstr.*, **50**, 13,852 (1956).
333. A. Ya. Yakubovich and G. V. Motsarev, *Dokl. Akad. Nauk SSSR*, **88**, 87 (1953); *Chem. Abstr.*, **48**, 143 (1954).
334. A. Ya. Yakubovich and G. V. Motsarev, *Zh. Obshch. Khim.*, **23**, 1547 (1953); *Chem. Abstr.*, **48**, 10,642 (1954).
335. J. D. Austin, C. Eaborn, and J. D. Smith, *J. Chem. Soc.*, **1963**, 4744.
336. W. E. Evison and F. S. Kipping, *J. Chem. Soc.*, **1931**, 2774.
337. V. Chvalovský and V. Bažant, *Chem. Prům.*, **16**, 207 (1966); *Chem. Abstr.*, **65**, 5478 (1966).
338. A. Ya. Yakubovich and G. V. Motsarev, *Zh. Obshch. Khim.*, **23**, 1059 (1953); *Chem. Abstr.*, **48**, 8186 (1954).
339. A. Ya. Yakubovich and G. V. Motsarev, *Zh. Obshch. Khim.*, **23**, 1414 (1953); *Chem. Abstr.*, **47**, 12,281 (1953).
340. H. Sakurai, K. Tominaga, and M. Kumada, *Bull. Chem. Soc. Jap.*, **39**, 1820; *Chem. Abstr.*, **66**, 1073 (1967).

341. Y. Sakata and T. Hashimoto, *Yakugaku Zasshi*, **79**, 872 (1959); *Chem. Abstr.*, **54**, 357 (1960).

342. R. A. Benkeser, T. V. Liston, and G. M. Stanton, *Tetrahedron Lett.*, **1960**, 1.

343. C. Combes, *Compt. Rend.*, **122**, 622 (1896).

344. L. R. Vyle and F. S. Kipping, *J. Chem. Soc.*, **125**, 2616 (1924).

345. A. K. Ghosh, C. E. Hansing, A. I. Stutz, and A. G. MacDiarmid, *J. Chem. Soc.*, **1962**, 403.

346. R. H. Benkeser, D. I. Hoke, and R. A. Hickner, *J. Amer. Chem. Soc.*, **80**, 5294 (1958).

347. C. L. Frye, *J. Amer. Chem. Soc.*, **86**, 3170 (1964).

348. F. S. Kipping and A. G. Murray, *J. Chem. Soc.*, **1928**, 1427.

349. K. A. Andrianov, S. E. Yakushkina, T. M. Karaseva, and N. V. Pertsova, *Vysokomol. Soedin.*, **8**, 352 (1966); *Chem. Abstr.*, **65**, 2361 (1966).

350. E. W. Beck, W. H. Daudt, H. J. Fletcher, M. J. Hunter, and A. J. Barry, *J. Amer. Chem. Soc.*, **81**, 1256 (1959).

351. J. L. Speier, *J. Amer. Chem. Soc.*, **74**, 1003 (1952).

352. F. W. G. Fearon and H. Gilman, *J. Organometal. Chem.*, **6**, 577 (1966).

353. C. Tamborski and E. J. Soloski, *J. Organometal. Chem.*, **10**, 385 (1967).

354. F. S. Kipping and N. W. Cusa, *J. Chem. Soc.*, **1935**, 1088.

355. T. J. Maass and H. W. Post, *Rec. Trav. Chim. Pays-Bas*, **81**, 88 (1962).

356. R. H. Meen and H. Gilman, *J. Org. Chem.*, **20**, 73 (1955).

357. S. Dyankov and D. Shopov, *C. R. Acad. Bulg. Sci.*, **19**, 503 (1966); *Chem. Abstr.*, **65**, 12,070 (1966).

358. C. A. Kraus and R. J. Rosen, *J. Amer. Chem. Soc.*, **47**, 2739 (1925).

359. R. A. Benkeser, R. E. Robinson, and H. Landesman, *J. Amer. Chem. Soc.*, **74**, 5699 (1952).

360. C. R. Hance and C. R. Hauser, *J. Amer. Chem. Soc.*, **74**, 1856 (1952).

361. O. Schmitz-DuMont, W. Jansen, and W. Schaal, *Z. Anorg. Allg. Chem.*, **339**, 113 (1965).

362. H. Gilman and G. E. Dunn, *J. Amer. Chem. Soc.*, **73**, 5077 (1951).

363. P. J. Morris, F. W. G. Fearon, and H. Gilman, *J. Organometal. Chem.*, **9**, 427 (1967).

364. L. M. Nazarova, *Zh. Obshch. Khim.*, **31**, 1119 (1961); *Chem. Abstr.*, **55**, 23,404 (1961).

365. R. A. Benkeser and D. J. Foster, *J. Amer. Chem. Soc.*, **74**, 5314 (1952).

366. H. Gilman, W. H. Atwell, P. K. Sen, and C. L. Smith., *J. Organometal. Chem.*, **4**, 163 (1965).

367. F. W. G. Fearon and H. Gilman, *J. Organometal. Chem.*, **10**, 409 (1967).

368. H. Gilman, R. A. Benkeser, and G. E. Dunn, *J. Amer. Chem. Soc.*, **72**, 1689 (1950).

369. H. Gilman and O. L. Marrs, *J. Org. Chem.*, **30**, 1942 (1965).

370. B. N. Dolgov and Yu. N. Volnov, *Zh. Obshch. Khim.*, **1**, 91 (1931); *Chem. Abstr.*, **25**, 4535 (1931).

371. G. Calingaert and H. A. Beatty, *J. Amer. Chem. Soc.*, **61**, 2748 (1939).

372. G. Calingaert, H. A. Beatty, and H. R. Neal, *J. Amer. Chem. Soc.*, **61**, 2755 (1939).

373. G. Calingaert, H. Soroos, and V. Hnizda, *J. Amer. Chem. Soc.*, **62**, 1107 (1940).

374. P. D. George, L. H. Sommer, and F. C. Whitmore, *J. Amer. Chem. Soc.*, **77**, 1677 (1955).

375. F. H. Pollard, G. Nickless, and P. C. Uden, *J. Chromatogr.*, **19**, 28 (1965).

376. J. L. Speier and R. E. Zimmerman, *J. Amer. Chem. Soc.*, **77**, 6395 (1955).

377. S. N. Borisov, M. G. Voronkov, and B. N. Dolgov, *Izv. Akad. Nauk SSSR*, **1957**, 1396; *Chem. Abstr.*, **52**, 7136 (1958).

378. J. W. Jenkins, N. L. Lavery, P. R. Guenther, and H. W. Post, *J. Org. Chem.*, **13**, 862 (1948).

379. R. W. Coutant and A. Levy, *Amer. Chem. Soc., Div. Petrol. Chem., Preprints*, **11** (3), 291 (1966); *Chem. Abstr.*, **66**, 37,294 (1967).

380. R. O. Sauer, U.S. Patent 2,647,136 (1953); *Chem. Abstr.*, **48**, 8252 (1954).

381. H. Gilman, R. A. Tomasi, and D. Wittenberg, *J. Org. Chem.*, **24**, 821 (1959).

382. S. Yoshino, K. Kojima, and E. Matsuhara, *J. Chem. Soc. Jap. Pure Chem. Sect.*, **74**, 397 (1953).

383. G. J. Sleddon, German Patent 1,111,184 (1961); *Chem. Abstr.*, **57**, 13,804 (1962).

384. E. M. Soshestvenskaya, *Zh. Obshch. Khim.*, **26**, 231 (1956); *Chem. Abstr.*, **50**, 13,785 (1956).

385. W. Noll, German Patent 825,087 (1951); *Chem. Abstr.*, **49**, 11,703 (1955).

386. T. Hoshino and K. Kojima, Japanese Patent 1872 (1953); *Chem. Abstr.*, **48**, 4880 (1954).

387. K. A. Andrianov and V. M. Kotov, *Dokl. Akad. Nauk SSSR*, **167**, 811 (1966); *Chem. Abstr.*, **65**, 3898 (1966).

388. K. A. Andrianov and V. M. Kotov, *J. Organometal. Chem.*, **7**, 211 (1967).

389. F. C. Whitmore, L. H. Sommer, and J. Gold, *J. Amer. Chem. Soc.*, **69**, 1976 (1947).

390. R. O. Sauer and F. M. Hadsell, *J. Amer. Chem. Soc.*, **70**, 3590 (1948).

391. M. Kumada, *J. Chem. Soc. Jap. Ind. Chem. Sect.*, **55**, 373 (1952); *Chem. Abstr.*, **48**, 10,543 (1954).

392. J. O. Koehler and H. Lamprey, *Advan. Chem. Series*, **23**, 217 (1959); *Chem. Abstr.*, **54**, 6519 (1960).

393. P. D. Zemany and F. P. Price, *J. Amer. Chem. Soc.*, **70**, 4222 (1948).

394. B. N. Dolgov, M. G. Voronkov, and S. N. Borisov, *Zh. Obshch. Khim.*, **27**, 709 (1952); *Chem. Abstr.*, **51**, 16,283 (1957).

395. C. Eaborn, *J. Chem. Soc.*, **1953**, 494.

396. J. Rathouský, O. Kruchňa, and V. Bažant, *Collect. Czech. Chem. Commun.*, **25**, 1807 (1960); *Chem. Abstr.*, **54**, 24,478 (1960).

397. B. N. Dolgov, S. N. Borisov, and M. G. Voronkov, *Zh. Obshch. Khim.*, **27**, 2062 (1957); *Chem. Abstr.*, **52**, 6159 (1958).

398. R. O. Sauer, U.S. Patent 2,730,540 (1956); *Chem. Abstr.*, **50**, 12,108 (1956).

399. H. R. McEntee, U.S. Patent 2,786,861 (1957); *Chem. Abstr.*, **51**, 13,903 (1957).

400. Yu. P. Egorov, K. S. Pushchevaya, E. D. Lubuzh, V. M. Vdovin, and A. D. Petrov, *Izv. Akad. Nauk SSSR*, **1963**, 822; *Chem. Abstr.*, **59**, 10,102 (1963).

401. V. M. Vdovin, K. S. Pushchevaya, and A. D. Petrov, *Izv. Akad. Nauk SSSR*, **1961**, 1275; *Chem. Abstr.*, **56**, 1470 (1962).

402. V. M. Vdovin, K. S. Pushchevaya, N. A. Belikova, R. Sultanov, A. F. Plate, and A. D. Petrov, *Dokl. Akad. Nauk SSSR*, **136**, 96 (1961); *Chem. Abstr.*, **55**, 17,478 (1961).

403. N. S. Nametkin, V. M. Vdovin, E. Sh. Finkelshtein, K. S. Konobeevskij, and V. D. Oppengeim, *Dokl. Akad. Nauk SSSR*, **162**, 585 (1965); *Chem. Abstr.*, **63**, 7119 (1965).

404. V. M. Vdovin, K. S. Pushchevaya, and A. D. Petrov, *Dokl. Akad. Nauk SSSR*, **141**, 843 (1961); *Chem. Abstr.*, **56**, 14,191 (1962).

405. N. S. Nametkin and V. M. Vdovin, *J. Polym. Sci., Part C*, **4**, 1043 (1963).

406. N. S. Nametkin, V. M. Vdovin, and V. I. Zavyalov, *Izv. Akad. Nauk SSSR*, **1965**, 1448; *Chem. Abstr.*, **63**, 18,273 (1965).

407. N. S. Nametkin, V. D. Oppengeim, V. I. Zavyalov, K. S. Pushchevaya, and V. M. Vdovin, *Izv. Akad. Nauk SSSR*, **1965**, 1543; *Chem. Abstr.*, **64**, 3708 (1966).

408. V. M. Vdovin, N. S. Nametkin, V. I. Zavyalov, and K. S. Pushchevaya, *J. Prakt. Chem.*, **23**, 281 (1964); *Chem. Abstr.*, **61**, 3210 (1964).

409. N. S. Nametkin, V. M. Vdovin, and V. I. Zavyalov, *Dokl. Akad. Nauk SSSR*, **162**, 824 (1965); *Chem. Abstr.*, **63**, 8501 (1965).

410. K. A. Andrianov, V. I. Pakhomov, and V. M. Gelperina, *Dokl. Akad. Nauk SSSR*, **162**, 79 (1965); *Chem. Abstr.*, **63**, 5756 (1965).

411. H. Gilman and W. H. Atwell, *J. Amer. Chem. Soc.*, **86**, 5589 (1964).

412. N. S. Nametkin, V. Vdovin, and P. L. Grinberg, *Dokl. Akad. Nauk SSSR*, **155**, 849 (1964); *Chem. Abstr.*, **60**, 15,901 (1964).

413. N. S. Nametkin, V. Vdovin, and P. L. Grinberg, *Izv. Akad. Nauk SSSR*, **1964**, 1133; *Chem. Abstr.*, **61**, 7039 (1964).

414. D. R. Weyenberg and L. E. Nelson, *J. Org. Chem.*, **30**, 2618 (1965).

415. G. Fritz, W. Kemmerling, G. Sonntag, H. J. Becher, E. A. V. Ebsworth, and J. Grobe, *Z. Anorg. Allg. Chem.*, **321**, 10 (1963).

416. W. A. Kriner, *J. Poly. Sci., Part A-1*, **4**, 444 (1966).

417. L. H. Sommer, O. F. Bennett, P. G. Campbell, and D. R. Weyenberg, *J. Amer. Chem. Soc.* **79**, 3295 (1957).

418. H. Gilman and W. H. Atwell, *J. Amer. Chem. Soc.*, **87**, 2678 (1965).

419. R. Müller, R. Köhne, and H. Beyer, *Ber.*, **95**, 3030 (1962).

420. R. Müller and W. Müller, *Ber.*, **97**, 1111 (1964).

421. N. S. Nametkin, V. M. Vdovin, P. L. Grinberg, and E. D. Babich, *Dokl. Akad. Nauk SSSR*, **161**, 358 (1965); *Chem. Abstr.*, **63**, 625 (1965).

422. H. Gilman and W. H. Atwell, *J. Amer. Chem. Soc.*, **86**, 2687 (1964).

423. W. H. Knoth, Jr. and R. V. Lindsley, Jr., *J. Org. Chem.*, **23**, 1392 (1958).

424. R. West, *J. Amer. Chem. Soc.*, **76**, 6012 (1954).

425. J. Goubeau, T. Kalmar, and H. Hofmann, *Ann. Chem.*, **659**, 39 (1962).

426. V. M. Vdovin, N. S. Nametkin, K. S. Puschchevaya, and A. V. Topchiev, *Izv. Akad. Nauk SSSR*, **1963**, 274; *Chem. Abstr.*, **58**, 13,980 (1963).

427. R. A. Benkeser, J. L. Noe, and Y. Nagai, *J. Org. Chem.*, **30**, 378 (1965).

428. A. G. Brook and J. B. Pierce, *J. Org. Chem.*, **30**, 2566 (1965).

429. M. Kumada, J. Nakajima, M. Ishikawa, and Y. Yamamoto, *J. Org. Chem.*, **23**, 293 (1958).

430. A. G. Brook, K. H. Pannell, G. E. LeGrow, and J. J. Sheeto, *J. Organometal. Chem.*, **2**, 491 (1964).

431. A. G. Brook, C. M. Warner, and M. E. McGriskin, *J. Amer. Chem. Soc.*, **81**, 981 (1959).

432. A. G. Brook, W. W. Limburg, D. M. MacRae, and S. A. Fieldhouse, *J. Amer. Chem. Soc.*, **89**, 704 (1967).

433. L. L. Shchukovskaya and R. I. Palchik, *Izv. Akad. Nauk SSSR*, **1964**, 1556.

434. V. Bažant, V. Chvalovský, and J. Rathouský, *Organosilicon Compounds*, Vol. 1, Czechoslovak Academy of Sciences, Prague, 1965, pp. 212–242.

435. Ibid., Vol. 2.

436. C. Eaborn and R. W. Bott, in *Organometallic Compounds of the Group IV Elements*, Vol. 1, Part I, A. G. MacDiarmid, Ed., Marcel Dekker, New York, 1968, pp. 105–536.

437. M. Kumada, K. Naka, and M. Ishikawa, *J. Organometal. Chem.*, **2**, 136 (1964).

438. G. Fritz and J. Grobe, *Z. Anorg. Allg. Chem.*, **299**, 302 (1959); *Chem. Abstr.*, **53**, 18,055 (1959).

439. G. Fritz and J. Grobe, *Angew. Chem.*, **70**, 701 (1958); *Chem. Abstr.*, **53**, 10,259 (1959).

440. G. Fritz, B. Raabe, and J. Grobe, *Angew. Chem.*, **70**, 402 (1958).
441. G. Fritz and B. Raabe, *Angew. Chem.*, **68**, 381 (1956).
442. G. Fritz and B. Raabe, *Z. Naturforsch.*, *B*, **11**, 57 (1956); *Chem. Abstr.*, **50**, 13,727 (1956).
443. M. G. Voronkov, B. N. Dolgov, and G. B. Karpenko, *Zh. Obshch. Khim.*, **24**, 269 (1954); *Chem. Abstr.*, **49**, 4505 (1955).
444. B. N. Dolgov, G. V. Golodnikov, and N. E. Glushkova, *Zh. Obshch. Khim.*, **26**, 1688 (1956); *Chem. Abstr.*, **51**, 1828 (1957).
445. B. N. Dolgov, G. V. Golodnikov, and K. G. Golodova, *Dokl. Akad. Nauk SSSR*, **117**, 987 (1957); *Chem. Abstr.*, **52**, 8039 (1958).
446. G. Fritz, *Angew. Chem.*, **69**, 308 (1957).
447. G. Fritz, *Z. Naturforsch.*, *B*, **12**, 66 (1957); *Chem. Abstr.*, **51**, 13,746 (1957).
448. A. L. Smith and H. A. Clark, *J. Amer. Chem. Soc.*, **83**, 3345 (1961).
449. G. Fritz, D. Habel, and G. Teichmann, *Z. Anorg. Allg. Chem.*, **303**, 85 (1960).
450. G. Fritz and G. Teichmann, *Ber.*, **95**, 2361 (1962).
451. G. Fritz and G. Teichmann, *Angew. Chem.*, **70**, 701 (1958); *Chem. Abstr.*, **53**, 10,249 (1959).
452. D. N. Andreev, *Angew. Chem.*, **70**, 512 (1958).
453. D. N. Andreev, *Trudy Konf. Khim. Prakt. Prim. Kremneorg. Soed.*, Leningrad, **1**, 152 (1958).
454. H. A. Dewhurst, *J. Phys. Chem.*, **63**, 1976 (1959).
455. H. A. Dewhurst and L. E. S. Pierre, *J. Phys. Chem.*, **64**, 1063 (1960).
456. L. E. S. Pierre and H. A. Dewhurst, *J. Phys. Chem.*, **64**, 1060 (1960).
457. C. J. Wolf and A. C. Stewart, *J. Phys. Chem.*, **66**, 1119 (1962).
458. J. L. Weininger, *J. Amer. Chem. Soc.*, **83**, 3388 (1961).
459. E. L. Warrick, *Ind. Eng. Chem.*, **47**, 2388 (1955).
460. S. Iwayanagi, H. Nakane, and M. Hideshima, *Chem. High Polym.*, **15**, 333 (1958); *Chem. Abstr.*, **54**, 10,391 (1960).
461. L. E. S. Pierre, H. A. Dewhurst, and A. M. Bueche, *J. Polym. Sci.*, **36**, 105 (1959).
462. A. Charlesby, *J. Polym. Sci.*, **17**, 379 (1955).
463. A. Charlesby and D. G. Lloyd, *Proc. Roy. Soc.*, *Ser. A.*, **254**, 343 (1960); *Chem. Abstr.*, **54**, 18,036 (1960).
464. W. K. W. Chen, R. B. Mesrobian, D. S. Ballantine, D. J. Metz, and A. Glines, *J. Polym. Sci.*, **23**, 903 (1957).
465. V. Chvalovský, V. Matoušek, and V. Bažant, *Chem. Prům.*, **7**, 377 (1957).
466. Z. M. Manulkin, *Zh. Obshch. Khim.*, **20**, 2004 (1950); *Chem. Abstr.*, **45**, 5611 (1951).
467. L. H. Sommer, E. Dorfman, G. M. Goldberg, and F. C. Whitmore, *J. Amer Chem. Soc.*, **68**, 488 (1946).
468. G. Fritz, G. Teichmann, and H. Thielking, *Angew. Chem.*, **72**, 209 (1960).
469. C. Tamborski and H. W. Post, *J. Org. Chem.*, **17**, 1400 (1952).
470. M. I. Batuev, A. D. Petrov, V. A. Ponomarenko, and A. D. Matveeva, *Zh. Obshch. Khim.*, **26**, 2336 (1956); *Chem. Abstr.*, **51**, 4979 (1957).
471. V. A. Ponomarenko, and V. F. Mironov, *Izv. Akad. Nauk SSSR*, **1954**, 497; *Chem. Abstr.*, **49**, 9495 (1955).
472. C. L. Agre and W. Hilling, *J. Amer. Chem. Soc.*, **74**, 3899 (1952).
473. A. D. Petrov and G. I. Nikishin, *Izv. Akad. Nauk SSSR*, **1956**, 243; *Chem. Abstr.*, **50**, 13,726 (1956).
474. L. H. Sommer, D. L. Bailey, J. R. Gould, and F. C. Whitmore, *J. Amer. Chem. Soc.*, **76**, 801 (1954).
475. A. G. Brook and H. Gilman, *J. Amer. Chem. Soc.*, **77**, 2322 (1955).

476. F. C. Whitmore, L. H. Sommer, J. Gold and R. E. van Strien, *J. Amer. Chem. Soc.*, **69**, 1551 (1947).
477. G. D. Cooper, *J. Org. Chem.*, **21**, 1214 (1956).
478. G. D. Cooper, *J. Amer. Chem. Soc.*, **76**, 3713 (1954).
479. G. D. Cooper, *J. Amer. Chem. Soc.*, **76**, 2499 (1954).
480. C. Tomasino, Ph.D. Thesis, University of Florida, 1959, *Diss. Abstr.*, **20**, 103 (1959).
481. V. Bažant and V. Matoušek, *Collect. Czech. Chem. Commun.*, **24**, 3758 (1959).
482. E. Larsson, *Kgl. Fysiograf. Sellskap. Lund Forh.*, **25**, 1 (1955).
483. A. D. Petrov and L. L. Shchukovskaya, *Dokl. Akad. Nauk SSSR*, **86**, 551 (1952); *Chem. Abstr.*, **47**, 12,225 (1953).
484. A. D. Petrov and S. I. Sadykh-Zade, *Dokl. Akad. Nauk SSSR*, **85**, 1297 (1952); *Chem. Abstr.*, **47**, 4281 (1953).
485. R. A. Benkeser and R. G. Severson, *J. Amer. Chem. Soc.*, **73**, 1424 (1951).
486. L. H. Sommer and N. S. Marans, *J. Amer. Chem. Soc.*, **73**, 5135 (1951).
487. H. Gilman and F. I. Marshall, *J. Amer. Chem. Soc.*, **71**, 2066 (1949).
488. R. A. Benkeser and H. R. Krysiak, *J. Amer. Chem. Soc.*, **75**, 4528 (1953).
489. G. Illuminati, J. F. Nobis, and H. Gilman, *J. Amer. Chem. Soc.*, **73**, 5887 (1951).
490. R. A. Benkeser and H. R. Krysiak, *J. Amer. Chem. Soc.*, **76**, 6353 (1954).
491. R. A. Benkeser, R. A. Hickner, D. I. Hoke and O. H. Thomas, *J. Amer. Chem. Soc.*, **80**, 5289 (1958).
492. L. M. Stock and H. C. Brown, *J. Amer. Chem. Soc.*, **82**, 1942 (1960).
493. L. M. Stock and H. C. Brown, *J. Amer. Chem. Soc.*, **84**, 1668 (1962).
494. H. C. Brown and L. M. Stock, *J. Amer. Chem. Soc.*, **84**, 3298 (1962).
495. C. Eaborn, *J. Chem. Soc.*, **1956**, 4858.
496. C. Eaborn and R. C. Moore, *J. Chem. Soc.*, **1959**, 3640.
497. S. V. Sunthankar and H. Gilman, *J. Amer. Chem. Soc.*, **72**, 4884 (1950).
498. R. Müller and L. Klenk, *J. Prakt. Chem.*, **1**, 129 (1955); *Chem. Abstr.*, **54**, 1376 (1960).
499. Y. Sakata and T. Hashimoto, *J. Pharm. Soc. Japan*, **79**, 878 (1959); *Chem. Abstr.*, **54**, 358 (1960).
500. Y. Sakata and T. Hashimoto, *J. Pharm. Soc. Japan*, **80**, 728 (1960); *Chem. Abstr.*, **54**, 24,480 (1960).
501. S. V. Sunthankar and H. Gilman, *J. Org. Chem.*, **15**, 1200 (1950).
502. C. Eaborn, *J. Chem. Soc.*, **1953**, 3148.
503. D. I. Hoke, Ph.D. Thesis, Diss. Abstr., **18**, 1980 (1958).
504. W. Schroeder, Ph.D. Thesis, Diss. Abstr., **18**, 1984 (1958).
505. H. H. Szmant, O. M. Devlin, and G. A. Brost, *J. Amer. Chem. Soc.*, **73**, 3059 (1951).
506. A. Ladenburg, *Ann.*, **173**, 143 (1874).
507. A. Ladenburg, *Ber.*, **7**, 387 (1874).
508. R. F. Toomey, Ph.D. Thesis, Diss. Abstr., **21**, 1386 (1960).
509. A. Ya. Yakubovich and G. V.Motsarev, *Dokl. Akad. Nauk SSSR*, **91**, 277 (1953); *Chem. Abstr.*, **48**, 8750 (1954).
510. T. V. Liston, Ph.D. Thesis, Diss. Abstr., **21**, 1063 (1960).
511. G. V. Motsarev and A. Ya. Yakubovich, *Zh. Obshch. Khim.*, **27**, 1318 (1957); *Chem. Abstr.*, **52**, 2783 (1958).
512. G. V. Motsarev and A. Ya. Yakubovich, *Zh. Obshch. Khim.*, **28**, 2727 (1958); *Chem. Abstr.*, **53**, 9111 (1959).
513. T. Hashimoto, *J. Pharm. Soc. Japan*, **80**, 730 (1960); *Chem. Abstr.*, **54**, 24,480 (1960).

514. H. Gilman and E. A. Zuech, *J. Org. Chem.*, **26**, 3481 (1961).
515. A. Polis, *Ber.*, **19**, 1012 (1886).
516. D. Vorländer, *Ber.*, **58**, 1893 (1925).
517. H. Gilman and D. H. Miles, *J. Org. Chem.*, **23**, 326 (1958).
518. A. R. Gilbert, G. D. Cooper, and R. W. Shade, *Ind. Eng. Chem.*, **51**, 665 (1959).
519. J. W. Ryan, *J. Amer. Chem. Soc.*, **84**, 4730 (1962).
520. K. A. Andrianov, V. I. Pakhomov, and V. M. Gelperina, *Dokl. Akad. Nauk SSSR*, **162**, 79 (1965); *Chem. Abstr.*, **63**, 5756 (1965).

Oxymetalation

WILLIAM KITCHING

Department of Chemistry, University of Queensland,
Brisbane, Queensland, Australia

I. INTRODUCTION AND SCOPE

Although the field of organometallic chemistry is more than 100 years old, only relatively recently (e.g., 1950 onward) have chemists commenced to examine thoroughly and reexamine the behavior of carbon–metal compounds. The richness of the field presently defies assessment, but already highly exciting and technologically important discoveries have been made. Much of the recent progress may be traced to the availability of new techniques that greatly facilitate structural and other deductions. In this context, we should recognize the skill and insight of many of the early chemists, particularly in the zinc, magnesium, mercury, and platinum areas, whose discoveries heralded the birth of modern organometallic chemistry.

Much of this early work lay dormant for 50 years or more, but its rediscovery, closer examination, and extension have followed in rapid succession. One such area of endeavor is oxymetalation chemistry, which dates to the turn of the century, when German chemists characterized and examined a number of addition compounds of mercury(II) salts and olefins. However, only recently have details of the processes involved and the structures of the oxymetalation "adducts" been established. A number of reviews are available that discuss certain aspects of this chemistry.[1,2,3] The review by Chatt[1] excellently summarizes the position until 1951, while an article by the present author discusses oxymetalation more generally (up to 1966).[2] The stereochemistry of oxymercuration has been focused on,[3] but the coverage is incomplete and somewhat out of date. This topic will be fully treated in the present discussion. In an article of this type it is not possible to cover the literature exhaustively.

The organization employed in this chapter is arbitrary but has been designed with the idea of stressing the generality of this type of reaction. More recent aspects will, of course, demand the most attention. Beside mechanistic and structural considerations, considerable stress is placed here on known and possible synthetic applications.

II. NATURE OF OXYMETALATION AND OXYMETALLICS

The detailed steps involved in the formation of oxymetallics may vary considerably with the metal ion, but the overall result is similar and may be formally represented as in Eq. (1):

$$\begin{matrix} & & & M(OAc)_{x-1} \\ & & & | \\ \diagdown C = C \diagdown \quad + \ M(OAc)_x & \xrightarrow{\ R-OH\ } & \diagdown C - C \diagup & + \ HOAc \qquad (1) \\ \diagup \qquad \diagdown & & \diagup | \quad \diagdown & \\ & & OR & \end{matrix}$$

Thus an olefin, generally, reacts with an oxy salt of a metal to produce a saturated, substituted alkyl metal derivative. In some cases, additional stabilization of the metal (other than a single σ-bond to carbon) is required; other ligands and, in some cases, intramolecular ene- coordination (particularly in the case of Pt^{II}, Pd^{II}, and Rh^I may be necessary for survival. This differing behavior will be discussed fully in later sections. In some instances metal halides (e.g., $HgCl_2$) and even anionic halo complexes (e.g., Na_2PdCl_4) may react directly, but this capability is largely restricted to Pt^{II} and Pd^{II}. The intervention of neighboring groups may also result in some structural reorganization. The use of alcohols as solvents leads generally to mercuri-substituted alkyl ethers, although, in poorly nucleophilic solvents, anion competition may produce a mixture of ether and acetate products. Solvents other than alcohols are sometimes employed, e.g., acetic acid, piperidine, etc.; in these cases acetates and mercuri-substituted N-alkylpiperidines are produced. As generally performed then, oxymetalation with Hg^{II}, Tl^{III} and Pb^{IV} leads initially to substituted alkyl metal acetates. In many cases, these compounds are more readily characterized as the halides, and simple treatment with alkali metal halide leads to anion exchange and the oxymetallic halide. The latter possess the distinct advantage of being far less physiologically active, and the characteristic demetalation reactions are far less favored.

Most is known of oxymercuration, which has been studied intermittently since the turn of the century, and a relatively clear picture of this process is emerging. The chemical similarity between the iso-electronic Hg^{II}, Tl^{III}, and Pb^{IV} was recognized only recently; the latter two oxymetalations are of more recent vintage. However, these oxymetallics are far more chemically reactive, and only a few such compounds have been satisfactorily characterized, although their intervention in a host of reactions seems reasonable. The oxymetallics from Pt^{II}, Pd^{II}, and Rh^I have additional structural and other features not shared by Hg^{II} and Tl^{III}, but chemical comparisons are not unrewarding. The oxymercurials are generally air-stable crystalline solids, possessing the usual attributes of organomercurials as regards structure and chemistry, and the clearer features of oxymercuration have provided guide lines for the recent work on other oxymetalations.

Oxymetalation may be mechanistically categorized in a number of ways, each of which has features of merit and emphasizes different similarities to other reaction mechanisms. The following discussion is not to be considered dogmatic in any sense, and discussion of the mechanistic details of oxy-metalation will be reserved until later. Mechanistic categorizing becomes an increasingly difficult venture, and the following applies largely to the actual outcome of the reaction without serious mechanistic implications. Briefly, consideration will be given to insertion and electrophilic addition descriptions of oxymetalation.

The insertion reaction[4,5] among metal compounds appears to be rather general and is encountered with almost surprising frequency in organo-metallic chemistry. The term *insertion* should be applied descriptively to the product, without mechanistic overtones, since there is no doubt that many "insertion" reactions proceed by fundamentally different mechanisms. How-ever, the term itself has a particular chemical attraction and does serve as a somewhat unifying concept for many widely different reactions between un-saturated molecules generally and metal derivatives. For example, com-pounds incorporating metal–oxygen, metal–carbon, metal–hydrogen, metal–nitrogen, metal–halogen, and even metal–metal bonds have reacted with one or more of olefins, dienes, cyanides, carbonyl compounds, carbon monoxide, carbon disulfide, and sulfur dioxide.[5] Thus the reaction of ketones with organomagnesium compounds may be viewed as an insertion into the carbon–magnesium bond.[4]

$$\begin{matrix} \diagdown \\ \diagup \end{matrix} C{=}O + R\text{-mg} \longrightarrow \begin{matrix} \diagdown \\ \diagup \end{matrix} C \begin{matrix} O\text{-mg} \\ \diagdown R \end{matrix} \qquad (2)$$

In the present context, however, we are largely concerned with "olefin insertion" into metal–oxygen or metal–halogen bonds. Here insertion is the addition of an essentially covalent metal compound M—Z to a neutral un-saturated molecule (the olefin), forming a new carbon metal system in which the unsaturation has been removed.

$$M{-}Z + Y: \longrightarrow M{-}Y{-}Z \qquad (3)$$

e.g.,

$$Hg(OAc)_2 + CH_2{=}CH_2 \longrightarrow AcOHg{-}CH_2{-}CH_2{-}OAc$$

The generality of the reaction in this sense is emphasized by Davies,[6] who has probed the region of trialkyltin and lead methoxide additions to polar multiple bonds. The virtue in considering oxymetalation in the realm of insertion reactions mainly is to place it in a reaction zone generally important among both transition and nontransition metals. This broader perspective then suggests that oxymetalation may be easily extended to metals not yet explored.

Mechanistic information available suggests, however, that as a reaction type oxymetalation may be placed with profit in the area of electrophilic additions to olefins, and the available data appear to be best rationalized on this basis. Thus oxymercuration proceeds more or less readily with a wide assortment of olefins,[1,2,3] and effects of neighboring groups, olefin structure, nucleophilic competition, metal salt electrophilicity, and stereochemical outcome find a cogent rationale in this context. In a broad sense, then, an electrophilic mercuric species, e.g., $Hg(OAc)_2$, $^{\oplus}HgOAc$ (solvated), etc., may first form a π-complex with the olefin, which then undergoes nucleophilic attack to yield the product oxymercurial. The stereochemical consequences of π-complexation as a discrete intermediary stage and the polar nature of the transition state will be discussed fully in the section on mechanism. The above suffices at this stage to justify categorization as an electrophilic olefin addition.

What may be considered to be troublesome features of these reactions are the reversibility of oxymetalation (deoxymetalation), as in Eq. (4), and the ease with which demetalation[7] may occur (Eq. (5)). The latter seems to involve carbonium ion species.

$$\underset{\underset{OR}{|}}{\overset{\overset{HgX}{|}}{C-C}} + HX \rightleftharpoons C=C + HgX_2 + ROH \qquad (4)$$

$$\underset{\underset{OR}{|}}{\overset{\overset{HgX}{|}}{C-C}} \longrightarrow \underset{\underset{OR}{|}}{C-\overset{\oplus}{C}} \longrightarrow products \qquad (5)$$

Deoxymetalation is particularly important in the mercury area, and deoxymercuration is a well-studied phenomenon. This normally occurs in the presence of halo acids or strongly coordinating anions.[2] In many instances, the necessity arises during synthesis to neutralize the acid produced (cf. Eq. (1)) in the forward or oxymetalation step. Oxymercurials are generally stable in the presence of acetic acid, but neutralization can be required if the Hg^{II} salt is derived from a strong acid. However, the presence of halide ion is important. In the cases of Tl^{III} or Pb^{IV}, subsequent reaction in the sense of Eq. (5) assumes greater relative importance, presumably because of the higher oxidation potential of $Tl^{III}-Tl^{I}$ compared with that for the $Hg^{II}-Hg^{0}$ couple. Tl^{I} and Pb^{II} are also better leaving groups than Hg^{0} under these conditions. Thus isolation of many Tl^{III} or Pb^{IV} oxymetallics is seriously hampered by this very facile process, particularly if solvolyzing solvents such as alcohols and carboxylic acids are used. In fact, no well characterized oxymetallic of Pb^{IV} has been described. However, a large number of reactions of Tl^{III} and Pb^{IV} carboxylates with olefins appear to find a consistent interpretation in terms of the formation and heterolytic decomposition of an organo-metal intermediate.[7]

Progressing now to the transition metal derivatives, largely Pt^{II} and Pd^{II}, the difference emerges that many of the isolable compounds in this area have as their precursors the π-bonded olefin complexes.[8,9] Many are diolefin complexes, which in the presence of base and alcohol react in the sense that one double bond is saturated by $OR^{\ominus}$ and a carbon–metal σ-bond (Eq. (6)). (The lower case nomenclature for the metal has been employed to indicate the bonds of interest.)

$$\text{(structure)} \xrightarrow[\text{ROH}]{\text{base}} \text{(structure)} \tag{6}$$

In other cases, this is not a necessary approach, since certain benzylic and allylic amines[10] react directly with Pd^{II} or Pt^{II} salts to yield oxymetallics:

$$\text{(structure)} \xrightarrow[\text{PdCl}_2]{\text{ROH}} \text{(structure)} \tag{7}$$

In some processes, the overall result of which is olefin oxidation, (e.g., Pd^{II} and ethylene), oxymetallics are strongly implied as intermediates, but no direct observations have been reported.

This brief discussion then suffices to outline the nature of the chemistry; we now embark on more detailed discussion of it.

The prefix "oxy" reduces the subject to manageable proportions, since a number of reactions, which might be termed "halometalation" are known:

$$\text{C=C} + MCl_n \longrightarrow \text{C---C} \tag{8}$$

Thus phosphorus halides[11] add to, or react with, olefins under certain conditions, as does boron trichloride (BCl_3).[12] The former (as well as PCl_3)[13] may well react by an electrophilic mechanism. The addition of arsenic trichloride[14,15] to acetylene once had great military importance (the vesicant Lewisite), and this reaction seems to involve an electrophilic arsenic species. However, these examples may be excluded on the additional ground that phosphorus, boron, and arsenic are "metals" with questionable metallic credentials. The scope of this article is essentially as defined in Eq. (1); the bulk of material will concern the metals mercury, thallium, lead, palladium, and platinum. Undoubtedly, reactions involving metals have been described that may involve oxymetallics, but only desultory information is available. There are many gaps in the periodic table, in which it appears that metallic systems under suitable conditions could oxymetalate, but many of the heavier elements of the Periodic Table do not form strong covalent bonds to carbon, so that many electrophilic processes may be readily reversed (cf. aromatic mercuration). The high solvation energy of many metal cations may suggest unfavorable thermodynamics in some cases, but there seems little question that a number of electrophilic oxymetalations await discovery by some intrepid chemical explorer.

III. SYNTHESIS OF OXYMETALLICS

A. Oxymercuration

The general approach to synthesis of oxymercurials is straightforward and normally involves the reaction of mercuric acetate (or in some cases Hg^{II} salts of stronger acids) directly with the olefin in a suitable, usually aqueous or alcoholic, medium. The reaction is generally assumed to be complete when a sample of the reaction mixture fails to produce a yellow precipitate of mercuric oxide on basification. Oxymercurials, except for anion exchange, undergo no rapid reaction under these conditions. When indications are that the reaction is complete, the addition of the stoichiometric amount of alkali metal halide (usually chloride) leads to a rapid ligand exchange at mercury, producing the halomercury derivative, which may be recrystallized from typical organic solvents. This sequence of reactions is outlined in Eq. (9).

$$\text{C=C} + Hg(OAc)_2 \xrightarrow{\text{ROH}} \underset{\underset{HgOAc}{\mid}}{\overset{\overset{OR}{\mid}}{\text{C—C}}} + HOAc \qquad (9)$$

$$\xrightarrow{\text{KCl}} \underset{\underset{HgCl}{\mid}}{\overset{\overset{OR}{\mid}}{\text{C—C}}}$$

Aqueous media produce alcohols, while alcoholic solvents lead to the corresponding ethers. Mercuric halides are generally unreactive, while mercuric nitrate is commonly used in aqueous preparations. However, since oxymercurials rapidly regenerate the original olefin in the presence of halides and acids (see below), control of the acidity (in the above case, nitric acid would be produced) of the solution is important. In practice, the mercuric nitrate is carefully neutralized until basic salt appears, which is dissolved by the addition of the olefin. This alternation of neutralization and addition is then continued:

$$C_2H_4 + Hg(NO_3)_2 + NaOH \longrightarrow HOCH_2CH_2HgNO_3 + NaNO_3 \qquad (10)$$

and the product is isolated as the halomercurial.

Most oxymercurials have considerable acetic acid tolerance, and the preparation of β-mercuric-substituted alkyl acetates is effected by employing acetic acid as a solvent (Eq. 11).[16]

$$C_2H_4 + Hg(OAc)_2 \xrightarrow{\text{HOAc}} \xrightarrow{\text{KCl}} ClHgCH_2CH_2OAc \qquad (11)$$

Alkyl acetates may also be produced when mercuric acetate is used in an alcohol solvent of poor nucleophilicity. Thus in t-butanol, both ether and acetate products are formed.

An interesting preparative procedure involved the addition of ethylene to mercuric chloride in piperidine solution to yield 1-(2'-chloromercuriethyl)-piperidine,

which may be reduced to N-ethylpiperidine.[17,18] More recently, the ammono-mercuration reaction has been further reported, in which the elements of —NHCOMe and —HgX are added to the double bond by treatment of the olefin with $Hg(NO_3)_2$—HNO_3—CH_3CN. The reaction of norcarane[20] with dry $Hg(NO_3)_2$ in acetonitrile proceeds with ring-opening to give (after NaCl treatment) 2-chloromercurimethyl-N-acetylcyclohexylamine. The details of this reaction are as yet unclear.

B. Oxythallation and Oxyplumbation

The wide range of conditions suitable for synthesis of oxymercurials does not apply in the above cases. This situation is a result largely of the survival problem experienced by oxythallation adducts under acidic or solvolyzing conditions.[7] Thus acetic acid, or even partially aqueous solvents, must be avoided generally, the former since solvolytic demetalation proceeds rapidly under these conditions and the latter, since the hydrolysis of the starting Tl^{III} or Pb^{IV} carboxylates is facile. The conditions employed have utilized thoroughly dried chloroform as the solvent, and a stoichiometric amount of the metal carboxylate. Lead tetraacetate is sometimes difficult to obtain entirely free of acetic acid; this, of course, would promote solvolytic reaction. The oxythallation adducts that have been characterized have been very soluble in chloroform and are precipitated by the addition of dry pentane.[21]

No oxyplumbation adducts have been characterized, only Pb^{II} acetate and organic acetates being isolated.[7]

$$\ce{>C=C< + Tl(OAc)3 ->[Dry][CHCl3]} \underset{\underset{Tl(OAc)_2}{|}}{>C-C<}\overset{\overset{OAc}{|}}{} \xrightarrow{pentane} \text{addition product} \qquad (12)$$

C. Oxypalladation and Oxyplatination

Because of the similarity of the areas, discussion may be conveniently fused. The above compounds normally may be considered examples of square planar (dsp^2) Pt^{II}, Pd^{II} and Rh^{I}, containing metal–carbon σ and π bonds. Four-coordination normally is achieved by halo-bridging.[8,9] As indicated previously in (Eq. (6), the precursors of these oxymetallics are normally the corresponding diene complexes. The salts of these metals may undergo several, not necessarily mutually exclusive, reactions with dienes (or more highly unsaturated olefins). The metal salt may be reduced with the production of organic oxidation products, or a monoolefin complex (i.e., nonchelate) may be formed. Commonly, however, chelation may occur as indicated in Eq. 6. Thus interaction of a number of dienes, e.g., 1,5-cyclo-octadiene, dicyclopentadiene, dipentene, 1,5-hexadiene, in alcohol solvents with the appropriate metal salt leads to diene complexes[8,9] of form (diene MCl_2), where M = Pt, Pd, or [diene $MCl]_2$, M = Rh. With anhydrous sodium carbonate in alcohol, the diene complexes generally yield crystalline, stable alkoxy halides of formula (diene $OR)_2 M_2X_2$ where M = Pt, Pd, in which one double bond has been saturated by —OR and a σ-bond to the metal. The position as regards the formation of corresponding alkoxy rhodium compounds is not clear,[22] and few data are available.

In some cases, the direct interaction of benzylic amines and allylic[10] and propargylic amines[23] with Pd^{II} salts produces oxypalladation products.

$$\ce{\overset{CH}{\underset{CH2}{\|}}\underset{\underset{\underset{CH3}{\diagdown}}{N}}{\overset{CH2}{\diagup}}\overset{CH2}{\diagdown}CH3 + Li2PdCl4 ->[ROH] } \quad \ce{H2C\overset{\overset{OR}{|}}{\underset{\underset{Pd}{|}}{CH}}\overset{CH2}{\diagdown}\underset{/\backslash}{\overset{|}{}}\underset{CH3}{\overset{CH2}{\diagdown}} \overset{}{} CH3} \qquad (13)$$

In the cases of the benzylic amines, the structures and presumably the mechanisms are distinctly different and fall into the area of aromatic substitution by a metal ion.[24]

IV. STRUCTURES OF OXYMETALLICS

The molecular structures of the products of oxymetallation of olefins are now well understood, and this situation has arisen largely as a result of the advent of nuclear magnetic resonance spectroscopy. Most is known of the oxymercurials, and the structures of the less stable thallium compounds conform to the same pattern. The last few years have seen NMR spectroscopy resolve the problems of the structures of oxypalladation and oxyplatination compounds, first described over a century ago.

A. Oxymercurials

Before the availability of spectroscopic techniques, structural deductions were, of necessity, based on chemical reactions. However, such reactions presented quite formidable interpretative difficulties to early workers, some of whom postulated "loose" molecular complexes, while others preferred truly saturated structures resulting from addition. The apparently enigmatic reactions of oxymercurials have been discussed in detail elsewhere;[1,2,3] it is necessary only to say that the chemical reactivity of oxymercurials is readily accommodated in the framework of modern mechanistic organic chemistry.

Although the chemical evidence seemed overwhelming, and there could be little serious question of the saturated nature of oxymercurials, it became the task of the emerging physical and spectroscopic techniques to authenticate the structures. The first results were reported by Cotton and Leto,[35] who examined the 40MHz spectra of a number of ethylene-derived oxymercurials and demonstrated their saturated nature. Certain features of the spectra have been further discussed.[36,37]

A large amount of proton NMR, i.r., and some actual crystal structure data[2] adequately testify to the σ-bonded nature of oxymercurials. Also, ^{199}Hg—'H spin coupling in the spectra of some oxymercurials has been discussed and treated theoretically.[37,38]

B. Oxythallation Adducts

Few such products have been isolated, and their structures closely resemble those of the oxymercurials.[2] The NMR spectra of such compounds are complicated because of long-range ^{203}Tl and ^{205}Tl—'H spin coupling (^{203}Tl, ^{205}Tl, I = 1/2; 100% magnetically active), but in one report the proton spectra of the norbornene-derived adduct has been discussed in detail and will be treated later. The chemistry (mainly dethallation reactions)[7] of these adducts and their proton magnetic resonance (PMR) spectra appear consistent only with σ-bonded formulations.

C. Oxypalladation and Oxyplatination Adducts

Interest in the structures of these compounds has been revived by a number of recent reports, discussing mainly the proton NMR spectra in relation to stereochemical outcome. Spectral and chemical reduction results confirm the gross features of the structures preferred originally by Chatt.[8,9] Thus the compounds can be regarded as analogous to oxymercurials, except that the coordination ability of Pt^{II} and Pd^{II} is satisfied by the neighboring double bond. In the derivatives of allylic amines, this latter role is played by neighboring nitrogen.[10] Thus the square planar coordination sites are occupied by *cis* bridging chlorines, a C–metal σ-bond, and a carbon–metal π-bond. Details of the NMR spectra will be discussed in the larger section on mechanism, in relation to stereochemistry.

The chemical shifts of protons in oxymetallics show no strange features and the presence of metal–$'$H spin coupling in the case of ^{199}Hg, ^{203,205}Tl, and ^{195}Pt has valuable diagnostic implications, and can indicate conformational preferences.

V. MECHANISMS OF OXYMETALATION

With the now universal acceptance of the fact that oxymetallics result from saturation of a double bond by *oxy* and metal functions, the question arises as to how this occurs. A substantial body of data, the interpretations of which were conflicting, is available, but much of this is ambiguous in nature, and of questionable value.[1] The data relating to mechanism has been reviewed recently and a generally consistent picture of oxymetalation has emerged.[2]

Although the stereochemical course of a reaction is a property of its mechanism, the stereochemistry of oxymetalation may be discussed separately, and then considered in relation to actual mechanistic schemes. Much of the confusion that has characterized research in oxymetalation may be traced initially to uncertainty over the structure of the products themselves, but more recently to the stereochemical outcome.

A. Stereochemistry of Oxymercuration

The most acceptable methods for stereochemical determinations involve direct examination by physical methods. Analogies and inferences based on involved and sometimes poorly understood degradative sequences are not sufficient, although the outcome of reactions generally understood (e.g., rates of elimination) may be highly suggestive. Difficulties in determining the configuration of mercurated alcohols and ethers by what are hoped to be stereospecific cleavages of the C—Hg bond must be employed with caution, since the outcome appears to depend seriously on the nature of the solvent and some other factors.

In 1935 Wright[40] considered oxymercuration of simple olefins to be *cis*, since molecular hydroxy- or alkoxymercuric acetate was thought to add as a discrete unit to the double bond. This view was vigorously restated in 1947.[41] However, in an incisive manner, Lucas, Hepner, and Winstein,[42] largely on mechanistic grounds and presumed similarity between "bromonium ions" and "mercurinium ions" (see below) suggested that the oxymercuration of simple olefins may well be *trans*.

There was no disagreement that oxymercuration was stereospecific, since isomeric olefins yield pure diastereoisomeric pairs, one only from each isomer.[40,43-45] The question was whether the specificity was *trans* or *cis*. The cyclohexene-derived mercurials appeared particularly suitable for structural studies, since constraints imposed by the ring system removed problems associated with rotation.

Methoxy-mercuration of cyclohexene has been well studied,[41] and the initially formed 1-chloromercuri-2-methoxycyclohexene (the "α" isomer) may be converted (epimerization of the C—Hg bond) to the β-isomer, thus providing the two diastereoisomers.[41] In some cases, the epimeric mixture is

separated by selective destruction of the α isomer with HCl (deoxymercuration). Despite some lack of confidence in the data, the crystal structures of the "α," "β" mercurials clearly established *trans* and *cis* configurations, respectively.[46] Thus the *kinetically* formed oxymercurial (i.e., the one relevant to discussion of reaction mechanism) has the *trans* configuration in the case of cyclohexene and presumably for other simple unstrained olefins. For strained monocyclic olefins the situation is different, and *cis* oxymercuration of *trans*-cyclo-octene appears to occur.[47] Perhaps addition to cyclobutene and cyclopropene might occur *cis* also.

Proton NMR spectroscopy is in clear agreement with these conclusions.[48] In the α-cyclohexene oxymercurial proton, H_1 has two coupling constants of

10Hz and one of 3.5 Hz, the former indicating coupling to two axial protons (H_2, H_6) and to one equatorial proton (H_6). Thus the hydroxyl group (at C_2) does not occupy an axial position, and the oxymercurial must have the *trans* configuration. These interpretations were confirmed by Wolfe and Campbell,[49] who obtained the spectra of 2-deuteroxycyclohexylmercuric acetate (**1**) and compared it with that of the hydroxymercurial derived from cyclohexene-3,3,6,6-d_4 (**2**).

(1)   (2)

In (1) an unresolved multiplet at 5.85τ was assigned to H_a, while H_b was a sextet and analysis indicated it was coupled to two other protons (10 Hz) and a third (3 Hz). However, J_{AB} could not be unambiguously evaluated. However, considerable simplification results in (2), since H_A and H_B lead to a simple AB quartet with $J_{AB} = 10.3$ Hz, which is near to the maximum observed for vicinal axial protons. Consequently, *trans* addition has occurred.

Dipole moment measurements[51] have been employed to provide data on the configurations of epimeric oxymercurials; but, in many cases, the method has led to incorrect conclusions. The main difficulty is associated with the uncertainty of the C—Hg—X angle, and Wright[31] suggested that this angle may be as low as 80°. Depending on the conformation, the dipole moment can alter seriously as arbitrary conformations are employed. If, however, the C—Hg—X angle is taken as 180°, which seems more reasonable and in line with stereochemistry of Hg^{II} in its organic compounds, the dipole moments can indicate configuration. Calculations show that the epimer with the lower dipole moment is *trans*, as would be anticipated. However, complications due to *cis* interactions between Hg^{II} and oxy-groups and solvation effects must be recognized. Particular care must be exercised in the cases of polyfunctional compounds in which dipole moments can hardly be considered reliable.

The observation has been made that the epimeric oxymercurial with the lower dipole moment has an enhanced deoxymercuration rate.[3] This is consistent with a normal *trans* elimination mechanism for deoxymercuration. Since the enthalpy of activation for deoxymercuration of α-2-methoxycyclohexylmercuric iodide was ca. 8–9 kcal/mole lower than that for the β-isomer; since entropies of activation were essentially the same, the conclusion seemed unavoidable that the α form was the *trans* isomer.[50,51] This agrees with the crystal structure data,[46] PMR evidence,[48,49] and dipole moments.[3]

This method necessitates the comparison of rates for both α and β isomers; it has been used (particularly HCl deoxymercuration) for selective destruction of the "α" isomer in a mixture of "α" and "β" isomers during the equilibration process.

A reaction sequence, which can be considered[52] to provide stereochemical suggestions, is based on the addition of bis-(trinitromethyl)mercury(II) to olefins, which may proceed as below

$$\text{C}{=}\text{C} + [\text{C(NO}_2)_3]_2\text{Hg} \longrightarrow (\text{NO}_2)_3\text{C}{-}\overset{|}{\text{C}}{-}\overset{|}{\text{C}}{-}\text{HgC(NO}_2)_3$$

$$\text{C}{=}\text{C} + [\text{C(NO}_2)_3]_2\text{Hg} + \text{H}_2\text{O} \longrightarrow \text{HO}{-}\overset{|}{\text{C}}{-}\overset{|}{\text{C}}{-}\text{HgC(NO}_2)_3 + \text{HC(NO}_2)_3$$

Formation of the alcohol (and its stability in the presence of trinitromethane $K = 7 \times 10^{-1}$) was considered to occur only when *cis* addition occurred, since the *trans* isomer was thought to deoxymercurate under these conditions of acidity. Derivatives of the first type are particularly stable to deoxymercuration, since such a process involves C—C bond rupture. Thus isolation of the alcohol was considered diagnostic for *cis* addition. Unfortunately, the addition of $\text{Hg(C(NO}_2)_3)_2$ to cyclohexene always yields trinitromethyl 2-trinitromethylcyclohexylmercury, whatever the solvent, so that it could indicate that hydroxymercuration or alkoxymercuration had proceeded *trans*. This requires verification. This method clearly is suspect when structural features confer additional acid stability on the oxymercurial. Ring formation, e.g., from *o*-allylphenol[30] and lactonization, etc., generally lead to enhanced acid tolerance. Nitro mercuration of cyclohexene to yield 1-

$$\text{C}{=}\text{C} + \text{Hg(NO}_2)_2 \xrightarrow{\text{H}_2\text{O}} \underset{\text{NO}_2}{\overset{\text{HgNO}_2}{\text{C}{-}\text{C}}} \xrightarrow{\text{KCl}} \underset{\text{NO}_2}{\overset{\text{HgCl}}{\text{C}{-}\text{C}}}$$

chloromercuri-2-nitrocyclohexane also proceeds in a *trans* fashion on the basis of proton NMR results.[53]

Thus the general outcome of oxymercuration or nitromercuration of simple unstrained olefins is *trans* addition, while *trans*-cyclooctene and presumably *trans*-cyclononene (perhaps cyclobutene, cyclopropene) yield *cis* addition products.

That *trans* could be generally altered to *cis* addition by employing strained bicyclic olefins has now been demonstrated, and pioneered largely by Traylor.[32,33]

Studies of the oxymercuration of strained, bicyclic olefins have been most illuminating since the first definite example of *cis* oxymercuration was located in this area. The first report of the oxymercuration of the norbornenes concluded that *trans* addition had occurred,[31] largely on the basis of chemical criteria, now known to be misleading, and dipole moments.

Oxymercuration of norbornene by mercuric acetate in methanol produced a mixture of methoxy and acetoxy products. Such acetates are generally not produced with unstrained olefins, except when the alkoxide ion is poorly nucleophilic, e.g., *t*-butoxide. The product mixture was considered[31] to arise from nucleophilic competition for an intermediate mercurinium ion.

Misidentification of reduction products was largely responsible for the above suggestions of *trans* addition. Subsequently, Traylor[32,33] demonstrated conclusively that norbornene-derived mercurials had the *cis-exo*-configuration, and no skeletal rearrangement accompanied the addition process.

In addition to dipole moment and chemical evidence (reduction experiments produced *exo*-norborneol), PMR data[48] strongly support the *cis-exo* addition mode.

In the adduct H_3 is coupled to two protons with J = 6.8 Hz and 2.1 Hz, while H_2 has one coupling constant, J = 6.8 Hz. Comparison with *cis* and *trans* 2,3-coupling constants[56] established for the *endo-endo* and *exo-exo* and *trans*-bornane-2,3-diols indicated that H_2 and H_3 were *cis*. The absence of coupling between H_2 and H_1 suggests an *endo* position for H_2, and establishes *cis-exo* oxymercuration.

Oxymercuration of *exo*- and *endo*-dicyclopentadiene[55,31,32] and benzonorbornadiene also proceeds in a *cis-exo* fashion, and in the former cases there is no addition to comparatively strain-free cyclopentene ring. In the oxymercuration of *endo*-dicyclopentadiene, there is an absence of derivatives

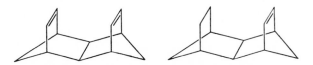

of *exo*-dicyclopentadiene, which is particularly interesting since the addition of ionic reagents to the *endo* hydrocarbon is customarily accompanied by rearrangement.

Oxymercuration of the related norbornadiene was originally reported[56] as yielding a completely nortricyclenic mercurial, as a result of 2:6 homoconjugative addition. However, it was subsequently learned that kinetic control led to a *cis*-2,3-*exo* product.[21]

Also, *cis,exo*-oxymercuration was indicated for the *endo-endo* diene and *endo-endo* monoene shown.[21]

The observations that the oxymercurials from the strain-free cyclohexene and strained norbornene had the *trans* and *cis* configurations, respectively, would indicate that a bicyclic olefin (or suitable monocyclic olefin, for that matter) representing a key blend of strain and electronic factors might produce both *cis* and *trans* oxymercurials. This appears to be the case with bicyclo[2.2.2]octene, since both *cis* and *trans*-3-chloromercuribicyclo[2.2.2]-octan-2-ols were produced, with no rearranged products.[33] The stereochemical outcome could be altered by adjustment of reaction conditions. The

configurations of the *cis* and *trans* mercurials were established by reduction to the known bicyclo[2.2.2]octan-2-ols.[33]

Thus far, stereochemical conclusions have been based on PMR data, dipole moments, rates of deoxymercuration (faster for *trans* epimer), and in one case, an actual X-ray structural determination. Two additional methods, developed largely by Traylor and Baker,[32,33] and subsequently further investigated, are the method of stereospecific chemical reduction, and an infrared technique. The first involves stereospecific reduction in the sense that the —HgX group is replaced by deuterium. Common reagents to effect this are sodium amalgam in D_2O and $LiAlD_4$ and $NaBD_4$. These methods have since been employed more generally. The infrared technique depends on the observation that, in hydroxy mercurials, ν_{OH} differs from that of the parent alcohol by an amount that is a function of the Hg—O distance. Thus $\Delta\nu$ would be greater for *cis* than for *trans* dispositions of —OH and —HgX, since the —O—Hg-interactions responsible for the shifts would be a functon of the Hg—O distance. Comparisons with hydroxymercurials of known configuration supported the assignment of *trans* configurations to β-hydroxymercurials, for which ν_{OH} differed from that of the parent alcohol by less than 10 cm^{-1}, and *cis* configurations to those in which $\Delta\nu(OH)$ was greater than 18 cm^{-1}. These methods are illustrated with *endo*-dicyclopentadiene.

Considerable confusion initially accompanied stereochemical assignments of the oxymercurial derived from 5-norbornene-2-*endo*-carboxylic acid.

However, it is clear from detailed 60 and 100 mHz spectra that the halomercuri group is *exo* as shown and lactonization (neighboring carboxyl group participation) occurs.[57-59] This has also been demonstrated for a number of 2- and 3-methyl-substituted acids and esters.[59] The same stereochemistry operates for oxymercuration of 2-*endo*-hydroxymethyl-5-norbornenes.[58] Again *trans* addition has occurred, and in 2- and 3- substituted 5-*endo*-substituted norbornenes, ring closure occurs with an *exo* mercuri group. However, *endo* mercuri attack appears to occur when suitable *syn*-7-substituents are present.[58]

In the case of the *syn* and *anti*-7-(2-hydroxyethyl)-norbornene, both *cis,exo* and *trans* cyclic mercurials are produced.[60]

The effects of neighboring groups on the oxymercuration of norbornenes not leading entirely to ring closure (e.g., *endo*-5-cyano-*endo*-5-carbomethoxy-2-norbornenes) have been studied by Traylor,[58] and previously also by Henbest.[61] Solvent effects largely determine the propensity to ring closure. A number of products were isolated in the cyano case.[58] Factor and Traylor have also studied the oxymercuration of 1,4,7,7-tetramethylnorbornene, as well as *syn*-7-bromonorbornene,[62] both of which oxymercurate *cis,exo*. (These results will be discussed further in the section on mechanism.) Oxymercuration of the 2,3-*endo*-5-norbornenedicarboxylic acids, contrary to a previous report, also proceeds in a *trans* fashion to yield *exo* mercury substituent.[59]

Yurev and co-workers have studed the oxymercuration of some 7-oxa-norbornane compounds,[63] which appeared to proceed with *cis,exo* stereochemistry, with little rearrangement. The alcohol and acetate can be formed, depending on the conditions.

B. Stereochemistry of Oxythallation

Although a limited number of oxythallation adducts have been characterized, the only stable examples suitable for stereochemical inquiries were derived from norbornene and norbornadiene. Stereochemical determinations by PMR measurements are not straightforward in these cases, since the spectra are complicated by large proton-thallium spin couplings. Employing the Nuclear Overhauser Effect to make spectral assignments, Anet demonstrated that oxythallation occurs in a *cis,exo* manner.[39]

In the case of strained bicyclic olefins, then, oxythallation has the same stereochemical outcome as oxymercuration, and mechanistic analogy might seem in order. However, there are some data which indicate that oxythallation of unstrained olefins may not be as clearly *trans* as is oxymercuration.

Nothing is known of the stereochemistry of oxyplumbation, other than inferences based on the stereochemical outcome of $Pb(OAc)_4$ olefin-oxidation, which in certain cases proceeds through the oxyplumbation adduct.

C. Stereochemistry of Oxypalladation and Oxyplatination

The structures and stereochemistries of the methoxy platinum(II) and palladium(II) complexes formed by the reaction between the well-known diolefin complexes and methanol in the presence of base have been determined, and the available data reviewed.[2,34] Previously,[8,9] the type of metal-ligand bonding had been established, although the stereoisomerism associated with the organic ligand had not been evaluated. The latter questions have been probed mainly by NMR measurements. The procedure may be illustrated with the methoxy(endo-dicyclopentadiene)platinum(II) and palladium(II) complexes:[34]

(3)   (4)

The two nonequivalent double bonds in endo-dicyclopentadiene provide two different sites for the alkoxy-metalation. cis-Addition, either exo or endo, may occur. The final position of the lone double bond, (i.e., whether it is positioned closer to the methoxy or metal addend) actually doubles the number of possibilities. Rearrangement accompanying addition (to yield exo dicyclopentadiene derivatives) must also be considered. The norbornene-type of double bond (5, 6) is more reactive than the comparatively unstrained 2, 3 double bond.

Reduction yielded only octahydro-exo-5-methoxy-4,7-endomethano-indene (5), which established the position on the ring and the exo nature of the methoxyl. No rearrangement had apparently occurred.

(5)

Examination of the PMR spectrum of the pyridine derivative (6) established the endo mode of attachment of the metal; $J_{AX} \sim 2$ Hz confirms the exo nature of H_A and consequently endo metal attachment.

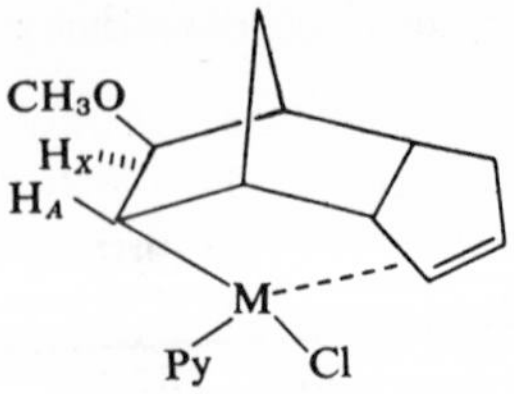

(6)

The location of the double bond is as shown, since here, most profitable coordination to the metal can occur. These conclusions agree with the solid state structure based on an X-ray analysis.[64]

Because of instability and poorly resolved spectra, the stereochemistry of oxymetalation of dipentene and 1,5-cyclooctadiene was not established conclusively, although *trans* addition was suggested.[34]

Oxyplatination and -palladation of norbornene was also studied and shown to have the *trans* stereochemistry,[34] with *exo* methoxyl, and no rearrangement occurred.

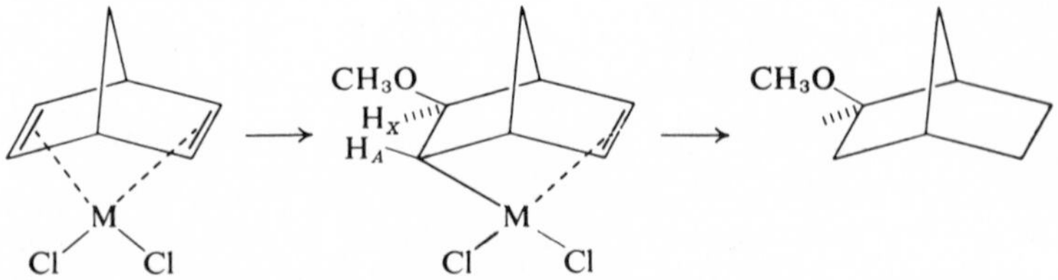

On the basis of what seem to be rather tenuous arguments (NMR chemical shift data), Anderson and Burreson concluded that oxypalladation of 1,5-cyclooctadiene proceeded *trans*.[65] Subsequently, on the basis of the stereo-chemical results of photolyses of oxypalladium adducts of this diene, the reversed stereochemistry was suggested,[68] i.e., *cis* oxypalladation of cyclo-octadiene. *cis*-Oxymetalation (platinum and palladium) may be more general

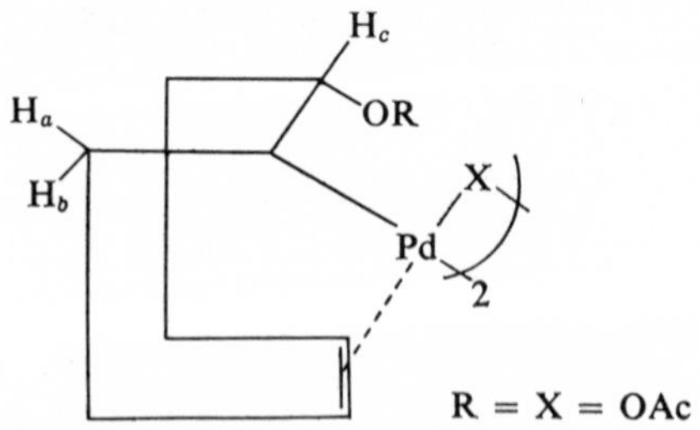

R = X = OAc

than previously thought, particularly if the loss of palladium hydride does not lead to a strained olefinic system (see below).

The above structural conclusions were in agreement with results by Green and Hancock,[67] although some resonance assignments differed. *exo*-Oxymetalation of norbornadiene had occurred.

These oxypalladation adducts may be considered to correspond to the intermediates proposed in the Pd^{II} oxidation of olefins, which are thought to decompose to oxidation products via the loss of a Pd^{II} hydride, where the β-hydrogen is *cis* to the palladium. This then raises the question as to why the oxymetal adducts of norbornadiene and dicyclopentadiene, and, separately, 1,5-cyclooctadiene, do not decompose rapidly by such a pathway.[34] (Even Pd^{II} alkyls with stabilizing phosphine ligands, perhaps better than olefins, decompose rapidly if β-hydrogens are present.) The former would produce strained olefin systems, so that this might prevent such a decomposition. If the 1,5-cyclooctadiene adduct is *trans*, the loss of Pd^{II} hydride (β-hydrogen *cis* to palladium) should be favorable, since no strained olefin is produced. This stability, however, is consistent with *cis* oxymetalation of cycloocta-1,5-diene, since H_c is *trans* to palladium, and a square planar ligand array involves distortion of the cyclooctene ring, so that neither H_a nor H_b is *cis* to palladium. This rationale is supported by Anderson and Burreson's results.[66] Shaw[68] has recently discussed the stereochemistry of addition reactions to coordinated olefins generally, and concluded that the lack of rotation about the metal-olefin axis in the case of chelating diolefins prevented the favored *cis* addition, so that *trans* oxymetalation occurs. However, it seems clear that oxymetalation of cycloocta-1,5-diene is *cis*, so that this simplified and general rationale may be inadequate.[69]

Examples of amino-palladation and platination have also been reported,[70] but the stereochemistry of the reaction seems unknown at present. Similarly, the stereochemical outcome of the reactions of diene-palladium chloride with carbanions (e.g., ethyl malonate + base) also is not clear.[71,72]

Having indicated the known features of the stereochemistry of oxymetalation, the task now is to relate these to plausible mechanisms for the formation of the compounds from olefins and metal salts. Most is known of oxymercuration, and the general features of this reaction appear to be well understood. Mechanisms, once proposed in the context of *cis* addition and elimination for oxymercuration of cyclohexene, for example, will not be treated here.[73]

D. Oxymercuration

The oxymercuration reaction has been demonstrated to be reversible in a number of investigations, but perhaps that by Kreevoy, et al., is most revealing.[74] The reverse reaction can be considered as deoxymercuration.

$$CH_3-CH{=}CH-CH_3 + HgCl_2 + H_2O \rightleftharpoons CH_3-\underset{\underset{OH}{|}}{CH}-\underset{\underset{HgCl}{|}}{CH}-CH_3 + H^\oplus + Cl^\ominus$$

The *threo* and *erythro* mercurials were produced.

Threo (from *cis*)   Erythro (from *trans*)

Equilibrium constants of $K_P = 2.62 \times 10^{-9}$ mole^2 mm^{-1} and 9.0×10^{-10} mole^2 mm^{-1} for the *cis* and *trans* cases, respectively, were obtained, and constancy was exhibited over appreciable concentration ranges. The relative constancies of the final physical constants (e.g., conductivity) established that the oxymercuration-deoxymercuration sequence is stereospecific. If a small fraction of one olefin were converted to the other by such a sequence, the values of K_P would drift toward a common value. The measured K_P values and the known free energies of formation of the olefins indicated that the free energy of isomerization of the *threo* and *erythro*-3-chloromercuri-2-butanols was essentially zero. The data also appeared to indicate that HgCl$_2$-olefin, π-complexes were not present in significant concentrations.

Data of a semiquantitative nature[75] confirmed the appreciable stability of the mercurials derived from *o*-allylphenol toward HCl induced deoxymercuration. However, the fairly ready reversibility established for aqueous halo-acid systems does not apply for the situation in neutral organic solvents. The details of deoxymercuration will be presented shortly.

E. The Status of the Mercurinium Ion

Although an alternative *cis* oxymercuration mechanism for unstrained olefins, e.g., cyclohexene was proposed,[73] this now is certainly incorrect.[2] Most authors now agree that initial rapid complexing of the olefin with Hg^{II} precedes the actual σ-bonding steps.

Some years ago, distribution studies on the system cyclohexene-mercuric nitrate-nitric acid ($\mu = 1$) indicated that π complexation in the sense below occurred rapidly, without complications from C—Hg σ bond formation.[42]

$$C_6H_{10} + Hg^{2+} + H_2O \rightleftharpoons C_6H_{10}HgOH^{\oplus} + H^{\oplus}$$

Such π-complexes were considered as intermediates in oxymercuration (suggested to regulate *trans* addition) and called mercurinium ions. This intermediate is a commonly accepted tenet in the oxymercuration mechanism. The actual structure of the mercurinium ion was considered initially in terms of resonance theory,[43] but in recent years several approaches based on molecular orbital theory have been utilized in discussions of the bonding in olefin-metal complexes.[76] In the case of the mercurinium ion, bonding may result from interaction of a $6sp$ hybrid orbital of mercury with the carbon $2p$ orbitals of the olefin to form a two-electron, triangular, three-orbital system, in which each orbital has considerable overlap with the remaining two. Additional stabilization resulting from $5d$-π^* interaction may be considered,[50] but such "back-bonding" would appear less important than in the Pt^{II} case. The system may be considered to conform to the Hückel criterion for aromaticity ($n = 0$). The effects of solvent, etc., may modify the state of hybridization of Hg^{II} to a significant extent.

Waters and Kiefer[77] have described the methoxymercuration of allene- and methyl-substituted allenes. In the latter cases electrophilic attack leads to mono-adducts in which the mercury is bound to the central carbon atom, whereas attack at unsubstituted π-bonds (e.g., allene itself) occurs terminally to produce an allyl mercury intermediate that undergoes further addition to a 1,3-bisacetoxymercuri ketal, which is easily hydrolyzed to the α,α'-dimercuri-substituted ketones. Methyl substitution leads to substantial rate enhancements.

$$CH_2{=}C{=}CH_2 \xrightarrow[\text{MeOH}]{\text{Hg(OAc)}_2} \left[CH_2{=}\underset{\overset{|}{OCH_3}}{C}{-}CH_2HgOAc \right] \longrightarrow AcOHgCH_2{-}\underset{\overset{|}{OCH_3}}{\overset{\overset{OCH_3}{|}}{C}}{-}CH_2HgOAc$$

$$AcOHgCH_2{-}\overset{\overset{O}{\|}}{C}{-}CH_2HgOAc \xleftarrow{H_2O}$$

The results of stereochemical and other arguments (e.g., steric effects) favored a σ-bridged mercurinium ion intermediate. The high yields and orderly effects on rate and orientation, etc., indicated a stabilized intermediate, in contrast to proton addition that forms a high energy intermediate, which then undergoes a number of nondiscriminating reactions (e.g., elimination, solvolysis, etc.).

A number of attempts to verify the existence of mercurinium ions as discrete intermediates has been made. Until quite recently their intermediacy was largely based on analogy with (d^{10})Ag$^+$-olefin complexes[78] and bromonium ions,[79] and their ease of explaining *trans* addition. The use of the NMR method appeared to be the starting point for attempts to detect such ions directly. However, we must recognize initially that very low stationary concentrations of such species would make direct and unambiguous identification difficult. Detailed kinetic studies provided no evidence for the Hg^{II}-olefin complex, but the possibility of such intermediates could not be excluded.[80]

The first report interpreting spectral data in terms of the cyclohexene-mercurinium ion was due to Sokolov, Ustnyuk, and Reutov,[81] who reasoned that the major obstacle to direct observation might be the rapidity of nucleophilic attack by $OR^{\ominus}$ leading to the product covalent mercurial. The choice of a nitrile system as solvent seemed to be quite an advantage. Ions (7) and (8) were considered to be equienergetic and in equilibrium. The resonance of

(7)   (8)

the olefinic protons of cyclohexene was 4.64τ in acetonitrile, 4.87τ in the presence of a small amount of nitric acid. At an equimolar concentration of cyclohexene and $Hg(NO_3)_2$, new signals at ca. 2.0τ and 2.5τ were interpreted in terms of (7) and related ions. Temperature and concentration effects seemed consistent with this view. It is of interest that π-complexation to Pt^{II} usually leads to upfield shift of the olefin proton resonance.

Subsequently, Japanese workers reported more data for the ethylene-$Hg(NO_3)_2$—H_2O system and interpreted the results in terms of the existence (in high concentration) of the ethylene-mercurinium ion.[82] Most aspects of the interpretation seemed strange; on thorough reexamination,[83] it was established for both $Hg(NO_3)_2$ and $Hg(ClO_4)_2$—H_2O—C_2H_4 systems that the signals additional to those from $HOCH_2CH_2HgOH$, were assignable to the ether $(XHgCH_2CH_2)_2O$. Subsequently, the ethers were actually isolated from the reaction mixture and identified.[84] There was some evidence that ether formation occurred in basic conditions also.[35] In the analogous reactions of propene, there was no indication of ether formation.[84] The kinetics and stereochemistry, and other data, appear best interpreted in terms of mercurinium intermediates in oxymercuration.[2]

F. Kinetics of Oxymercuration

The reversibility of oxymercuration, general *trans* addition to unstrained simple olefins, and the intermediacy of the mercurinium ion provide considerable mechanistic information. Much of the available kinetic data on the forward (oxymercuration) and reverse reactions (deoxymercuration) has been presented previously and interpreted,[2] and only more recent data will be covered here.

The reaction under aqueous conditions with uncomplexed Hg^{II} proceeds according to the following stoichiometry, and is called hydroxymercuration. The stereochemistry (see above) is known, but there appears to be a surprising

$$CH_2\!\!=\!\!CH\!\!-\!\!R + H_2O + Hg^{2+} \longrightarrow {}^{\oplus}HgCH_2CHROH + H^{\oplus}$$

shortage of reliable kinetic data, perhaps because of the rapidity of the reaction. Kinetics of reactions employing complexed Hg^{II} (e.g., acetate, chloride) have been described previously. The reaction is known generally to proceed in the Markovnikov manner.[2] Halpern and Tinker[82] established the kinetics of hydroxymercuration of 20 olefins, and second-order kinetics were observed for these quite fast reactions.

$$\frac{d}{dt}[\text{oxymercurial}] = \frac{d[H^+]}{dt} = k[Hg^{2+}]\left[\begin{array}{c}\diagdown \qquad \diagup \\ C\!\!=\!\!C \\ \diagup \qquad \diagdown\end{array}\right]$$

Catalysis by oxygen or hydrogen peroxide was not observed (contrary to an earlier claim);[73] this removed what some authors considered to be a troublesome feature of the ionic addition mechanism. The effects of acids implied little difference in reactivity between $Hg^+(OH)$, $Hg(OH)_2$, and Hg^{2+}, which is somewhat surprising and may be due in part to unjustified faith in the hydrolysis constants for Hg^{2+}. Any reaction between olefin and Hg_2^{2+} appears to be negligible.

A simple interpretation of the kinetics would be a rate-determining bimolecular reaction between olefin and Hg^{2+}. This would not recognize the possible role of the mercurinium ion, and such an approach seems unreasonable (see above). The results of Halpern and Tinker[80] do place some restrictions on the possible role of such a mercurinium intermediate, however.

The rate-determining formation of an olefin-Hg complex is consistent with the kinetics but unreasonable in comparison with behavior of other d^{10} ions (e.g., Ag^+) toward olefins and the rates of formation of other Hg^{II} complexes. The more attractive pathway involves the mercurinium ion in a rapid preequilibrium, followed by a rate-controlling reaction with water (or other nucleophile) to yield the hydroxymercuration product. Strict adherence to first-order behavior, as the olefin concentration was increased substantially, allowed the estimation of formation constants for the complex, e.g., for ethylene 100 mole^{-1}.

The rate of hydroxymercuration increases with the presence of electron-donating alkyl groups on the olefin and decreased by electron-withdrawing substituents, e.g. (—Cl, —CN).[80] This behavior is expected for electrophilic addition. A ρ^* value of -3.3 (from the plot of log k vs. σ^*) was obtained and implies a high degree of charge on the carbon bearing the substituent in the transition state, i.e., carbonium ion character and a nonsymmetrical charge distribution in the mercurinium ion. However, some bridging in the transition state does seem necessary (i.e., not an open carbonium ion) to account for the

$$\left[\begin{array}{c} | \quad\quad | \\ -C\!\!-\!\!-\!\!-\!\!C^{\delta+}\!\!-\!\!R \\ \diagdown\!\diagup \\ Hg \end{array} \right]^{\oplus}$$

failure to observe nonspecificity in successive oxymercuration-deoxymercuration sequences with olefins such as 2-butenes[74] and stilbene.[85]

Other kinetic data on methoxymercuration by $Hg(OAc)_2$ in methanol have been discussed[41] and interpreted[2] in terms of the mercurinium ion mechanism, which can explain solvent effects, stereochemistry, and other evidences of ionic participation.

$$Hg(OCOCH_3)_2 \rightleftharpoons {}^{\oplus}HgOCOCH_3 + CH_3COO^{\ominus}$$

G. Deoxymercuration

Information on some fine details of the oxymercuration-deoxymercuration (microscopic reversal) sequence has been provided by Kreevoy in some elegant and exhaustive studies. The ready stereospecific regeneration of the parent olefin by a number of reagents is well known to be a characteristic

feature of this class of compounds.[1,2] Winstein, Traylor and Garner reviewed the iodide-ion induced deoxymercuration as a *trans* elimination process,[86] and the greater rate of the α-cyclohexylmercurial (*trans*) over the β appeared strong support for such a mechanism.

Initial studies by Kreevoy[87] established the kinetics of deoxymercuration by acid to be first order in mercurial; values of k_1/H^+ were tolerably in-

$$2\,CH_3CH(OR)CH_2HgI + H_3O^\oplus \longrightarrow CH_3CH{=}CH_2 + H_2O + CH_3CH(OR)CH_2Hg^\oplus$$
$$+ ROH + HgI_2$$

variant, confirming the presence of a proton in the transition state. The possibility of fast and reversible π-complex formation prior to the rate-determining step was eliminated.

Kreevoy probed the nature of the slow step from studies of the α and β-2-methoxycyclohexylmercuric iodides and concluded that the product of this step was the mercurinium ion.[50] The actual nature of the transition state

was deduced[88-90] from studies of secondary hydrogen isotope effects and $\sigma^*\rho^*$ correlations in which $\rho^* = -2.77$. A transition state picture with roughly equal contributions from protonated starting state, mercuric-olefin complex, and the cation was considered consistent with the data.

Halide ions may cause substantial catalysis of deoxymercuration, and Kreevoy showed that the overall rate constant for deoxymercuration of 2-methoxyethylmercuric iodide in the presence of hydronium and iodide ions had the form[91]

$$k_2^0 = K_2 + k_3[I^\ominus] + k_4[I^-]^2$$

This catalysis by none, one, or two iodide ions was possible, the effect emanating from iodide complexation of mercury. Catalysis by chloride would be much weaker.

Replacement of the alkoxide function with a better leaving group would be expected to favor a nonacid catalyzed, neutral solvolytic type of deoxymercuration. This was the case with 2-iodoethylmercuric esters.[92] Iodide catalysis of solvolytic deoxymercuration was also demonstrated.[93]

$$2RCOOCH_2CH_2HgI \longrightarrow RCOO^\ominus + CH_2{=}CH_2 + HgI_2$$
$$+ RCOOCH_2CH_2Hg^\oplus$$

$$\underset{\underset{\displaystyle |}{CH_2CN}}{CH_3COOCH}{-}CH_2HgI + I^\ominus \longrightarrow HgI_2 + CH_3COO^\ominus + CH_2{=}CH{-}CH_2CN$$

These investigations completed the picture of the $H^\oplus$—$I^\ominus$ deoxymercuration, since catalysis by zero or one proton, one or two iodide ions, and all combinations thereof had been kinetically demonstrated for dilute aqueous solution.

H. Oxymercuration of Bicyclic Alkenes

The mechanisms proposed by Winstein and Kreevoy for the oxymetalation and deoxymetalation reactions are seen to be self-consistent and explain the results for simple unstrained olefins. However, norbornene oxymercurates *exo,cis* and bicyclo[2.2.2]octene may yield both *cis* and *trans* products. How the general mechanism may be modified has been discussed by Traylor in a number of important papers.[32,33]

The mercurinium ion proposal was still a key tenet in the overall scheme, and its fate was considered to depend on the electrophilicity of the addend, and the rigidity and strain in the olefin. *cis,exo*-Addition, then, was attributed to a twist strain, operative in the second step of the usual two-step addition mechanism. This, of course, does not explain the completely *exo* approach

(9)

of the electrophile to give (9) as shown. Another feature of importance was that *cis* or *frontside* opening of the mercurinium ion was favored, since the nucleophile may be considered to be already located on that side by its attachment to mercury. This could almost place oxymercuration in the realm

of molecular or four-center additions.

Neighboring groups manifest themselves rather dramatically in oxymer-curation of certain substituted norbornenes, and even poor neighboring groups, such as hydroxyl and carboxyl, override the features that normally lead to *cis,exo* oxymercuration. Some examples are shown and the stereo-chemistry is based largely on PMR spectra and reduction experiments producing compounds of known configurations.[58,62] Endo mercury attack

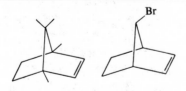

with *syn*-7-hydroxymethyl-2-norbornene occurs to yield a ring-closed mer-curial.[58,60]

Traylor has also provided some data on the favored exclusive formation of the *exo*-complex(I), which was considered due to steric effects. In this case *syn*-7 substitution should retard *exo* approach, as it does in some other cases. However, oxymercuration of 1,4,7,7-tetramethylnorbornene and *syn*-7-bromonorbornene, proceed exclusively *cis,exo*.[62] This absence of effects due

to the 7,7-dimethyl group would suggest steric effects to be not the pre-dominant directive effect for *exo* approach, and some electronic effect seems primarily responsible. Resonance effects are generally accepted to be un-important in oxymercuration-deoxymercuration, and classical cations seem not to be involved, as do nonclassical ions, on the basis of the effects of

$$\text{Hg(OAc)}_2 \xrightarrow{\text{H}_2\text{O}} \text{NaBH}_4 \longrightarrow$$

48%   48%

1-methyl substituent. However, no entirely satisfactory rationale has been presented for the observed *exo* stereospecificity in these *cis* oxymercurations and other *cis* electrophilic additions, but there does appear to be some presently undefined electronic dissimilarity between the *exo* and *endo* sides.

Effects of added sodium acetate on *cis* and *trans* hydroxy or methoxy mercurations are striking and suggest different mechanisms for *cis* and *trans* oxymercurations.[62] The former appear to proceed by cyclic transition states (molecular additions), while the absence of acetate effects for *trans* addition is in line with the mechanism already outlined. Attempts have been made to relate the stereochemical outcome of norbornene-oxymercuration to the nonclassical ion problems,[94] but some problems of definitive identifications of reaction intermediates exist, so that any comparisons of this sort are somewhat conjectural.

I. Oxythallation and Oxyplumbation

Unfortunately, isolation problems of oxythallation and oxyplumbation adducts are acute, so that the stereochemistry and general structure of these classes of compounds are poorly understood. Oxythallation of norbornene and norbornadiene produce *cis,exo* products,[39] so that mechanisms similar to those discussed for oxymercuration may be in action. In the case of simple unstrained olefins (e.g., cyclohexene) isolation of the presumed organothallium compound has not been possible, so that the stereochemistry is unknown. Inferences on the stereochemistry, however, have been made from the nature of the oxidation products resulting from heterolytic decomposition (demetalation) of the presumed intermediate.[95,96] The situation with oxyplumbation is one of extreme paucity and no characterized oxyplumbation adduct has been reported. Again, however, it is tempting to suggest that electrophilic mechanisms (whether they involve "thallinium," "plumbinium" ions or concerted *cis* additions) again operate. More will be said in the discussion on oxidation by metal acetates, many of which appear to involve organometallic (oxymetalation) intermediates.

J. Oxyplatination and Oxypalladation

Little detail is available on the conversion of the chelating diolefin complexes of Pt^{II} and Pd^{II} to the σ-bonded alkoxy compounds on treatment with alcohol and base, although a number of suggestions has been made.[34,67,69] *trans*-Addition in the case of norbornadiene and dicyclopentadiene complexes and *cis*-addition in the case of cyclo-1,5-octadiene seem to occur.[66] Coordination of the olefin may make it more receptive to nucleophilic attack, catalyzed by added acetate or sodium carbonate. The oxypalladation step

proposed in Pd^{II} oxidations occurs in the primary sphere of Pd^{II} and a *cis* step is indicated. This will be discussed in the section on oxidation.

VI. REACTIONS OF OXYMETALLICS

A. Oxidation Processes

The oxidation of alkenes and other related compounds by metal salts has been known and exploited for some time,[97,98] but only recently has any real insight into the oxidation mechanisms been available. Some of this knowledge has been summarized before,[2] but investigation generally is quite intense because of the experimental usefulness and industrial importance of such oxidations. This is particularly true for oxidation by Pd^{II}.

B. Hg^{II} Oxidation

This is a long-known process, and Shearer and Wright considered that oxidation of alkenes proceeded by formation of an oxymercurial which was oxidized by a second mole of mercuric salt.[99] Radical pathways were envisaged under certain conditions.[100] These reactions have been reformulated and heterolytic mechanisms proposed.[2,101]

Perhaps the clearest picture is available of oxidation by Hg(OAc)$_2$ in acetic acid, a well-known allylic oxidation method. In a general survey of allylic oxidation, Wiberg and Nielsen reported that cyclohexene yielded the allylic cyclohexenyl acetate,[102] and tracer studies suggested the intervention of a symmetrical intermediate,

From studies of α-pinene oxidation,[102] it appeared that an allylic mercurial may have been involved (its formation being rate-determining), which decomposed (demercuration) to yield the ionic intermediate. Thus oxymercurial formation was not essential for the oxidation process.

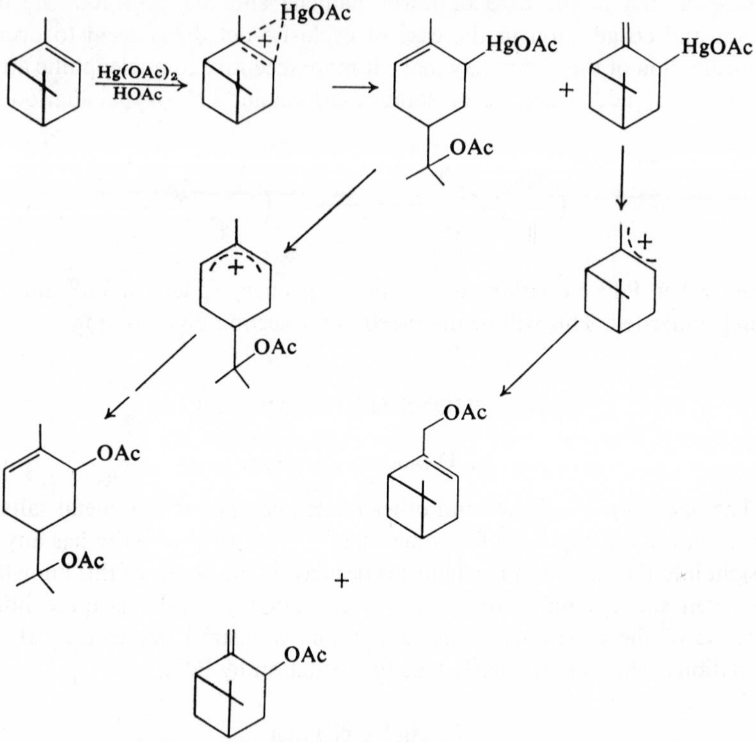

Strong evidence that allylic mercurials are involved in the oxidation of simple olefins by $Hg(OAc)_2$ in acetic acid was provided by Winstein, et al.,[103] in their thorough studies of the chemistry of allylic mercurials. Butenyl-mercuric acetate, alone or in the presence of $Hg(OAc)_2$ in acetic acid, under-goes a demercuration reaction to produce pure secondary acetate. The $Hg(OAc)_2$ appears strongly to promote this demercuration, by a route shown below.

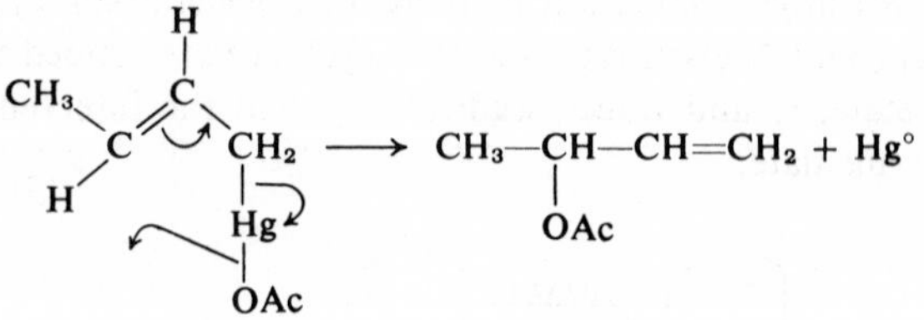

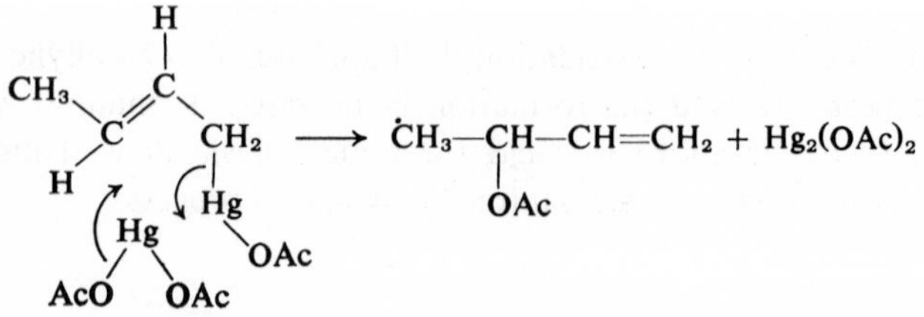

Although pure allyl mercury compounds display proton NMR spectra for "frozen" σ-structures, the addition of HgX_2 in small amounts changes the spectrum to that expected for equilibrating σ-species.[103] In the case of the butenyl mercurials, the equilibrium must be heavily in favor of the primary isomer, as judged by the chemical shift data. The same situation applies for crotylmagnesium and palladium systems.

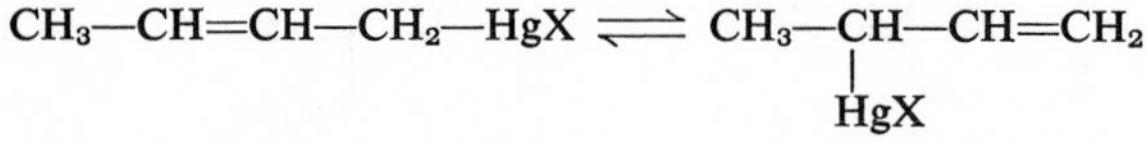
CH₃—CH=CH—CH₂—HgX
CH₃—CH—CH=CH₂
HgX

On this basis, if oxidation of 1- and 2-butene involved allylic mercurials, any secondary allylic mercurial formed from 2-butene (see below) should rapidly become primary and demercurate, as shown above to yield exclusively secondary acetate. The data of Winstein, et al., are in agreement with this,[103] since for a series of 1- and 2-olefins (C_4 to C_8), secondary acetate is formed in high yield. Mechanisms of the S_Ei and S_E^2 appear involved. Oxymercurial formation is not essential for the oxidation outcome.

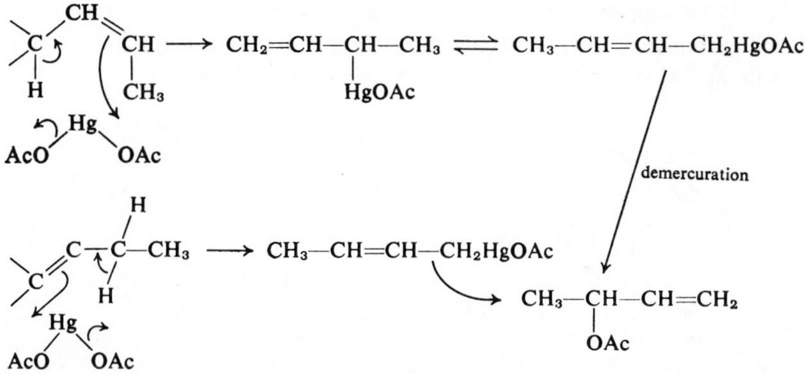
CH
C
H
CH
CH₃
Hg
AcO
OAc
CH₂=CH—CH—CH₃
HgOAc
CH₃—CH=CH—CH₂HgOAc
demercuration
H
C
C—CH₃
C
H
Hg
AcO
OAc
CH₃—CH=CH—CH₂HgOAc
CH₃—CH—CH=CH₂
OAc

Kinetics and substituent effects were consistent with the rate-determining formation of the allylic mercurials. However, it should be made clear that widely differing olefins may be oxidized by different pathways with lower product specificities. A point of particular importance is that rapidly interconverting or equilibrating, allylic organometallics may account for results of tracer experiments which indicated the intervention of a symmetrical intermediate.[104]

Wolfe, et al.,[104] also probed details of the cyclohexene oxidation and oxidized cyclohexene-3,3,6,6-d_4 to 3-acetoxycyclohexene, which seemed to be a mixture of the following cyclohexenes:

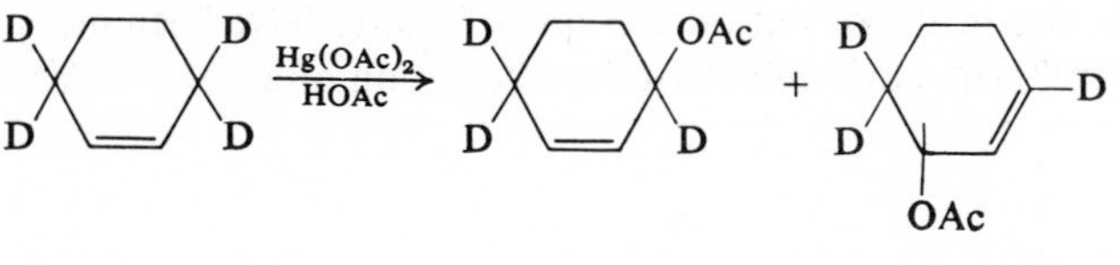
D
D
D
D
Hg(OAc)₂
HOAc
D
OAc
D
D
+
D
D
D
OAc

This result again was considered consistent with a symmetrical intermediate being involved, but not with the equilibration of allylic mercurials. Unfortunately, cyclohexenyl mercurials have not been made (although often attempted), so that the necessary solvolytic demercuration experiments have

not been conducted. Certainly, in the case of simple olefins, the intervention of allylic mercurials appears to be a very logical explanation.

C. Tl^{III} Oxidation

In contrast to oxidation by Hg^{II}, which in simple cases involves allylic mercurials, Tl^{III} oxidation seems best explained by dethallation reactions of organothallium intermediates,[7] produced by oxythallation reactions.

Grinstead initially reported that oxidation of ethylene and 2-hexene produced carbonyl products, glycols and esters.[105] He considered an oxythallation-dethallation sequence the most probable explanation.

The intervention of acetonium ion intermediates has also been considered perhaps most clearly by Anderson and Winstein.[106] The stereochemistry of the Tl^{III} oxidation of cyclohexene in dry and moist acetic acid was probed. In dry solvent, cis and trans diacetates, ring-contracted products, and cyclohexenyl acetate (allylic oxidation) were observed. Moist acetic acid resulted in glycol monoacetates as additional products. The diacetates were mainly cis (81%) in moist solvent but largely trans (85%) in dry solvent. This reversal in stereochemistry under aqueous conditions has been considered to support the intervention of acetoxonium ions; again oxythallation-dethallation was considered. Other data, interpreted along similar lines, have been described by Lee and Price[96] and Kabbe.[107]

The kinetics of the oxidation and other features have been investigated by Henry,[108–110] who concluded that decomposition of an oxythallation adduct

$$\frac{-d}{dt}[C_2H_4] = k_2[Tl^{3+}][C_2H_4]$$

$$Tl^{3+} + H_2O + C_2H_4 \xrightarrow{\text{slow}} {}^{2+}TlCH_2CH_2OH + H^{\oplus}$$

$${}^{2+}TlCH_2CH_2OH \xrightarrow[\text{H}_2\text{O}]{\text{fast}} HOCH_2CH_2OH + CH_3CHO + H^{\oplus}$$

was involved. Under favorable nonaqueous conditions, such oxythallation adducts have been isolated,[21] and in aqueous solution containing excess acetate ion.[69]

The lack of proton inhibition (which means that the oxymetalation adduct cannot be in equilibrium with Tl^{3+} and ethylene) and isotope effects indicated the oxymetalation step to be rate-determining, i.e., a rearrangement of a π- to a σ-Tl^{III} complex. The transition state appeared to have more carbonium ion character than that for oxymercuration and may imply reduced

stereochemical control. Markovnikov oxythallation was indicated; over a range of acetate ion concentrations, the only important species was $Tl(OAc)_2^{\oplus}$. Increased branching in the olefin and electrolyte addition greatly accelerate Tl^{III} oxidation.[69]

Decomposition of the oxythallation adduct has been compared to the hydrolysis of certain chlorohydrins,[69] except that the leaving group is Tl^+. This pathway is consistent with the chemistry of monoalkylthallium(III) compounds, which decompose rapidly by solvolytic pathways.[7] More details

and discussion are available in the paper by Henry.[69]

D. Pb^{IV} Oxidation

The chief features of oxidation with Pb^{IV} have been evaluated by Criegee,[111] and it is not surprising that the pathways postulated resemble those postulated for the iso-electronic Tl^{III}. The products of alkene oxidation are usually diacetates, ring-enlarged products, rearranged acetates, and products of allylic oxidation. Heterolytic routes predominate under polar conditions, and again an oxyplumbation adduct determines the outcome.[2,7]

$$Pb(OAc)_4 \rightleftharpoons {}^{\oplus}Pb(OAc)_3 + OAc^{\ominus}$$

The oxidation of α-pinene has been examined in considerable detail,[111,112,10] and Whitham[15] established that *cis*-2-acetoxy-3-pinene was the primary product which, however, underwent ready isomerization in acetic acid to *trans*-verbenyl acetate. The proposed mechanism involved *cis* oxyplumbation.

In the case of cyclohexene, Pb^{IV} allylic oxidation also occurs, but here an allylic lead compound yielding a symmetrical intermediate may be involved.[102,106] However, preparations of allylic lead(IV) triacylates have not been reported and appear quite difficult to obtain.

E. Pd^{II} Oxidation (Aqueous)

The oxidation of olefins by Pd^{II} salts has been known for some time and is employed industrially to convert ethylene to acetaldehyde (the Wacker process).[114] Aqueous Pd^{II} converts olefins to carbonyl compounds, and a number of recent articles have discussed the available data in considerable detail.[115,116] The newer features will be considered here.

The overall reaction may be represented as below.

$$C_2H_4 + \tfrac{1}{2}O_2 \xrightarrow{\text{PdCl}_2,\ \text{CuCl}_2} C_2H_4O$$

and thus the process is essentially nonconsuming in Pd^{II} or Cu^{II}. Other olefins are oxidized to ketones. It has been confirmed that the reaction does not involve hydration and subsequent oxidation of the alcohol.[115] In the case of ethylene, deuterium-labeling experiments have established that vinyl alcohol (the enol of acetaldehyde) is not a significant intermediate.[117]

The main features of the mechanism appear to be understood and are based largely on the results of Smidt[114] and Henry,[69,118,119] the latter employing a reactor of high gas-liquid mixing efficiency to detect the initial formation of olefin-Pd^{II} complexes. The kinetics are first order in ethylene and Pd^{II} and strongly inhibited by chloride ion and protons. The complete rate expression was established as

$$\frac{-d}{dt}[C_2H_4] = \frac{k[PdCl_3(C_2H_4)^-]}{[Cl^-][H^+]} = \frac{kK_1[PdCl_4{}^{2-}][C_2H_4]}{[Cl^-]^2[H^+]}$$

where K_1 pertains to

$$PdCl_4{}^{2-} + C_2H_4 \overset{K_1}{\rightleftharpoons} PdCl_3(C_2H_4)^{\ominus} + Cl^{\ominus}$$

This rate expression suggests, and it is generally agreed, that π-complexation is the first step in the sequence, followed by loss of another chloride to give an aquated π-complex.

$$PdCl_3(C_2H_4)^- + H_2O \overset{K_2}{\rightleftharpoons} PdCl_2 \cdot H_2O \cdot C_2H_4 + Cl^{\ominus}$$

Attack of hydroxide on the complex (proton inhibition) can be ruled out on kinetic grounds,[118] and three additional plausible paths consistent with the kinetics can be written. Kinetic isotope effects are very small, indicating

$$PdCl_2(OH)(C_2H_4)^- + H_2O \xrightarrow{\text{slow}} [Cl_2(H_2O)PdCH_2CH_2OH]^-$$

$$\downarrow \text{fast}$$

$$CH_3CHO + H_3^{\oplus}O + 2Cl^{\ominus} + Pd^{\circ}$$

that the rupture of C—H bonds is not rate-determining. This leaves the rearrangement of a π- to a σ-complex (oxypalladation) as the most plausible route.

The intermediacy of oxypalladation adducts is now accepted,[2] and their mode of decomposition has been studied. Both Tl^{II} and Pd^{II} oxidations involve oxymetalation adducts, but, although the products of Tl^{III} oxidation are consistent with the heterolysis of the C—Tl bond, the products from Pd^{II} reactions are not consistent with this idea.[69] No glycol derivatives are ever found, even when a hydride shift is impossible.

A reasonable decomposition route for the oxypalladation adduct is suggested by the chemistry of Pd^{II} alkyls. Alkyl palladium(II) systems, with a β-hydrogen are unstable, apparently due to a β-elimination, giving olefin and a Pd^{II} hydride.[69] Methyl Pd^{II} systems are not prone to this fragmentation

$$R-CH_2-CH_2-\overset{\overset{\displaystyle L}{|}}{\underset{\underset{\displaystyle L}{|}}{Pd}}-Cl \longrightarrow R-CH=CH_2 + HCl + Pd^0 + 2L$$

route. However, this elimination pathway cannot be directly extrapolated to the oxypalladation adduct, since elimination would produce vinyl alcohol, which would rearrange to acetaldehyde, which would contain one deuterium if the system were conducted in D_2O. This is not the experimental outcome.

$$ClPdCH_2CH_2OD \xrightarrow{D_2O} ClPdH + CH_2=CHOD \longrightarrow$$
$$HCl + Pd^0 + CH_2DCHO$$

A number of suggestions to overcome this obstacle has been proposed and discussed by Henry[69] and others;[2,115] perhaps the most effective is one in which Pd^{II} hydride elimination is not completed before electron reorganization yields acetaldehyde. This could be a Pd^{II}-assisted shift of the hydride.

$$\underset{ClPd---H}{\overset{\overset{\displaystyle H \quad H}{\overset{\displaystyle |}{} \overset{\displaystyle |}{}}}{H-C-C-O-H}} \longrightarrow Pd^0 + HCl + CH_3CHO$$

A recent suggestion[120] involves Pd^{II} hydride elimination, followed by re-addition and a solvolysis step. In practice, the distinction between the two methods above could be difficult. Some distinction could be made under

$$HOCH_2CH_2PdCl_2^\ominus \rightleftharpoons (HOCH=CH_2)PdHCl_2^\ominus$$

$$\begin{array}{ccc}
\overset{\oplus}{O}H_2 & & OH \\
| & & | \\
CH_3{-}CH + [PdCl_2]^{2-} & \xleftarrow{\text{ } H_2O \text{ }} & CH_3{-}C{-}PdCl_2^\ominus \\
| & & | \\
OH & & H
\end{array}$$

$$\longrightarrow CH_3CHO + H_3O^\oplus$$

nonaqueous conditions, e.g., in methanol or acetic acid (see below), where —OH would be replaced by OR, and the only path available is a solvolytic one, so that 1,1-di-substituted ethanes would result from ethylene oxidation. There are some data along these lines, but probably inconclusive at the present time.[69] It would appear, however, that the presence of Cu^{II} is generally essential for the formation of higher boiling dioxygenated products.[69,121]

The oxidation of olefins other than ethylene yields ketones generally;[114] 1-olefins produce methyl ketones with some aldehyde formation, which depends on a number of operational factors. Oxidation rates are higher for terminal olefins and *cis* isomers, and a change from purely aqueous conditions is desirable for higher olefins.[115] Aqueous N,N-dimethylformamide has been used widely.[122] Under certain conditions π-allyl palladium complexes are formed.[117,123] Some synthetic applications of the π-allyl palladium compounds are related to their oxidation by $PdCl_2$, sodium dichromate, or manganese dioxide to yield unsaturated carbonyl compounds.[115,123]

F. Pd^{II} Oxidation (Nonaqueous)

In contrast to the oxidation of ethylene under aqueous conditions, the reaction in acetic acid leads to vinyl acetate. However, few data are available

$$CH_2{=}CH_2 + HOAc + PdCl_2 \xrightarrow{\text{ NaOAc }} CH_2{=}CHOAc + HCl + Pd^0$$

for higher olefins, much of it conflicting in nature, largely because little or no consideration has been given to isomerization—both olefinic and oxygen positional.[123] Only one report specifically recognizes and makes allowances for these complications.[124] The available data have been discussed by Schultz and Gross[121] and Bird.[115] Schultz and Gross have considered mechanisms for the formation of higher boiling products, e.g., ethylidene diacetate, etc., from ethylene in some of these situations. The role played by Cu^{II} salts, which favor such products, has also been assessed.[121]

However, there is again general agreement that oxidation by Pd^{II} under nonaqueous conditions, e.g., acetic acid, again involves oxypalladation intermediates; in this way it is possible to rationalize the products from the

$$\text{CH}_3\text{CH}_2\text{CH}{=}\text{CH}_2 \begin{cases} \longrightarrow \quad \underset{\underset{\text{OAc}}{|}}{\text{CH}_3\text{CH}_2}{-}\underset{\underset{\text{PdOAc}}{|}}{\text{CH}}{-}\text{CH}_2 \xrightarrow{-\text{HPdOAc}} \underset{80\%}{\text{CH}_3\text{CH}_2}\underset{|}{-}\underset{\text{OAc}}{\text{CH}}{=}\text{CH}_2 \\[2mm] \underset{9\%}{\text{CH}_3\text{CH}{=}\text{CH}{-}\text{CH}_2\text{OAc}} \\[2mm] \longrightarrow \quad \underset{\underset{\text{AcOPd}}{|}}{\text{CH}_3\text{CH}_2}{-}\underset{\underset{\text{OAc}}{|}}{\text{CH}}{-}\text{CH}_2 \xrightarrow{-\text{HPdOAc}} \underset{9\%}{\text{CH}_3\text{CH}_2\text{CH}{=}\text{CH}{-}\text{OAc}} \end{cases}$$

$$\text{CH}_3\text{CH}{=}\text{CHCH}_3 \longrightarrow \underset{\underset{\text{AcOPd}}{|}}{\text{CH}_3}{-}\underset{\underset{\text{OAc}}{|}}{\text{CH}}{-}\text{CH}{-}\text{CH}_3 \xrightarrow{-\text{HPdOAc}} \underset{97\%}{\text{CH}_2}{=}\text{CH}{-}\underset{\underset{\text{OAc}}{|}}{\text{CH}}{-}\text{CH}_3$$

$$\underset{1\%}{\text{CH}_3\text{CH}}{=}\underset{\underset{\text{OAc}}{|}}{\text{CH}}{-}\text{CH}_3$$

Pd(OAc)$_2$ oxidation of the butenes.[124] This study indicated that Markovnikov oxypalladation was favored, followed by the elimination of HPdX, preferentially producing allylic acetate. Thus 1-olefins give mainly enol acetate, while 2-olefins give mainly allylic acetate; 1- and 2-olefins give different allylic acetate. The π-allyl palladium species were demonstrated to be insignificant reaction intermediates. Solvent and other effects on the course of these reactions can be severe.[121]

The Pd(OAc)$_2$ oxidation of α-olefins, carrying alkyl or aryl groups on the β-carbon atom, can lead to 1,1,4,4-tetra-substituted 1,3-butadienes, and oxidation seems to occur exclusively at the terminal vinyl carbon atom.[125] The key intermediate was considered to be a binuclear π-olefin palladium complex.

Among others, the synthesis of vinyl acetate from vinyl chloride in the presence of Pd[II][126] and certain carbonylation reactions of olefins[127] appear to involve β-oxy or β-chloroalkyl palladium complexes.

Further discussion of these oxidations and mechanistic proposals may be found in Refs. 2, 69, 114, 115, 121, 188.

Because of the synthetic importance of the Pd[II] oxidation method, a tabular survey of a wide variety of oxidations is included, together with some actual experimental procedures.

G. Table I. Oxidation of Olefins by Pd^{II} to Carbonyl Compounds

TABLE I

Oxidation of Olefins by Pd^{II} to Carbonyl Compounds

Olefin	Carbonyl compound(s)	Yields, %	Refs.
Ethylene	Acetaldehyde	90	128–132
Propene	Mainly acetone		129,133,139
1- and 2-Butene	Methyl ethyl ketone,	95	130,133,135
	butyraldehyde	5	
Isobutene	Methacrolein,	35	136,137
	isobutyraldehyde	12	136,137
	t-Butanol, isobutyraldehyde		138
	Acetone, t-butanol		139
1,3-Butadiene	Crotonaldehyde	> 90	134,139
1-Pentene	Pentan-2-one	> 90	134
2-Pentene	Pentan-2-one	> 90	134
1,4-Pentadiene	Pent-2-en-1-al	> 90	134
Cyclopentene	Cyclopentanone	> 90	134
2-Methyl-1-butene	α-Methylcrotonaldehyde,		137
	2-methylbutyraldehyde		137
2-Methylbut-2-ene	α-Methylcrotonaldehyde,		137
	2-methylbutan-3-one		137
1-Hexene	2-Hexanone	90	134,140
Cyclohexene	Cyclohexanone		106,129,
			134,141
2-Methyl-2-pentene	Mesityl oxide	20	137
2-Methyl-1-pentene	Mesityl oxide		137
3-Methyl-2-pentene	3-Methylpent-2-en-4-one	60	137
1-Heptene	2-Heptanone	90	134,140,142
1-Octene	2-Octanone	> 90	134
1-Nonene	2-Nonanone	> 90	134
1-Decene	2-Decanone	> 90	134
Dodec-1-ene	2-Dodecanone	> 80	122
Styrene	Acetophenone	> 90	134,135
Allylbenzene	Methyl benzyl ketone	> 90	134
Indene	β-Indanone	> 90	134
Stilbene	Desoxybenzoin	90	141
1,1-Diphenylethylene	Benzophenone,		141
	1,1,4,4-tetraphenylbutadiene		

Some additional examples are located in Ref. 115.

In Table II are assembled some data pertaining to the oxidation of olefins in carboxylic acids, leading to the formation of vinyl and allylic esters.

H. Table II. Oxidation of Olefins by Pd^{II}-forming Vinyl and Allylic Esters

TABLE II

Oxidation of Olefins by Pd^{II}-forming Vinyl and Allylic Esters

Olefin	Carboxylic acid	Esters	Refs.
Ethylene	Formic	Vinyl formate	143
	Acetic	Vinyl acetate	144–146
	Propionic	Vinyl propionate	143
	Butyric	Vinyl butyrate	145
	Isobutyric	Vinyl isobutyrate	147
	Crotonic	Vinyl crotonate	145
	Hexanoic	Vinyl hexanoate	143
	Benzoic	Vinyl benzoate	147
Propene	Acetic	Propenyl, isopropenyl, allyl, and isopropyl acetates	124,143, 148
	Propionic	Isopropenyl propionate	143
1-Butene	Acetic	But-1-en-2-yl, but-1-en-3-yl, but-2-en-2-yl, but-2-en-1-yl acetates	18,124, 149
cis,trans-2-Butene	Acetic	But-1-en-3-yl acetate	124,150
iso-Butene	Acetic	Methallyl acetate	151
1-Pentene	Acetic	Pent-2-en-1-yl and pent-1-en-2-yl acetates	124
cis-2-Pentene	Acetic	Pent-1-en-3-yl and pent-3-en-2-yl acetates	124
1-Hexene	Acetic	Hex-2-en-1-yl acetate	152
	Propionic	Hexenyl propionate	152
Cyclohexene	Acetic	3-Cyclohexenyl acetate	95
Hept-1-ene	Acetic	Hept-2-en-1-yl acetate	152
Oct-1-ene	Acetic	Oct-1- and -2-enyl acetates	153
Oct-2-ene	Acetic	s-Octenyl acetates	154
Dec-1-ene	Acetic	Dec-2-en-1-yl acetate	152

I. Table III. Oxidation of π-Allylpalladium Chloride Systems[137]

TABLE III

Oxidation of π-Allylpalladium Chloride Systems [137]

System	Products
Isobutene-MnO_2—H_2SO_4	Methacrolein (40%)
2-Methyl-1 or 2-butene	
$\quad MnO_2$—H_2SO_4	α-Methylcrotonaldehyde,
	$\quad$ methyl isopropenyl ketone (84%)
$\quad PdCl_2$	Methyl isopropenyl ketone (57%)
$\quad$ Buffered $PdCl_2$	β-Methylcrotonaldehyde (37%)
2-Methyl-1- or -2-pentene	
$\quad Na_2Cr_2O_7, H_2SO_4$	2-Methylpenten-3-one (26%)
$\quad MnO_2, H_2SO_4$	2-Methyl-2-pentenal (18%)
$\quad$ Buffered $PdCl_2$	Mesityl oxide (28%)
3-Methyl-2-pentene	
$\quad Na_2Cr_2O_7, H_2SO_4$	3-Methyl-2-penten-4-one (26%)
$\quad MnO_2, H_2SO_4$	3-Methyl-2-penten-4-one (38%)
2,3-Dimethyl-1 or -2-butene	2,3-Dimethyl-2-butenal (13%)
$\quad MnO_2, H_2SO_4$	
3-Ethyl-2-pentene	
$\quad$ Unbuffered $PdCl_2$	3-Ethyl-2-pentene-4-one trace
$\quad$ Buffered $PdCl_2$	3-Ethyl-2-pentene-4-one trace
$\quad Na_2Cr_2O_7, H_2SO_4$	3-Ethyl-2-pentene-4-one (74%)
2,4-Dimethyl-2-pentene	2,4-Dimethyl-2-pentenal (28%)
$\quad MnO_2, H_2SO_4$	
2,4,4-Trimethyl-2-pentene	2,4,4-Trimethyl-2-pentenal (19%)
$\quad Na_2Cr_2O_7, H_2SO_4$	

In Tables IV–VI, literature data pertaining to allylic oxidations of the following type with Hg^{II}, Pb^{IV}, and Tl^{III} are given.

J. Table IV. Allylic Oxidation with Hg[II]

TABLE IV

Allylic Oxidation with Hg[II]

Reaction system	Products	Refs.
a. Chemical structures and experimental data		
Hg(OAc)₂ — Acetic acid at reflux (3 hr) 1:1 olefin:oxidant	OAc (32%) + recovered olefin (34%)	155
As above, 2 hr at 140° 2:1 olefin:oxidant	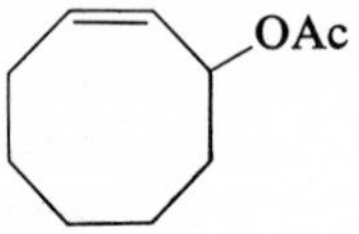 OAc (57%)	156
Hg(OAc)₂ — Acetic acid at reflux (6 hr) 1:1 ratio	OAc (20%)	157
Hg(OAc)₂ — Acetic acid, 10 hr at 120° 1:2 ratio	OAc (40%)	157
Hg(OAc)₂ — Acetic acid, 75° 1:2	(24%) OAc Rearrangement	158
Hg(OAc)₂ — Acetic acid, 1 hr 1:2	R, OH, H R = Ph PhCH₂ C₆H₁₁; % yield 71 45 47; temperature 95 70 70	159

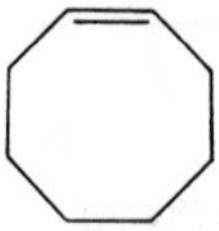

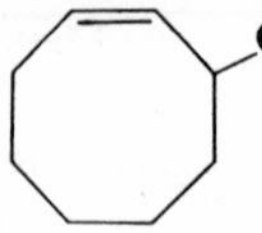

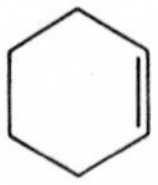

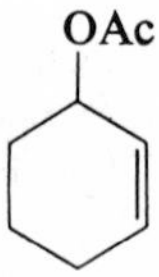

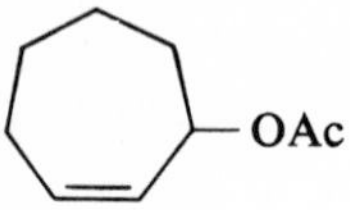

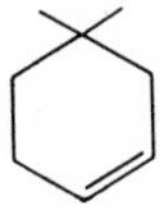

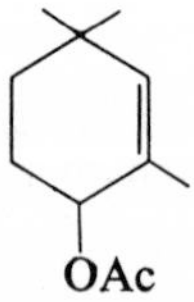

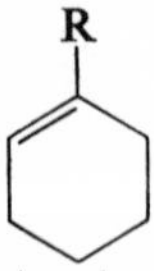

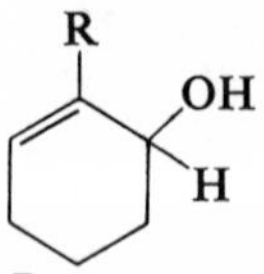

(*continued*)

TABLE IV (*continued*)

Reaction system	Products	Refs.
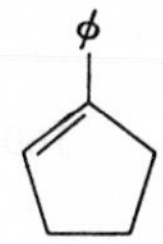 Hg(OAc)$_2$ Acetic acid, 1 hr at 80° 1:2	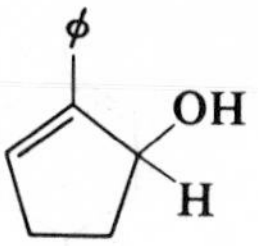 + Hg$_2$(OAc)$_2$ After hydrolysis	159
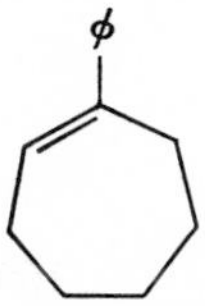 Hg(OAc)$_2$ Acetic acid, 1 hr at 80°	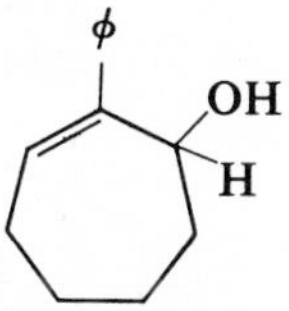 (54%) After hydrolysis	159
	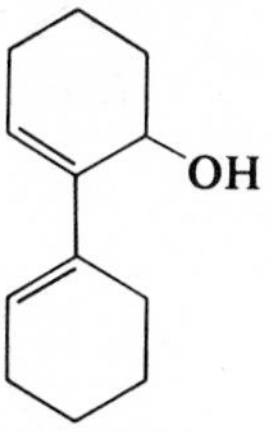 (40%) After hydrolysis	159
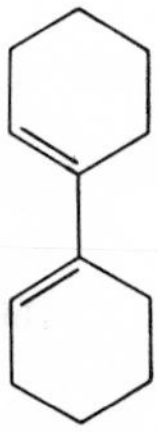 Hg(OAc)$_2$ Acetic acid, 1 hr at 65° 1:2	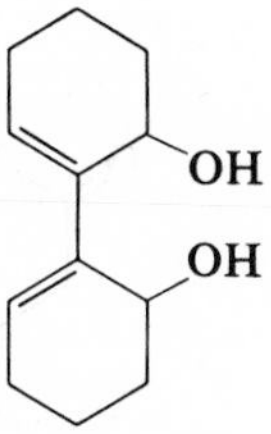 Acetic acid 95°	159
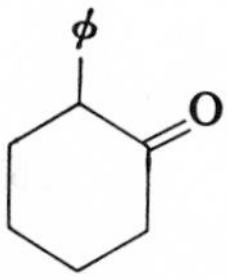 Hg(OAc)$_2$ Acetic acid 1:2	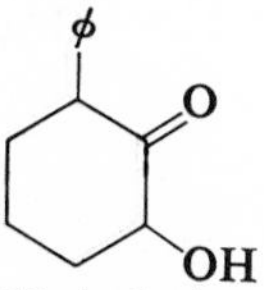 (68%) Hydrolysis	159

(*continued*)

TABLE IV (*continued*)

Reaction system	Products	Refs.
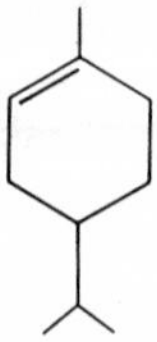 Hg(OAc)$_2$ Acetic acid, 2.5 hr at 140° 1:2	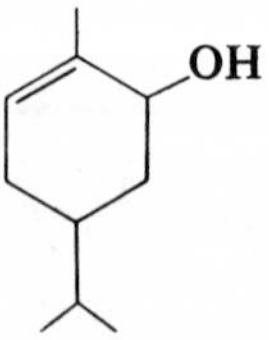 After saponification, 2 moles of oxidant appeared optimum	160
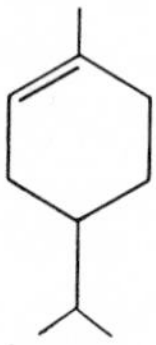 Hg(OAc)$_2$ Acetic acid, 2 hr at 70° 1:2	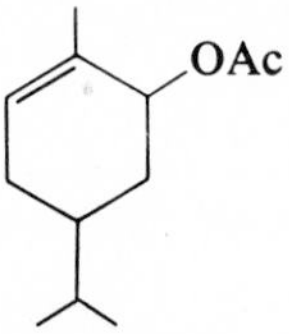 (95%) Racemic	160
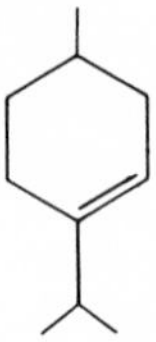 Hg(OAc)$_2$ 130–140° 1:1 No solvent	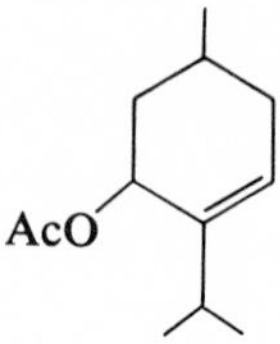	160
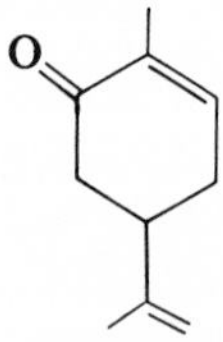 Hg(OAc)$_2$ No temperature reported	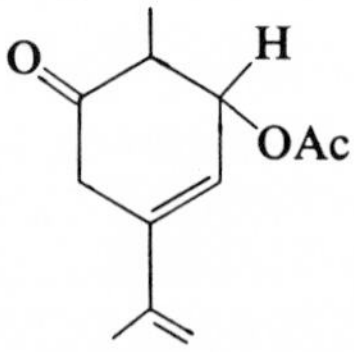	160
 Hg(OAc)$_2$ 140° No solvent (2 hr) 1:1	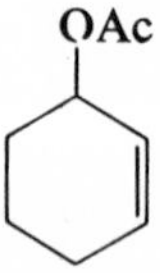 (23%) + Hg°	161

(*continued*)

TABLE IV (*continued*)

Reaction system	Products	Refs.
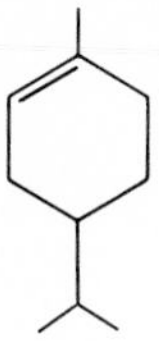 Hg(OAc)₂ 1:1	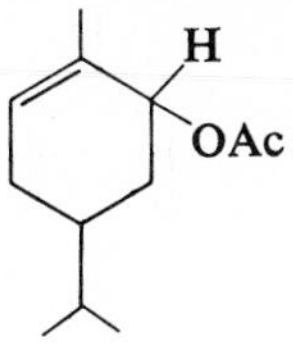 **H** OAc (54%)	161
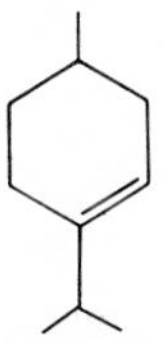 Hg(OAc)₂ 2 hr at 140° 1:1	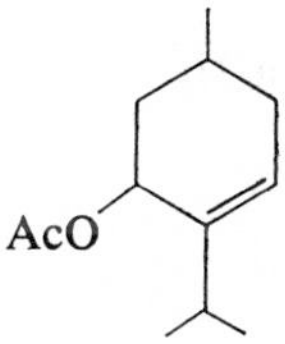 AcO	161
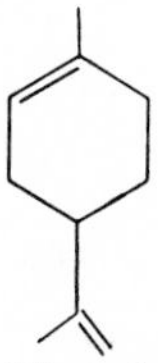 Hg(OAc)₂ No solvent	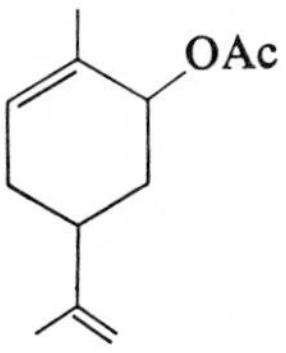 OAc (22%)	161
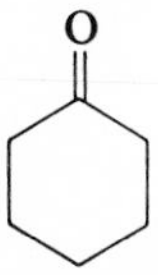 Hg(OAc)₂ 1:1 No solvent	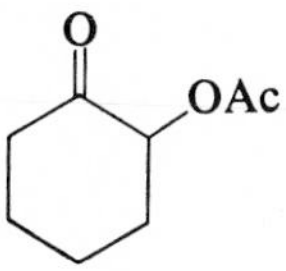 OAc (20%)	161
Hg(OAc)₂ 150–200°, no solvent Also methylcyclohexene, carvene, methene, and aromadendrene	OAc Hg° + HOAc No yields	162

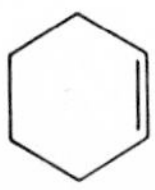

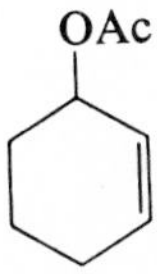

(continued)

TABLE IV (*continued*)

Reaction system	Products	Refs.
 1:1 Trace of HOAc 30 min at 120–130°; then 30 min at 155°	(5%) OAc Rearrangement	163
 AcO 1:2 Hg(OAc)$_2$ 3:2 HOAc—CHCl$_3$ 18 hr at ca. 20°	 AcO	164 (39%)
 AcO H Hg(OAc)$_2$ in AcOH—CHCl$_3$ 24 hr at 20°	 AcO H	165 (72%)
 RO R = p-NO$_2$C$_6$H$_4$CO Hg(OAc)$_2$ in HOAc—CHCl$_3$ (1:1) 15 hr at 20°	 RO H OAc ca. 5%	166

(*continued*)

TABLE IV (*continued*)

Reaction system	Products	Refs.

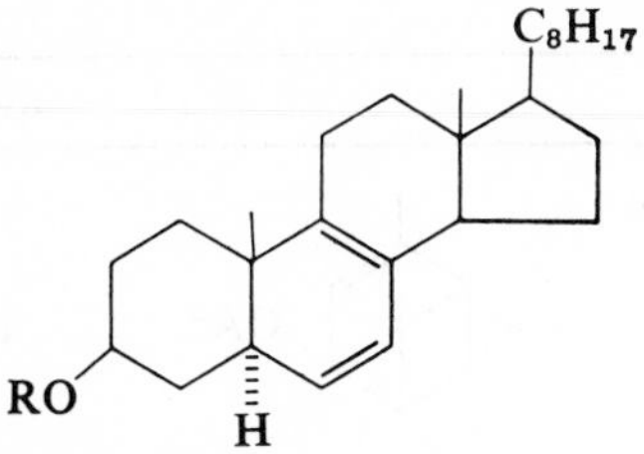

Hg(OAc)$_2$CHCl$_3$—HOAc
1 hr at 20°

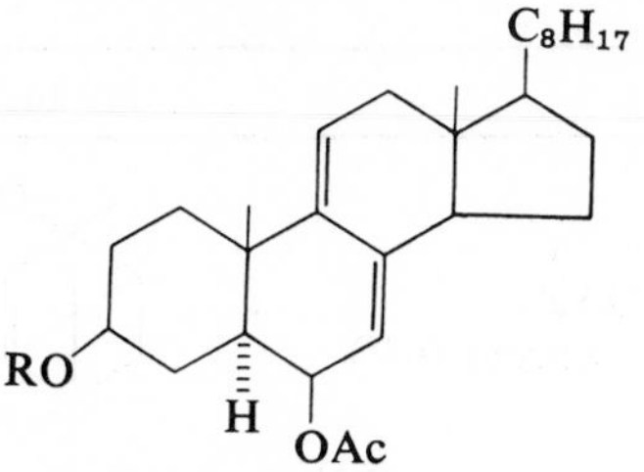

No yield given

167

b. *Allylic oxidation of excess* C_nH_{2n} *by* $Hg(OAc)_2$ *in* $HOAc$[103]

n	Olefin	Allylic % secondary acetate (at 50°)	Rate-Constant 10^6K sec^{-1}
4	1-	99.7	1.1 ± 0.1
4	*cis*-2	99	
4	*trans*-2	93.5 (at 75°)	
5	1-	99.6	1.6 ± 0.1
5	*cis*-2	98.0	
6	1-	97.5	
8	1-	99.6	1.0 ± 0.2

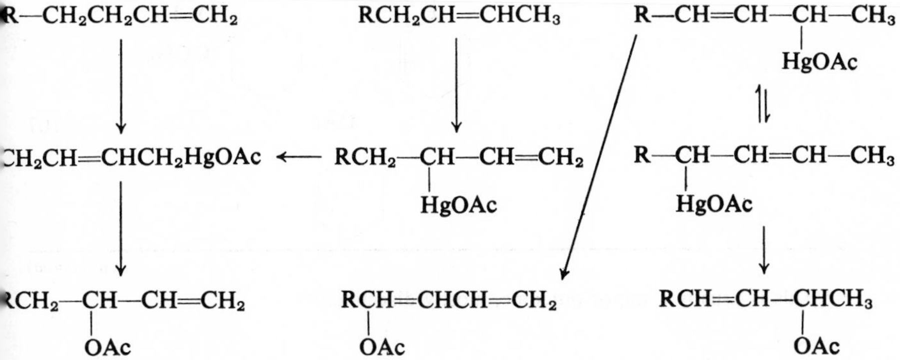

K. Table V. Allylic Oxidation with Pb^{IV} *

TABLE V

Allylic Oxidation with Pb^{IV}*

System	Products	Refs.
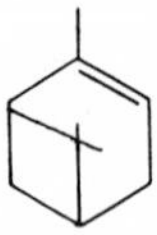 Pb(OAc)$_4$ Dry benzene (65°)	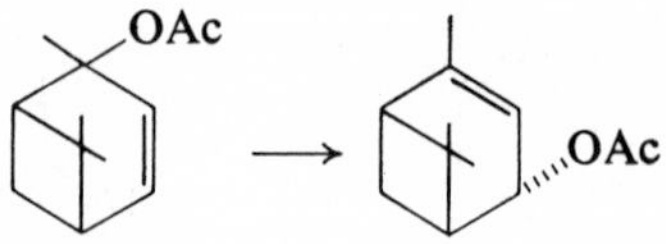	113
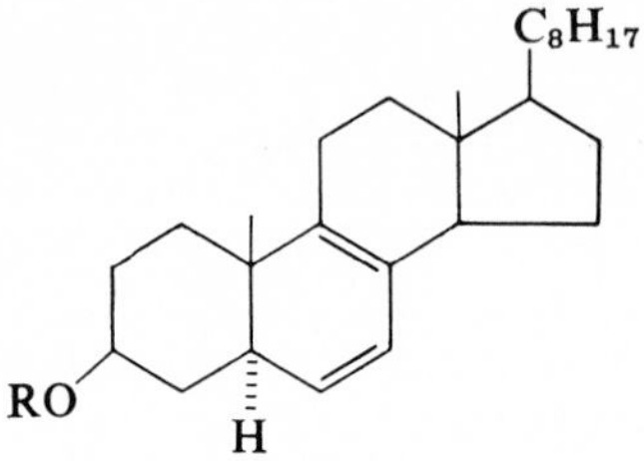	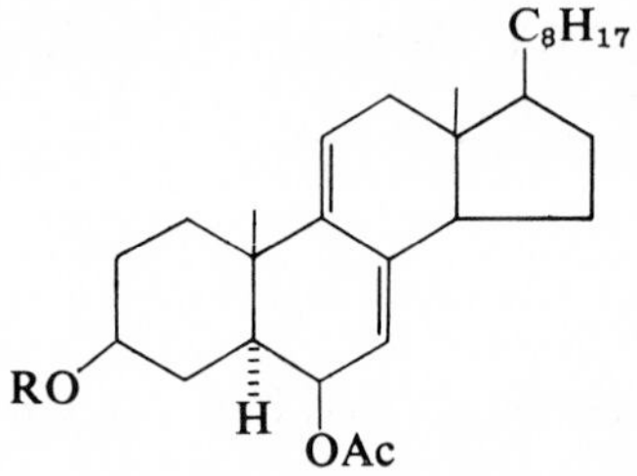	166
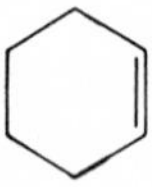 Pb(OAc)$_4$ HOAc	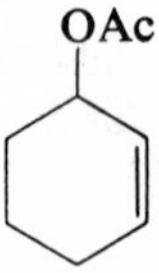 37% + diacetates Ring contraction products	106
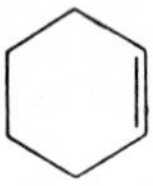 Pb(OAc)$_4$ MeOH	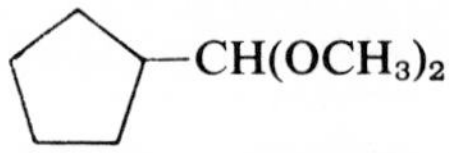 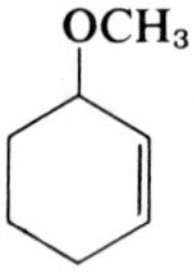 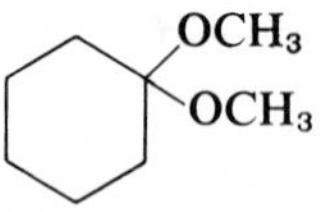 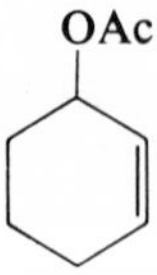	107

(continued)

* This is usually a minor outcome, mostly diacetates.

TABLE V (*continued*)

System	Products	Refs.
	(C₆H₆) (HOAc)	168
	34%	169
		170
(+)	(±) 12.5% (C₆H₆) 17% (HOAc)	102, 171, 172

L. Table VI. Allylic Oxidation with Tl^{III}*

TABLE VI

Allylic Oxidation with Tl^{III}*

$$CH_2=C\underset{\diagdown CH_3}{\overset{\diagup CH_3}{}} \xrightarrow{Tl(OAc)_3} \underset{\diagup CH_3 \quad (5\%)}{\overset{AcOCH_2\diagdown}{}}C=CH_2 \qquad 107$$

3hr at 80°
Minor allylic oxidation with butenes   (Unpublished)

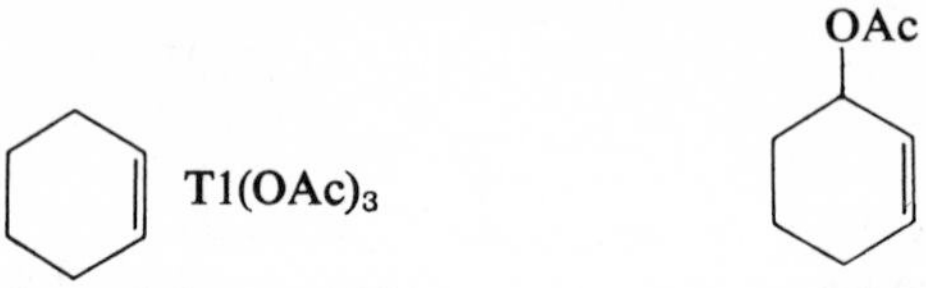

$Tl(OAc)_3$

OAc

2–3% (25°)
11% (95°)   95,96

Several days at 20°   + Diacetates and ring
                                       contraction products

* This again is a minor outcome, diacetates being major products. Few examples have been reported.

VII. FRIEDEL-CRAFT REACTIONS

The reaction of olefins with aromatic compounds in the presence of mercuric salt and catalyst is a new type of Friedel-Craft synthesis and the mechanism and synthetic utility of the scheme have been explored by Ichikawa, et al.[175,176] The reactions fall into the content of electrophilic aromatic substitution.

$$ArH + CH_2=CH_2 + HgZ_2 \longrightarrow ArCH_2CH_2Z + Hg + HZ$$

or

$$2ArH + CH_2=CH_2 + HgZ_2 \longrightarrow ArCH_2CH_2Ar + Hg + 2Hz$$

Also, β-arylethyl acetates may be formed.

The nature of the catalysts and reaction conditions were in harmony with an ionic reaction. An intermediate organomercurial of the type $ArCH_2CH_2\text{-}HgZ$ was isolated and appeared to eliminate aromatic mercuration as a

A. Table VII. Reactions of Alkenes with Aromatics in the Presence of Hg^{II} and Catalyst[176,177]

TABLE VII

Reactions of Alkenes with Aromatics in the Presence of Hg^{II} and Catalyst[176,177]

Alkene	Aromatic	Product	Catalyst
Ethylene	Benzene	*sym*-Diphenylethane β-Arylethyl acetate β-Arylethyl alcohol Bibenzyl	H_2SO_4, H_3PO_4, etc.
Ethylene	Anisole	*p*-Anisil 1-(*o*-Methoxyphenyl)-2- (*p*-methoxyphenyl)ethane	H_3PO_4 (98%)
Ethylene	Anisole	β-(*p*-Methoxyphenyl)ethyl acetate	$HClO_4$ (60%)
Ethylene	Toluene	β-(*p*-Tolyl)ethyl (95%) acetate and some *o*-tolyl (5%)	$HClO_4$ (60%) or H_3PO_4
Ethylene	*o*-Xylene	*p*-(1-*o*-Xylyl)ethyl acetate	$HClO_4$ or H_3PO_4
	Naphthalene	β-(Naphthyl)ethyl acetate,	$HClO_4$ or H_3PO_4
		di-(α-naphthyl)ethane	$HClO_4$ or H_3PO_4
Ethylene	Chlorobenzene	β-(*o*-Chlorophenyl)ethyl acetate,	$HClO_4$ or H_3PO_4
		β-(*p*-Chlorophenyl)ethyl acetate	$HClO_4$ or H_3PO_4
Propylene	Anisole	1-(*p*-Methoxyphenyl)-2-propyl acetate	$HClO_4$, BF_3
2-Butene	Anisole	3-(*p*-Methoxyphenyl)-2-butyl acetate	H_3PO_4, $HClO_4$, BF_3
Styrene	Anisole	1-Phenyl-1,2-bis-(*p*-methoxy- phenyl)ethane	$HClO_4$
Cyclohexene	Anisole	Methoxyphenylcyclohexene, di-(methoxyphenyl)- cyclohexane	$HClO_4$

possible pathway.[177] The mechanism most in accord with Ichikawa's data and subsequent work (mainly by Jensen) in organomercurial solvolysis,[7] appears to be the following:

$$R—CH{=}CH_2 + HgZ_2 \rightleftharpoons R—\underset{\underset{Z}{|}}{C}H—CH_2HgZ$$

$$R—\underset{\underset{Z}{|}}{C}H—CH_2HgZ + H^\oplus \rightleftharpoons R—CH{\cdots}CH_2 + HZ$$

Subsequent steps probably involve $HClO_4$ catalyzed solvolysis:

$$RHgX \longrightarrow R^\oplus + Hg^0 + X^\ominus \longrightarrow R - X \quad \text{etc.}$$

A free carbonium ion, however, is not the active electrophilic species, as judged by lack of rearrangement in suitable systems.[180] For a more complete discussion the reader is referred to the original work.[2,175-177]

This synthetic approach was extended to ethyl acetoacetate in place of aromatics,[179] and from ethylene and $Hg(OAc)_2$, in the presence of BF_3—CH_3COOH complex as catalyst, ethyl α-(2-acetoxyethyl)acetoacetate, via ethyl α-(2-chloromercuryethyl)acetoacetate. The full potential of this reaction, involving active methylene compounds, was explored,[180] as outlined below.

$$
\begin{array}{c}
\overset{\displaystyle R_2}{\underset{\displaystyle OAc}{\overset{|}{\underset{|}{R_1-C}}}}\overset{\displaystyle}{\underset{\displaystyle HgOAc}{\overset{|}{\underset{|}{-CH}}}}-R_3 + R_4-\overset{\displaystyle H}{\underset{\displaystyle H}{\overset{|}{\underset{|}{C}}}}-R_5
\end{array}
\xrightarrow[\text{catalyst}]{\text{HClO}_4}
\overset{\displaystyle H}{\underset{\displaystyle R_1-\overset{|}{\underset{|}{C}}-CH-HgOAc}{\overset{|}{\underset{|}{R_4-C-R_5}}}}
$$

Oxymercurial   Active methylene R_2 R_3

(1-5)

$\swarrow$ H$_2$O, NaCl

$$
\overset{\displaystyle R_5 \quad R_1 \quad R_3}{R_4-CH-\overset{|}{\underset{|}{C}}-CH-HgCl}
\qquad
\underset{\displaystyle R_2}{}
$$

(6-12)

(1) $R_1, R_2, R_3 = H$
(2) $R_1 = R_3 = H; R_2 = CH_3$
(3) $R_1 = R_3 = H; R_2 = C_6H_5$
(4) $R_1 = H; R_2 = R_3 = CH_3$
(5) $R_1 = R_2 = CH_3; R_3 = H$
(6) $R_1 = R_2 = R_3 = H; R_4 = R_5 = CH_3CO$
(7) $R_1 = R_2 = R_3 = H; R_4 = CH_3CO, R_4 = C_6H_5CO$
(8) $R_1 = R_2 = R_3 = H; R_4 = R_5 = C_6H_5CO$
(9) $R_1 = R_3 = H; R_2 = CH_3; R_4 = R_5 = CH_3CO$
(10) $R_1 = R_3 = H; R_2 = C_6H_5; R_4 = R_5 = CH_3CO$
(11) $R_1 = C_6H_5; R_2 = R_3 = H; R_4 = CH_3CO; R_4 = C_6H_5CO$
(12) $R_1 = C_6H_5; R_2 = R_3 = H; R_4 = C_6H_5CO; R_5 = EtOCO$

A requirement for reaction was that substantial concentration of enol form be present for the active methylene reagent. The isolated mercurials above also served as sources of cyclopropanes by base- (or in some cases, acid-) promoted demercurations. The mechanisms that may be operative are outlined below.[180]

$$
\underset{\displaystyle Ac}{\overset{\displaystyle Ac}{\diagdown}}CH-CH_2CH_2HgCl
\underset{\text{base}}{\rightleftharpoons}
\underset{\displaystyle Ac}{\overset{\displaystyle Ac}{\diagdown}}\overset{\displaystyle \ominus}{\underset{\displaystyle \cdot\cdot}{C}}-CH_2CH_2HgCl
$$

$\downarrow$

$$
\underset{\displaystyle CH_2 \triangle CH_2}{\overset{\displaystyle CH_3CO \diagup \diagdown COCH_3}{C}}
$$

Dimedone also reacts with the ethylene-oxymercurial to form a substituted ethyl mercurial, which decomposes with base to form the spiro compound shown.[181] The slower acid-induced demercuration was considered to be an

$$CH_3-C\overset{O}{\overset{\parallel}{-}}C=\overset{OH}{\overset{|}{C}}-CH_3 \xrightarrow{-H^+}$$

intramolecular alkylation.[180]

The general scheme of synthesis through oxymetallics was extended to Tl^{III}[18] and Pb^{IV}, and the reactions of acetylacetone with a number of olefins in the presence of Tl^{III}[182] and Pb^{IV}[183] were studied. The actual details are outlined in Table VIII. Although no intermediate organothallium or organolead compounds were isolated, the conclusion seems highly reasonable that oxythallation and oxyplumbation are key steps in the processes.

$$RCH=CH_2 + Tl(OAc)_3 \xrightarrow{R'OH} RCH-CH_2-Tl(OAc)_2$$
$$OR'$$

$$CH_3-CO-CH-COCH_3 \xleftarrow{\quad} CH_3COCH_2COCH_3$$
$$R-CH-CH_2Tl(OAc)_2$$

$$H^\oplus \downarrow$$

$$-TlOAc-HOAc$$

$$CH_3-C=C-\overset{O}{\overset{\parallel}{C}}-CH_3 \xrightarrow{-H^\oplus} \text{dihydrofuran}$$

B. Table VIII. Reactions of Olefins with Active Methylene Compounds in the Presence of Tl^{III} and Pb^{IV} [182,183]

TABLE VIII

Reactions of Olefins with Active Methylene Compounds in the Presence of Tl^{III} and Pb^{IV} [182,183]

Metal acetate	Olefin	Substrate	Product(s)
Tl, HClO$_4$ HOAc	C$_2$H$_4$	Acetylacetone	3-Acetyl-2-methyl-4,5-dihydrofuran (90%), 1,1-diacetylcyclopropane (4%), pentan-1-acetoxy-4-one (2%)
Tl, HClO$_4$ HOAc	Styrene	Acetylacetone	3-Acetyl-2-methyl-4-phenyl-4,5-dihydrofuran (69%)
Tl, HClO$_4$ MeOH	Styrene		3-Acetyl-2-methyl-4-phenyl-4,5-dihydrofuran, 1,1-dimethoxy-2-phenylethane
Tl,HClO$_4$ HOAc	Ethylene	Anisole	Ethyleneglycol diacetate (78%), anisylethyl acetate (18%)
Pb^{IV}, HClO$_4$ Benzene-HOAc (7:1)	Styrene		Acetoxyacetylacetone (20%) 3-Acetyl-2-methyl-5-phenyl-4,5-dihydrofuran (20%)

VIII. CHEMICAL REDUCTION OF OXYMERCURIALS

In the determination of structures of oxymetallics referred to previously, a method of locating the site of metal atom attachment to the organic fragment was stereospecific reduction in a deuterium environment, to yield the deutero-substituted compound. The paper by Bordwell and Douglass surveys the scope,[184] selectivity, and possible mechanisms of these reductions, usually performed with sodium amalgam in D$_2$O, or boro-hydrides or deuterides. However, from a synthetic point of view, the ready reduction of oxymercurials provides a convenient way to obtain alcohols and ethers from the alkenes in two steps.

Depending on the nature of the reducing agent and structural features in the mercurial, etc., the reduction of alkylmercurials may proceed as below

$$R-Hg-Y \longrightarrow R-Hg-R \longrightarrow R-H + Hg°$$

However, when R contains a β-alkoxy group (as in oxymercurials), deoxymercuration may become a very important side reaction. Reducing agents that have been used are sodium amalgam (which produces largely R—H),

A. Table IX. Examples of Chemical Reduction of Selected Oxymercurials

TABLE IX

Examples of Chemical Reduction of Selected Oxymercurials

Oxymercurial	Reduction System	Product	Refs
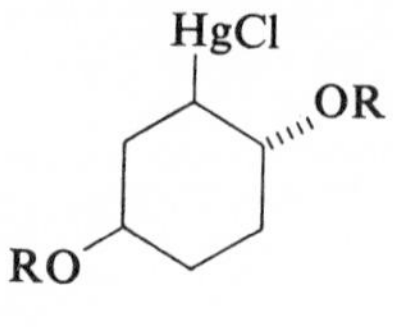 HgCl, OR, RO	$NH_2NH_2 \cdot H_2O$; $OH^\ominus$ Reflux 16 hr	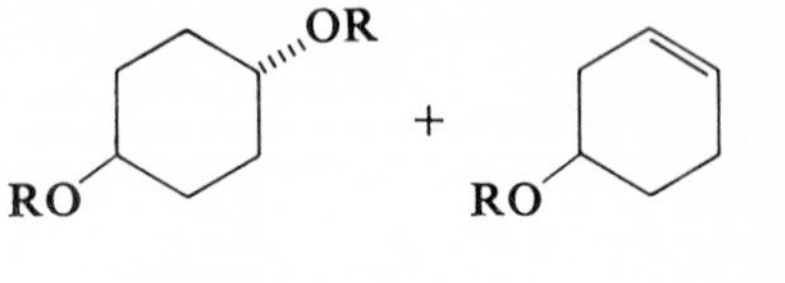 OR, RO + RO 38% R = Me 35% R = Me 70% R = H	61
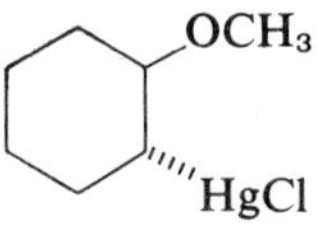 OCH₃, HgCl	$NaBH_4$ alkaline H_2O	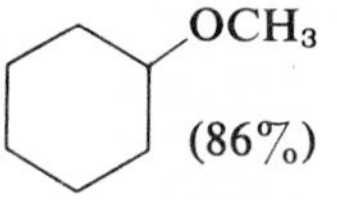 OCH₃ (86%)	184
	NH_2NH_2 Long reflux	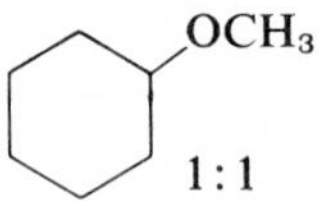 OCH₃ 1:1 + deoxymercuration	
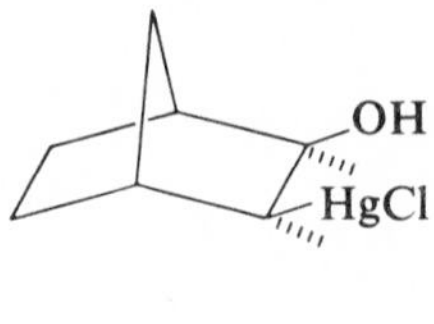 OH, HgCl	$NH_2NH_2, OH^\ominus$ 6-hr reflux	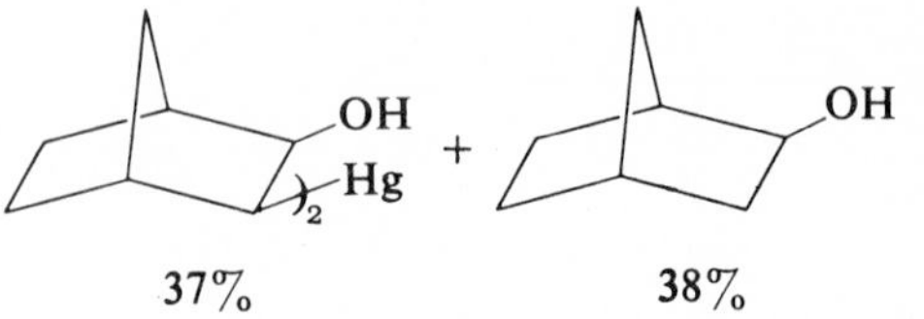 OH, Hg₂ + OH 37% 38%	32
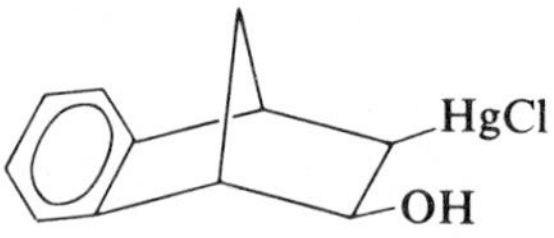 HgCl, OH	NaHg, $OH^\ominus$ 6 hr	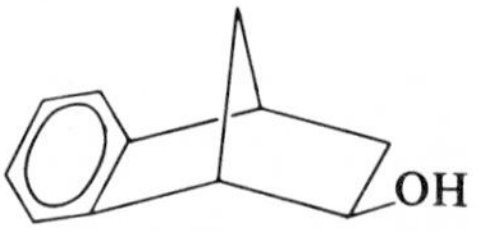 OH	32
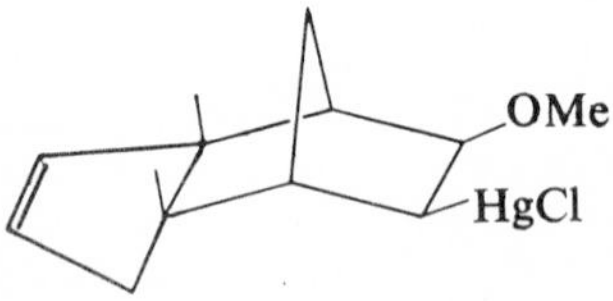 OMe, HgCl	Na(Hg)ₓ H_2O	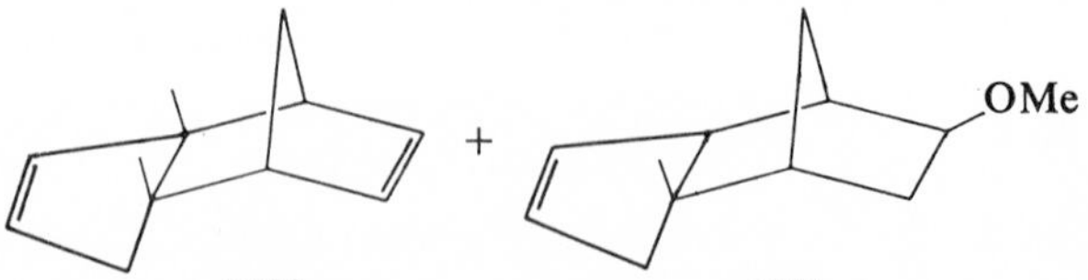 + OMe 50% 50%	55

(continued)

TABLE IX (*continued*)

Oxymercurial	Reduction System	Product	Refs.

sodium stannite and hydrazine (reduction to R_2Hg stage), and sodium trimethoxyborohydride.[100] Some examples of these reductions are given in Table IX. Reduction occurs readily when Y in RHgY is strongly electronegative (as —Br, Cl, OAc, —OR, —OH) but slowly when Y = R.

The main value of the $NaBH_4$/alkali system is that deoxymercuration is essentially eliminated. As regards mechanisms for these reductions Bordwell and Douglass considered the following as likely:[184]

$$H_3\overset{\ominus}{B}\text{\tiny{''''}}Y \longrightarrow H_3\overset{\ominus}{B}\text{---}Y \longrightarrow R\text{---}H + Hg°$$

$$\begin{array}{c} H \downarrow Hg \\ | \\ R \end{array} \quad \left(\begin{array}{c} H\text{---}Hg \\ | \\ R \end{array} \right)$$

Deuterium-labeling experiments indicated that the source of the hydrogen is the borohydride and not the water. The observed retention of configuration is consistent with the following:

$$\overset{H\text{---}BH_3}{\underset{/}{\overset{|}{\underset{\text{''''}}{C}}}\text{---}Hg\text{---}Y} \longrightarrow \overset{H}{\underset{/}{\overset{|}{\underset{\text{''''}}{C}}}\text{---}Hg}$$

although the reduction seemed to depart from a stereospecific path under some conditions.

The route of oxymercuration, followed by reduction with $BH_4^{\ominus}$, is of preparative value for alcohols, ethers, and lactones, and was originally discussed by Henbest.[61] Bordwell and Douglass, in their studies, effected the following conversions: Methallyl alcohol → 2,2,5,5-tetramethyl-1,4-dioxan; 1-alkoxy-2-propanol → 2,6-dimethyl-1,4-dioxan; 5-hexen-2-ol or 1,5-hexadiene → 2,5-dimethyltetrahydrofuran; 1,5-cyclooctadiene → 1,5-epoxycyclooctane; and 4-cycloocten-1-ol → 1,4-epoxycyclooctane. The latter two are particularly important syntheses of oxabicyclononanes, since other routes have associated stereochemical and isomerization problems.[184]

H. C. Brown and co-workers have developed this technique to the point of great synthetic utility; their methods are described in a number of papers.[94,185,186] The method is particularly important, since it provides a convenient method for the Markovnikov hydration of alkenes. The procedure seems broadly applicable, and no problem was encountered at the preparative level. Previously, it was customary to isolate the mercurial (usually as the chloride) and then effect the reduction step. However, the work of Brown indicates that there is no particular disadvantage in carrying out the demercuration stage with $NaBH_4$ in situ without isolating the oxymercurial. Little or no rearrangement appeared to accompany the hydration, as in the case of hydroboration-oxidation.

$$\underset{\underset{Me}{|}}{\overset{\overset{Me}{|}}{Me\text{---}C}}\text{---}CH\text{=}CH_2 \xrightarrow{HB} \xrightarrow{[O]} \underset{\underset{Me}{|}}{\overset{\overset{Me}{|}}{Me\text{---}C}}\text{---}\underset{\underset{OH}{|}}{CH_2}\text{---}CH_2$$

$$\xrightarrow{Hg(OAc)_2,\ NaBH_4} \underset{\underset{Me\ \ OH}{|\ \ \ |}}{\overset{\overset{Me}{|}}{Me\text{---}C}}\text{---}CH\text{---}CH_3$$

A typical procedure, as described by Brown is given below.

B. Preparation of 2-Hexanol from 1-Hexene

To a magnetically stirred solution of mercuric acetate (3.19 g, 10 mM) in water (10 cc) and tetrahydrofuran (10 cc) was added 1-hexene (10 mM); the solution was stirred for ca. 10 min at room temperature to bring about the oxymercuration. Sodium hydroxide ($3M$ soln, 10 cc) was added, followed by 10 cc of a $0.5M$ NaBH$_4$ solution in $3.0M$ NaOH. Reduction is very rapid and the mercury settles out. Sodium chloride is added to saturate the upper layer, and the ether layer contains 2-hexanol in high yield (ca. 96%).

The results for some representative olefins are outlined in Table X.

C. Table X. Hydration of Alkenes by Oxymercuration-Reduction Sequence

TABLE X

Hydration of Alkenes by Oxymercuration-Reduction Sequence

Alkene	Reaction time,[a] min		Yield, %
1-Hexene	10	2-Hexanol	94
1-Dodecene[b]	70	2-Dodecanol	89
cis-2-Pentene	10	65% 2-, 35% 3-Pentanol	96
trans-2-Pentene	15	54% 2-, 46% 3-Pentanol	93
2-Methyl-1-butene	5	2-Methyl-2-butanol	88
2-Methyl-2-butene	10	2-Methyl-2-butanol	93
3,3-Dimethyl-1-butene	20	3,3-Dimethyl-2-butanol	92
2,3-Dimethyl-2-butene	35	2,3-Dimethyl-2-butanol	84
2,4,4-Trimethyl-1-pentene	30	2,4,4-Trimethyl-2-pentanol	94
Cyclopentene	1 hr	Cyclopentanol	89
Cyclohexene	11	Cyclohexanol	97
Cyclooctene[b]	3 hr	Cyclooctanol	86
1-Methylcyclopentene	6	1-Methylcyclopentanol	91
1-Methylcyclohexene	5	1-Methylcyclohexanol	98
Methylenecyclohexane	5	1-Methylcyclohexanol	97
Styrene	5	1-Phenylethanol	94
α-Methylstyrene	10	2-Phenyl-2-propanol	93

[a] Time to complete the oxymercuration stage.
[b] Heterogeneous system.

In contrast to the usual addition of methyl Grignard reagent to bicyclic ketones to produce *endo* tertiary alcohol, the oxymercuration-demercuration sequence produces the epimeric tertiary alcohol.[186] The hydration occurs from the more accessible side of the molecule, which leads to the preferential formation of the *cis*-dimethyl cyclopentanols:

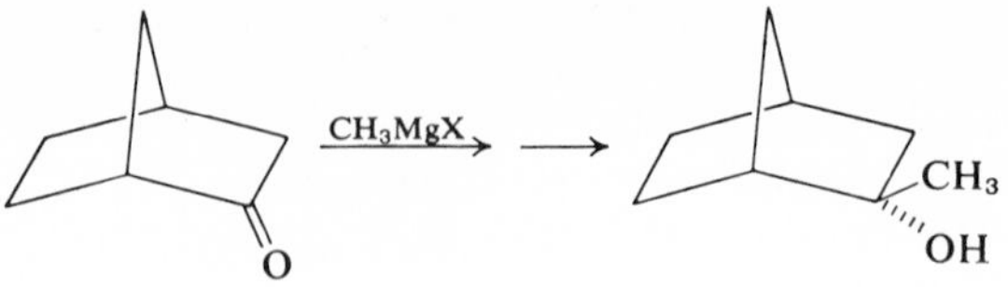

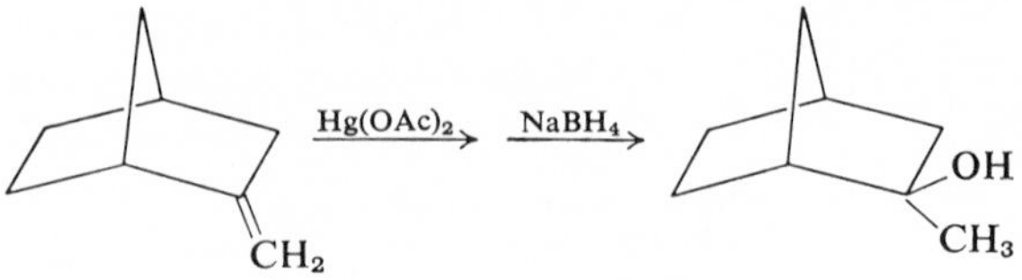

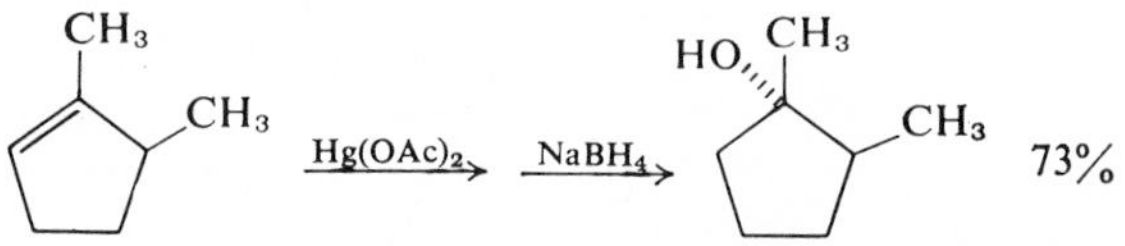

and the *exo* alcohols in the cases of the bicyclics. The results of these stereo-selectivities are assembled in Table XI.[186] In the cases of norbornene, 7,7-dimethylnorbornene and related compounds, *exo* alcohols of high iso-meric purity are obtained.

D. Table XI. Hydration of Bicyclic Alkenes by Oxymercuration-Reduction Sequence

TABLE XI

Hydration of Bicyclic Alkenes by Oxymercuration-Reduction Sequence

Alkene	Reaction time	Products
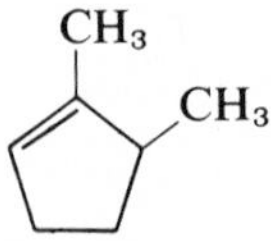	5 min	73% *cis*-1,2-Dimethylcyclopentanol, 27% *trans*-1,2-dimethylcyclo-pentanol
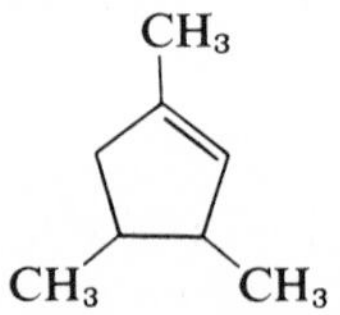	15 min	76% *cis,cis*-1,2,4-Trimethyl-cyclopentanol, 24% *trans,trans*-1,3,4-Trimethyl-cyclopentanol

(*continued*)

TABLE XI (*continued*)

Alkene	Reaction time	Products
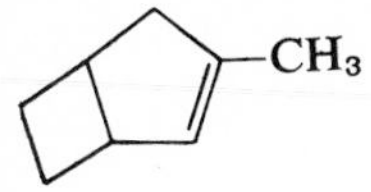 —CH$_3$	5 min	78% *exo* (*t*-OH) 22% *endo*
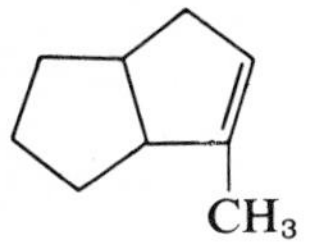 CH$_3$	5 min	84% *exo* 16% *endo*
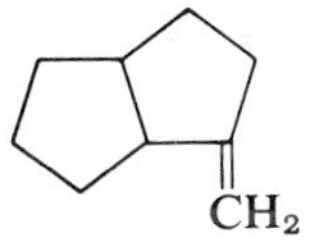 CH$_2$	5 min	89% *exo* 11% *endo*
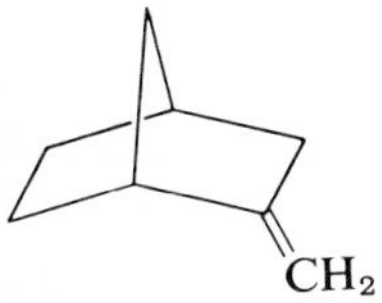 CH$_2$	5 min	99.5% *exo* 0.5% *endo*
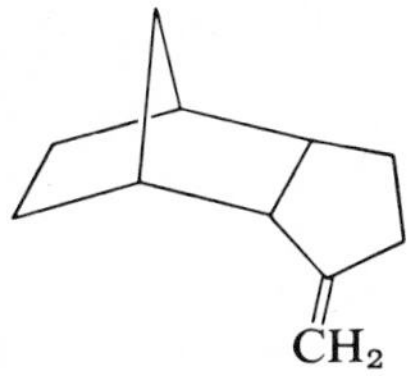 CH$_2$	1 min	100% *exo*
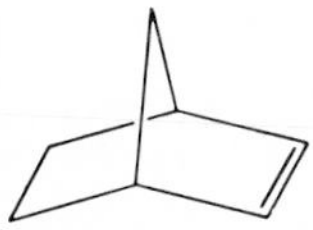	½ min	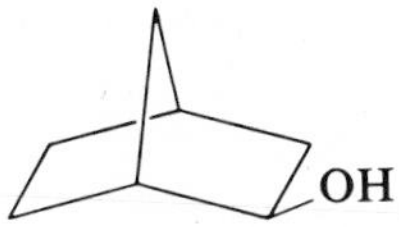 OH 100% yield 99.8% *exo*
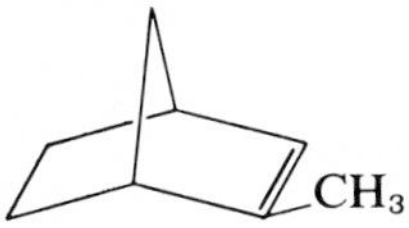 CH$_3$	½ min	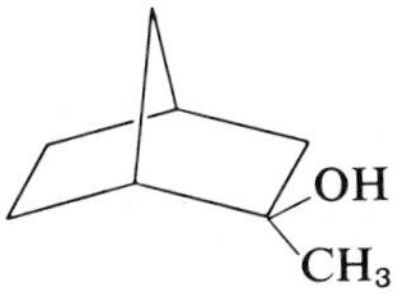 OH CH$_3$ 86% yield 99.8% *exo*
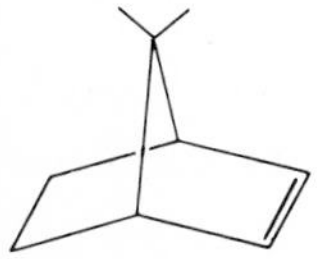	15 min	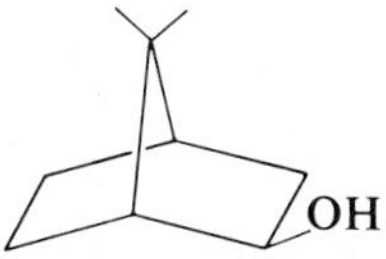 84% yield 99.8% *exo* OH

(*continued*)

TABLE XI (*continued*)

Alkene	Reaction time	Products

5 min

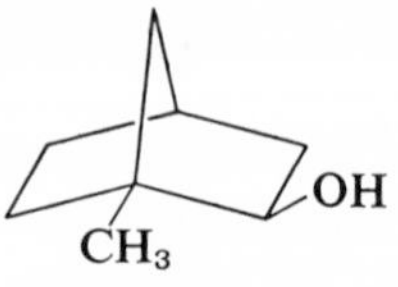

48%   48%

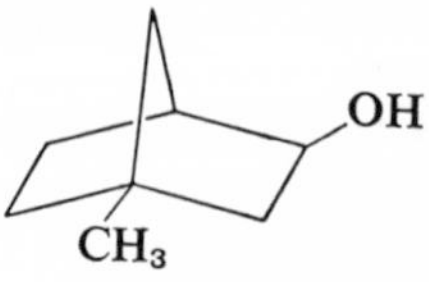

100% yield + some isomerized
tertiary alcohol

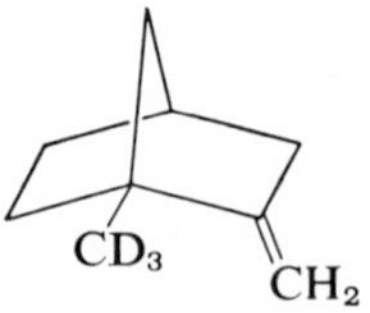

~5 min   (?)

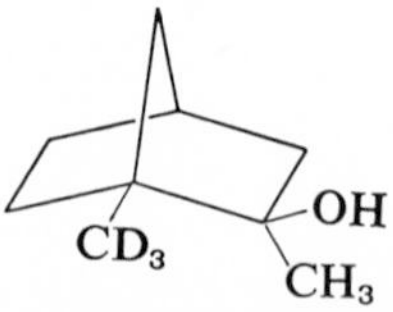

Metal hydride reductions of other oxymetallics have been reported but pertain exclusively to the location of the metal atom attachment;[2] at the present stage they have no broadly based synthetic scope.

IX. CHEMICAL REACTIONS OF OXYTHALLATION AND OXYPLUMBATION ADDUCTS

The general equation to describe these reactions is written below, but there is little evidence on these classes of compounds, of which only a few examples

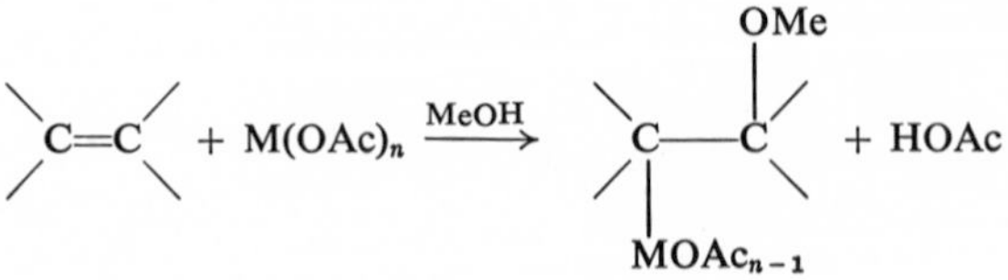

$$\underset{/}{\overset{\backslash}{C}}=\underset{\backslash}{\overset{/}{C}} + M(OAc)_n \xrightarrow{MeOH} \underset{/\ \ |}{\overset{\backslash\ \ |}{C-C}} + HOAc$$

OMe ... MOAc$_{n-1}$

are known. Criegee[111] appears to have isolated the first definite example of an oxythallation adduct from the reaction of styrene and thallic acetate in

$$C_6H_5-CH=CH_2 \xrightarrow[\text{MeOH}]{(TlOAc_3)} C_6H_5-CH-CH_2Tl(OAc)_2$$
$$\qquad\qquad\qquad\qquad\qquad\quad |$$
$$\qquad\qquad\qquad\qquad\qquad OCH_3$$

methanol. On heating this adduct, dethallation occurred to produce acetoxy products, including that due to a phenyl migration

$$C_6H_5-\underset{\underset{OCH_3}{|}}{CH}-CH_2Tl(OAc)_2 \xrightarrow[-TlOAc]{130°} C_6H_5-\underset{\underset{OCH_3}{|}}{CH}-\overset{\oplus}{CH_2}$$

$$C_6H_5-\underset{\underset{OCH_3}{|}}{CH}-CH_2OAc \qquad C_6H_5CH_2-\underset{\underset{OCH_3}{|}}{\overset{OAc}{\overset{|}{CH}}}$$

Treatment with LiAlH$_4$ led to deoxythallation (cf. Hg). Also o-allylphenol produces a stable dihydrobenzofuran derivative.[107]

The clearest information on such oxythallation adducts was due to Pande and Winstein,[21] who prepared and studied the adducts from norbornadiene and norbornene, and demonstrated oxythallation to be somewhat analogous to oxymercuration. A dry chloroform solution of norbornadiene reacts with thallic acetate to produce an adduct that could be precipitated with pentane. NaBH$_4$ leads largely to deoxythallation, but sodium amalgam produces the reduction product.

The *cis,exo* stereochemistry of the adducts was established by Anet,[39] from detailed NMR examination, utilizing the Nuclear Overhauser Effect. The spectra are considerably complicated by large, long range [205]Tl and [203]Tl—H spin couplings. Some idea of these spin interactions can be obtained from the following table.

Assignment	$J(Tl-H)$ (same sign)	(Chemical shift τ)
H_1	649	7.13
H_2	797	6.50
H_3	624	5.07
H_4	263	7.46
H_6 *exo*	817	8.29

Of five protons γ to the thallium H_6 *exo* has $J \sim 817$ Hz and H_4 has $J \sim 263$ Hz. A coupling constant $J_{H_2-H_3} \sim 6.6$ Hz was considered consistent with a *cis,endo* relation of H_2 and H_3. A similar approach was used for the norbornadiene adduct, which also has the *cis,exo* stereochemistry.

Acetolysis of these adducts occurs rapidly at room temperature, by C—Tl bond heterolysis to produce carbonium ions.[21] Few details are available because of the high lability of these adducts, leading to deplumbation

and solvolysis products. Consequently, no stable characterized adducts have been reported, although Pande and Winstein have reported that norbornene yields an adduct on treatment with $Pb(OAc)_4$ in chloroform,[21] but attempts to characterize it failed.

However, the products of the reactions between olefins and $Pb(OAc)_4$ are generally explained as involving such adducts (see below). Some indirect evidence was produced by Ichikawa, et al., who studied the reaction of $Pb(OAc)_4$ and anethole in acetic acid.[187] Iodometric analyses confirmed a

$$MeO—C_6H_4—CH{=}CH—CH_3 + Pb(OAc)_4 \xrightarrow{HOAc} MeO—C_6H_4—\underset{\underset{OAc}{|}}{CH}—\underset{\underset{OAc}{|}}{CH}—CH_3$$
$$+ Pb(OAc)_2$$

rapid decrease in Pb^{IV} concentration, with the formation of a color on mixing. This suggested rapid attainment of an equilibrium most plausibly oxyplumbation. A slower second-order reaction followed, leading to diacetates,

$$\text{anethole} + \text{Pb(OAc)}_4 \rightleftharpoons \text{adduct}$$

$$\text{adduct} \longrightarrow \text{products}$$

The major products of alkene-Pb(OAc)_4 reactions in acetic acid (under polar conditions) are diacetates,[7] with some allylic oxidation and other products (see above). The formation of diacetates is reasonably clear, although the path to allylic oxidation is not settled.[27]

(acetoxy participation?)

X. CHEMICAL REACTIONS OF OXYPALLADATION AND OXYPLATINATION ADDUCTS

The investigations have been confined largely to their structural determinations by spectroscopic and reduction methods. These have been discussed previously. An interesting reactivity difference has been noted between the Pt^{II} complexes below on treatment with HCl.[34,67]

The conversion to the diene complex by treatment with HCl is complete in 15 min at room temperature, whereas the Pt^{II} complex requires boiling for several hours. There is sufficient acid in commercial chloroform to catalyze the change to the ethoxy compound in the presence of ethanol.

The most important aspects of the reactions of these adducts (particularly Pd^{II}) are discussed in the section on Pd^{II} oxidations.

XI. SUMMARY AND CONCLUSIONS

An attempt has been made to organize a large number of observations into the framework of a single reaction type: oxymetalation. The structures, mechanisms, and synthetic utility have been discussed, and give promise of an unusually productive and fertile area in organic and organometallic chemistry. Although, at this stage, our understanding of the structures and mechanisms appears to be more advanced than synthetic developments, this situation may be rapidly adjusted. The extension of the reaction to other metals can be anticipated with some confidence, and more thorough examination of the Tl^{III} and Pb^{IV} reactions is warranted. Electrophilic and related additions to olefins would seem to be a common reaction of suitable metal ions, with interesting applications in mechanism and synthesis.

XII. EXPERIMENTAL PROCEDURES

In this section the details of the syntheses of a number of oxymetallics of mercury, thallium, platinum, and palladium are described; they illustrate the general approaches.

1. 2-(Bromomercuri-)ethanol[25]

Mercuric nitrate monohydrate ($Hg(NO_3)_2/H_2O$; 16.32 g, 0.047 mole) was dissolved in H_2O (300 cc) and glacial acetic acid (3 cc). This was chilled in a refrigerator and saturated with ethylene from a storage cylinder. With the ethylene bubbling, NaOH ($\sim 1M$) was added dropwise, until a yellow basic precipitate formed and persisted. When this had dissolved, more alkali was added and the procedure continued until no precipitate was formed on the addition of alkali. To the filtered alkaline solution was added KBr (5.6 g, 0.047 mole). After 1 hr, the solution was acidified with solid CO_2 and a copious precipitate formed. Yield 12–13 g (70–80%).

2. Acetoxyethylmercuric acetate[27]

Ethylene from a storage cylinder was introduced into a magnetically stirred solution of mercuric acetate (20 g, 0.062 mole) in glacial acetic acid (30 cc) at room temperature. When the crystals of mercuric acetate had dissolved and the NaOH test for mercuric ion was negative (ca. 3 hr), the reaction mixture was filtered. The removal of acetic acid (~ 15 cc) under vacuum caused the deposition of 17 g of raw crystals. (Yield $\sim 80\%$). Recrystallization from ligroin gave 12 g of mercurial mp 96–97°.

3. 4-Chloromercuric-3-methoxy-1-butene[28]

To a solution of 31.8 g (0.1 mole) of mercuric acetate in methanol (300 cc) at 0° was added 16.3 g (0.3 mole) of 1,3-butadiene in methanol (40 cc). After 5 min at this temperature, the system gave a negative test for mercuric ion, and was filtered into 100 cc of 10% aqueous NaCl. The precipitated oil was taken up in 100 cc of chloroform, washed with water, and evaporated, leaving 29.1 g (91%) of crude product, mp 40–44°. Recrystallization from methanol (which separates a small amount of 1,4-dichloromercuri-2,3-dimethoxybutane) yielded the product, mp 49–50°.

4. α-2-Methoxycyclopentylmercuric chloride [29]

Alpha denotes the kinetically formed *trans* isomer.

A suspension of mercuric acetate (89.4 g, 0.28 mole) in methanol (400 cc), containing cyclopentene (20 cc, bp 44–44.8°) became homogeneous after it was treated with 78 ml (0.195 mole) of 10% aqueous NaOH, and the solution filtered. The filtrate was treated with aqueous 5% NaCl to precipitate 64 g (88%) of the mercurial mp, 76–77°. Crystallization from ethanol (charcoal) produced pure α-2-methoxycyclopentylmercuric chloride, mp 83–84°.

5. β-2-Methoxycyclopentylmercuric chloride [29]

The β denotes the mercurial resulting from epimerization at C_1, and has the *cis* configuration.

A solution of 16.7 g (0.05 mole) of the α-mercurial in 80 cc of 5% aqueous NaOH (ca. 0.1 mole) was heated almost to boiling. Over an hour, hydrazine hydrate (85%; 0.5 cc, 0.008 mole) was added and the mixture was refluxed for 1 hr. Upon cooling, metallic mercury (3.6 g) separated. The aqueous phase was filtered, treated with NaCl and then with CO_2 to yield an oil (9.6 g). This was added to methanol (30 cc) and followed by concentrated HCl (1.33 cc, 0.013 mole). After exactly 1 min, the solution was poured into 10% alkali solution (20 ml, 0.05 mole). The precipitates were separated and the mercurial obtained by treating the filtrate with CO_2. The mercurial (6.0 g, 40%), mp 56–57°) was crystallized from methanol, mp 59°.

The above two procedures also serve for the homologous, cyclohexene-derived mercurials.

6. 1-Acetoxymercurimethyl-1,2-dihydrobenzofuran [30]

A solution of mercuric acetate (23.7 g, 0.074 mole) in 100 cc of water was slowly added with stirring to a suspension of 10 g of *o*-allylphenol in water (100 cc). The reaction mixture was stirred for an additional hour, during which time a gray oil separated. The aqueous solution was decanted and, on standing, crystals separated out. Subsequently (after several hours), the oil solidified. The crystals and the oil were crystallized from water or alcohols, forming white plates, mp 80–81°, in nearly quantitative yield.

7. cis-Exo-3-Hydroxy-2-chloromercuribicyclo[2.2.1]heptane [31,32]

A reaction mixture consisting of norbornene (0.94 g, 0.01 mole), mercuric acetate (3.18 g, 0.01 mole), and nitric acid (0.2 ml) in water (40 cc) was allowed to react for 1 hr and then treated with aqueous NaCl (0.01 mole).

The product (85%) melted at 125–127° and could be crystallized from 50% aqueous ethanol. Omission of the nitric acid leads to the production of some acetate, which may be saponified.

8. cis-exo-3-Methoxy-2-chloromercuribicyclo[2.2.1]heptane[31,32]

To norbornene in methanol (0.46 g, 0.005 mole in 25 cc) was added mercuric acetate (1.6 g, 0.005 mole) and a trace of acidic catalyst. After 1 hr, the solution was chilled to 5–10°, and treated with aqueous NaCl (0.005 mole). Filtration of the product (ca. 95% yield) and recrystallization from carbon tetrachloride gave the pure mercurial, mp 120–121°, in greater than 90% yield.

9. cis-2-Acetoxy-3-(chloromercuri)-bicyclo[2.2.2]octane[33]

A mixture consisting of bicyclo[2.2.2]octene (2.0 mM), mercuric acetate (0.7 g, 2.2 mM), and glacial acetic acid (6 cc) was stirred for 15 min. The mercuric acetate dissolved, and the solution gave no mercuric oxide on treatment with a base. This mixture was poured rapidly into a cold (0°) solution of NaCl (0.2 g in 50 cc) to precipitate a colorless solid, which melted at about 10° (85%).

10. cis-exo-2-Acetoxy-3-(diacetatothallic)-bicyclo[2.2.1]heptane[21]

A dry chloroform solution of norbornene (1 molar equivalent) was shaken with thallic acetate (1 mole) to produce a solution of the oxythallation product. The addition of dry pentane gave a high yield of the oxythallation product, mp 150–151°. This can be crystallized from chloroform-pentane.

The same general procedure serves for the preparation of the oxythallation adduct of norbornadiene, styrene, and o-allylphenol.

No oxyplumbation products have been isolated and characterized.

11. Dicyclopentadiene dichloroplatinum(II)[8]

Dicyclopentadiene (8 cc) was added to sodium chloroplatinite (Na_2PtCl_4 hydrate) (8 g) in propanol (200 cc) and shaken at room temperature for several days. The crystals that formed were filtered and washed with ether and dried. Reprecipitation from a chloroform solution with ether gave pure product, 200–220° (decomp.). Other alcohols may be employed as solvents.

12. Di-μ-chlorobis(3a,4,7,7a-tetrahydro-exo-6-methoxy-endo-4,7-methanoindene-endo-5σ,2π)diplatinum(II)[34]

Dicyclopentadienedichloroplatinum(II) (0.4 g) was suspended in methanol (30 cc) and heated to boiling; then sodium acetate (ca. 0.3 g) was added. The solids dissolved and, subsequent to further heating, a white product formed.

This was filtered, dried, and recrystallized from chloroform-ether (90%), mp 210–220°.

The methoxy derivatives of Pt^{II} and Pd^{II} of other diolefins are formed by analogous reactions.

13. Di-μ-chloro-bis(2-methoxy-3,N,N-dimethylaminopropyl)-dipalladium(II)[10]

Lithium chloropalladate(II) (1.30 g, 0.005 mole) in methanol (20 cc) was mixed with N,N-dimethylallylamine (0.85 g, 0.01 mole) in methanol (15 cc). A yellow precipitate formed but soon redissolved. The product crystallized from solution at −20°, and was filtered, yielding 1.20 g (97%) mp 124–126°.

14. Preparation of Thallic Acetate

Oxythallation usually employs thallium(III) acetate as the thallium source; the procedure we have found most suitable for its preparation follows.

Thallic oxide ($Tl_2O_3 \cdot 50$ g) and 300 cc of glacial acetic acid were stirred at 65° until the brown-black mass had passed into solution (~1 day). The solution was filtered and on cooling and concentration, deposited 73 g (85%) of white crystals. The solid was collected, filtered, and dried in vacuo, and stored in a moisture-free environment. Thallic carboxylates are rapidly hydrolyzed.

15. Typical Oxidizing Procedures

In this section, the procedures typically employed for $M(OAc)_n$ oxidation of simple olefins are given.

a. $Hg(OAc)_2$ Oxidation of Allylbenzene.[173] Allylbenzene (10.4 g, 0.088 mole) and mercuric acetate (42 g, 0.14 mole) were refluxed in acetic acid (200 cc) for 40 hr. The reaction solution was poured into water (600 cc) and Hg precipitated (ca. 60–80%). The water suspension was extracted with ether or pentane (6 × 80 cc), washed with water and saturated sodium bicarbonate solution, and dried.

The ether or pentane was removed and the residue distilled at ca. 130° (6.5 mm) to give approximately 11 g (75%) of acetate product, which is ca. 90–95% cinnamyl acetate (v.p.c.) (NMR 8.07τ(3); 5.40τ (2, J = 6Hz); 3.6–3.7τ (2, multiplet). Substantial amounts (ca. 40%) of the secondary isomer, 2-phenylallyl acetate, are formed, but under conditions of prolonged reflux, isomerization to the primary isomer occurs.

b. $Tl(OAc)_3$ Oxidation of Cyclohexene.[96] Anhydrous thallic acetate in acetic acid was stirred during the dropwise addition to cyclohexene (1:2 ratio). Sampling to determine the state of the reaction was conducted. On completion, the solution was poured into concentrated aqueous $NaHCO_3$, and the aqueous layer was extracted several times with chloroform. Sometimes the aqueous layer was extracted with ether and dried (Na_2SO_4).

The solvent was removed and the residue examined by g.l.c. Separation was effected by distillation and g.l.c.

c. $Pb(OAc)_4$ *Oxidation of* (+) *Carvomenthene.*[102] A solution of (+) carvomenthene (8.6 g, 62 mM) was added to lead tetraacetate (13.0 g, 29 mM) in acetic acid (50 ml). The reaction solution was heated for 4 hr in a steam bath and poured into water (150 ml). No PbO_2 was produced. Potassium hydroxide (50 g) was added to the solution and extracted with ether, which was washed ($NaHCO_3$), dried (Na_2SO_4), and concentrated using a rotary evaporator, yielding a crude product (9.3 g). Distillation yields starting material (3.8 g), monoacetates (2.0 g, bp 110–118°) and some higher boiling substances (3.2 g, largely diacetates). The monoacetates contained 6.4% reactant and 48% (17% yield) carvotanacetol acetates (60% *trans*).

d. $Pd(OAc)_2$ *Oxidation of 1-Butene.*[124,174] 1-Butene (excess) and Pd-$(OAc)_2$ (ca. 800 mg) in acetic acid (ca. 15 cc) were thermostatted at 25° for ca. 40 hr. Palladium metal formed fairly rapidly and was produced almost quantitatively (ca. 400 mg Pd, 98%). V.p.c. analysis indicated a number of components. Neutralization (aqueous $NaHCO_3$) and extraction with pentane, etc., were followed by v.p.c. isolation of the components. The structures of the products reported are indicated in Table II.

XIII. APPENDIX

Since the time of writing, a number of important papers have appeared, which are discussed briefly below.

A review article discussing the formation of charged carbon species from organometallic precursors has appeared (W. Kitching, *Rev. Pure Appl. Chem.*, **19**, 1 (1969)) and the cleavage of cyclopropanes by metal acetates, conducted mainly by Ouellette and co-workers is discussed in this report.

South and Ouellette (A. South and R. J. Ouellette, *J. Amer. Chem. Soc.*, **90**, 7064 (1968)) have discussed in detail the thallic acetate cleavage of several arylcyclopropanes and have proposed mechanisms. Important information contained in this paper relates to the preparation of thallic acetate, and the procedure is outlined below.

A mixture of 10 g (0.022 mole) of thallic oxide in acetic acid (100 ml) and water (25 ml) was stirred at 50° for 4 hr. The residual solid was removed by suction, and the acetic acid removed under reduced pressure. The solid was dissolved in a minimum amount of acetic acid at 75°, and the thallic acetate crystallized upon cooling. The solid was suction-filtered and dried under a continuous vacuum. A 73.7% yield (12.3 g, 0.032 mole) was obtained and the dry solid stored in a desiccator. The product was found to be 98% pure by analysis.

Thallous and thallic acetates form a double salt.

In the oxymercuration area, a number of papers have appeared. Waters, Linn, and Caserio (W. L. Waters, W. S. Linn, and M. C. Caserio, *J. Amer. Chem. Soc.*, **90**, 6741 (1968) have discussed methoxymercuration in the general framework of addition reactions of allenes. Under the conditions employed, *trans* addition was the outcome.

Johnson and Rickborn (M. R. Johnson and B. Rickborn, *Chem. Commun.*, **1968** 1073); J. Org. Chem. (Submitted Private Correspondence) have focused on the stereoselectivity in the oxymercuration of cyclohex-2-enol, cyclohex-2-enyl methyl ether and cyclohex-2-enyl acetate, and reported findings at variance with some earlier work. Moon and Waxman (S. Moon and B. H. Waxman, *Chem. Commun.*, **1967**, 1283) found that oxymercuration, on the basis of product analysis (diols) from borohydride reduction, of cyclohex-2-enol did not occur with a high degree of stereoselectivity, and solvent effects were operative. Thus in acetonitrile (5% H_2O) nearly pure *trans*-3-hydroxy product was obtained, and this system could prove synthetically useful. Other solvents were less specific.

Further information on the oxymercuration of cyclic allenes has appeared (G. C. Joshi and D. Devaprabhakara, *J. Organometall. Chem.*, **15**, 497 (1968)), and 1,2-cyclononadiene, 1,2-cyclodecadiene, and 1,2-cyclotridecadiene gave readily characterized oxymercuration products.

Baird and Buza (W. C. Baird and M. Buza, *J. Org. Chem.*, **33**, 4105 (1968)) have studied the oxymercuration-demercuration of *syn* and *anti*-7-hydroxy and 7-acetoxy norbornenes, which produced high yields of *exo, syn* and *exo*, and *anti*-2,7-dihydroxynorbornanes, respectively. There was a clear preference for the *syn* double bond; this was rationalized in terms of stabilization of the transition state by the *syn*-oxygen function and double bond coordinating to the mercury. Such stabilization would be unfavorable for anti-7-groups. In the case of 7-acetoxynorbornadiene, the hydroxyl group was introduced *exo* and *syn* to the 7-acetoxyl group. Thus the electronic stabilizing effect seems to override the anticipated retardative steric effect for *exo,syn* oxymercuration.

An important symposium featuring homogeneous reactions of palladium was held recently (*Division of Petroleum Chemistry Abstracts*, **14** (1969)) in conjunction with the American Chemical Society Meeting, in Minneapolis, Minnesota, April 13, 1969. A number of reports discussed reactions involving oxypalladation steps. A long abstract outlined the work of I. I. Moiseev of the USSR. P. M. Henry produced evidence that oxypalladation was involved in vinyl ester exchange. These abstracts have been published.

REFERENCES

1. J. Chatt, *Chem. Rev.*, **48**, 1 (1951).
2. W. Kitching, *Organometal. Chem. Rev.*, **3**, 61 (1968).
3. N. S. Zefirov, *Usp. Khim.*, **34**, 1272 (1965).
4. R. F. Heck, *Advan. in Chem. Series.*, No. 49, **181** (1965).
5. M. F. Lappert and B. Prokai, *Advan. Organometal. Chem.*, **5**, 225 (1967).
6. A. J. Bloodworth and A. G. Davies, *Proc. Chem. Soc.*, 315 (1963).
7. W. Kitching, *Rev. Pure. Appl. Chem.*, **19**, 1 (1969).
8. J. Chatt, L. M. Vallarino, and L. M. Venanzi, *J. Chem. Soc.*, **1957**, 2496.
9. J. Chatt, L. M. Vallarino, and L. M. Venanzi, *J. Chem. Soc.*, **1957**, 3413.
10. A. C. Cope, J. M. Kliegman, and E. C. Friedrich, *J. Amer. Chem. Soc.*, **89**, 287 (1967).
11. G. K. Fedorova and A. V. Kirsanov, *Zh. Obshch. Khim.*, **30**, 4044 (1960).
12. M. F. Lappert, *Angew. Chem.*, **72**, 353 (1960).
13. G. M. Kosolapoff, *J. Amer. Chem. Soc.*, **74**, 4119 (1952).
14. S. J. Green and T. S. Price, *J. Chem. Soc.*, **119**, 448 (1921).
15. P. D. Bartlett, H. P. Dauben, and L. J. Rosen, U.S. Patent, 2,465,834; *Chem. Abstr.*, **43**, 5412 (1949).
16. G. Hugel and J. Hibou, *Chim. Ind. (Milan)*, Special Number, Feb. 1929, p. 296.
17. R. K. Friedlina and N. S. Kochetkova, *Bull. Acad. Sci.*, USSR, *Classe Sci. Chim.*, 128 (1945).
18. E. R. Allen, J. Cartlidge, M. M. Taylor, and C. F. Tipper, *J. Phys. Chem.*, **63**, 1437 (1959).
19. D. Chow, J. A. Robson, and G. F Wright, *Can. J. Chem.*, **43**, 312 (1965).
20. V. I. Sokolov, N. B. Rodina, and O. A. Reutov, *J. Gen. Chem. USSR*, **36**, 973 (1966).
21. K. C. Pande and S. Winstein, *Tetrahedron Lett.*, **1964**, 3393.
22. J. Chatt and L. M. Venanzi, *J. Chem. Soc.*, **1957**, 4735.
23. T. Yukawa and S. Tsutsumi, *Inorg. Chem.*, **7**, 1458 (1968).
24. W. Kitching, *Organometal. Chem. Rev.*, **3**, 35 (1968).
25. K. A. Hofmann and J. Sand, *Ber.*, **33**, 1540 (1900).
26. A. N. Nesmeyanov, and R. K. Friedlina, *Ber.*, **69**, 1631 (1936).
27. K. Ichikawa, K. Fujita, and H. Ouchi, *J. Amer. Chem. Soc.*, **81**, 5316 (1959).
28. K. H. McNeely and G. F Wright, *J. Amer. Chem. Soc.*, **77**, 2553 (1955).
29. A. G. Brook, R. Donovan, and G. F Wright, *Can. J. Chem.*, **31**, 536 (1953).
30. R. Adams, F. L. Roman, and W. N. Sperry, *J. Amer. Chem. Soc.*, **44**, 1781 (1922).
31. M. J. Abercrombie, A. Rodgman, K. R. Bharucha, and G. F Wright, *Can. J. Chem.*, **37**, 1328 (1959).
32. T. G. Traylor and A. W. Baker, *J. Amer. Chem. Soc.*, **85**, 2746 (1963).
33. T. G. Traylor, *J. Amer. Chem. Soc.*, **86**, 244 (1964).
34. J. K. Stille and R. A. Morgan, *J. Amer. Chem. Soc.*, **88**, 5135 (1966).
35. F. A. Cotton, J. R. Leto, *J. Amer. Chem. Coc.*, **80**, 4823 (1954).
36. P. R. Wells and W. Kitching, *Tetrahedron Lett.*, **1963**, 1531.
37. S. Brownstein, *Disc. Faraday Soc.*, **34**, 25 (1962).
38. E. F. Kiefer and W. L. Waters, *J. Amer. Chem. Soc.*, **87**, 4401 (1965).
39. F. A. L. Anet, *Tetrahedron Lett.*, **1964**, 3399.
40. G. F Wright, *J. Amer. Chem. Soc.*, **57**, 1993 (1935).
41. J. Romeyn and G. F Wright, *J. Amer. Chem. Soc.*, **69**, 697 (1947).
42. H. J. Lucas, F. R. Hepner, and S. Winstein, *J. Amer. Chem. Soc.*, **61**, 3102 (1939).
43. W. H. Brown and G. F Wright, *J. Amer. Chem. Soc.*, **62**, 2412 (1940).

44. M. H. Thomas and F. E. W. Wetmore, *J. Amer. Chem. Soc.*, **63**, 136 (1941).
45. A. M. Birks and G. F Wright, *J. Amer. Chem. Soc.*, **62**, 2412 (1940).
46. A. G. Brook and G. F Wright, *Acta Cryst.*, **4**, 50 (1951).
47. V. I. Sokolov, private communication.
48. M. M. Anderson and P. M. Henry, *Chem. Ind. (London)*, **50**, 2053 (1961).
49. S. Wolfe and P. G. Campbell, *Can. J. Chem.*, **43**, 1184 (1965).
50. M. M. Kreevoy and F. R. Kowitt, *J. Amer. Chem. Soc.*, **82**, 739 (1960).
51. T. G. Traylor and S. Winstein, Abstracts 135th Meeting, Amer. Chem. Soc., Boston, 1959, p. 82–O.
52. N. S. Zefirov, L. P. Prikazchikova and Y. K. Yurév, *Dokl. Akad. Nauk SSSR*, **124**, 834 (1959).
53. G. B. Bachman and M. L. Whitehouse, *J. Org. Chem.*, **32**, 2303 (1967).
54. F. A. L. Anet, *Can. J. Chem.*, **39**, 789 (1961).
55. J. K. Stille and S. C. Stinson, *Tetrahedron*, **20**, 1387 (1964).
56. S. Winstein and M. Shatavsky, *Chem. Ind. (London)*, **1956**, 56.
57. F. R. Jensen and J. J. Miller, *Tetrahedron Lett.*, **1966**, 4861.
58. A. Factor and T. G. Traylor, *J. Org. Chem.*, **33**, 2607 (1968).
59. D. N. Ford, W. Kitching, and P. R. Wells, *Aust. J. Chem.*, **22**, 1157 (1969).
60. R. S. Bly, R. K. Bly, O. A. Bedenbaugh, and O. R. Vail, *J. Amer. Chem. Soc.*, **89**, 881 (1967).
61. H. B. Henbest and B. Nicholls, *J. Chem. Soc.*, **1959**, 227.
62. A. Factor and T. G. Traylor, *J. Org. Chem.*, **33**, 2615 (1968).
63. Y. K. Yurév, N. S. Zefirov, and L. P. Prikazchikova, *Zh. Obshch. Khim.*, **32**, 2744 (1962).
64. W. A. Whitla, H. M. Powell and L. M. Venanzi, *Chem. Commun.*, **1966**, 310.
65. C. B. Anderson and B. J. Burreson, *J. Organometal. Chem.*, **7**, 181 (1967).
66. C. B. Anderson and B. J. Burreson, *Chem. Ind., (London)*, **1967**, 620.
67. M. Green and R. I. Hancock, *J. Chem. Soc., A*, 2054 (1967).
68. B. L. Shaw, *Chem. Commun.*, **1968**, 464.
69. P. M. Henry, *Advan. in Chem. Series*, **70**, 126 (1968).
70. G. Paiaro, A. De Renzi, and R. Palumbo, *Chem. Commun.*, **1967**, 1150.
71. B. F. G. Johnson, J. Lewis, and M. S. Subramanian, *Chem. Commun.*, **1966**, 117.
72. J. Tsuji and M. Tatahashi, *J. Amer. Chem. Soc.*, **87**, 3275 (1965).
73. G. F Wright, *Amer. N. Y. Acad. Sci.*, **65**, 436 (1967).
74. M. M. Kreevoy, L. C. Schaleger and J. C. Ware, *Trans. Faraday Soc.*, **58**, 2433 (1962).
75. R. L. Rowland and E. F. Kluchesky, *J. Amer. Chem. Soc.*, **73**, 5490 (1951).
76. M. J. S. Dewar, *Bull. Soc. Chim. Fr.*, **18**, C79 (1951).
77. W. L. Waters and E. F. Kiefer, *J. Amer. Chem. Soc.*, **89**, 6261 (1967).
78. K. S. Pitzer, *J. Amer. Chem. Soc.*, **67**, 1127 (1945).
79. S. Winstein and H. J. Lucas, *J. Amer. Chem. Soc.*, **60**, 836 (1938).
80. J. Halpern and H. B. Tinker, *J. Amer. Chem. Soc.*, **89**, 6427 (1967).
81. V. I. Sokolov, Y. A. Ustnyuk, and O. A. Reutov, *Doklady Akad. Nauk SSSR*, **173**, 1103 (1967).
82. Y. Saito and M. Matsuo, *Chem. Commun.*, **1967**, 961.
83. W. Kitching, A. J. Smith, and P. R. Wells, *Chem. Commun.*, **1968**, 370.
84. W. Kitching, A. J. Smith and P. R. Wells, *Aust. J. Chem.*, **21**, 2395 (1968).
85. M. M. Kreevoy, N. Takashina, and L. L. Schaleger, Abstracts, 137th National Meeting of Amer. Chem. Soc., Cleveland, Ohio, Apr. 1960.
86. S. Winstein, T. G. Traylor and C. S. Garner, *J. Amer. Chem. Soc.*, **77**, 3741 (1955).

87. M. M. Kreevoy, *J. Amer. Chem. Soc.*, **81**, 1099 (1959).
88. M. M. Kreevoy, J. W. Gilje, L. T. Ditsch, W. Batorewics, and M. A. Turner, *J. Org. Chem.*, **27**, 726 (1962).
89. M. M. Kreevoy and L. T. Ditsch, *J. Amer. Chem. Soc.*, **82**, 6127 (1960).
90. L. T. Schaleger, M. A. Turner, T. C. Chamberlin, and M. M. Kreevoy, *J. Org. Chem.*, **27**, 3421 (1962).
91. M. M. Kreevoy, G. Stokkev, R. A. Kretchmer, and A. K. Ahmed, *J. Org. Chem.*, **28**, 3184 (1963).
92. M. M. Kreevoy and G. B. Bodein, *J. Org. Chem.*, **27**, 4539 (1962).
93. M. M. Kreevoy and M. A. Turner, *J. Org. Chem.*, **29**, 1639 (1964).
94. H. C. Brown, J. H. Kawakami, and S. Ikegami, *J. Amer. Chem. Soc.*, **89**, 1526 (1967).
95. C. B. Anderson and S. Winstein, *J. Org. Chem.*, **26**, 238 (1961).
96. J. B. Lee and M. J. Price, *Tetrahedron*, **20**, 1017 (1964).
97. L. Balbiano, *Gazz. Chim. Ital.*, **36**, 237 (1906).
98. A. Leys, *Bull. Soc. Chim.*, **4**, 262 (1907).
99. D. A. Shearer and G. F Wright, *Can. J. Chem.*, **33**, 1002 (1955).
100. J. H. Robson and G. F Wright, *Can. J. Chem.*, **38**, 1 (1960).
101. K. Ichikawa and H. Ouchi, *J. Amer. Chem. Soc.*, **82**, 3876 (1960).
102. K. B. Wiberg and S. D. Nielsen, *J. Org. Chem.*, **29**, 3353 (1964).
103. Z. Rappoport, P. D. Sleezer, S. Winstein, and W. G. Young, *Tetrahedron Lett.*, **1965**, 5119.
104. S. Wolfe, P. G. C. Campbell, and G. E. Palmer, *Tetrahedron Lett.*, **1966**, 4203.
105. R. R. Grinstead, *J. Org. Chem.*, **26**, 238 (1961).
106. C. B. Anderson and S. Winstein, *J. Org. Chem.*, **28**, 605 (1963).
107. H. J. Kabbe, *Ann.*, **656**, 204 (1962).
108. P. M. Henry, *J. Amer. Chem. Soc.*, **87**, 990 (1965).
109. P. M. Henry, *J. Amer. Chem. Soc.*, **87**, 4423 (1965).
110. P. M. Henry, *J. Amer. Chem. Soc.*, **87**, 1597 (1966).
111. R. Crigee, *Angew. Chem.*, **70**, 173 (1958).
112. Y. Matsubaara, *J. Chem. Soc. Jap.*, **78**, 907 (1957).
113. G. H. Whitham, *J. Chem. Soc.*, **1961**, 2232.
114. J. Smidt, et al., *Angew Chem., Intern. Ed. Engl.*, **1**, 80 (1962). (Also references therein.)
115. C. W. Bird, *Transition Metal Intermediates in Organic Synthesis*, Logos Press, London, 1966, p. 88.
116. A. Aguilo, *Advan. Organometal. Chem.*, **5**, 321 (1967).
117. See I. I. Moiseev, M. N. Warhaftig, and J. H. Sirikin, *Dokl. Akad. Nauk SSSR*, **130**, 820 (1960).
118. P. M. Henry, *J. Amer. Chem. Soc.*, **86**, 3246 (1964).
119. P. M. Henry, *J. Amer. Chem. Soc.*, **88**, 1595 (1966).
120. R. Jira, J. Sedlmeier, and J. Smidt, *Ann.*, **693**, 99 (1966).
121. R. G. Schultz and O. E. Gross, *Advan. in Chem. Series*, **70**, 97 (1968).
122. W. H. Clement and C. M. Selwitz, *J. Org. Chem.*, **29**, 241 (1964).
123. R. Huttel, J. Kratzer, and M. Bechter, *Chem. Ber.*, **94**, 766 (1961).
124. W. Kitching, Z. Rappoport, S. Winstein, and W. G. Young, *J. Amer. Chem. Soc.*, **88**, 2054 (1966).
125. H. C. Volger, *Rec. Trav. Chim. Pays-Bas*, **86**, 677 (1967).
126. H. C. Volger, *Rev. Trav. Chim., Pays-Bas*, **87**, 1 (1968).
127. J. Tsujc and K. Ohno, *Advan. in Chem. Series*, **70**, 155 (1968).

128. N. Berndt, L. Hoerning, O. Probst, W. Schmidt, U. Schwenk, and E. Weber, U.S. Patent, 3,122,586; *Chem. Abstr.*, **61**, 1758 (1964).

129. D. R. Bryant, J. E. McKeon, and P. S. Starcher, French Patent, 1,395,129; *Chem. Abstr.*, **63**, 9816 (1965).

130. Consortium für Elektrochemische Industrie, British Patent, 884,962; *Chem. Abstr.*, **59**, 5024 (1963).

131. Farbwerke Hoechst A.G., Belgian Patent 635,230; *Chem. Abstr.*, **61**, 11,894 (1964).

132. K. I. Matveev, A. M. Osipov, and L. N. Stroganova, USSR Patent 176,258; *Chem. Abstr.*, **64**, 11,086 (1966).

133. W. Riemenschneider, W. Schmidt, and L. Hoernig, German Patent, 1,136,685, *Chem. Abstr.*, **58**, 12,423 (1963).

134. J. Smidt, W. Hafner, and R. Jira, U.S. Patent, 3,080,425; *Chem. Abstr.*, **59**, 7375 (1963).

135. Japan Oil Co., British Patent 960,195; *Chem. Abstr.*, **61**, 6922 (1964).

136. Badische Anilin und Soda-Fabrik, A.G., Belgian Patent, 658,285, *Chem. Abstr.*, **64**, 6499 (1966).

137. R. Huttel and H. Christ, *Chem. Ber.*, **97**, 1439 (1964).

138. Farbwerke Hoechst, A.G., British Patent, 898,790; *Chem. Abstr.*, **61**, 8189 (1964).

139. J. Smidt, W. Hafner, R. Jira, R. Sieber, and H. Kojer, *Angew. Chem.*, **71**, 176 (1959).

140. W. Hafner, R. Jira, J. Sedlmeier, and J. Smidt, *Chem. Ber.*, **95**, 1575 (1962).

141. R. Huttel, T. Kratzer, and M. Beechter, *Chem. Ber.*, **94**, 766 (1961).

142. R. F. Neale, French Patent, 1,409,190; *Chem. Abstr.*, **64**, 6567 (1966).

143. J. E. McKeon and P. S. Starcher, Belgian Patent, 629,885; *Chem. Abstr.*, **61**, 2976 (1964).

144. E. W. Stern and M. L. Spector, *Proc. Chem. Soc.*, 370 1961.

145. Japan Synthetic Chemical Industry Co., Belgian Patent, 618,071; *Chem. Abstr.*, **59**, 12,715 (1963).

146. J. B. Williamson, British Patent, 1,003,347; *Chem. Abstr.*, **63**, 17,909 (1965).

147. Fabwerke Hoechst A.G., Netherland Patent Appl., 6,504,302; *Chem. Abstr.*, **64**, 12,554 (1966).

148. Imperial Chemical Industries, Belgian Patent, 634,595; *Chem. Abstr.*, **60**, 14,394 (1964).

149. A. P. Belov and I. I. Moiseev, *Izv. Akad. Nauk SSSR, Ser. Khim.*, 139 (1966).

150. Imperial Chemical Industries, Belgian Patent, 635,426; *Chem. Abstr.*, **61**, 11,896 (1964).

151. H. Holzrichter, W. Kroenig and B. Frenz, French Patent, 1,346,219; *Chem. Abstr.*, **60**, 11,902 (1964).

152. M. N. Vargaftik, I. I. Moiseev, Y. K. Syrkin, and V. V. Yakshiu, *Izv. Akad. Nauk SSSR, Ser. Khim.*, 930 (1962).

153. D. Clark, P. Hayden, W. D. Walsh, and W. E. Jones, British Patent, 964,001; *Chem. Abstr.*, **61**, 13,199 (1964).

154. D. Clark and W. D. Walsh, British Patent, 988,011; *Chem. Abstr.*, **63** 1706 (1965).

155. A. C. Cope, M. R. Kinter, and R. T. Keller, *J. Amer. Chem. Soc.*, **76**, 2757 (1954).

156. S. Akiyoshi, *Chem. Abstr.*, **52**, 12,907 (1958).

157. E. C. Friedrich and S. Winstein, unpublished results.

158. I. Alkonyi, *Ber. Bunsenges. Phys. Chem.*, **95**, 279 (1962).

159. W. Treibs and M. Weissenfels, *Ber. Bunsenges. Phys. Chem.*, **93** 1374 (1960).

160. W. Treibs, G. Lucius, H. Kogler, and H. Breslauer, *Ann. Chim (Paris)*, **59**, 59 (1953).

161. W. Treibs and H. Bast., *Ann. Chim. (Paris)*, **561**, 165 (1949).

162. W. Treibs, *Naturwissenschaften*, **35**, 125 (1945).
163. P. Karrer and C. H. Eugstev, *Helv. Chim. Acta*, **34**, 1400 (1951).
164. C. Djerassi, J. Rono and G. Rosenkranz, *J. Org. Chem.*, **16**, 754 (1951).
165. C. Djerassi, G. Rosenkranz, J. Rono, and F. Batres, *J. Org. Chem.*, **16**, 298 (1951).
166. A. Windaus, U. Riemann, and G. Zuhlsdorff, *Ann. Chim.* (*Paris*), **552**, 135 (1942).
167. D. H. R. Barton and W. J. Rosenfelder, *J. Chem. Soc.*, **1951**, 2381.
168. Z. Alkonyi, *Chem. Ber.*, **96**, 1873 (1963).
169. R. L. Clarke, K. Dobriner, A. Mooradian, and C. M. Martini, *J. Amer. Chem. Soc.*, **77**, 661 (1955).
170. L. F. Feiser and R. Stevenson, *J. Amer. Chem. Soc.*, **76**, 1728 (1954).
171. A. Kergomard, *Ann. Chim.* (*Paris*), **8**, 153 (1953).
172. T. Aratani, *Nippon Kagaku Zasshi*, **78**, 1534 (1957); *Chem. Abstr.*, **54**, 1587 (1960).
173. Unpublished results.
174. Unpublished procedures.
175. K. Ichikawa, H. Tozaki, I. Ueki, and H. Shingu, *J. Chem. Soc. Jap.*, *Pure Chem. Sect.*, **79**, 267 (1951).
176. K. Ichikawa, S. Fukushima, H. Ouchi, and M. Tsuchida, *J. Amer. Chem. Soc.*, **80** 6005 (1958).
177. K. Ichikawa, S. Fukushima, H. Ouchi, and M. Tsuchida, *J. Amer. Chem. Soc.*, **81**, 3401 (1959).
178. F. R. Jensen and R. J. Ouellette, *J. Amer. Chem. Soc.*, **83**, 4477 (1961).
179. K. Ichikawa, H. Ouchi, and S. Fukushima, *J. Org. Chem.*, **24**, 1129 (1959).
180. K. Ichikawa, O. Itoh, T. Kawamura, M. Fujiwara, and T. Ueno, *J. Org. Chem.*, **31**, 447 (1966).
181. K. Ichikawa, O. Itoh, and T. Kawamura, *Bull. Chem. Soc.*, *Jap.*, **41**, 1240 (1968).
182. K. Ichikawa, S. Vemura, and T. Sugita, *Tetrahedron*, **22**, 407 (1966).
183. K. Ichikawa and S. Vemura, *J. Org. Chem.*, **32**, 493 (1967).
184. F. G. Bordwell and M. L. Douglass, *J. Amer. Chem. Soc.*, **88**, 993 (1966).
185. H. C. Brown and P. Geoghegan, *J. Amer. Chem. Soc.*, **89**, 1524 (1967).
186. H. C. Brown and W. J. Hammar, *J. Amer. Chem. Soc.*, **89**, 1525 (1967).
187. K. Ichikawa, Y. Takeuchi, and O. Itoh, *Bull. Inst. Chem. Res.*, *Kyoto Univ.*, **40**, 317 (1962).
188. R. Jira and W. Freiesleben, "Organometallic Reactions," Chapter 1.

Errata

Page 36   Column 1, eighth entry:
should be "3,3-Dimethyl-1-butene" (not "2,2-dimethyl-1-butene")

Page 39   Column 1, line 4 from bottom:
delete hyphen so as to read "p-Chlorocinnamic acid"

Page 55   Column 5, fourth entry from bottom:
change "1,2,2-triacetoxyethane" to "1,1,2-triacetoxyethane"

$$CH_3\overset{\overset{\textstyle O}{\|}}{C}-O-CH_2-CH(-O-\overset{\overset{\textstyle O}{\|}}{C}-CH_3)_2$$

Page 61   Column 6, fourth entry from bottom:
should be "2,4,5-trimethylbenzyl acetate"

Page 65   Column 7, line 6·   read   "2-Methyl-2-ethyl-1,3-dioxolane"
(not "2-methyl-1-ethyl-1,3-dioxolane")

Page 74   Paragraph 1, line 1:   read   "Allyl chloride has been *obtained* as an oxidation . . . "

Page 75   Line 6 from bottom: delete "C" in 160° C

Page 78   Column 1, next to the last entry: insert "e" in [1,2-Pentamethylene-π-allyl PdCl]$_2$

Page 79   Paragraph 2, line 5: delete "C" in 160° C

Page 90   Column 2, last line: read   "p-anisylmercury chloride"

Page 95   Top right: shift phenyl in figure to second C atom

$$CH_3CHCH_2CHO$$

Page 100   Paragraph 5, line 2: delete "C"

Page 101   Paragraph 2, line 2: delete "C"

Page 106   Paragraph 4, line 2: read   "besides" (not "beside")

Page 109   Column 1, next to the last entry: read   "N,N-Diethyl-3-methyl"

Page 109   Column 4, fourteenth entry: read   "Biacetyl" (not "Diacetyl")

Page 138   Column 3, line 11: must be "2-Butene" (not "1-Butene")

399

Page 143   Column 1, line 11:   read   [(Hexamethyl-Dewar-benzene)-PdCl$_2$] (insert bracket)

Page 153   Line 3 from the bottom: read   "besides" (not "beside")

Page 320   VII: read   "Friedel-Crafts" (not "Friedel-Craft")

Page 320:   XII, 7, 8, and 10:   read   *"cis,exo"* (not "cis.Exo-")

Page 362   Column 1, fifth entry: read   "Isobutene" (not "*iso*-Butene")

Page 363   Column 2, lines 12, 13, and 14:   read   "3-Ethyl-2-penten-4-one"
           (not "3-Ethyl-2-pentene-4-one")

Page 364   Column 1, fourth structure:

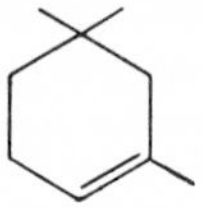

not

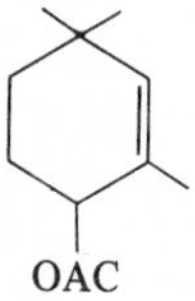

OAC

Page 372   VII;   read   "CRAFTS" (not "CRAFT")
           Page 1, line 2:   read "Crafts" (not "Craft")

Page 378   Line 4 of equations on the arrow: read   "Na(Hg)$_x$" (not "NaHg")

Page 379   Third arrow from bottom in table: read   "Na(Hg)$_x$" (not "Na/Hg")

Page 379   Second arrow from bottom in table: read
           "heterogeneous" (not "hetereogeneous")

Page 382   Table XI, column 3, third entry: read   *"cis,cis*-1,3,4-Trimethylcyclopentanol, . .
           (not *"cis,cis*-1,2,4-Trimethyl . . .")

Page 386   Paragraph 1, line 3 (just above equations):   read   " . . .to dethallation. . ."
           (not ". . .to deplumbation. . .")

Subject Index